Modern Silicon Carbide Power Devices

Modern Silicon Carbide Power Devices

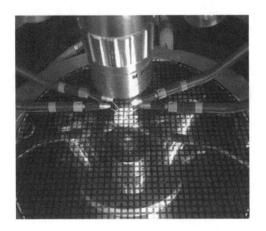

B Jayant Baliga
North Carolina State University, USA

World Scientific

NEW JERSEY · LONDON · SINGAPORE · BEIJING · SHANGHAI · HONG KONG · TAIPEI · CHENNAI · TOKYO

Published by

World Scientific Publishing Co. Pte. Ltd.

5 Toh Tuck Link, Singapore 596224

USA office: 27 Warren Street, Suite 401-402, Hackensack, NJ 07601

UK office: 57 Shelton Street, Covent Garden, London WC2H 9HE

British Library Cataloguing-in-Publication Data
A catalogue record for this book is available from the British Library.

MODERN SILICON CARBIDE POWER DEVICES

ISBN 978-981-128-427-4 (hardcover)
ISBN 978-981-128-428-1 (ebook for institutions)
ISBN 978-981-128-429-8 (ebook for individuals)

For any available supplementary material, please visit
https://www.worldscientific.com/worldscibooks/10.1142/13623#t=suppl

Dedication

The author proposed the development of wide band gap semiconductor based power devices in 1979. He would like to dedicate this book to the management at the General Electric Company for supporting his vision by providing resources to make the first wide band gap power devices out of Gallium Arsenide in the 1980s. He would also like to dedicate the book to the companies that sponsored his Power Semiconductor Research Center in the 1990s allowing demonstration of the first high performance silicon carbide diodes and MOSFETs.

About the Author

Professor Baliga is internationally recognized for his leadership in the area of power semiconductor devices. In addition to over **700 publications** in international journals and conference digests, he has authored and edited **27 books** (*"Power Transistors"*, IEEE Press 1984; *"Epitaxial Silicon Technology"*, Academic Press 1986; *"Modern Power Devices"*, John Wiley 1987; *"High Voltage Integrated Circuits"*, IEEE Press 1988; *"Solution Manual: Modern Power Devices"*, John Wiley 1988; *"Proceedings of the 3rd Int. Symposium on Power Devices and ICs"*, IEEE Press 1991; *"Modern Power Devices"*, Krieger Publishing Co. 1992; *"Power Electronics Technology and Applications I,"* IEEE Press 1992; *"Proceedings of the 5th Int. Symposium on Power Devices and ICs"*, IEEE Press 1993; *"Power Semiconductor Devices"*; PWS Publishing Company 1995; *"Solution Manual: Power Semiconductor Devices"*; PWS Publishing Company 1996; *"Cryogenic Operation of Power Devices"*, Kluwer Press 1998; *"Power Electronics Technology and Applications II,"* IEEE Press 1998; *"Silicon RF Power MOSFETs"*,

World Scientific Publishing Company 2005; *"Silicon Carbide Power Devices"*, World Scientific Publishing Company 2006; *"Fundamentals of Power Semiconductor Devices"*, Springer Science, 2008; *"Solution Manual: Fundamentals of Power Semiconductor Devices"*, Springer Science, 2008; *"Advanced Power Rectifier Concepts"*, Springer Science, 2009; *"Advanced Power MOSFET Concepts"*, Springer Science, 2010; *"Advanced High Voltage Power Device Concepts"*, Springer Science, 2011; Chinese Edition of *"Fundamentals of Power Semiconductor Devices"*, Author, Springer-Science 2012; *"The IGBT Device: Physics, Design, and Applications"*, Elsevier Press, 2015; Chinese Edition of *"Advanced High Voltage Power Devices Concepts"*, Author, China Machine Press 2015; *"Gallium Nitride and Silicon Carbide Power Devices"*, World Scientific Publishing Company 2017; *"Fundamentals of Power Semiconductor Devices"*, Second Edition, Springer Science, 2019; *"Wide Bandgap Semiconductor Power Devices"*, Elsevier Press, 2019; *"The IGBT Device: Physics, Design, and Applications"*, Second Edition, Elsevier Press, 2022). In addition, he has contributed chapters to another 24 books. He holds **123 U.S. Patents** in the solid-state area. In 1995, one of his inventions was selected for the *B.F. Goodrich Collegiate Inventors Award* presented at the *Inventors Hall of Fame*. In 2016, he was inducted into the **National Inventors Hall of Fame** as the sole inventor of *the Insulated Gate Bipolar Transistor*.

Professor Baliga obtained his Bachelor of Technology degree in 1969 from the Indian Institute of Technology, Madras, India. He was the recipient of the *Philips India Medal* and the *Special Merit Medal (as Valedictorian)* at I.I.T, Madras. He obtained his Masters and Ph.D. degrees from Rensselaer Polytechnic Institute, Troy NY, in 1971 and 1974, respectively. His thesis work involved Gallium Arsenide diffusion mechanisms and **pioneering work** on the growth of InAs and GaInAs layers using **Metal-Organic CVD (MOCVD)** techniques. At R.P.I., he was the recipient of the *IBM Fellowship* in 1972 and the *Allen B. Dumont Prize* in 1974.

From 1974 to 1988, Dr. Baliga performed research and directed a group of 40 scientists at the General Electric Research and Development Center in Schenectady, NY, in the area of Power Semiconductor Devices and High Voltage Integrated Circuits. During this time, **he pioneered the concept of combining MOS and Bipolar physics to create a new family of discrete devices.** He is the **inventor of the IGBT** which is now in production by many international semiconductor companies.

This invention is widely used around the globe for air-conditioning, home appliance (washing machines, refrigerators, mixers, etc.) control, factory automation (robotics), medical systems (CAT scanners, MRI machines), and electric street-cars/bullet-trains, as well as for the drive-train in all electric and hybrid-electric cars. IGBT-based motor control **improves efficiency by over 40 percent**. The IGBT is essential for deployment of Compact Fluorescent Lamps (CFLs) to replace incandescent lamps producing **efficiency improvement by 75 percent**. Since two-thirds of the electricity in the world is used to run motors and twenty percent of the electricity in the world is used for lighting, the availability of IGBTs has produced a cumulative electrical **energy savings of 103,000 Terra-Watt-Hours** during 1990-2020. In addition, the IGBT enabled the introduction of the electronic ignition system for running spark plugs in the internal combustion engine of gasoline powered cars and trucks. The resulting 10 percent improvement in fuel efficiency has **saved consumers 1.86 trillion gallons of gasoline** during 1990-2020. The cumulative impact of these electrical energy and gasoline savings is a **cost savings of over $ 33 Trillion for consumers**, and a **reduction in Carbon Dioxide emissions from Coal-Fired power plants by over 180 Trillion pounds**. For this achievement, he has been labeled the *"man with the smallest carbon footprint on earth"*. Most recently, the IGBT has enabled creation of very compact, light-weight, and inexpensive defibrillators used to resuscitate cardiac arrest victims. Deployment of these portable defibrillators in fire-trucks, paramedic vans, in buildings, and on-board airlines, is projected by the American Medical Association (AMA) to save 100,000 lives per year in the US. *Scientific American Magazine* named him one of the '*Eight heroes of the semiconductor revolution*' in their 1997 special issue commemorating the Solid-State Century for his development of the IGBT. The IGBT is also an essential component for widespread deployment of electric vehicles in the future and for expansion of wind and solar renewable power generation. It is estimated that this will **reduce carbon dioxide emission by 34 Trillion pounds each year**.

Dr. Baliga is also the originator of the concept of merging Schottky and p-n junction physics to create a new family of **JBS power rectifiers** that are commercially available from various companies. This concept originally implemented for silicon devices has become an essential concept for the commercialization of silicon carbide high voltage Schottky rectifiers.

In 1979, Dr. Baliga developed a theoretical analysis resulting in the **Baliga's Figure of Merit (BFOM)** which relates the resistance within power rectifiers and FETs to the basic semiconductor properties. He predicted that the performance of Schottky power rectifiers and power MOSFETs could be enhanced by several orders of magnitude by replacing silicon with other materials such as gallium arsenide and silicon carbide. This is forming the basis of a new generation of power devices in the 21st Century.

In August 1988, Dr. Baliga joined the faculty of the Department of Electrical and Computer Engineering at North Carolina State University, Raleigh, North Carolina, as a Full Professor. In 1997, in recognition of his contributions to NCSU, he was given the highest university faculty rank of *Distinguished University Professor of Electrical Engineering*. In 2018, he was made the *Progress Energy Distinguished University Professor of Electrical* Engineering.

He established an international consortium in 1991 at NCSU called the ***Power Semiconductor Research Center*** (**PSRC**) to support research in the area of power semiconductor devices and high voltage integrated circuits, and has served since then as its Founding Director. Under his leadership, PSRC was able to acquire **$ 6 million** in support from global companies for a decade. His research interests include the modeling of novel device concepts, device fabrication technology, and the investigation of the impact of new materials, such as GaAs and Silicon Carbide, on power devices. The first high performance **SiC Schottky rectifiers and power MOSFETs** were demonstrated at PSRC in the 1990s resulting in the release of products by many companies during the last 10 years.

In 2008, Professor Baliga was a key member of an NCSU team - partnered with four other universities - that was successful in being granted a **$ 50 million** Engineering Research Center called **FREEDM** from the National Science Foundation for the development of micro-grids that allow integration of renewable energy sources. He served as the sub-thrust leader for the development of power devices from wide-band-gap semiconductors for utility applications during this 10-year program.

Professor Baliga was a key member of an NCSU team that won a **$ 140 million** Manufacturing Institute named **PowerAmerica Institute** announced by President Obama in 2014. This institute will foster manufacturing wide bandgap semiconductor power devices in the United States based on his proposal in 1979 and basic work on demonstrating devices in the 1990s at PSRC/NCSU. He has created **PRESiCE**^{TM}, an open domain manufacturing technology for SiC power devices at a foundry in Texas, which has been licensed by one company for producing products. He has also created the next generation of high frequency SiC power devices for electric vehicles and renewable energy generation.

Professor Baliga has received numerous awards in recognition for his contributions to semiconductor devices. These include two *IR 100 awards* (1983, 1984), the **Dushman and Coolidge Awards at GE** (1983), and being selected among the *100 Brightest Young Scientists in America* by Science Digest Magazine (1984). He was elected *Fellow of the IEEE* in 1983 at the age of 35 for his contributions to power semiconductor devices. In 1984, he was given the *Applied Sciences Award* by the world famous sitar maestro Ravi Shankar at the Third Convention of Asians in North America. He received the 1991 **IEEE William E. Newell Award**, the highest honor given by the Power Electronics Society, followed by the 1993 **IEEE Morris E. Liebman Award** for his contributions to the emerging *Smart Power Technology*. In 1992, he was the first recipient of the BSS Society's *Pride of India Award*. At the age of 45, he was elected as Foreign Affiliate to the prestigious **National Academy of Engineering**, and was one of only 4 citizens of India to have the honor at that time (converted to regular Member in 2000 after taking U.S. Citizenship). In 1998, the University of North Carolina system selected him for the *O. Max Gardner Award*, which recognizes the faculty member among the 16 constituent universities who has made the *greatest contribution to the welfare of the human race*. In December 1998, he received the **IEEE J.J. Ebers Award**, the highest recognition given by the IEEE Electron Devices Society for his technical contributions to the Solid-State area. In June 1999, he was honored at the Whitehall Palace in London with the **IEEE Lamme Medal**, one of the highest forms of recognition given by the IEEE Board of Governors, for his contributions to development of an apparatus/technology of benefit to society.

In April 2000, he was honored by his Alma Mater IIT-Madras as a *Distinguished Alumnus*. In November 2000, he received the *R.J. Reynolds Tobacco Company Award for Excellence in Teaching, Research, and Extension* for his contributions to the College of Engineering at North Carolina State University. In 2011, Dr. Baliga was selected to receive the *Alexander Quarles Holladay Medal for Excellence*, which recognizes members of the NCSU faculty who over their careers have made outstanding contributions to the University through their research, teaching, and extension services. In 1998, he received the **O. Max Gardner Award**, as the faculty member who has made the 'the greatest contribution to the welfare of the human race', by the University of North Carolina Board of Governors.

In 1999, Prof. Baliga founded a company, *Giant Semiconductor Corporation*, with seed investment from Centennial Venture Partners, to acquire an exclusive license for his patented technology from North Carolina State University with the goal of bringing his NCSU inventions to the marketplace. A company, *Micro-Ohm Corporation*, subsequently formed by him in 1999, has been successful in licensing the **GD-TMBS power rectifier** technology to several major semiconductor companies for world-wide distribution. These devices have application in power supplies, battery chargers, and automotive electronics. It has become the most successful rectifier product during the last 30 years. In June 2000, Prof. Baliga founded another company, *Silicon Wireless Corporation*, to commercialize a novel **super-linear silicon RF transistor** that he invented for application in cellular base-stations and grew it to 41 employees. This company (renamed *Silicon Semiconductor Corporation*) was located at Research Triangle Park, N.C. It received an investment of $ 10 million from *Fairchild Semiconductor Corporation* in December 2000 to co-develop and market this technology. Based upon his additional inventions, this company also produced a **new generation of Power MOSFETs (SSCFETs and JBSFETs)** for delivering power to microprocessors in notebooks and servers. This technology was licensed by his company to Linear Technologies Corporation with transfer of the know-how and manufacturing process. Voltage Regulator Modules (VRMs) using his transistors are currently available in the market for powering microprocessor and graphics chips in laptops and servers. His **GD-MOSFET invention**, commercialized by *Giant Semiconductor Corporation*, is widely manufactured for use in low voltage power electronics.

In 2010, Dr. Baliga was inducted into the Engineering Design Magazine's "**Engineering Hall of Fame**" for his invention, development, and commercialization of the Insulated Gate Bipolar Transistor (IGBT), joining well known luminaries (e.g. Edison, Tesla, and Marconi) in the electrical engineering field. The award announcement states: *"While working at General Electric in the late 1970s, Baliga conceived the idea of a functional integration of MOS technology and bipolar physics that directly led to the IGBT's development... it remains undeniable that Baliga's vision and leadership played a critical role in moving the IGBT from a paper-based concept to a viable product with many practical applications."*

President Obama personally presented Dr. B. Jayant Baliga with the **National Medal of Technology and Innovation**, the highest form of recognition given by the United States Government to an Engineer, in a ceremony at the White House on October 21, 2011. Dr. Baliga's award citation reads: *For development and commercialization of the Insulated Gate Bipolar Transistor and other power semiconductor devices that are extensively used in transportation, lighting, medicine, defense, and renewable energy generation systems.* His IGBT innovation has saved world-wide consumers $ 33 Trillion while reducing carbon dioxide emissions by 150 Trillion pounds during 1990-2020.

In October 2012, Governor Beverly Purdue presented Dr. Baliga the **North Carolina Award for Science**. This is the highest award given by the State of North Carolina and the Governor to a civilian. On October 4, 2013, he was inducted into the **Rensselaer Alumni Hall of Fame** by Rensselaer Polytechnic Institute President Shirley Jackson. The ceremony included unveiling his portrait etched on a window in Thomsen Hall in the Darrin Communications Center.

On August 23, 2014, Dr. Baliga received the **IEEE Medal of Honor** *'For the invention, implementation, and commercialization of power semiconductor devices with widespread benefits to society'* in a ceremony held in Amsterdam, The Netherlands. He joins the company of previous semiconductor pioneers Gordon Teal, John Bardeen, Robert Noyce, William Shockley, Jack Kilby, Leo Esaki, Alfred Cho, Andrew Grove, Herbert Kroemer, Nick Holonyak, Gordon Moore, and Robert Dennard.

In June 2015, he received the **Global Energy Prize** for the 'invention, development, and commercialization of the Insulated Gate Bipolar Transistor – one of the most important innovations for the control and distribution of energy' together with Nobel Laurate Shuji Nakamura for his work on the development of the blue LEDs. This recognition given in Saint Petersburg, Russian Federation, is considered the highest global award in the energy area.

In December 2015, he was honored by the IEEE Electron Devices Society as a **Celebrated Member**. Only 6 people out of the 10,000 members of this society had been selected for this recognition at that time as *"legendary individuals in the field of electron devices"*.

He was inducted into the **National Inventors Hall of Fame** in 2016 as the sole inventor of the Insulated Gate Bipolar Transistor (IGBT). This is the highest global recognition for an inventor. The National Inventors Hall of Fame has recognized only 500 patents out of over 10 million issued to date. Past notable recipients include Thomas Edison, Alexander Graham Bell, Nicola Tesla, and the Wright Brothers.

He was made a Fellow of the **National Academy of Inventors** in 2017 for his many inventions at the university. This is the highest honor given to inventors from academia.

In 2018, he was inducted into the **IEEE ISPSD Hall of Fame**. This award recognizes his role in creating and establishing a new international conference by serving as the first Technical Program Chair and the second General Chairman. He set up the basic structure for review of papers by a technical program committee and procedures for selection of papers for presentation at the conference that have now been used for 30 years.

Preface

Power semiconductor devices are a key component of all power electronic systems. It is estimated that at least 50 percent of the electricity used in the world is controlled by power devices. With the wide spread use of electronics in the consumer, industrial, medical, and transportation sectors, power devices have a major impact on the economy because they determine the cost and efficiency of systems. After the initial replacement of vacuum tubes by solid state devices in the 1950s, semiconductor power devices have taken a dominant role with silicon serving as the base material.

Bipolar power devices, such as bipolar transistors and thyristors, were first developed in the 1950s. Their power ratings and switching frequency increased with advancements in the understanding of the operating physics and availability of more advanced lithography capability. The physics underlying the current conduction and switching speed of these devices has been described in my textbook[1]. Since the thyristors were developed for high voltage DC transmission and electric locomotive drives, the emphasis was on increasing the voltage rating and current handling capability. The ability to use neutron transmutation doping to produce high resistivity n-type silicon with improved uniformity across large diameter wafers enabled increasing the blocking voltage of thyristors to over 5000 volts while being able to handle over 2000 amperes of current in a single device.

Meanwhile, bipolar power transistors were developed with the goal of increasing the switching frequency in medium power systems. Unfortunately, the current gain of bipolar transistors becomes low when it is designed for high voltage operation at high current density. The popular solution to this problem, using the Darlington configuration, had the disadvantage of increasing the on-state voltage drop resulting in an increase in the power dissipation. In addition to the large control currents required for bipolar transistors, they suffered from second breakdown failure modes. These issues produced a cumbersome design with snubber networks, which raised the cost and degraded the efficiency of the power control system.

In the 1970s, the power MOSFET product was first introduced by International Rectifier Corporation. Although initially hailed as a replacement for all bipolar power devices due to its high input impedance and fast switching speed, the power MOSFET has success-fully cornered the market for low voltage (< 100 V) and high switching speed (> 100 kHz) applications but failed to make serious inroads in the high voltage arena. This is because the on-state resistance of power MOSFETs increases very rapidly with increase in the breakdown vol-tage. The resulting high conduction losses, even when using larger more expensive die, degrade the overall system efficiency.

Charge-coupled device physics allowed reducing the resistance of the silicon devices significantly in the 1990s[2]. The approach using a source connected electrode under the gate in trenches has become widely commercialized for 50-200 V blocking voltage range. The approach with columns of p-type and n-type vertical columns for the drift region has been commercialized for the 600-900 V blocking voltage range.

In recognition of the short comings of silicon bipolar transistors and power MOSFETs in the 1970s, I proposed two new thrusts in 1979 for the power device field. The first was based upon the merging of MOS and bipolar device physics to create a new category of power devices[3]. My most successful innovation among MOS-Bipolar devices has been the *Insulated Gate Bipolar Transistor (IGBT)*. Soon after commercial introduction in the early 1980s, the IGBT was adopted for all medium power electronics applications[4]. Today, it is manufactured by more than a dozen companies around the world for consumer, industrial, medical, and other applications that benefit society. The triumph of the IGBT is associated with its huge power gain, high input impedance, wide safe operating area, and a switching speed that can be tailored for applications depending upon their operating frequency.

The second approach that I suggested in 1979 for enhancing the performance of power devices was to replace silicon with wide band gap semiconductors. The basis for this approach was an equation that I derived relating the on-resistance of the drift region in unipolar power devices to the basic properties of the semiconductor material. This equation has since been referred to as *Baliga's Figure of Merit (BFOM)*. In addition to the expected reduction in the on-state resistance with higher carrier mobility, the equation predicts a reduction in on-resistance as the inverse of the cube of the breakdown electric field strength of the semiconductor material.

In the 1970s, there was a dearth of knowledge of the impact ionization coefficients of semiconductors. Consequently, an association of the breakdown electric field strength was made with the energy band gap of the semiconductor[5]. This led to the conclusion that wide band gap semiconductors offer the opportunity to greatly reduce the on-state resistance of the drift region in power devices. With a sufficiently low on-state resistance, it became possible to postulate that unipolar power devices could be constructed from wide band gap semiconductors with lower on-state voltage drop than bipolar devices made out of silicon. Since unipolar devices exhibit much faster switching speed than bipolar devices because of the absence of minority carrier stored charge, wide band gap based power devices offered a much superior alternative to silicon bipolar devices for medium and high power applications. Device structures that were particularly suitable for development were identified as Schottky rectifiers to replace silicon P-i-N rectifiers, and power Field Effect Transistors to replace the bipolar transistors and thyristors prevalent in the 1970s.

The first attempt to develop wide band gap based power devices was undertaken at the General Electric Corporate Research and Development Center, Schenectady, NY, under my direction. The goal was to leverage a 13-fold reduction in specific on-resistance for the drift region predicted by the BFOM for Gallium Arsenide. A team of 10 scientists was assembled to tackle the difficult problems of the growth of high resistivity epitaxial layers, the fabrication of low resistivity ohmic contacts, low leakage Schottky contacts, and the passivation of the GaAs surface. This led to an enhanced understanding of the breakdown strength[6] for GaAs and the successful fabrication of high performance Schottky rectifiers[7] and MESFETs[8]. Experimental verification of the basic thesis of the analysis represented by BFOM was therefore demonstrated during this period. Commercial GaAs based Schottky rectifier products were subsequently introduced in the market by several companies.

In the later half of the 1980s, the technology for the growth of silicon carbide was developed with the culmination of commercial availability of wafers from CREE Research Corporation. Although data on the impact ionization coefficients of silicon carbide was not available, early reports on the breakdown voltage of diodes enabled estimation of the breakdown electric field strength. Using these numbers in the BFOM predicted an impressive 100-200 fold reduction in the specific on-resistance of the drift region for silicon carbide based unipolar devices.

In 1988, I joined North Carolina State University and subsequently founded the *Power Semiconductor Research Center (PSRC)* – an industrial consortium – with the objective of exploring ideas to enhance power device performance. Within the first year of the inception of the program, silicon carbide Schottky barrier rectifiers with breakdown voltage of 400 volts were successfully fabricated with on-state voltage drop of about 1 volt and no reverse recovery transients[9]. By improving the edge termination of these diodes, the breakdown voltage was found to increase to 1000 volts. With the availability of epitaxial silicon carbide material with lower doping concentrations, silicon carbide Schottky rectifiers with breakdown voltages over 2.5 kV were successfully fabricated at PSRC[10]. These results motivated many other groups around the world to develop silicon carbide based power rectifiers. In this regard, it has been my privilege to assist in the establishment of national programs to fund research on silicon carbide technology in the United States, Japan, and Switzerland-Sweden. Meanwhile, accurate measurements of the impact ionization coefficients for 6H-SiC and 4H-SiC in defect free regions were performed at PSRC using an electron beam excitation method[11]. Using these coefficients, a BFOM of over 1000 is predicted for SiC providing even greater motivation to develop power devices from this material.

The first silicon carbide power Schottky didoes were observed to exhibit an increase in leakage current by 5-orders of magnitude with increasing reverse bias. This can lead to thermal runaway failure of the diodes. The JBS rectifier concept, first proposed for silicon devices in the 1980s, was found to be essential for addressing this problem in silicon carbide Schottky diodes[12]. The silicon carbide JBS rectifiers were commercialized in 2005 and have a well-established market today as anti-parallel diodes for silicon IGBTs.

Although the fabrication of high performance, high voltage Schottky rectifiers has been relatively straight-forward, the development of a suitable silicon carbide MOSFET structure has been more problematic. The existing silicon power D-MOSFET and U-MOSFET structures do not directly translate to suitable structures in silicon carbide. The interface between silicon carbide and silicon dioxide, as a gate dielectric, needed extensive investigation due to the large density of traps that prevent the formation of high conductivity inversion layers. Even after overcoming this hurdle, the much higher electric field in the silicon dioxide when compared with silicon devices, resulting from the much larger electric field in the underlying silicon carbide, leads to reliability problems. Fortunately, a structural innovation, called the ACCUFET, to overcome both problems was proposed and demonstrated at PSRC[13]. In this structure, a buried P^+ region is used to shield the gate region from the high electric field within the SiC drift region. This concept is applicable to devices that utilize either accumulation channels or inversion channels. Devices with low specific on-resistance have been demonstrated at PSRC using both 6H-SiC and 4H-SiC with epitaxial material capable of supporting over 5000 volts[14]. This device structure has been subsequently emulated by several groups around the world.

Although many papers have been published on silicon carbide device structures and process technology, no comprehensive book written by a single author was available that provides a unified treatment of silicon carbide power device structures until I wrote and published a book in 2006[15]. This new book has been prepared to update the information on silicon carbide power devices. Many innovative silicon carbide power MOSFET structures that were created during the last 15 years are described in this book. A novel bi-directional switch, called BiDFET, is discussed here due to its enabling revolutionary advances in power electronics with matrix converters.

The emphasis in the book is on the physics of operation of the devices. The analyses provide general guidelines for understanding the design and operation of the various device structures. For designs that may be pertinent to specific applications, the reader should refer to the papers published in the literature, the theses of my M.S. and Ph.D. students, as well as the work reported by other research groups. Comparison with silicon devices is provided to enable the reader to understand the benefits of silicon carbide devices.

In the introduction chapter, the desired characteristics of power devices are described with a broad introduction to potential applications. The second chapter provides the properties of silicon carbide that have relevance to the analysis and performance of power device structures. Issues pertinent to the fabrication of silicon carbide devices are reviewed here because the structures analyzed in the book have been constructed with these process limitations in mind. The third chapter discusses breakdown voltage, which is the most unique distinguishing characteristic for power devices, together with edge termination structures. This analysis is pertinent to all the device structures discussed in subsequent chapters of the book.

The fourth chapter describes the basic thesis for development of wide bandgap power devices. The reduction in the specific on-resistance of the drift region is analyzed with design rules for choosing its doping and thickness. Information about super-junction silicon power MOSFFETs has been included here for comparison with the silicon carbide devices. The benefits of applying the super-junction structure to silicon carbide is also analyzed.

Chapter 5 describe the physics of operation of the basic Schottky rectifiers made from silicon carbide. The advantages of the low drift region resistance are made evident here. The problem of high reverse leakage current due to Schottky barrier lowering and tunneling are described high-lighted. Chapter 6 describes solutions for this problem by using P-N junctions to shield the Schottky contact in the silicon carbide JBS rectifier structure.

A brief analysis of silicon carbide P-i-N rectifiers is given in the seventh chapter. It is shown here that these structure are useful only when the blocking voltage exceeds 10 kV. The unique problem of bipolar degradation in silicon carbide P-i-N rectifiers is described here. Chapter 8 describes the silicon carbide MPS rectifier structure which allows significant improvement in the trade-off curve between on-state voltage drop and reverse recovery switching losses. These diodes are pertinent to blocking voltages above 10 kV for utility scale applications.

Chapter 9 discusses power JFET and MESFET structures with planar and trench gate regions. These normally-on structures can be used to construct the *Baliga-Pair* circuit[16], described in chapter 10, which has been shown to be ideally suitable for motor control applications. This represents one option for taking advantage of the low specific on-resistance of the silicon carbide drift region which has been commercialized by some companies.

Chapter 11 provides a description of silicon carbide planar-gate power MOSFET structures with emphasis on problems associated with simply replicating structures originally developed in silicon technology. Innovative approaches to prevent high electric field in the gate oxide of silicon carbide power MOSFETs are discussed here. Accumulation-mode structures are shown to provide the advantages of larger channel mobility and lower threshold voltage leading to a reduction in the specific on-resistance. Many structural innovations are described here for improving the high-frequency-figures-of-merit. The benefits of reducing the gate oxide thickness are explored as well.

In chapter 12, issues with adopting the silicon trench-gate MOSFET structure to silicon carbide are enunciated followed by analysis of solutions to these problems. Once again, methods for shielding the gate oxide are shown to enable reduction of the electric field in the gate oxide to acceptable levels. The shielding also ameliorates the base reach-through problem allowing a reduction of the base width and hence the channel resistance contribution.

Chapter 13 describes the silicon carbide JBSFET structure where a JBS diode is integrated with the MOSFET device. This is important for preventing bipolar current flow via the MOSFET body diode. It also reduces switching power losses and eliminates the need for an external JBS anti-parallel diode for the silicon carbide power MOSFET.

The application of the super-junction concept to silicon carbide power devices is reviewed in chapter 14. This approach is relatively immature at this time but holds significant promise for future reduction of specific on-resistance in silicon carbide devices with high (> 5 kV) breakdown voltages.

One of short-comings of silicon carbide power MOSFETs that can impede their acceptable for motor drive applications such as electric vehicles is their poor short-circuit withstand capability. Structural modifications lead to a trade-off between obtaining a short circuit time of 10 µs that is expected of silicon IGBTs and an increase in on-resistance and switching losses. The BaSIC topology, with a silicon MOSFET in series with the silicon carbide power MOSFET, has been demonstrated to provide an elegant solution as discussed in chapter 15. A short-circuit time of 10 µs has been achieved with this approach with less than 5 % increase in the on-resistance.

A bi-directional switch with symmetrical high voltage blocking capability and low on-resistance in the first and third quadrant has been long sought after for matrix converter applications. Such a device, called the BiDFET, has been recently created and manufactured in a foundry. This technology is described in chapter 16.

Interest in silicon carbide IGBTs has been growing for utility scale applications where the blocking voltage exceeds 15-kV. These devices are analyzed in chapter 17. An optimized silicon carbide IGBT structure is described here that avoid high [dV/dt] during the turn-off transient.

The manufacturing technology for silicon carbide power MOSFETs and JBS diodes is reviewed in chapter 18. This technology, called PRESiCE^{TM}, was created over a 5 year time from at NCSU using a 6-inch foundry.

The concluding chapter 19 gives a short description of promising applications for the silicon carbide devices. It is shown that these devices enable increasing the operating frequency in power circuits leading to significant reduction in the size and weight of systems. A modest gain in efficiency of 1-5 percent over silicon devices has been reported by using these wide band gap power devices.

Experimental results are included throughout the book whenever pertinent to each chapter. This provides a historical context and a brief summary of the state of the art for silicon carbide devices. However, the analytical models provided in the book are fundamental in nature and will not become obsolete.

I am hopeful that this book will be used for the teaching of courses on solid state devices and that it will make an essential reference for the power device industry. To facilitate this, analytical solutions are provided throughout the book that can be utilized to understand the underlying physics and model the structures.

Ever since my identification of the benefits of utilizing wide band gap semiconductors for the development of superior power devices thirty-five years ago, it has been my mission to resolve issues that would impede their commercialization. I wish to thank the sponsors of the Power Semiconductor Research Center, the Office of Naval Research, and the PowerAmerica Institute for supporting this mission during the past 30 years. They provided the resources required to create many breakthroughs in the silicon carbide technology which enabled comercialization of the technology. The establishment of the PowerAmerica Institute in 2015 was a major step forward in bringing down the cost of the wide band gap power device technology. This has now accelerated its market penetration in years to come. I look forward to observing the benefits accrued to society by adopting the technology for conservation of fossil fuel usage resulting in reduced environmental pollution.

Prof. B. Jayant Baliga
July 2023

References

[1] B. J. Baliga, "Fundamentals of Power Semiconductor Devices", Second Edition, Springer, 2019.

[2] B. J. Baliga, "Advanced Power MOSFET Concepts", Springer-Science, 2010.

[3] B. J. Baliga, "Evolution of MOS-Bipolar Power Semiconductor Technology", Proceedings IEEE, pp. 409-418, April 1988.

[4] B. J. Baliga, "The IGBT Device: Physics, Design, and Applications", Second Edition, Elsevier Press, 2023.

[5] B. J. Baliga, "Semiconductors for High Voltage Vertical Channel Field Effect Transistors", J. Applied Physics, Vol. 53, pp. 1759-1764, March 1982.

[6] B. J. Baliga, R. Ehle, J. R. Shealy, and W. Garwacki, "Breakdown Characteristics of Gallium Arsenide", IEEE Electron Device Letters, Vol. EDL-2, pp. 302-304, November 1981.

[7] B. J. Baliga, A. R. Sears, M. M. Barnicle, P. M. Campbell, W. Garwacki, and J. P. Walden, "Gallium Arsenide Schottky Power Rectifiers", IEEE Transactions on Electron Devices, Vol. ED-32, pp. 1130-1134, June 1985.

[8] P. M. Campbell, W. Garwacki, A. R. Sears, P. Menditto, and B. J. Baliga, "Trapezoidal-Groove Schottky-Gate Vertical-Channel GaAs FET", IEEE Electron Device Letters, Vol. EDL-6, pp. 304-306, June 1985.

[9] M. Bhatnagar, P. K. McLarty, and B. J. Baliga, "Silicon-Carbide High-Voltage (400 V) Schottky Barrier Diodes", IEEE Electron Device Letters, Vol. EDL-13, pp.501-503, October 1992.

[10] R. K. Chilukuri and B. J. Baliga, "High Voltage Ni/4H-SiC Schottky Rectifiers", International Symposium on Power Semiconductor Devices and ICs, pp. 161-164, May 1999.

[11] R. Raghunathan and B. J. Baliga, "Temperature dependence of Hole Impact Ionization Coefficients in 4H and 6H-SiC", Solid State Electronics, Vol. 43, pp. 199-211, February 1999.

[12] B. J. Baliga, "Advanced Power Rectifier Concepts", Springer-Science, 2009.

[13] P. M. Shenoy and B. J. Baliga, "High Voltage Planar 6H-SiC ACCUFET", International Conference on Silicon Carbide, III-Nitrides, and Related Materials, Abstract Tu3b-3, pp. 158-159, August 1997.

[14] R. K. Chilukuri and B. J. Baliga, PSRC Technical Report TR-00-007, May 2000.

[15] B. J. Baliga, "Silicon Carbide Power Devices", World Scientific Press, 2006.

[16] B. J. Baliga, See Chapter 7 in "Power Semiconductor Devices", pp. 417-420, PWS Publishing Company, 1996.

Contents

Chapter 11   Planar-Gate Power MOSFETs   287

Chapter 1

Introduction

Modern society has become increasingly reliant upon electrical appliances for comfort, transportation, and healthcare. This has motivated great advances in power generation, power distribution and power management technologies based on enhancements in the performance of power devices that regulate the flow of electricity. After the displacement of vacuum tubes by solid state devices in the 1950s, the industry relied upon silicon bipolar devices, such as bipolar power transistors and thyristors. Although the ratings of these devices grew rapidly to serve an ever broader system need, their fundamental limitations in terms of the cumbersome control and protection circuitry led to bulky and costly solutions. The advent of MOS technology for digital electronics enabled the creation of a new class of devices in the 1970s for power switching applications as well. These silicon power MOSFETs have found extensive use in high frequency applications with relatively low operating voltages (under 100 volts). The merger of MOS and bipolar physics enabled creation of yet another class of devices in the 1980s. The most successful innovation in this class of devices has been the Insulated Gate Bipolar Transistor (IGBT)[1]. The high power density, simple interface, and ruggedness of the IGBT have made it the technology of choice for all medium and high power applications.

Power devices are required for systems that operate over a broad spectrum of power levels and frequencies. The applications for power devices are shown as a function of circuit operating frequency in Fig. 1.1. High power systems, such as HVDC power distribution and locomotive drives that require the control of megawatts of power, operate at relatively low frequencies. As the operating frequency increases, the power ratings decrease for the devices with typical microwave devices handling about 100 watts. Although all of these applications are served by mainly by silicon devices today, devices based on gallium nitride and silicon carbide are now being adopted. Until recently, thyristors were the only devices available with sufficient voltage and current ratings favored for the HVDC power distribution applications. The ratings of IGBTs have now grown to levels where they are now preferred to thyristors for voltage source converters and FACTs designs[1].

The medium frequency and power applications such as electric trains, hybrid-electric cars, home appliances, compact fluorescent lamps, medical equipment, and industrial motor drives also utilize the IGBT. Power MOSFETs are preferred for the high frequency applications operating from low power source voltages. These applications include power supplies for computers and laptops, power management in smart phones, and automotive electronics.

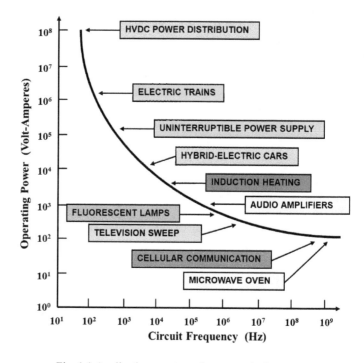

Fig. 1.1 Application spectrum for power devices.

Another approach for classification of applications for power devices is based on their current and voltage handling requirements as shown in Fig. 1.2. On the high power end of the chart, silicon thyristors are available that can individually handle over 6000 volts and 2000 amperes enabling the control of over 10 megawatts of power by a single monolithic device. These devices are suitable for the HVDC power transmission and locomotive drive (traction) applications. During last 10 years, silicon IGBT modules have been developed with blocking voltages of up to 6500 volts and current handling capability above 1000 amperes. This has allowed the IGBT to increasingly replace thyristors in HVDC and traction applications[1].

For the broad range of systems that require operating voltages between 300 volts and 3000 volts with significant current handling capability, the IGBT has been found to be the optimum solution since the 1990s. These applications span all sectors of the economy including consumer, industrial, transportation, lighting, medical, defense, and renewable energy generation[1].

When the current requirements fall below 1 ampere, it is feasible to integrate multiple devices on a single monolithic chip to provide greater functionality for systems such as telecommunications and display drives. However, when the current exceeds a few amperes, it is more cost effective to use discrete silicon power MOSFETs with appropriate control ICs to serve applications such as automotive electronics and switch mode power supplies[2].

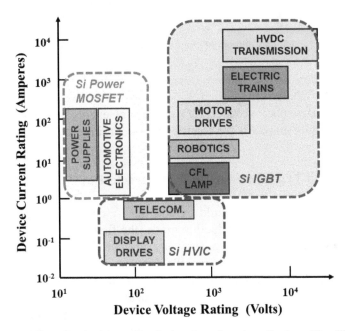

Fig. 1.2 Ratings required for power devices for selected applications. The silicon technology appropriate for various applications is shown.

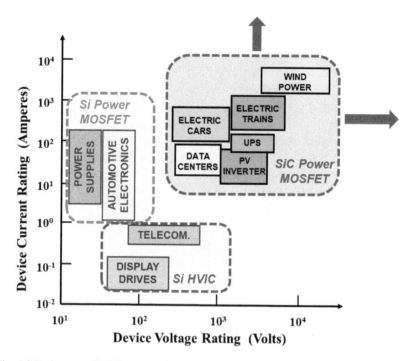

Fig. 1.3 Ratings required for power devices for selected applications. The silicon carbide technology appropriate for various applications is shown.

Silicon carbide power devices are being targeted towards the applications shown in Fig. 1.3. They have already been used in commercialized photovoltaic (PV) residential energy generators. Their major emerging market is for electric cars and trains.

1.1 Ideal and Typical Power Device Characteristics

An ideal power rectifier should exhibit the *i-v* characteristics shown in Fig. 1.4. In the forward conduction mode, the first quadrant of operation the figure, it should be able to carry any amount of current with zero on-state voltage drop. In the reverse blocking mode, the third quadrant of operation in the figure, it should be able to hold off any value of voltage with zero leakage current. Further, the ideal rectifier should be able to instantaneously switch between the on-state and the off-state with zero switching time. The ideal power rectifier would then dissipate no power while allowing control of the direction of current flow in circuits.

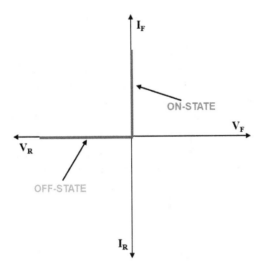

Fig. 1.4 Characteristics of an ideal power rectifier.

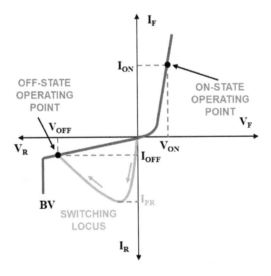

Fig. 1.5 Characteristics of a typical silicon P-i-N power rectifier.

Actual silicon power rectifiers exhibit the *i-v* characteristics illustrated in Fig. 1.5. They have a finite voltage drop (V_{ON}) when carrying current (I_{ON}) on the on-state leading to 'conduction' power loss. The doping concentration and thickness of the drift region of the silicon power device must be carefully chosen based upon the desired breakdown voltage (BV)^2. Smaller drift region doping levels with larger thickness are needed to support larger voltages. This increases the on-state voltage drop in rectifiers with increasing blocking voltage ratings. They also have a finite leakage current (I_{OFF}) when blocking voltage (V_{OFF}) in the off-state producing power loss. In addition, silicon power rectifiers switch from the on-state to the off-state in a finite time interval and display a large reverse recovery current, shown by the green line in Fig. 1.5, with a peak value I_{PR} than can be several times larger than the on-state current level before settling down to the off-state operating point. The reverse recovery process can produce power losses as great as those observed in the on-state.

The finite power dissipation in the power rectifier produces internal heating. This limits the maximum on-state current density to maintain an acceptable maximum junction temperature. The power dissipated in a power rectifier is given by:

$$P_D = (V_{ON} * J_{ON}) + (V_{OFF} * J_{OFF}) + P_{SW} \qquad [1.1]$$

where the first term is the on-state power loss, the second term is the off-state power loss, and the third term is the switching power loss per cycle. The on-state current density (J_{ON}) is determined by the maximum junction temperature ($T_{J,MAX}$):

$$T_{J,MAX} = \frac{P_D}{R_\theta} + T_A \qquad [1.2]$$

where R_θ is the thermal impedance and T_A is the ambient temperature. The power dissipation in power devices increases when their voltage rating is increased due to an increase in the on-state voltage drop and switching loss per cycle. The typical on-state current density for silicon power devices ranges from 25 to 150 A/cm^2 depending up on the blocking voltage rating and the packaging technology.

The *i-v* characteristics of an ideal power switch designed for operation from a DC power source are illustrated in Fig. 1.6. As in the case of the ideal rectifier, the ideal transistor conducts current in the on-state with zero voltage drop and blocks voltage in the off-state with zero leakage current. In addition, the ideal device can operate with a high current and voltage in the active region with the forward current in this mode controlled by the applied gate bias. The spacing between the characteristics in the active region is uniform for an ideal transistor indicating a gain that is independent of the magnitude of the forward current and voltage.

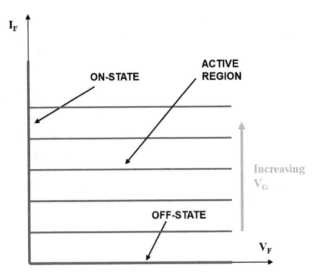

Fig. 1.6 Characteristics of an ideal transistor.

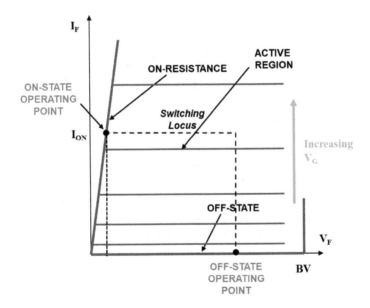

Fig. 1.7 Characteristics of a typical transistor.

The *i-v* characteristics of a typical power switch are illustrated in Fig. 1.7. This device exhibits a finite resistance when carrying current in the on-state as well as a finite leakage current while operating in the off-state (not observable in the figure because its value is much lower than the on-state current levels). The breakdown voltage of a typical transistor is also finite as indicated in the figure with 'BV' where the current abruptly increases. The typical transistor can operate with a high current and voltage in the active region. This current is controlled by the base current for a bipolar transistor while it is determined by a gate voltage for a MOSFET or IGBT (as indicated in the figure). It is preferable to have gate voltage controlled characteristics because the drive circuit is compact and can be integrated to reduce its cost. The spacing between the characteristics in the active region is non-uniform for a typical transistor with a square-law behavior for devices operating with channel pinch-off in the current saturation mode[2]. Recently, devices operating under a new super-linear mode have been proposed and demonstrated for wireless base-station applications[3].

1.2 Unipolar Power Rectifiers

Bipolar power devices operate with the injection of minority carriers during on-state current flow. These carriers must be removed when the switching the device from the on-state to the off-state. This is accomplished by either charge removal via the gate drive current or via the electron-hole recombination process. These processes introduce significant power losses that degrade the power management efficiency. It is therefore preferable to utilize unipolar current conduction in a power device.

The commonly used unipolar power diode structure is the Schottky rectifier that utilizes a metal-semiconductor barrier to produce current rectification[2]. The high voltage Schottky rectifier structure also contains a drift region, as show in Fig. 1.8, which is designed to support the reverse blocking voltage. The resistance of the drift region increases rapidly with increasing blocking voltage capability as discussed later in this book. Silicon Schottky rectifiers are commercially available with blocking voltages of up to 150 volts. Beyond this value, the on-state voltage drop of silicon Schottky rectifiers becomes too large for practical applications[2]. Silicon P-i-N rectifiers are favored for designs with larger breakdown voltages due to their lower on-state voltage drop despite their slower switching properties. As shown later in the book, silicon carbide Schottky rectifiers have much lower drift region resistance enabling design of very high voltage devices with low on-state voltage drop. These devices are excellent replacements for silicon P-i-N rectifiers used as fly-back or free-wheeling diodes with IGBTs in inverters.

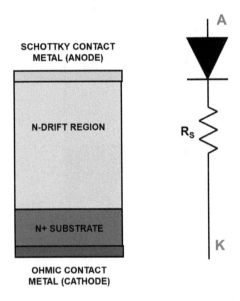

Fig. 1.8 Power Schottky rectifier structure and its equivalent circuit.

A major problem observed in Schottky rectifiers is the large increase in the reverse leakage current with increasing reverse bias voltage. An increase in reverse leakage current by more than one-order of magnitude occurs due to Schottky barrier lowering and pre-breakdown impact ionization in silicon devices[2]. A much worse increase in leakage current by six orders of magnitude due to Schottky barrier lowering and tunneling is observed for silicon carbide and gallium nitride Schottky rectifiers. This is a serious problem for high temperature operation and stability for these rectifiers.

The rapid increase in leakage current for Schottky rectifiers with increasing reverse bias voltage can be mitigated by using the *Junction-Barrier controlled Schottky (JBS)* structure shown in Fig. 1.9. This structure contains P^+ regions surrounding the Schottky contacts. A depletion region extends from the junction during reverse blocking and forms a potential barrier under the Schottky contact. This suppresses the electric field at the Schottky contact. The lower electric field at the

Schottky contact reduces the Schottky barrier lowering and tunneling at the contact[4].

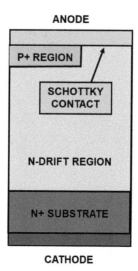

Fig. 1.9 The JBS power rectifier structure.

1.3 Bipolar Power Rectifiers

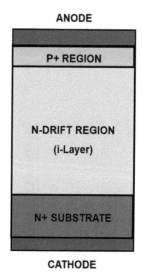

Fig. 1.10 The P-i-N power rectifier structure.

The silicon P-i-N rectifier was commercialized in the 1950s. It is a bipolar device whose structure is illustrated in Fig. 1.10. Current flow in the on-state current occurs by the injection of minority (holes) from the P$^+$ region into the N-drift region. The minority carrier concentration exceeds the doping concentration of the drift region at operating on-state current levels. This is defined as *high-level injection*. The concentration of holes and electrons becomes equal in the drift region due to charge neutrality. These injected mobile carriers greatly reduce the resistance of the drift region allowing the P-i-N rectifier to carry high on-state current density with a small on-state voltage drop. The presence of the electrons and holes in the drift region is referred to as *stored charge*.

The stored charge in the drift region of the P-i-N rectifier must be removed before it is able to support a large reverse bias voltage. It undergoes a *reverse recovery process* during which a high reverse current is observed as illustrated in Fig. 1.5. The reverse recovery process produces considerable power dissipation not only in the P-i-N rectifier but also the transistor used to control its current flow[2]. This results in reduced efficiency and increases the cost of the power electronics.

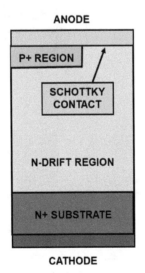

Fig. 1.11 The MPS Power Rectifier Structure.

The stored charge in the P-i-N rectifier can be greatly reduced while maintaining a low on-state voltage drop by using the MPS rectifier structure[4] shown in Fig. 1.11. Although similar in structure to the JBS rectifier, the principle of operation of the MPS rectifier is quite different. In the JBS rectifier, the on-state voltage drop is too low (~ 0.5 volts for silicon devices and 1.5 volts for silicon carbide devices) for the P-N junction to inject minority carriers into the drift region. In contrast, the on-state voltage drop for the MPS rectifier exceeds the built-in potential of the P-N junction. The injected minority carriers from the P-N junction produce conductivity modulation of the drift region as in the case of the P-i-N rectifiers. However, the stored charge is reduced in the MPS rectifier because the minority carrier density is zero at the Schottky contact. MPS rectifiers have a superior trade-off curve between on-state voltage drop and reverse recovery current when compared with P-i-N rectifiers.

1.4 Unipolar Power Transistors

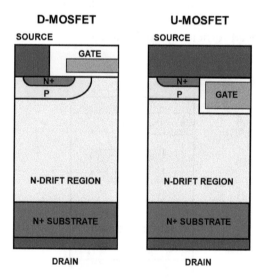

Fig. 1.12 The silicon power MOSFET structures.

Power switches can be designed as normally-on (depletion-mode) structures or as normally-off (enhancement-mode) structures. All power switches used by the industry are normally-off or enhancement mode devices. Normally-on structures create problems of large destructive shoot through currents when turning-on the power electronics because the gate drive required to keep these devices in the off-state has not yet been generated. The most commonly used unipolar power transistor is the silicon power Metal-Oxide-Semiconductor Field-Effect-Transistor or MOSFET. Although other structures, such as JFETs or SITs have been explored[5], they have not been popular for power electronic applications because of their normally-on behavior. Any proposed gallium nitride of silicon carbide device structure must be compatible with this important power circuit requirement to be acceptable for use by the industry. The Baliga-Pair discussed later in the book allows employment of normally-on SiC or GaN FET structures to create a normally-off switch.

The commercially available silicon power MOSFET products are based up on the structures shown in Fig. 1.12. The D-MOSFET was first commercially introduced in the 1970s and contains a 'planar-gate' structure. The P-base region and the N^+ source regions are self-aligned to the edge of the polysilicon gate electrode by using ion-implantation of boron and phosphorus with their respective drive-in thermal cycles. The n-type channel is defined by the difference in the lateral extension of the junctions under the gate electrode[2]. The device supports positive voltage applied to the drain across the P-base/N-drift region junction. The voltage blocking capability is determined by the doping and thickness of the drift region. Although low voltage (< 100 V) silicon power MOSFET have low on-resistances, the drift region resistance increases rapidly with increasing blocking voltage limiting the performance of silicon power MOSFETs to below 200 volts. It is common-place to use the Insulated Gate Bipolar Transistors (IGBT) for higher voltage designs.

The silicon U-MOSFET structure became commercially available in the 1990s. It has a gate structure embedded within a trench etched into the silicon surface. The N-type channel is formed on the side-wall of the trench at the surface of the P-base region. The channel length is determined by the difference in vertical extension of the P-base and N^+ source regions as controlled by the ion-implant energies and drive times for the dopants. The silicon U-MOSFET structure was developed to reduce the on-state resistance by elimination of the JFET component within the D-MOSFET structure[2].

An important innovation for silicon power MOSFETs is the concept of charge coupling to alter the electric field distribution in the drift region and allow it to support high voltages with large doping concentrations in the drift region[6]. The first charge coupled vertical silicon power MOSFET proposed in 1997 was the GD-MOSFET structure shown in Fig. 1.13 on the left-hand-side[7,8]. In comparison with the U-MOSFET structure, this device contains a deep trench region with a source connected electrode. A uniform electric field is generated in the drift region by using a graded doped drift region with high doping concentrations[9]. Breakdown voltages well above the parallel-plane breakdown voltage can be achieved using this idea. The specific on-resistance of these devices has been shown to be well below (5 to 25 times) that for the conventional silicon devices for blocking voltages ranging from 50 to 1000 volts[6]. Many companies have released products using this approach since 2005.

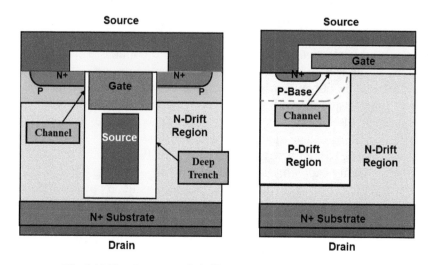

Fig. 1.13 The charge-coupled silicon power MOSFET structures.

An alternate charge-coupled silicon power MOSFET announced in 1999 was the COOLMOS[T] structure shown in Fig. 1.13 on the right hand side. Here, the charge coupling is accomplished across the vertical P-N junction formed between columns of P and N drift regions[10]. Many studies have been performed to optimize this device structure for blocking voltages of 500 to 1000 volts[6]. It has been demonstrated that the COOLMOS structure has about 3 to 10 times lower specific on-resistance than the conventional silicon power MOSFETs at a breakdown voltage of 600 volts. Many companies have commercialized this device structure under various names since 2005.

Any proposed SiC power switch technology must compete with not only the conventional silicon power MOSFET structures but also the new charge coupled silicon power MOSFETs. The charge coupled silicon devices offer much better performance but require a more expensive fabrication process. This difference must also be taken into account.

1.5 Bipolar Power Devices

The commonly available silicon power bipolar devices were the bipolar transistor and the gate turn-off thyristor or GTO[2]. These devices were originally developed in the 1950s and widely used for power switching applications until the 1970s when the availability of silicon power MOSFETs and IGBTs supplanted them. The structures of the bipolar junction transistor (BJT) and the gate turn-off thyristor (GTO) are shown in Fig. 1.15. In both devices, injection of minority carriers into the drift region modulates its conductivity reducing the on-state voltage drop. However, this charge must be subsequently removed during switching resulting in high turn-off power losses. These devices require a large control (base or gate) current which must be implemented with discrete components leading to an expensive bulky system design. They also need snubber circuits for safe turn-off, which adds cost, complexity and power losses to the power electronics.

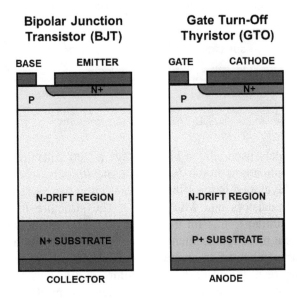

Fig. 1.15 The silicon bipolar device structures.

Several groups have worked on the development of bipolar transistors[11,12,13,14] and GTOs[15,16] using silicon carbide. The large junction potential for silicon carbide results in a relatively high on-state voltage drop for these devices when compared with commercially available silicon devices. Recently, interest has shifted from the SiC BJT and GTO to the development of silicon carbide IGBTs. For this reason, this book does not cover the physics and characteristics of these devices.

1.6 MOS-Bipolar Power Devices

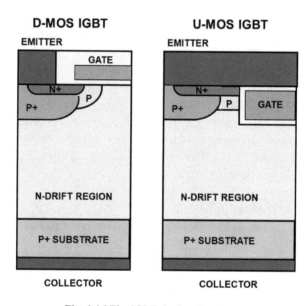

Fig. 1.16 The IGBT device structures.

The most widely used silicon high voltage (>300 volt) device for power switching applications is the *Insulated Gate Bipolar Transistor* (IGBT) which was developed in the 1980s by combining the physics of operation of bipolar transistors and MOSFETs[17]. The structure of the IGBT is deceptively similar to that for the power MOSFET as shown in Fig. 1.16 if viewed as a mere replacement of the N^+ substrate with a P^+ substrate. However, this substitution creates a four-layer parasitic thyristor which can latch up resulting in destructive failure due to loss of gate control. Fortunately the parasitic thyristor can be defeated by the addition of the P^+ region within the cell[2]. The benefit of the P^+ substrate is the injection of minority carriers into the N-drift region resulting in greatly reducing its resistance. This has enabled the development of high voltage IGBT products with high current carrying capability. The main disadvantage of the Si IGBT is a slow switching speed that increases the turn-off power losses. This problem was solved by using electron irradiation to reduce the lifetime in the drift region[2]. Extensive applications of the silicon

IGBT has occurred in all segments of the economy in the last 40 years with enormous benefits to society[1].

The development of the IGBT in silicon carbide has been analyzed and attempted by a few research groups[18,19,20]. The large junction potential and high resistance of the P^+ substrate for silicon carbide results in a relatively high on-state voltage drop for these devices when compared with commercially available silicon devices. Their switching speed is also compromised by the injected stored charge in the on-state. Significant improvements in the characteristics of SiC IGBTs has more recently been achieved by optimization of the buffer layer[21]. The chapter in this book on SiC IGBT describes the physics of operation of these devices and demonstrates a method to avoid the high transient voltages observed in the reported devices.

1.7 Summary

The motivation for the development of silicon carbide and gallium nitride unipolar devices has been reviewed in this chapter. Although excellent unipolar silicon Schottky rectifiers and power MOSFETs are commercially available with breakdown voltages below 200 volts, the resistance of their drift region increases rapidly at higher breakdown voltages producing significant power losses in applications. This problem can be overcome using silicon carbide and gallium nitride based unipolar devices. These devices also offer low switching losses enabling increasing the circuit operating frequency which reduces the size of passive components and filters in applications.

References

[1] B. J. Baliga, "The IGBT Device: Physics, Design, and Applications of the Insulated Gate Bipolar Transistor", Elsevier Press, 2015; Second Edition 2023.

[2] B. J. Baliga, "Fundamentals of Power Semiconductor Devices", Springer-Science, 2008.

[3] B. J. Baliga, "Silicon RF Power Devices", World Scientific Press, 2005.

[4] B. J. Baliga, "Advanced Power Rectifier Concepts", Springer-Science, New York, 2010.

[5] B. J. Baliga, "Modern Power Devices", John Wiley and Sons, 1987.

[6] B. J. Baliga, "Advanced Power MOSFET Concepts", Springer-Science, New York, 2010.

[7] B. J. Baliga, "Vertical Field Effect Transistors having improved Breakdown Voltage Capability and Low On-state Resistance", U.S. Patent # 5,637,898, Issued June 10, 1997.

[8] B. J. Baliga, "Power Semiconductor Devices having improved High Frequency Switching and Breakdown Characteristics", U.S. Patent # 5,998,833, Issued December 7, 1999.

[9] B. J. Baliga, "Trends in Power Discrete Devices", IEEE International Symposium on Power Semiconductor Devices and ICs, Abstract P-2, pp. 5-10, 1997.

[10] L. Lorenz, et al, "COOLMOS – A New Milestone in High Voltage Power MOS" IEEE International Symposium on Power Semiconductor Devices and ICs, pp. 3-10, 1999.

[11] E. Danielsson, et al, "Extrinsic base design of SiC Bipolar Transistors", Silicon Carbide and Related Materials, pp. 1117-1120, 2003.

[12] I. Perez-Wurfll, et al, "Analysis of Power Dissipation and High Temperature Operation in 4H-SiC Bipolar Junction Transistors", Silicon Carbide and Related Materials, pp. 1121-1124, 2003.

[13] J. Zhang, et al, "High Power (500V-70A) and High Gain (44-47) 4H-SiC Bipolar Junction Transistors", Silicon Carbide and Related Materials, pp. 1149-1152, 2003.

[14] A. Agarwal, et al, "SiC BJT Technology for Power Switching and RF Applications", Silicon Carbide and Related Materials 2003, pp. 1141-1144, 2004.

[15] P. Brosselard, et al, "Influence of different Peripheral Protections on the Breakover Voltage of a 4H-SiC GTO Thyristor", Silicon Carbide and Related Materials, pp. 1129-1132, 2003.

[16] A. K. Agarwal, et al, "Dynamic Performance of 3.1 kV 4H-SiC Asymmetrical GTO Thyristors", Silicon Carbide and Related Materials, pp. 1349-1352, 2003.

[17] B. J. Baliga, "Evolution of MOS-Bipolar Power Semiconductor Technology", Proceedings of the IEEE, pp. 409-418, 1988.

[18] T. P. Chow, N. Ramaungul, and M. Ghezzo, "Wide Bandgap Semiconductor Power devices", Materials Research Society Symposium, Vol. 483, pp. 89-102, 1998.

[19] R. Singh, "Silicon Carbide Bipolar Power Devices – Potentials and Limits", Materials Research Society Symposium, Vol. 640, pp. H4.2.1-12, 2001.

[20] J. Wang, et al, "Comparison of 5kV 4H-SiC N-channel and P-channel IGBTs", Silicon Carbide and Related Materials, pp. 1411-1414, 2000.

[21] J. W. Palmour, "Silicon Carbide Power Device development for Industrial Markets", IEEE Int. Electron Devices Meeting, Abstract 1.1.1, pp. 1-8, 2014.

Chapter 2

Material Properties and Processing

The basic electronic properties of the semiconductor determine the electrical characteristics of the power diodes and transistors. The knowledge of these material properties has been gathered over the years by preparation of the material with different doping concentrations. The measured properties for silicon carbide are reviewed and compared with those for silicon in this chapter. Although initial development of SiC power devices was performed using the available 6H-SiC polytype, all modern SiC power devices are being manufactured using the 4H-SiC polytype due to its superior properties. Only the 4H-SiC polytype is therefore included in this chapter. The basic material properties are then used to obtain electrical parameters (such as the built-in potential) which are relevant to the analysis of the performance of power devices discussed in the rest of the book.

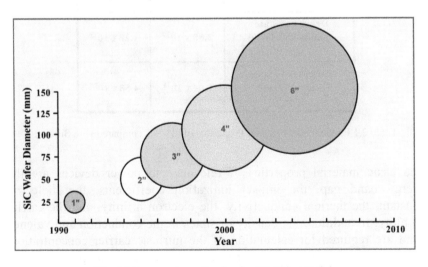

Fig. 2.1 Increase in wafer size for 4H-SiC material.

21

The 4H-SiC material is commercially available from several vendors for the development and manufacturing of power devices because of its superior properties. Manufacturers have now eliminated the micropipes in this material so that it is no longer a concern when fabricating devices. The diameter of commercially available 4H SiC wafers has been increased from 1 inch in size in the early 1990s to 6 inches in size by 2005 as shown in Fig. 2.1. Most 4H SiC based power devices are now manufactured using 6 inch diameter wafers although it is anticipated that 8 inch diameter wafers will go into production in the near future.

2.1 Fundamental Properties

Properties	Silicon	4H-SiC
Energy Band Gap (eV)	1.11	3.26
Relative Dielectric Constant	11.7	9.7
Thermal Conductivity (W/cm K)	1.5	3.7
Electron Affinity (eV)	4.05	3.8
Density of States Conduction Band (cm^{-3})	2.80×10^{19}	1.23×10^{19}
Density of States Valency Band (cm^{-3})	1.04×10^{19}	4.58×10^{18}

Table 2.1 Fundamental Material Properties of 4H-SiC compared with Silicon.

The basic material properties of relevance to power devices are the energy band gap, the impact ionization coefficients, the dielectric constant, the thermal conductivity, the electron affinity, and the carrier mobility. In addition, the density of states in the conduction and valence band are required for calculation of the intrinsic carrier concentration. This section provides a summary of the fundamental properties of the 4H poly-type of silicon carbide[1,2,3], and compares them with those for silicon[4]. The intrinsic carrier concentration and the built-in potential extracted by using this information have been computed and compared with those for silicon in this section.

2.2 Energy Band Gap

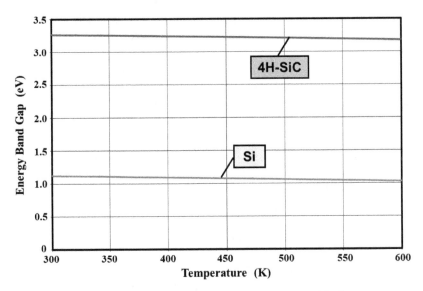

Fig. 2.2 Energy band gap for 4H-SiC compared with Si.

4H silicon carbide has an energy band gap that is much larger than that for silicon allowing its classification as a wide band gap semiconductor. The energy band gap of semiconductors decreases with increasing temperature due to thermal expansion of the lattice. A semi-empirical formula for change in band gap for silicon with temperature[5] is given by:

$$E_G(\text{Si}) = 1.169 - \frac{4.9 \times 10^{-4}\, T^2}{T + 655} \qquad [2.1]$$

where T is the absolute temperature in °K.

Similarly, the temperature dependence of the band gap for 4H-SiC[6] is given by:

$$E_G(4\text{H}-\text{SiC}) = 3.30 - \frac{8.20 \times 10^{-4}\, T^2}{T + 1800} \qquad [2.2]$$

The energy band gap for 4H-SiC can be compared with that for Si in Fig. 2.2. The energy band gaps for 4H-SiC at room temperature (300 °K) is 3.26 eV, about 3 times larger than that for silicon. Since a larger band gap results in a smaller generation of carriers in the depletion regions of devices, the theoretical bulk leakage current for 4H-SiC devices which utilize P-N junctions to support voltages is very small. However, in practical devices, the leakage current is much larger than predicted by space charge generation due to surface generation at the edge terminations.

The larger band gap for 4H-SiC is also favorable for producing metal-semiconductor contacts with larger Schottky barrier heights. This enables reduction of the leakage current in high voltage Schottky rectifiers despite enhanced Schottky barrier lowering and tunneling current when compared to silicon devices. The larger Schottky barrier height for the gate contact in MESFETs (Metal Semiconductor Field Effect Transistors) is also favorable for control of the threshold voltage and reduction of leakage current.

2.3 Intrinsic Carrier Concentration

The intrinsic carrier concentration is the population of electrons and holes within an un-doped (intrinsic) semiconductor. The intrinsic carrier concentration is determined by the thermal generation of electron-hole pairs across the energy band gap of a semiconductor. Its value can be calculated by using the energy band gap (E_G) and the density of states in the conduction (N_C) and valence (N_V) bands:

$$n_i = \sqrt{n.p} = \sqrt{N_C.N_V}\, e^{-[E_G(T)/2kT]} \qquad [2.3]$$

where k is Boltzmann's constant (1.38 x 10^{-23} J/°K) and T is the absolute temperature in °K. For silicon, the intrinsic carrier concentration is given by:

$$n_i = 3.87x10^{16}T^{3/2}e^{-(7.02x10^3)/T} \qquad [2.4]$$

For 4H-SiC, it is given by:

$$n_i = 1.70x10^{16}T^{3/2}e^{-(2.041x10^4)/T} \qquad [2.5]$$

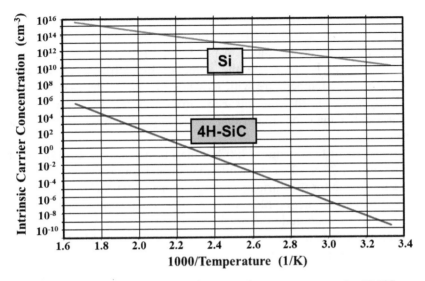

Fig. 2.3 Intrinsic carrier concentration versus inverse temperature for 4H-SiC compared with Si.

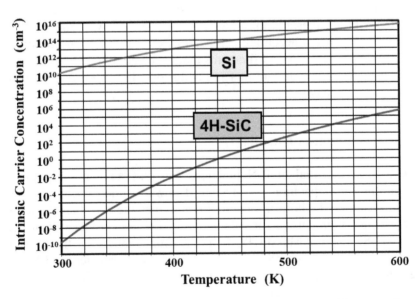

Fig. 2.4 Intrinsic carrier concentration versus temperature for 4H-SiC compared with Si.

Using these equations, the intrinsic carrier concentration can be calculated as a function of temperature. The results are plotted in Fig. 2.3

using the traditional method for making this plot on an inverse temperature scale for the x-axis. An additional Fig. 2.4 is provided here because it is easier to relate the value of the intrinsic carrier concentration to the temperature with its value plotted on the x-axis. It can be clearly observed that the intrinsic carrier concentrations for 4H SiC are far smaller than for silicon due to the large difference in band gap energy.

At room temperature (300°K), the intrinsic carrier concentration for silicon is 1.38 x 10^{10} cm^{-3} while that for 4H-SiC is 2.5 x 10^{-10} cm^{-3}. These low value for the intrinsic concentrations in 4H-SiC make the bulk generation current negligible. Surface generation currents are usually much larger in magnitude due to the presence of states within the band gap due to defects at the interface between the semiconductor and the dielectric applied to its surface.

For silicon, the intrinsic carrier concentration becomes equal to a typical doping concentration of 1 x 10^{14} cm^{-3} at a relatively low temperature of 470 °K or 197 °C. In contrast, the intrinsic carrier concentration for 4H-SiC is only 9 x 10^{4} cm^{-3} even at 600 °K or 327 °C. The development of mesoplasmas has been associated with the intrinsic carrier concentration becoming comparable to the doping concentration[7]. Mesoplasmas create current filaments that have very high current density leading to destructive failure in semiconductors. This is much less likely in silicon carbide devices.

2.4 Junction Built-in Potential

The built-in potential of P-N junctions can play an important role in determining the operation and design of power semiconductor devices. As an example, the built-in potential determines the zero-bias depletion width which is important for calculation of the on-resistance of planar-gate 4H-SiC power MOSFETs. It has a strong impact on the on-state voltage drop in JBS rectifiers, and is an important parameter used for the design of normally-off accumulation mode MOSFETs. These structures are discussed in detail later in the book.

The built-in voltage is given by:

$$V_{bi} = \frac{kT}{q} \ln\left(\frac{N_A^- . N_D^+}{n_i^2}\right)$$ [2.6]

where N_A^- and N_D^+ are the ionized impurity concentrations on the two sides of an abrupt P-N junction. For silicon, their values are equal to the doping concentration because of the small dopant ionization energy levels. This does not apply to silicon carbide in the neutral regions because of the much larger dopant ionization levels as discussed later in this chapter. However, the dopants are completely ionized within the depletion regions due to the prevailing electric field that removes any free carriers.

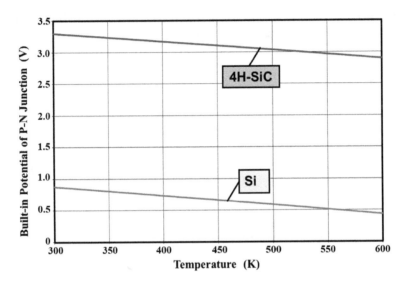

Fig. 2.5 Built-in Potential for a P-N Junction in SiC compared with Si.

The calculated junction built-in potential for 4H-SiC P-N junctions is plotted in Fig. 2.5 as a function of temperature. The product $(N_A^-.N_D^+)$ was assumed to be 10^{35} cm^{-6} in making the plots. This would be applicable for a typical doping concentration of 1 x 10^{19} cm^{-3} on the heavily doped side of the junction and 1 x 10^{16} cm^{-3} on the lightly doped side of the junction.

The built-in potential for 4H-SiC (3.229 V) are much larger than that for silicon (0.877 V) at 27 °C due to the far smaller values for the intrinsic carrier concentration. This can be a disadvantage due to the larger zero bias depletion width for silicon carbide as shown in the next section. As an example, the larger zero bias depletion width consumes space within the 4H-SiC planar-gate MOSFET cell structure increasing the on-resistance by constricting the area through which current can flow. In contrast, the larger built-in potential for SiC and its associated larger zero bias depletion width can be taken advantage of in making innovative device structures, such as the ACCUFET discussed later in the book, that are tailored to take advantage of the unique properties of SiC.

2.5 Zero Bias Depletion Width

The zero-bias depletion width of a P-N junction with high doping concentration on the p-side can be obtained using[8]:

$$W_0 = \sqrt{\frac{2\varepsilon_S V_{bi}}{q N_D}}$$

[2.7]

where N_D is the doping concentration on the n-side. The junction built-in potential for silicon and 4H-SiC at room temperature are 0.877 and 3.229 volts, respectively. The zero bias depletion width obtained by using these values is provided in Fig. 2.6 as a function of the doping concentration on the lightly doped side of the abrupt P-N junction.

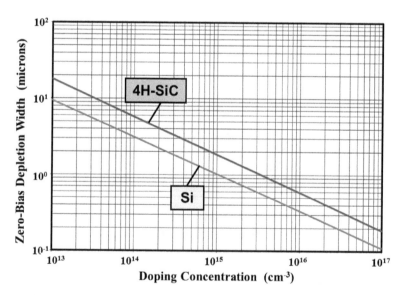

Fig. 2.6 Zero-bias depletion width in SiC P-N junctions compared with Si.

The zero bias depletion width for 4H-SiC P-N junctions is much (about 2x) larger than for the silicon case for the same doping concentration. However, it is worth noting that the doping concentration in SiC devices is also much greater for a given breakdown voltage than for silicon as discussed later in the chapter. In all cases, it can be observed from the figure that the zero bias depletion width can be substantial in size at low doping concentrations making it important to take this into account during device design and analysis.

2.6 Impact Ionization Coefficients

Impact ionization occurs in semiconductors when mobile electrons and holes are accelerated by high electric fields within depletion regions of reverse blocking junctions. The mobile charges gain energy during their motion which is imparted to the lattice during scattering events. When the electric field becomes sufficiently large, the energy gained by the mobile particles can excite electron-hole pairs across the energy band gap. These new electrons and holes are in turn accelerated by the electric field producing the generation of more electron-hole pairs. This precipitates avalanche breakdown of the junction with the on-set of a large amount of current flow which limits its maximum voltage withstand capability.

The main advantage of wide band gap semiconductors for power device applications is the larger electric field required for onset of impact ionization for these materials. A larger electric field is required for a semiconductor with a greater energy band gap because the mobile charges must gain more energy to create electron-hole pairs. The impact ionization process is characterized by using impact ionization coefficients defined as the number of electron-hole pairs created by a mobile particle moving through a distance of 1 cm with the imposed electric field.

The impact ionization coefficient (α) for semiconductors is described by Chynoweth's Law[9,10]:

$$\alpha = a.e^{-b/E} \qquad\qquad [2.8]$$

where E is the electric field component in the direction of current flow. The parameters a and b are constants that depend upon the semiconductor material and the temperature. For silicon, the impact ionization rate is much larger for electrons than for holes and been measured as a function of electric field and temperature[11,12]. The data can be modeled by using a_n = 7 x 10^5 per cm and b_n = 1.23 x 10^6 V/cm for electrons and a_p = 1.6 x 10^6 per cm and b_p = 2.0 x 10^6 V/cm for holes at room temperature[13]. The α_n and α_p for Si is plotted in Fig. 2.7. Large values are observed at an electric field of about 2 x 10^5 V/cm.

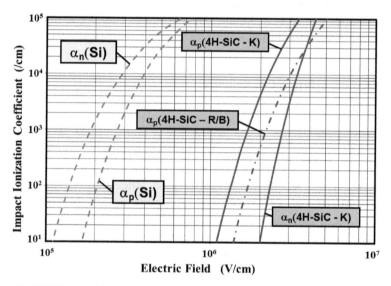

Fig. 2.7 Measured impact ionization coefficients in 4H-SiC compared with Si.

In the case of 4H-SiC, the impact ionization coefficients for holes have been found to be much larger than those for electrons which is opposite of that found for silicon. The impact ionization coefficients for 4H-SiC along the c-axis were measured as a function of temperature by using an electron beam excitation method by Raghunathan and Baliga[14]. This method allowed extraction of impact ionization rates in defect free regions of the material by isolating diodes containing defects with an EBIC (Electron Beam Induced Current) image. This was important because substantially enhanced impact ionization rates were discovered when the measurements were conducted at defect sites[15]. For defect free material, the extracted values for the impact ionization coefficient parameters for holes in 4H-SiC were found to be:

$$a_p(4H - SiC\ R\ /\ B) = 6.46x10^6 - 1.07x10^4 T \qquad [2.9]$$

with

$$b_p(4H-SiC\ R/B)=1.75x10^7 \qquad\qquad \text{[2.10]}$$

The α_p for 4H-SiC obtained by using these parameters is plotted in Fig. 2.7. Large values are observed at an electric field of about 2 x 10^6 V/cm.

The impact ionization coefficient parameters for holes and electrons in 4H-SiC have also been measured by Konstantinov and co-workers along the c-axis[16,17] by optical excitation. At room temperature, the measured values can be modelled using:

$$a_p(4H-SiC\ K)=8.07x10^6 \qquad\qquad \text{[2.11]}$$

with

$$b_p(4H-SiC\ K)=1.5x10^7 \qquad\qquad \text{[2.12]}$$

and

$$a_n(4H-SiC\ K)=3.13x10^8 \qquad\qquad \text{[2.13]}$$

with

$$b_n(4H-SiC\ K)=3.45x10^7 \qquad\qquad \text{[2.14]}$$

The α_n and α_p values obtained using these equations are also plotted in Fig. 2.7. The size of the optical excitation area is large compared with the e-beam method making it likely that the excitation area contains defects. This results is a larger reported value for α_n and α_p compared with the data from reference 18.

The impact ionization coefficients for 4H-SiC can be compared with those for silicon using Fig. 2.7. It can be seen that the onset of signi-ficant generation of carriers by impact ionization (i.e. when $\alpha = 10^3$ cm^{-1}) occurs in silicon at electric fields of about 2 x 10^5 V/cm. An electric field of about 2-3 x 10^6 V/cm is required in 4H-SiC to achieve the same magnitude for the impact ionization coefficient. As a consequence, breakdown in GaN and 4H-SiC devices occurs when the electric field is an order of magnitude larger than that for silicon.

The measured impact ionization coefficients for holes in 4H-SiC measured by Konstaninov and co-workers is larger than that reported by Raghunathan/Baliga. The α_n and α_p values measured by Konstantinov and co-workers is commonly used when modelling 4H-SiC devices to provide a match to the breakdown voltage observed for practical devices[18,19] where defects may be present within their active area. These coefficients are therefore used in this book for analysis of the breakdown voltage. However, as the defect density in the 4H-SiC wafers was reduced by improvements in growth technology, there are reports of breakdown voltages exceeding those predicted using the α_n and α_p values measured in reference 21. These improved breakdown voltages are more consistent with the breakdown voltages predicted by using the α_p values reported by Raghunathan/Baliga.

2.7 Bulk Electron Mobility

As in the case of silicon, the mobility for electrons is larger than that for holes in 4H-SiC. It is therefore favorable to make unipolar devices using N-type drift regions rather than P-type drift regions. The mobility for electrons and holes decreases with increasing doping due to coulombic scattering from the ionized donors and acceptors[12]. However, the drift region doping concentration for Si power devices is usually below 1 x 10^{16} cm^{-3} to achieve the desired breakdown voltage. The mobility becomes independent of doping level at such low doping levels. In contrast, the doping concentration for the drift region in 4H-SiC devices is substantially larger than in silicon devices for obtaining the same breakdown voltage as discussed in detail later in the book. It is therefore important to take into account the reduction mobility with doping level when analyzing the drift region in these materials. In addition, the reduction of mobility must be taken into account when analyzing the resistance of highly doped regions, such as the N$^+$ source region within the power MOSFET structure. Analytical models for the variation of the mobility with doping concentration over a broad range of doping levels are therefore required for analysis of 4H-SiC devices. This behavior has also been theoretically modeled taking into account acoustic and polar optical phonon scattering as well as intervalley scattering[20]. It is however common practice to use a curve fit to the measured mobility data during device analysis.

For n-type silicon, the measured data[21] for mobility of electrons at room temperature as a function of the doping concentration can be modeled using:

$$\mu_n(Si) = \frac{5.10x10^{18} + 92N_D^{0.91}}{3.75x10^{15} + N_D^{0.91}} \qquad [2.15]$$

At low doping levels, the electron mobility in silicon has a value of 1360 cm^2/V-s while at very high doping levels, it asymptotes to a value of 92 cm^2/V-s.

The mobility in 4H-SiC is anisotropic due to its hexagonal crystal structure. The mobility parallel to the c-axis is 20 % larger than perpendicular to the c-axis. Current flow is oriented along the c-axis in vertical discrete 4H-SiC power JBS diodes and power MOSFETs. The mobility parallel to the c-axis is therefore provided here because it is of greatest interest for analysis of vertical discrete 4H-SiC power devices. For n-type 4H-SiC, the mobility of electrons at room temperature as a function of the doping concentration can be modeled using[6]:

$$\mu_n(4H-SiC) = \frac{4.05x10^{13} + 20N_D^{0.61}}{3.55x10^{10} + N_D^{0.61}}$$ [2.16]

At low doping levels, the electron mobility in 4H-SiC has a value of 1140 cm^2/V-s, while at very high doping levels it asymptotes to a value of 20 cm^2/V-s. These values are consistent with experimental results[22,23,24]. Theoretical computation of the electron mobility in 4H-SiC has also been reported[25].

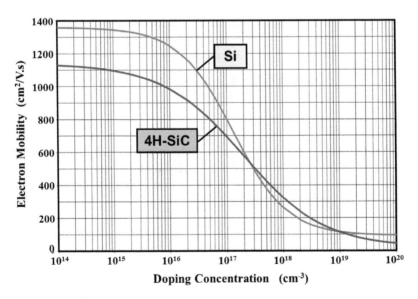

Fig. 2.8 Doping dependence of the bulk mobility for electrons in 4H-SiC compared with Si.

The electron mobility for silicon and 4H-SiC at room temperature is plotted in Fig. 2.8 as a function of doping concentration. In all cases, the mobility decreases with increasing doping due to enhanced coulombic scattering of electrons by the ionized donors. The drop off in mobility occurs at a doping concentration of 1 x 10^{17} cm^{-3} for Si and 4H-SiC. The data in Fig. 2.8 is useful for development of the power device models later in the book.

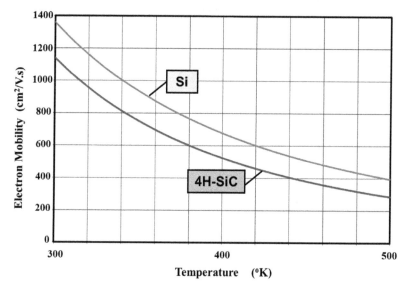

Fig. 2.9 Temperature dependence of the bulk mobility for electrons in 4H-SiC compared with Si.

The mobility in semiconductors decreases with increasing temperature due to enhanced phonon scattering[12]. This holds true for the electron mobility in silicon and 4H-SiC as shown in Fig. 2.9. For silicon, the temperature dependence of the electron mobility at low doping concentrations can be modeled using[26]:

$$\mu_n(Si) = 1360\left(\frac{T}{300}\right)^{-2.42} \qquad [2.17]$$

For 4H-SiC, the temperature dependence of the electron mobility at low doping concentrations can be modeled using[5]:

$$\mu_n(4H-SiC)=1140\left(\frac{T}{300}\right)^{-2.70} \qquad [2.18]$$

The variation of the mobility with temperature is shown in the above figure only up to 500 °K (227 °C) because power devices are usually not rated to operate at higher temperatures. Although there is considerable interest in the performance of silicon carbide devices at much higher temperatures due to its wide band gap structure, the operation of devices above 500 °K is problematic for products used in consumer and industrial products due to degradation of the ohmic contacts and the surface passivation. It is worth pointing out that the mobility for electrons reduces by a factor of about 2-times when the temperature rises to 125 °C and by a factor of about 3-times at 225 °C. This increases the resistance of the drift region in unipolar devices such as Schottky rectifiers and power MOSFETs. This an important effect that must be included during modelling of power devices. The increase in on-state resistance reduces the maximum current handling capability of these devices.

2.8 Bulk Hole Mobility

Although power devices are invariably based on electron transport in Si and 4H-SiC due to their larger mobility, information on the mobility for holes is required during design and analysis of devices, such as power MOSFETs. During switching transients, the capacitive charging currents flow through the p-base region of power MOSFETs. This current flow can trigger the turn-on of the parasitic bipolar transistor. Analysis of the resistance of the p-base region requires knowledge of the mobility for holes in the semiconductors.

It is useful to have models for the hole mobility as a function of doping concentration over a broad range of doping levels for silicon and 4H-SiC. For p-type silicon, the measured data[24] for mobility of holes at room temperature as a function of the doping concentration can be modeled using:

$$\mu_p(Si)=\frac{2.9x10^{15}+47.7N_A^{0.76}}{5.86x10^{12}+N_A^{0.76}} \qquad [2.19]$$

At low doping levels, the hole mobility in silicon has a value of 495 cm^2/V-s while at very high doping levels, it asymptotes to a value of 48 cm^2/V-s.

For p-type 4H-SiC, the mobility of holes at room temperature as a function of the doping concentration can be modeled using[3]:

$$\mu_p(4H - SiC) = \frac{4.05x10^{13} + 10N_A^{0.65}}{3.3x10^{11} + N_A^{0.65}}$$ [2.20]

At low doping levels, the hole mobility in 4H-SiC has a value of 120 cm^2/V-s, while at very high doping levels it asymptotes to a value of 10 cm^2/V-s.

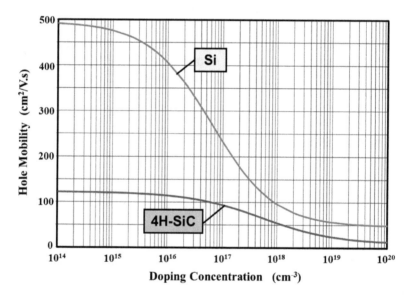

Fig. 2.10 Doping dependence of the bulk mobility for holes in 4H-SiC compared with Si.

The mobility for holes in silicon and 4H-SiC at room temperature is plotted in Fig. 2.10 as a function of doping concentration. In all cases, the mobility decreases with increasing doping due to enhanced coulombic scattering of holes by the ionized acceptors. The drop off in mobility occurs at a doping concentration of 1 x 10^{17} cm^{-3} for both cases. The mobility for holes in 4H-SiC is the low making the resistance of p-type regions a problem that needs special attention during device design. The data In Fig. 2.10 is useful for development of power device models later in the book.

The mobility in semiconductors decreases with increasing temperature due to enhanced phonon scattering. This holds true for the hole mobility in silicon and 4H-SiC as shown in Fig. 2.11. For silicon, the temperature dependence of the hole mobility at low doping concentrations can be modeled using[31]:

$$\mu_p(Si) = 495\left(\frac{T}{300}\right)^{-2.2}$$

[2.21]

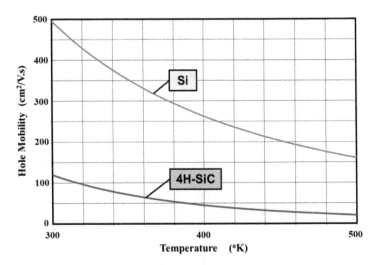

Fig. 2.11 Temperature dependence of the bulk mobility for holes in 4H-SiC compared with Si.

For 4H-SiC, the temperature dependence of the hole mobility at low doping concentrations can be modeled using[28,27]:

$$\mu_p(4H-SiC) = 120\left(\frac{T}{300}\right)^{-3.4}$$

[2.22]

The variation of the mobility with temperature is shown in Fig. 2.11 up to 500 °K (227 °C). Power devices are usually not rated to operate at higher temperatures. The mobility for holes reduces by a factor of about 2-times when the temperature rises to 125 °C and by a factor of about 3-times at 225 °C for silicon. A much greater reduction in the hole mobility occurs for 4H-SiC. In 4H-SiC, the hole mobility becomes 40 % of the room temperature value at 400 °K and 10 % the room temperature value at 500 °K. The low mobility for holes in 4H-SiC can create problems during current flow through the base regions of power MOSFETs under transient operation. The high resistance of p-base regions in 4H-SiC IGBTs could lead to latch-up of the internal thyristor as well.

2.9 Channel Electron Mobility

Power MOSFETs rely upon control of current flow through a channel induced under the MOS gate region. In silicon devices, the channel is formed using an inversion layer – electrons at the surface of a P-base region for n-channel devices and holes at the surface of an N-base region for p-channel devices. Silicon carbide power MOSFETs of interest are n-channel devices because of the much larger mobility for electrons than holes in bulk 4H-SiC material.

An n-channel region is formed by application a positive gate bias across the gate oxide to produce a strong electric field orthogonal to the semiconductor surface. Band bending at the semiconductor surface creates an inversion layer of electrons at the interface between the P-base region and the gate oxide at sufficiently large gate bias voltages[28]. The electrons in the inversion layer are confined very close to the interface.

Many additional mechanisms influence the scattering of electrons in the inversion layer when compared with bulk transport. They include Coulombic scattering by fixed charge in the gate oxide, charges in interface states, surface phonon scattering, and surface roughness scattering. Among these, surface roughness scattering is the most significant for inversion layers in 4H-SiC[29]. The wafer surface for 4H-SiC is much rougher than for silicon due to the off-axis orientation of the substrate required by epitaxial growth and the greater difficulty in polishing this material.

The typical variation of the effective or conductivity inversion layer mobility is shown schematically in Fig. 2.12. It has a peak value ($\mu_{P,EFF}$) close to the threshold voltage and then reduces with increasing gate bias. The value of the effective inversion layer mobility ($\mu_{G,EFF}$) at the gate bias voltage (V_G) is of interest for computation of the on-resistance for power MOSFETs. This behavior can be modelled using:

$$\mu_{EFF} = \frac{\mu_{P,EFF}}{1 + K_{inv}\left(V_G - V_{TH}\right)} \quad\quad [2.23]$$

where $\mu_{P,EFF}$ is the peak inversion layer mobility, K_{inv} is a constant that describes the rate of decrease in mobility with increasing electric field in the oxide, V_G is the gate bias and V_{TH} is the threshold voltage.

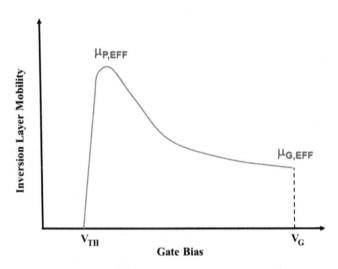

Fig. 2.12 Effective mobility in the inversion layer.

The effective inversion layer mobility for 4H-SiC was initially reported to be very low (< 0.1 cm^2/V-s). A high effective inversion layer mobility for 4H-SiC n-channel lateral MOSFETs was first reported in 1998[30,31]. Lateral MOSFETs fabricated using low temperature (410 $^\circ$C) deposited SiO$_2$ followed by a wet oxidation cycle at 1000 $^\circ$C for 400 minutes were found to exhibit peak inversion layer mobility of 176 cm^2/V-s at room temperature which reduced to 140 cm^2/V-s at high gate bias voltages. The effective mobility was found to increase with increasing temperature indicating presence of traps at the interface between the oxide and the semiconductor. These MOSFETs had a threshold voltage of 2 volts at room temperature. The results obtained using deposited oxide were subsequently reproduced with a peak mobility of 80 cm^2/V-s[32]. 10-kV 4H-SiC SiC power MOSFETs have been successfully fabricated using a deposited gate oxide followed by NO annealing[33]. These devices had a favorable threshold voltage of 7.5 V with a channel mobility of 15 cm^2/V-s.

However, it is preferable to utilize thermally grown oxide for the fabrication of power devices due to their superior breakdown strength. It was found that thermal oxidation of 4H-SiC in either dry or wet ambient produces a very high density of interface states that trap the electrons in the inversion layers. It is necessary to determine the concentration of very fast interface states[34]. The effective mobility measured with the presence of the interface states is very low due to the reduced mobile charge in the inversion layer. Hall measurements performed on inversion layers have determined that the inversion mobility is in the range of 100 cm^2/V-s.

During the last 20 years, considerable effort has been undertaken to understand the interface between SiO_2 and 4H-SiC and correlate this with the inversion layer mobility[47]. The best method for improvement of effective mobility in 4H-SiC for MOSFETs fabricated using thermally grown oxides has been reported to be by post-oxidation annealing in nitric oxide (NO) and nitrous oxide (N_2O). It has been reported that the channel mobility is inversely proportional to the interface state density. A significant reduction in the interface state density has been accomplished by performing annealing at 1175 °C in a nitric oxide (NO) ambient for 2 hours[35,36,37,38]. An effective channel mobility for electrons of 30-35 cm^2/V-s was achieved using this process at the operating gate bias. Subsequent work[39,40] has demonstrated that charge trapping sufficiently suppressed by the nitric oxide annealing leads to an effective channel mobility of about 60 cm^2/V-s.

It would be preferable to fabricate 4H-SiC power MOSFETs using ion-implanted P-base regions as in the case of silicon devices. Due to the low diffusion rate for dopants in the 4H-SiC, it is necessary to stagger the edge for the implantation of the P-base and N^+ source regions for the 4H-SiC devices[41,42] to create the DiMOSFET structure. The damage in the ion implanted regions must be removed by annealing followed by surface preparation to reduce interface states. The inversion layer mobility in n-channel lateral MOSFETs fabricated on aluminum implanted layers in 4H-SiC has been reported[43]. The ion-implant dose and energy was selected to achieve a doping concentration of 1 x 10^{17} cm^{-3} followed by annealing for 10 minutes at 1600 °C. The gate oxide was grown at 1200 °C and then placed in an alumina environment. Peak inversion layer mobility of 100 cm^2/V-s was observed with a high threshold voltage of about 10 volts.

High voltage power MOSFETs must be typically designed with a threshold voltage of 5 volts. This requires reducing the P-base doping concentration[44] to about 1 x 10^{16} cm^{-3}. Such low P-base doping concentration is comparable to the doping in the N-drift region leading to reach-through breakdown problems. To avoid this, it is necessary to include a deeper highly doped P-type barrier layer below the P-base region to create the shielded-base power MOSFET structure[45]. The shielded-base structure can also be achieved by using a retrograde ion-implantation profile to achieve a low doping concentration at the surface. This approach is widely practiced in the industry to manufacture 4H-SiC power MOSFETs as discussed later in the book. The inversion layer mobility has been measured on P-type epitaxial layers with doping concentration of 1 x 10^{16} cm^{-3} grown on top of aluminum ion-implanted highly doped (5 x 10^{18} cm^{-3}) shielding layers[46]. It was found to range from 20 to 30 cm^2/V-s when compared to 2 cm^2/V-s without the epitaxial layer.

2.10 Electron Velocity-Field Curves

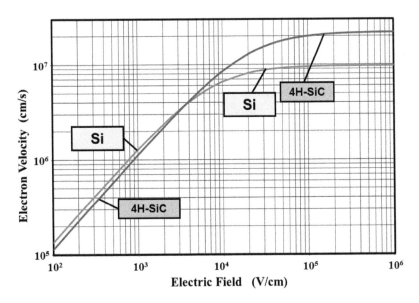

Fig. 2.13 Velocity-field curve for electrons at 300 °K in 4H-SiC compared with Si.

Power devices must operate with high electric fields in the drift region in order to support high voltages over short distances. The velocity for electrons and holes in semiconductors increases in proportion to the electric field at low values for the field. The proportionality constant is defined as the mobility which was described in the previous sections. At larger electric field values, the mobile carriers gain enough energy to generate optical phonon scattering in the semiconductors. This results in a saturation of the drift velocity at high electric fields. The velocity-field curves for electrons in the 4H-SiC can be compared with Si using Fig. 2.13.

The electron velocity-field curve at room temperature for Si with low doping concentrations can be modeled using the measured data[47]:

$$v_n(\text{Si}) = \frac{9.85 \times 10^6 \, E}{\left[1.04 \times 10^5 + \left(E^{1.3}\right)\right]^{0.77}} \qquad \text{[2.24]}$$

At low electric fields, the electron mobility in Si has a value of 1360 cm^2/V-s at small doping concentrations (below 1 x 10^{15} cm^{-3}). In this regime of operation, the electron velocity increases in proportion to the electric field until the field reaches a value of about 5 x 10^3 V/cm. The electron velocity then increases more slowly with increasing electric field until it saturates at an electric field of about 1 x 10^5 V/cm. The saturated drift velocity for electrons in silicon at 300 °K is 9.7 x 10^6 cm/s.

The electron velocity-field curve at room temperature for 4H-SiC with low doping concentrations can be modeled using the measured data[48,49]:

$$v_n(4\text{H}-\text{SiC}) = \frac{2.20 \times 10^7 \, E}{\left[2.27 \times 10^5 + \left(E^{1.25}\right)\right]^{0.8}} \qquad \text{[2.25]}$$

At low electric fields, the electron mobility in 4H-SiC has a value of 1140 cm^2/V-s at small doping concentrations (below 1 x 10^{15} cm^{-3}). In this regime of operation, the electron velocity increases in proportion to the electric field until the field reaches a value of about 1 x 10^4 V/cm. This electric field is much greater than that for silicon. After this, the electron velocity increases more slowly with increasing electric field until it saturates at an electric field of about 1 x 10^5 V/cm. The saturated drift velocity for electrons in 4H-SiC at 300 °K is 2.2 x 10^7 cm/s. This values is twice as large as that observed for silicon.

2.11 Hole Velocity-Field Curves

The velocity-field curves for holes in the 4H-SiC can be compared with Si using Fig. 2.14. The velocity-field curve for holes at room temperature for Si with low doping concentrations can be modeled using the measured data[42]:

$$v_p(\text{Si}) = \frac{8.91 \, x \, 10^6 \, E}{\left[1.41 \, x \, 10^5 + \left(E^{1.2}\right)\right]^{0.83}} \qquad [2.26]$$

At low electric fields, the hole mobility in Si has a value of 495 cm^2/V-s at small doping concentrations (below 1 x 10^{15} cm^{-3}). In this regime of operation, the hole velocity increases in proportion to the electric field until the field reaches a value of about 1 x 10^4 V/cm. The hole velocity then increases more slowly with increasing electric field until it saturates at an electric field of about 1 x 10^5 V/cm. The saturated drift velocity for holes in silicon at 300 °K is 8.9 x 10^6 cm/s.

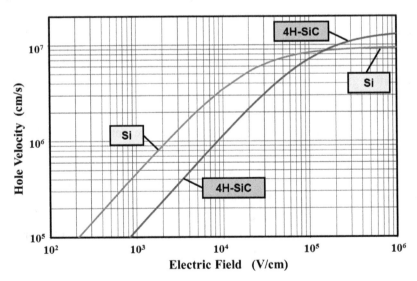

Fig. 2.14 Velocity-field curve at 300 °K for holes in 4H-SiC compared with Si.

The velocity-field curve for holes at room temperature for p-type 4H-SiC with low doping concentrations can be modeled using:

$$v_p(4H-SiC) = \frac{1.3 \times 10^7 \, E}{\left[1.16 \times 10^6 + \left(E^{1.2}\right)\right]^{0.83}}$$ [2.27]

At low electric fields, the hole mobility in 4H-SiC has a value of 120 cm^2/V-s at small doping concentrations (below 1×10^{15} cm^{-3}). In this regime of operation, the hole velocity increases in proportion to the electric field until the field reaches a value of about 1×10^5 V/cm. This electric field is much greater than that for silicon. After this, the hole velocity increases more slowly with increasing electric field until it saturates at an electric field of about 1×10^6 V/cm. The saturated drift velocity for holes in 4H-SiC at 300 °K is 1.3×10^7 cm/s. This values is smaller than the saturated drift velocity for electrons in 4H-SiC.

2.12 Dopant Ionization

At doping concentrations below 10^{19} cm^{-3}, the donor and acceptor level in semiconductors is located at a discrete position away from the band edges. The electron and hole carrier concentrations are not equal to the doping concentration because all of the dopant atoms are not ionized. The number of ionized dopants becomes smaller when the temperature is reduced and the doping concentration is increased. The conductivity of the drift region in power devices relies on the number of available free carriers for current transport which can be smaller than the doping concentration. In addition, the conductivity of base regions in power devices is reduced when all the dopant atoms are not ionized leading to greater parasitic resistances. The higher resistances of base regions can degrade dynamic performance of power devices. In this section, the behavior of dopants in n-type and p-type silicon is first provided as a baseline. The treatment of dopants in silicon carbide is then discussed and compared to that for silicon.

The number of ionized donors or equilibrium concentration of electrons in a semiconductor can be determined using:

$$n = N_D^+ = \frac{N_C}{2g_D} e^{\left(-\frac{E_{DI}}{kT}\right)} \left[\sqrt{1 + \frac{4N_D g_D}{N_C} e^{\left(\frac{E_{DI}}{kT}\right)}} - 1\right]$$ [2.28]

where N_C is the effective density of states in the conduction band, g_D is the degeneracy factor for donors, E_{DI} is the ionization energy for donors, k is Boltzmann's constant, T is the absolute temperature, and N_D is the donor doping concentration. Similarly, the number of ionized acceptors or equilibrium concentration of holes in a semiconductor can be determined using:

$$p = N_A^- = \frac{N_V}{2g_A} e^{\left(-\frac{E_{Al}}{kT}\right)} \left[\sqrt{1 + \frac{4N_A g_A}{N_V} e^{\left(\frac{E_{Al}}{kT}\right)}} - 1 \right] \qquad [2.29]$$

where N_V is the effective density of states in the valence band, g_A is the degeneracy factor for acceptors, E_{Al} is the ionization energy for acceptors, k is Boltzmann's constant, T is the absolute temperature, and N_A is the acceptor doping concentration. The degeneracy factor for donors is typically 2 and that for acceptors is typically 4.

2.12.1 Dopant Ionization in Silicon

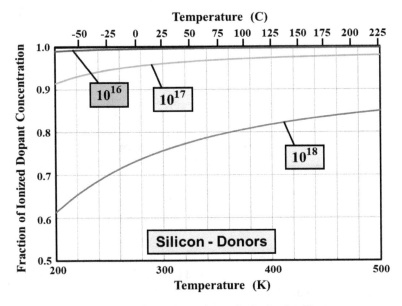

Fig. 2.15 Phosphorus donor dopant ionization in silicon.

The most commonly used n-type dopant for silicon is phosphorus which has an activation energy of 46 meV[50]. Using this value, the fraction of ionized donors (or the electron concentration) can be computed for various temperatures. The ionized donor concentration for silicon is shown in Fig. 2.15 for temperature ranging from 200 to 500 °K. The corresponding temperature in °C is also shown on the chart for convenience. Typical drift regions for silicon power devices have low doping concentrations below 10^{16} cm^{-3}. From Fig. 2.15, it can be concluded that all the donors are ionized in the drift region of silicon power devices for the entire temperature range (see red line). For higher doping concentrations, such as the n-type base regions of p-channel power MOSFETs, all the donors cannot be assumed to completely ionized especially at below room temperature (300 °K) (see green and blue lines).

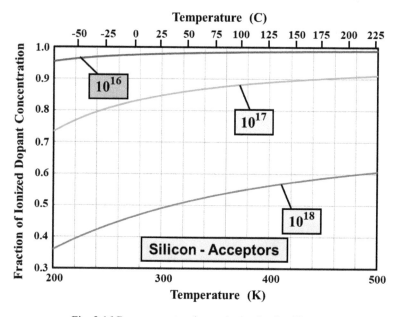

Fig. 2.16 Boron acceptor dopant ionization in silicon.

The most commonly used p-type dopant for silicon is boron which has an activation energy of 44 meV[74]. Using this value, the fraction of ionized acceptors (or the hole concentration) can be computed for various temperatures. The ionized acceptor concentration for silicon is shown in Fig. 2.16 for temperature ranging from 200 to 500 °K. The fraction of ionized acceptors is smaller than donors for the same temperature and dopant concentration. Typical drift regions for silicon power devices have low doping concentrations below 10^{16} cm^{-3}. From Fig. 2.16, it can be concluded that all the acceptors are ionized for the entire temperature range in the drift region of silicon power devices. For higher doping concentrations, such as the p-type base regions of n-channel power MOSFETs, all the donors cannot be assumed to completely ionized especially at below room temperature (300 °K).

2.12.2 Dopant Ionization in 4H-SiC

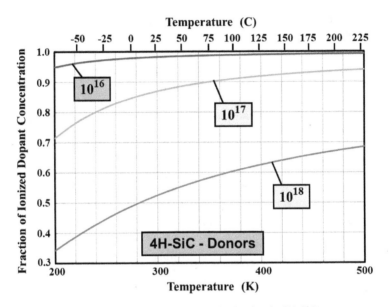

Fig. 2.17 Nitrogen donor dopant ionization in 4H-SiC.

The most commonly used n-type dopants for 4H-SiC are nitrogen and phosphorus with an activation energy of 61 meV[51]. Using this value, the fraction of ionized donors (or the electron concentration) can be computed for various temperatures. The ionized donor concentration for 4H-SiC is shown in Fig. 2.17 for temperature ranging from 200 to 500 °K. The corresponding temperature in °C is also shown on the chart for convenience. Typical drift regions for 4H-SiC power devices have low doping concentrations below 10^{16} cm^{-3}. From Fig. 2.17, it can be concluded that all the donors are ionized for the entire temperature range in the drift region of 4H-SiC power devices. For higher doping concentrations, such as the n-type base regions of p-channel power MOSFETs, all the donors cannot be assumed to completely ionized especially at below room temperature (300 °K).

The most commonly used p-type dopant for 4H-SiC is aluminum which has an activation energy of 200 meV[75]. Using this value, the fraction of ionized acceptors (or the hole concentration) can be computed for various temperatures. The ionized acceptor concentration for 4H-SiC is shown in Fig. 2.18 for temperature ranging from 200 to 500 °K. The fraction of ionized acceptors is much smaller than donors for the same temperature and dopant concentration due to the large activation energy. Typical drift region for 4H-SiC power devices have low doping concentrations below 10^{16} cm^{-3}. From Fig. 2.18, it can be concluded that only a small fraction of the acceptors are ionized for the entire temperature range in the drift region of 4H-SiC power devices. This will greatly increase the drift region resistance in unipolar devices. For higher doping concentrations, such as the p-type base regions of n-channel power MOSFETs, less than 10 % of the acceptors can be assumed to completely ionized even at elevated temperatures (500 °K). Conse-quently, the incomplete ionization of the p-type dopant has a strong impact on the parasitic resistance of the p-base regions within n-channel 4H-SiC power MOSFETs and IGBTs. This applies to all neutral regions of power devices. Within depletion regions, the acceptors will become fully ionized due to presence of the electric field.

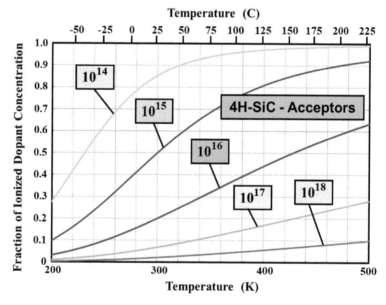

Fig. 2.18 Aluminum acceptor dopant ionization in 4H-SiC.

2.13 Recombination Lifetime

Silicon high voltage devices are designed to operate with the injection of minority carriers into the drift region to reduce its resistivity by the conductivity modulation phenomenon[12]. The recombination of holes and electrons plays an important role in determining the switching speed of these structures. The recombination process in semiconductors can occur from band-to-band but is usually assisted by the presence of deep levels in the band gap. The deep levels can also produce leakage current during reverse blocking in power devices by the generation of carriers in the depletion region.

Unipolar devices are of greatest interest for power switching applications in the case of silicon carbide. Using this material, high performance unipolar power devices are possible with blocking voltages of up to 10-kV. The minority carrier lifetime does not have an impact on the on-state and switching characteristics for unipolar devices, such as Schottky rectifiers and power MOSFETs. However, there has been interest in the development of silicon carbide power devices with blocking voltages exceeding 10-kV[52,53]. For these SiC ultra-high voltage devices, it is necessary to develop bipolar devices, such as IGBTs and GTOs. The minority carrier lifetime becomes of great importance in determining the on-state voltage drop and the switching speed for these devices[54].

Before 2000, the minority carrier lifetime values reported for 4H-SiC material were relatively low (10^{-9} to 10^{-7} seconds)[7]. This is consistent with diffusion lengths of between 1 and 2 microns measured by using the EBIC technique[55]. It is likely that these low values for the lifetime and diffusion lengths were associated with surface recombination. In 1999, Kimoto et al, demonstrated that surface recombination plays an important role in determining the switching speed of p-n junction diodes[56]. From their measurements, a low bulk lifetime of 0.33 μs and a surface recombination velocity of 5×10^4 cm/s were extracted. In 2003, Galeckas et al, pointed out that the lifetime in the N^+ 4H-SiC substrate used for power devices has a low lifetime of $10 - 100$ ns[57]. Consequently, the recombination of minority carriers in the epitaxial layers was accelerated by diffusion of minority carriers into the substrate.

A major breakthrough in improving the lifetime in the epitaxial drift layers for 4H-SiC power devices was accomplished by identification of the $Z_{1/2}$ defect as the dominant recombination center[58].

The reduction of the concentration of the $Z_{1/2}$ center has been accomplished by two methods- namely, carbon ion-implantation with annealing at 1700 °C and thermal oxidation at 1300 °C for long periods (e.g. 5 hours) followed by argon annealing at 1550 °C for 30 minutes[59]. This has allowed increasing the lifetime from 0.68 µs in as-grown layers to 6.6 µs after the oxidation treatment. Surface passivation using a plasma-enhanced chemical vapor deposited oxide (PECVD) layer that is annealed in nitric oxide at 1300 °C for 30 minutes was demonstrated to reduce the interface defect density leading to a lifetime of 13 µs.

In general, the lifetime (τ) in 4H-SiC drift regions is given by:

$$\frac{1}{\tau} = \frac{1}{\tau_{SRH}} + \frac{1}{\tau_{BB}} + \frac{1}{\tau_{AU}} \qquad [2.30]$$

where τ_{SRH} is the Shockley-Read-Hall (SRH) recombination lifetime, τ_{BB} is the band-to-band recombination lifetime, and τ_{AU} is the Auger lifetime[60]. In this expression, the SRH lifetime can be computed using[12]:

$$\tau_{SRH} = \tau_{p0} \left\{ \left[1 + e^{(E_i - E_F)/kT} \right] + \zeta \left[e^{(2E_i - E_r - E_F)/kT} \right] \right\} \qquad [2.31]$$

where τ_{p0} is the minority carrier lifetime in heavily doped n-type material, E_i is the intrinsic level position, E_F is the Fermi level position, E_r is the recombination center position, ζ is the capture cross-section ratio, k is Boltzmann's constant, and T is the absolute temperature.

The band-to-band lifetime is given by:

$$\tau_{BB} = \frac{1}{R_{BB} \left(n_0 + p_0 + \Delta n \right)} \qquad [2.32]$$

where R_{BB} is the band-to-band recombination coefficient, n_0 and p_0 are the equilibrium electron and hole concentrations and Δn is the excess carrier concentration. The band-to-band recombination coefficient[61] for 4H-SiC has a value of 1.5×10^{-12} cm^3/s.

The lifetime determined by the Auger recombination process is given by:

$$\tau_{AU} = \frac{1}{C_n \left(n_0^2 + 2n_0\Delta n + \Delta n^2 \right) + C_p \left(p_0^2 + 2p_0\Delta n + \Delta n^2 \right)} \qquad [2.33]$$

where C_n and C_p are the Auger recombination coefficients. For 4H-SiC, the Auger recombination coefficients[62] have a value of 5.0 x 10^{-31} cm^6/s for C_n and 2.0 x 10^{-31} cm^6/s for C_p.

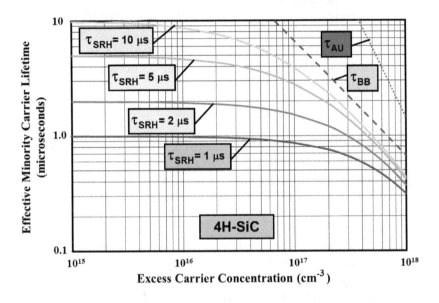

Fig. 2.19 Effective minority carrier lifetime in 4H-SiC.

The effective minority carrier lifetime in 4H-SiC obtained by using the above models is depicted in Fig. 2.19. The influence of band-to-band and Auger recombination begins to occur only when the excess (or injected) carrier concentration exceeds 10^{16} cm^{-3} and becomes pronounced at injected concentration of 10^{17} cm^{-3}. Such high injected carrier concentrations are observed in bipolar power devices such as PiN rectifiers, gate turn-off thyristors and IGBTs during on-state and surge current flow.

2.14 Lifetime Control

In the case of silicon power devices, the on-state resistance of unipolar devices become large at blocking voltages above 200 volts. Conse-quently, bipolar power devices such as PiN rectifiers and IGBTs have been developed for applications with higher blocking voltages. The switching speed of the bipolar devices depends on the minority carrier lifetime in the drift region. The lifetime in the drift region can be controlled most conveniently by using electron irradiation[63,64,65].

This process has also been applied successfully for controlling the minority carrier lifetime in 4H-SiC devices. It has been demonstrated that electron irradiation produces the $Z_{1/2}$ centers in 4H-SiC leading to a reduction of the minority carrier lifetime[66,67]. Although other defects are also generated by the electron irradiation, they can be removed by annealing at 900-1000 °C. The density of the $Z_{1/2}$ centers produced by electron irradiation is given by:

$$N_{Z_{1/2}} = K_{Z1/2} \cdot \phi_e \qquad [2.34]$$

where $K_{Z1/2}$ is the electron irradiation coefficient (cm^{-1}) that depends on the electron irradiation energy and ϕ_e is the electron irradiation fluence (cm^{-2}). The values for $K_{Z1/2}$ increase from 1.5 x 10^{-4} to 2 x 10^{-3} to 5 x 10^{-3} to 3 x 10^{-2} when the electron irradiation energy is increased from 116 to 160 to 200 to 250 keV.

Electron irradiation with higher energy has been studied to increase the penetration depth of the particles. Electron irradiation of 4H-SiC PiN rectifiers with drift layer thickness of 60 μm was performed using an energy of 2 MeV[68]. The $Z_{1/2}$ centers were confirmed to reduce the minority carrier lifetime. The reverse recovery current was diminished after the electron irradiation as expected with a significant increase in on-state voltage drop. The value for $K_{Z1/2}$ computed from the data in the paper is 0.1 – 0.2 cm^{-1} for 2 MeV electron irradiation.

Proton irradiation has also been applied to control the lifetime and characteristics of Si bipolar devices[12]. Proton irradiation produces a localized reduction in lifetime at a depth determined by the particle energy. This approach has been applied to 4H-SiC PiN power rectifiers with 10 kV blocking voltage capability by using 700 keV proton energy[69]. It was reported that the trade-off curve between on-state voltage drop and reverse recovery switching loss was superior with this proton radiation when compared with electron irradiation performed using 4.5 MeV energy. The proton radiation was found to produce the same $Z_{1/2}$ centers responsible for the reduction of the lifetime[70].

2.15 Contacts for Power Devices

In this section discusses contacts used for 4H-SiC devices. Ohmic contacts are required for the N$^+$ source and drain regions of the field effect transistors and the cathode region of Schottky rectifiers. Rectifying contacts are required for making Schottky rectifiers from 4H-SiC.

2.15.1 Metal-Semiconductor Contacts

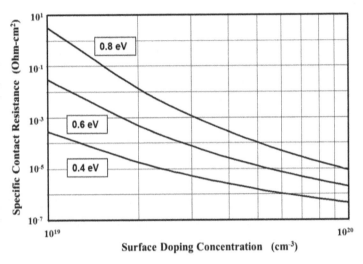

Fig. 2.20 Specific Resistance at Metal-Semiconductor Contacts.

Contacts to power devices are made by using metal films deposited on the surface of its semiconductor layers. A common requirement is to make ohmic contacts to n-type and p-type regions. This can be achieved by using a metal-semiconductor contact with low barrier height and a high doping concentration in the semiconductor to promote tunneling current across the contact. For metal-semiconductor contacts with high doping level in the semiconductor, the contact resistance determined by the tunneling process is dependent upon the barrier height and the doping level[71]:

$$R_c = \exp\left[\frac{2\sqrt{\varepsilon_S m^*}}{h}\left(\frac{\phi_{bn}}{\sqrt{N_D}}\right)\right] \qquad \text{[2.35]}$$

where ε_S is the dielectric constant, m^* is the electron effective mass, h is Boltzmann's constant, ϕ_{bn} is the metal-semiconductor barrier height, and N_D is the doping concentration in the semiconductor at the contact. It is important to obtain a specific contact resistance that is several orders of magnitude smaller than that of the drift region to take full advantage of the low specific on-resistance of the drift region in silicon carbide devices. This is also necessary because the contact areas are often only a small fraction (less than 10 percent) of the active area of most power device structures. Typically, specific contact resistances of less than 1 x 10^{-5} ohm-cm^2 are desirable to heavily doped n-type regions.

The specific contact resistance calculated using the above formula is plotted in Fig. 2.20 as a function of the doping concentration using the barrier height as a parameter. Unfortunately, the barrier heights of metal contacts to silicon carbide tend to be large due to its wide band gap. From the figure, it can be concluded that a specific contact resistance of 1 x 10^{-5} ohm-cm^2 can be obtained for a doping concentration of 5 x 10^{19} cm^{-3} if the barrier height is 0.6 eV.

2.15.2 Ohmic Contacts to n-Type 4H-SiC

High surface doping concentrations can be achieved for N-type 4H-SiC by using hot-implantation of nitrogen, phosphorus or arsenic followed by appropriate high temperature annealing[72]. Ohmic contacts with specific resistances of less than 10^{-5} Ohm-cm^2 have been reported to ion-implanted layers by using nickel and titanium[73,74] after annealing at 950-1000 °C for a few minutes. Contacts to highly doped n-type 4H-SiC have also been achieved by using titanium carbide[75] with specific contact resistance of 1 x 10^{-5} ohm-cm^2.

2.15.3 Ohmic Contacts to p-Type 4H-SiC

Ohmic contacts with low specific resistance can also be obtained for p-type 4H-SiC by using high doping concentrations with aluminum ion-implants. The best results are obtained using either titanium[76] annealed at 800 °C for a few minutes or by using titanium carbide[77] to yield a resistance of 2-4 x 10^{-5} Ohm-cm^2. Ohmic contacts to p-type 4H-SiC have also been reported by using nickel annealed at 1000 °C for a few minutes but the contact resistance is considerably larger (7 x 10^{-3} Ohm-cm^2).

2.15.4 Schottky Barrier Contacts to n-Type 4H-SiC

Metal-semiconductor contacts can be used to make 4H-SiC Schottky barrier rectifiers with high breakdown voltages. In this case, it is advantageous to have a relatively large barrier height to reduce the leakage current. The commonly used metals for formation of Schottky barriers to 4H-SiC are Titanium and Nickel. The barrier heights measured for these contacts range from 1.10 to 1.25 eV for Titanium and 1.30 to 1.60 eV for Nickel[78,79,80]. The use of these metals to fabricate high voltage device structures is discussed in subsequent chapters of the book.

2.16 Fabrication Technology for Silicon Carbide Devices

Due to the substantial infrastructure available to fabricate silicon devices, it is advantageous to manufacture silicon carbide devices using the same technology platform if possible. During the last fifteen years of research, it has been established that silicon carbide devices can be fabricated using the same equipment used for silicon devices in most instances. However, it has been found that much higher temperatures are needed for the annealing of ion implanted regions in silicon carbide to activate the dopants and remove the damage. In addition, the design of device structures in silicon carbide requires giving special consideration to the low diffusion coefficients for impurities. These unique issues are discussed in this section of the chapter.

2.16.1 Diffusion Coefficients and Solubility of Dopants

It is common-place to drive-in the dopants at a high temperature (e.g. 1000 °C) after ion-implantation to increase the junction depth when fabricating silicon power devices. The widely used double-diffused (DMOS) process for silicon planar-gate power MOSFETs utilizes the difference in the junction depth of the P-base and N^+ source regions to define the channel length without relying upon high resolution lithography to achieve sub-micron dimensions[12].

The diffusion coefficients for dopants in 4H-SiC can be compared with those in silicon using Fig. 2.21. Junction depths of $2 - 10$ μm can be obtained for phosphorus and boron dopants in silicon for making power MOSFET and IGBT device structures. Very large junction depths of $50 - 100$ μm can be achieved in silicon by diffusion at 1200 °C by using aluminum and gallium as dopants[81] to make PiN diodes and thyristors. In contrast, for silicon carbide the diffusion coefficients are very small even at relatively high temperatures. For nitrogen - the commonly used N-type dopant in 4H-SiC, the effective diffusion coefficient is reported as 5×10^{-12} cm^2/s even at 2450 °C. For aluminum - the commonly used P-type dopant in 4H-SiC, the effective diffusion coefficient is reported as 3 x 10^{-14} to 6 x 10^{-12} cm^2/s even at 1800 - 2000 °C. Due to the on-set of dissociation of the 4H-SiC material at these temperatures with an attendant generation of defects, it is not practical to drive dopants in silicon carbide after ion implantation. The design of power device structures in silicon carbide must take this limitation in process technology into account.

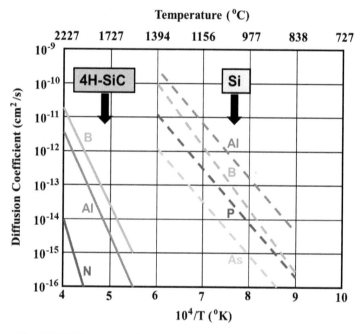

Fig. 2.21 Diffusion rates for dopants in 4H-SiC compared with silicon.

The solid solubility of dopants in silicon carbide has been reported to be comparable to that for dopants in silicon[5]. For nitrogen and aluminum, the solubility is in excess of 1 x 10^{20} cm^{-3}. Ion implanted nitrogen[82] and aluminum[83] doped layers have been formed with impurity concentrations ranging from 1 x 10^{19} cm^{-3} to 1 x 10^{20} cm^{-3}. These values are sufficient for the fabrication of most high voltage power device structures.

2.16.2 Ion Implantation and Annealing

A significant body of literature has developed on the ion implantation of impurities into silicon carbide and the subsequent annealing process to activate the dopants and remove lattice damage. The reader should refer to the proceeding of the conferences on 'Silicon Carbide and Related Materials' for an abundance of information on this topic and a book on the topic[54].

Although room temperature ion implantation can be successful, it has been found that hot-implantation produces a higher degree of impurity activation and a smaller number of defects. The hot-implants are usually performed in the 500-600 °C range followed by anneals performed at between 1200 and 1650 °C. At above 1600 °C, degradation of the silicon carbide surface is observed due to sublimation or evaporation[97,117]. The surface degradation can be mitigated by using a graphite boat to host the implanted wafer with another silicon carbide wafer placed on top (proximity anneals)[84] or by using carbon capping.

2.16.3 Gate Oxide Formation

Silicon bipolar power devices, such as the bipolar power transistor and the gate turn-off thyristor (GTO), were supplanted with MOS-gated devices in the 1980s. The silicon power MOSFET replaced the bipolar transistor for lower voltage (< 200 V) applications while the IGBT replaced bipolar transistors and GTOs for high voltage (>200V) applications. The main advantage of these MOS-gated device architectures was voltage controlled operation which greatly simplified the control circuit making it amenable to integration[12]. This feature must be extended to silicon carbide power devices to make them attractive from an applications perspective.

The issues that must be considered for the gate dielectric in MOS-gated silicon carbide devices are the quality of the oxide-semiconductor interface and the ability of the oxide to withstand higher electric fields than within silicon devices[85]. The quality of the oxide-semiconductor interface determines not only the channel mobility but impacts the threshold voltage of the devices.

In an MOS structure, the electric field in the oxide is related to the electric field in the semiconductor by Gauss's Law:

$$E_{ox} = \frac{\varepsilon_{semi}}{\varepsilon_{ox}} E_{semi} \approx 3 E_{semi} \qquad [2.36]$$

The maximum electric field at breakdown in the case of silicon is in the 3 x 10^5 V/cm range. Consequently, the maximum electric field in the oxide remains is about 1 x 10^6 V/cm, well below its breakdown field strength of 10^7 V/cm. In contrast, the maximum electric field for breakdown in silicon carbide is in the 3 x 10^6 V/cm range. Consequently, the electric field in the oxide can approach its breakdown strength and easily exceed a field of 3 x 10^6 V/cm, which is considered to be the threshold for reliable operation. One approach to overcome this problem is to use gate dielectric material with a larger permittivity[86,87]. In these references, it has been theoretically shown that the specific on-resistance can be reduced by an order of magnitude by using high dielectric constant gate material. A permittivity of about 15 (versus 3.85 for silicon dioxide) was found to be adequate for allowing full use of the high electric field strength for breakdown in silicon carbide without problems with unacceptably high oxide electric fields. One example of such a dielectric is zirconium oxide[88].

A second approach utilizes improved device structural architecture to screen the gate dielectric from the high electric fields within the silicon carbide. This is discussed in detail in the chapters on shielded planar and shielded trench gate MOSFETs in this book. Such devices can then be made using silicon dioxide whose properties are well understood. In this case, the silicon dioxide can be either grown by the thermal oxidation of silicon carbide or by the formation of the oxide using chemical vapor deposition processes. Many studies on both of these techniques are available in the literature.

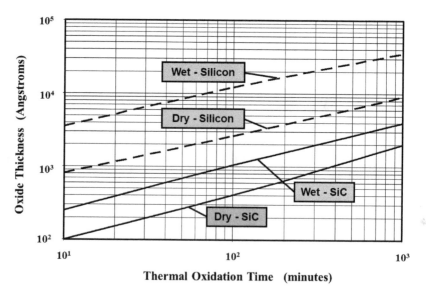

Thermal Oxidation Time   (minutes)

Fig. 2.22 Comparison of Thermal Oxidation of SiC with silicon at 1200 °C.

The thermal oxidation of SiC has been reviewed in the literature and the growth rate of the oxide has been compared with that on silicon surfaces[89]. Some selected data is shown in Fig. 2.22 to illustrate the much lower growth rate of thermal oxide on SiC when compared with silicon for both dry and wet oxidation conditions. The data shown in this figure are for 6H-SiC but similar values are applicable to the 4H-SiC polytype[90]. It is obvious that a much higher temperature and longer time duration is required for the growth of oxides on silicon carbide. This oxide has been shown to be essentially silicon dioxide with no carbon incorporated in the film because it is converted to gaseous carbon dioxide. The small amount of aluminum incorporated into the oxide grown on p-type SiC[91] has been found to have no adverse effect[57] on the MOS properties.

The gate dielectric produced with thermal oxidation of 6H-SiC has been found to be satisfactory for making MOSFETs with reasonable inversion layer mobility[92]. However, this method did not produce sufficiently high quality interfaces on 4H-SiC to make MOSFETs. It was discovered at PSRC that a low temperature oxide subjected to a wet nitrogen anneal enabled fabrication of n-channel inversion layer MOSFETs in 4H-SiC with an effective inversion layer mobility of 165 cm^2/V-s[44,45]. Although the gate oxide for these MOSFETs was unusually large (9000 angstroms), high performance MOSFETs with similar mobility values, were subsequently fabricated at PSRC using a gate oxide thickness of 850 angstroms[93]. An extensive evaluation of process conditions was performed at PSRC to determine their impact on the inversion layer mobility. This work has been validated by other groups[46]. In addition, inversion layer mobility in the range of 50 cm^2/V-s has been reported on thermally grown oxides subjected to annealing in nitric oxide[50,51,52,53,54]. These experiments were important to determine that power MOSFETs with low specific on-resistance can be developed from 4H-SiC.

2.16.4 Reactive Ion Etching of Trenches

The first silicon power MOSFETs were manufactured using the Double-diffused or DMOS process to form a planar gate architecture[94]. Although these devices offered excellent input impedance and fast switching performance for low voltage (< 100 volt) applications, their on-resistance was found to be limited by the presence of a JFET region. The JFET region could be eliminated by adopting a trench gate or UMOS process[12].

The trench gate structure in the silicon power MOSFET is fabricated by using reactive ion etching. An equivalent process for silicon carbide was not developed until the mid 1990s. Until then, alternative methods such as etching with molten KOH solutions or the use of amorphization of selective SiC regions was explored[95].

Reactive ion etching is the most convenient process for formation of trenches in silicon carbide enabling the fabrication of devices with processes compatible with silicon device manufacturing technology. Many gas compositions have been tried for the formation of trenches in silicon carbide. For application to power devices, the trenches should have a nearly vertical profile with a slightly rounded bottom to reduce electric field enhancement. The trench surface must be smooth and free of damage in order to reduce interface states and obtain high mobility along the inversion channel formed on the trench sidewalls. Reactive ion etching using a SF_6/O_2 mixture has been found to produce trenches that meet these requirements[96,97]. A silicon dioxide layer can be used as the hard mask for etching the trenches. Top and bottom corner rounding can be achieved by optimizing the chemistry. Smoothing of the trench sidewalls to remove etch induced defects is possible by sacrificial oxidation[98].

2.17 Summary

The electronic properties of 4H-SiC material that is relevant to power devices have been reviewed in this chapter. An improved knowledge of the impact ionization coefficients has allowed projection of very high performance for SiC based unipolar devices. These devices have become practical after several decades of effort. The behavior of the bulk electron and hole mobility as a function of electric field and temperature is provided in this chapter for enabling the design and analysis of these power devices. The current knowledge of surface mobility for 4H-SiC is provided to allow analysis of the channel region of power MOSFETs and IGBTs. The recombination lifetime in 4H-SiC is shown to be controlled by defects which can be adjusted using electron irradiation. The process technology for the fabrication of various unit steps for power devices is also provided here.

References

[1] G. L. Harris, "Properties of Silicon Carbide", IEE Inspec, 1995.

[2] M. Ruff, H. Mitlehner, and R. Helbig, "SiC Devices: Physics and Numerical Simulations", IEEE Transactions on Electron Devices, Vol. ED-41, pp. 1040-1054, 1994.

[3] N. G. Wright, et al, "Electrothermal Simulation of 4H-SiC Power Devices", Material Science Forum, Vol. 264, pp. 917-920, 1998.

[4] S. M. Sze, "Physics of Semiconductor Devices", John Wiley and Sons, 1981

[5] S. M. Sze and K. K. Ng, "Physics of Semiconductor Devices", Third Edition, pp. 15-16, John Wiley, New York, 2007.

[6] T. Kimoto and J.A. Cooper, "Fundamentals of Silicon Carbide Technology", pp. 17-18, John Wiley, New York, 2014.

[7] S. K. Ghandhi, "Semiconductor Power Devices", John Wiley and Sons, 1977.

[8] B. J. Baliga, "Fundamentals of Power Semiconductor Devices", Second Edition, Springer-Science, New York, 2019.

[9] A. G. Chynoweth, "Ionization Rates for Electrons and Holes in Silicon, Physical Review, Vol. 109, pp.1537-1545, 1958.

[10] A. G. Chynoweth, "Uniform Silicon P-N Junctions II. Ionization rates for Electrons", J. Applied Physics, Vol. 31, pp 1161-1165, 1960.

[11] C. R. Crowell and S. M. Sze, "Temperature dependence of Avalanche Multiplication in Semiconductors", Applied Physics Letters, Vol. 9, pp 242-244, 1966.

[12] R. Van Overstraeten and H. De Man, "Measurement of the Ionization Rates in Diffused Silicon P-N Junctions", Solid State Electronics, Vol. 13, pp. 583-590, 1970.

[13] B. J. Baliga, "Fundamentals of Power Semiconductor Devices", Second Edition, Section 2.1.5, Springer-Science, New York, 2019.

[14] R. Raghunathan and B. J. Baliga, "Temperature dependence of Hole Impact Ionization Coefficients in 4H and 6H SiC", Solid State Electronics, Vol. 43, pp. 199-211, 1999.

[15] R. Raghunathan and B. J. Baliga, "Role of Defects in producing Negative Temperature Dependence of Breakdown Voltage in SiC", Applied Physics Letters, Vol. 72, pp. 3196-3198, 1998.

[16] A. O. Konstantinov, et al, "Ionization Rates and Critical Electric Fields in 4H-SiC", Applied Physics Letters, Vol. 71, pp. 90, 1997.

[17] A. O. Konstantinov, et al, "Study of Avalanche Breakdown and Impact Ionization in 4H Silicon Carbide", Journal of Electronic Materials, Vol. 27, pp. 335-341, 1998.

[18] T. Kimoto and J. A. Cooper, "Fundamentals of Silicon Carbide Technology", pp. 29, John Wiley, New York, 2014.

[19] A. Akturk, et al, "Comparison of 4H-SiC Impact Ionization Models using Experiments and Self-Consistent Simulations", Journal of Applied Physics, Vol. 104, pp. 026101 1-3, 2008.

[20] H. Iwata and K. M. Itoh, "Theoretical Calculation of the Electron Hall Mobility in n-type 4H- and 6H-SiC", Materials Science Forum, Vol. 338-342, pp. 879-884, 2000.

[21] C. Jacobini, et al, "A Review of some Charge Transport Properties of Silicon", Solid State Electronics, Vol. 20, pp. 77-89, 1977.

[22] J. Pernot, et al, "Electrical Transport in n-type Silicon Carbide", Journal of Applied Physics, Vol. 90, pp. 1869-1875, 2001.

[23] S. Kagamuhara, et al, "Parameters required to Simulate Electrical Characteristics of SiC Devices for n-type 4H-SiC", Journal of Applied Physics, Vol. 96, pp. 5601-5607, 2004.

[24] T. Kimoto and J. A. Cooper, "Fundamentals of Silicon Carbide Technology", pp. 25, John Wiley, New York, 2014.

[25] H. Iwata and K. M. Itah, "Theoretical Calculation of the Electron Hall Mobility in n-type 4H- and 6H-SiC", Material Science Forum, Vol. 338-342, pp. 729-732, 2000.

[26] C. Canali, et al, "Electron Drift Velocity in Silicon", Phys. Rev. Vol. B12, pp. 2265-2284, 1975

[27] A. Koizumi, et al, "Temperature and Doping Dependencies of Electrical Properties in Al-Doped 4H-SiC Epitaxial Layers", Journal of Applied Physics, Vol. 106, 013716, 2009.

[28] B. J. Baliga, "Fundamentals of Power Semiconductor Devices", Second Edition, Chapter 6, Springer-Science, New York, 2019.

[29] T. Kimoto and J. A. Cooper, "Fundamentals of Silicon Carbide Technology", pp. 333, John Wiley, New York, 2014.

[30] S. Sridevan and B. J. Baliga, "Inversion Layer Mobility in SiC MOSFETs", Material Science Forum, Vol. 264-268, pp. 997-1000, 1998.

[31] S. Sridevan and B. J. Baliga, "Lateral n-Channel Inversion Mode 4H-SiC MOSFETs", IEEE Electron Device Letters, Vol. 19, pp. 228-230, 1998.

[32] D. Alok, E. Arnold, and R. Egloff, "Process dependence of Inversion-layer Mobility in 4H-SiC Devices", Material Science Forum, Vol. 338-342, pp. 1077-1080, 2000.

[33] S-H. Ryu, et al, "Critical Issues for MOS Based Power Devices in 4H-SiC", Materials Science Forum, Vol. 615-617, pp. 743-748, 2009.

[34] T. Kimoto and J. A. Cooper, "Fundamentals of Silicon Carbide Technology", pp. 247, John Wiley, New York, 2014.

[35] G. Y. Chung, et al, "Improved Inversion Channel Mobility for 4H-SiC MOSFETs following High Temperature Anneals in Nitric Oxide", IEEE Electron Device Letters, Vol. 22, pp. 176-178, 2001.

[36] J. R. Williams, et al, "Passivation of the 4H-SiC/SiO2 Interface with Nitric Oxide", Material Science Forum, Vol. 389-393, pp. 967-972, 2002.

[37] S. Dhar, et al "Effect of Nitric Oxide Annealing on the Interface Trap Density near the Conduction Band Edge of 4H-SiC at the oxide/(1120) 4H-SiC Interface", Applied Physics Letters, Vl. 84, pp. 1498-1500, 2004.

[38] C-Y Lu, et al, "Effect of Process Variations and Ambient Temperature on Electron Mobility at the SiO2/4H-SiC Interface", IEEE Transactions on Electron Devices, Vol. 50, pp. 1582-1588, 2003.

[39] S. Dhar, et al, "Inversion Layer Carrier Concentration and Mobility in 4H-SiC MOSFETs", Journal of Applied Physics, Vol. 108, pp. 054509, 2010.

[40] S. Dhar, et al, "Temperature Dependence of Inversion Layer Carrier Concentration and Hall Mobility in 4H-SiC MOSFETs", Material Science Forum, Vol. 717-720, pp. 713-716, 2012.

[41] B. J. Baliga and M. Bhatnagar, "Method of Fabricating Silicon Carbide Field Effect Transistor", U.S. Patent 5,322,802, Issued June 21, 1994.

[42] S-H Ryu, et al, "Design and Process Issues for Silicon Carbide Power DiMOSFETs", Material Research Society Symposium Proceedings, Vol. 640, pp. H4.5.1-H4.5.6, 2001.

[43] G. Gudjonsson, et al, "High Field-Effect Mobility in n-Channel Si Face 4H-SiC MOSFETs with Gate Oxide Grown on Aluminum Ion-Implanted Material", IEEE Electron Device Letters, Vol. 26, pp. 96-98, 2005.

[44] B. J. Baliga, "Fundamentals of Power Semiconductor Devices", Second Edition, Chapter 6, pp. 485-486, Springer-Science, New York, 2019.

[45] B. J. Baliga, "Silicon Carbide Semiconductor Devices having Buried Silicon Carbide Conduction Barrier Layers Therein", U.S. Patent 5,543,637, Issued August 6, 1996.

[46] S. Haney and A. Agarwal, "The Effects of Implant Activation Anneal on the Effective Inversion Layer Mobility of 4H-SiC MOSFETs", Journal of Electronic Materials, Vol. 27, pp. 666-671, 2008.

[47] C. Canali, et al, "Electron and Hole Drift Velocity Measurements in Silicon", IEEE Transactions on Electron Devices, Vol. ED-22, pp. 1045-1047, 1975.

[48] I. A. Khan and J. A. Cooper, "Measurements of High-Field Transport in Silicon Carbide", IEEE Transactions on Electron Devices, Vol. 47, pp. 269-273, 2000.

[49] T. Kimoto and J. A. Cooper, "Fundamentals of Silicon Carbide Technology", pp. 28, John Wiley, New York, 2014.

[50] S. M. Sze and K. K. Ng, "Physics of Semiconductor Devices", Third Edition, Wiley, New York, 2007.

[51] T. Kimoto and J. A. Cooper, "Fundamentals of Silicon Carbide Technology", pp. 513, John Wiley, New York, 2014.

[52] Q. Zhang, et al, "SiC Power Devices for Microgrids", IEEE Transactions on Power Electronics, Vol. 25, pp. 2889-2896, 2010.

[53] L. Cheng, et al, "Strategic Overview of High-Voltage SiC Power Device Development aiming at Global Energy Savings", Material Science Forum, Vols. 778-780, pp. 1089-1094, 2014.

[54] J. A. Cooper, et al, "Power MOSFETs, IGBTs, and Thyristors in SiC: Optimization, Experimental Results, and Theoretical Performance", IEEE International Electron Devices Meeting, Abstract 7.2.1, pp. 149-152, 2009.

[55] R. Raghunathan and B. J. Baliga, "EBIC Measurements of Diffusion Lengths in Silicon Carbide", 38th Electronic Materials Conference, Abstr. I-6, 1996.

[56] T. Kimoto, et al, "Performance Limiting Surface Defects in SiC Epitaxial p-n Junction Diodes", IEEE Transactions on Electron Devices, Vol. 46, pp. 471-477, 1999.

[57] A. Galeckas, J. Linnros, and M. Lindstedt, "Characterization of Carrier Lifetime and Diffusivity in 4H-SiC using Time-resolved Imaging Spectroscopy of Electroluminescence", Material Science and Engineering, Vol. B102, pp. 304-307, 2003.

[58] T. Kimoto and J. A. Cooper, "Fundamentals of Silicon Carbide Technology", pp. 174, John Wiley, New York, 2014.

[59] T. Kimoto, et al, "Enhancement of Carrier Lifetime in n-type 4H-SiC Epitaxial Layers by improving Surface Passivation", Applied Physics Express, Vol. 3, pp. 121201-1 – 121201-3, 2010.

[60] B. J. Baliga, "Fundamentals of Power Semiconductor Devices", Second Edition, pp. 59-75, Springer-Science, New York, 2019.

[61] N. Kaji, et al, "Ultrahigh-Voltage SiC p-i-n Diodes with Improved Forward Characteristics", IEEE Transactions on Electron Devices, Vol. 62, pp. 374-381, 2015.

[62] A. Galeckas, et al, "Auger Recombination in 4H-SiC: Unusual Temperature Behavior", Applied Physics Letters, Vol. 71, pp. 3269-3271, 1997.

[63] B. J. Baliga, "Fundamentals of Power Semiconductor Devices", Second Edition, pp. 75-80, Springer-Science, New York, 2019.

[64] B. J. Baliga, "Fast Switching Insulated Gate Transistors", IEEE Electron Device Letters, Vol. EDL-4, pp. 452-454, 1983.

[65] B. J. Baliga, "Switching Speed Enhancement in Insulated Gate Transistors by Electron Irradiation", IEEE Transactions on Electron Devices, Vol. ED-31, pp. 1790-1795, 1984.

[66] T. Kimoto and J. A. Cooper, "Fundamentals of Silicon Carbide Technology", pp. 177-179, John Wiley, New York, 2014.

[67] K. Danno, D. Nakamura, and T. Kimoto, "Investigation of Carrier Lifetime in Epilayers and Lifetime Control by Electron Irradiation", Applied Physics Letters, Vol. 90, pp. 202109-1 – 202109-3, 2007.

[68] P. Dong, et al, "Electron Radiation Effects on the 4H-SiC PiN Diodes Characteristics: An Insight From Point Defects to Electrical Degradation", IEEE Access, Vol. 7, pp. 170385-170391, 2019.

[69] P. Hazdra and S. Popelka, "Lifetime Control in SiC PiN Diodes Using Radiation Defects", Material Science Forum, Vol. 897, pp. 463-466, 2017.

[70] P. Hazdra, S. Popelka, and A. Schoner, "Optimization of SiC Power p-i-n Diode Parameters by Proton Irradiation", IEEE Tran. Electron Devices, Vol. 65, pp. 4483-4489, 2018.

[71] S. M. Sze, "Physics of Semiconductor Devices", page 304, John Wiley and Sons, 1981.

[72] S. Imai, et al, "Hot-Implantation of Phosphorus Ions into 4H-SiC", Materials Science Forum, Vol. 338-342, pp. 861-864, 2000.

[73] S. Tanimoto, et al, "Ohmic Contact Structure and Fabrication Process Applicable to Practical SiC Devices", Materials Science Forum, Vol. 389-393, pp. 879-884, 2002.

[74] T. Marinova, et al, "Nickel based Ohmic Contacts on SiC", Material Science and Engineering, Vol. B46, pp. 223-226, 1997.

[75] S. K. Lee, et al, "Low Resistivity Ohmic Titanium Carbide Contacts to n- and p-type 4H-SiC", Solid State Electronics, Vol. 44, pp. 1179-1186, 2000.

[76] J. Crofton, et al, "Titanium and Aluminum-Titanium Ohmic Contacts to p-type SiC", Solid State Electronics, Vol. 41, pp. 1725-1729, 1997.

[77] S. K. Lee, et al, "Electrical Characterization of TiC Contacts to Aluminum Implanted 4H-SiC", Applied Physics Letters, Vol. 77, pp. 1478-1480, 2000.

[78] A. Kestle, et al, "A UHV Study of Ni/SiC Schottky Barrier and Ohmic Contact Formation", Materials Science Forum, Vol. 338-342, pp. 1025-1028, 2000.

[79] K. V. Vassilevski, et al, "4H-SiC Schottky Diodes with high On/Off Current Ratio", Materials Science Forum, Vol. 389-393, pp. 1145-1148, 2002.

[80] R. Raghunathan, D. Alok, and B. J. Baliga, "High Voltage 4H-SiC Schottky Barrier Diodes", IEEE Electron Device letters, Vol. EDL-16, pp. 226-227, 1995.

[81] B. J. Baliga, "Deep Planar Gallium and Aluminum Diffusions in Silicon", Journal of the Electrochemical Society, Vol. 126, pp. 292-296, 1979.

[82] S. Blanque, et al, "Room Temperature Implantation and Activation Kinetics of Nitrogen and Phosphorus in 4H-SiC crystals", Materials Science Forum, Vol. 457-460, pp. 893-896, 2004.

[83] Y. Negoro, et al, "Low Sheet Resistance of High Dose Aluminum Implanted 4H-SiC using (1120) Face", Materials Science Forum, Vol. 457-460, pp. 913-916, 2004.

[84] R. K. Chilukuri, et al, "High Voltage P-N Junction Diodes in Silicon Carbide using Field Plate Edge Termination", Material Research Society Proceedings, Vol. 572, pp. 81-86, 1999.

[85] B. J. Baliga, "Critical Nature of Oxide/Interface Quality for SiC Power Devices", Microelectronics Engineering, Vol. 28, pp. 177-184, 1995.

[86] S. Sridevan, P. K. McLarty, and B. J. Baliga, "Silicon Carbide Switching Devices having Nearly Ideal Breakdown Voltage Capability and Ultra-Low On-State Resistance", U.S. Patent # 5,742,076, Issued April 21, 1998.

[87] S. Sridevan, P. K. McLarty, and B. J. Baliga, "Analysis of Gate Dielectrics for SiC Power UMOSFETs", IEEE Int. Symposium on Power Devices and ICs, pp. 153-156, 1997.

[88] V. V. Afanas'ev, et al, "Oxidation of Silicon Carbide: Problems and Solutions", Materials Science Forum, Vol. 389-393, pp. 961-966, 2002.

[89] J. A. Cooper, "Silicon Carbide MOSFETs", in 'Wide Energy Bandgap Electronic Devices', Edited by F. Ren and J. C. Zolper, World Scientific Press, 2003.

[90] A. Golz, et al, "Oxidation Kinetics of 3C, 4H, and 6H silicon carbide", Institute of Physics Conference Series, Vol. 142, pp. 633-636, 1996.

[91] S. Sridevan, P. K. McLarty, and B. J. Baliga, "On the Presence of Aluminum in Thermally Grown Oxides on 6H-SiC", IEEE Electron Device Letters, Vol. 17, pp. 136-138, 1996.

[92] L. A. Lipkin and J. W. Palmour, "Improved Oxidation Procedures for reduced SiO_2/SiC Defects". J. Electronic Materials, Vol. 25, pp. 909-915, 1996.

[93] S. Sridevan and B. J. Baliga, "Phonon Scattering limited Mobility in SiC Inversion Layers", PSRC Technical Report, TR-98-03.

[94] D. A. Grant and J. Gowar, "Power MOSFETs", John Wiley and Sons, 1989.

[95] D. Alok and B. J. Baliga, "A Novel Method for Etching Trenches in Silicon Carbide", J. Electronic Materials, Vol. 24, pp. 311-314, 1995.

[96] M. Kothandaraman, D. Alok, and B. J. Baliga, "Reactive Ion Etching of Trenches in 6H-SiC", J. Electronic Materials, Vol. 25, pp. 875-878, 1996.

[97] X. Tan and Q. Xie, "Trench Etch for SiC Power Devices", China Semiconductor Technology International Conference, pp. 1-3, 2022.

[98] C. Zheng, et al, "Low Roughness SiC Trench Formed by ICP Etching with Sacrificial Oxidation and Ar Annealing Treatment", IEEE International Symposium on Power Semiconductor Devices and ICs, pp. 354-357, 2021.

Chapter 3

Breakdown Voltage

The on-state resistance for silicon power MOSFETs becomes very high when their drift regions are designed to support more than 200 volts. This motived the development of the MOS-bipolar physics based silicon IGBT, which is now widely used for applications where the circuit voltages exceed 200 volts[1]. However, it is preferable to utilize a unipolar power switch, such as the power MOSFET, in power electronic applications, rather than a bipolar power device such as an IGBT, due to the much smaller switching power losses.

The main advantage of a wide band gap semiconductor for power device applications stems from the very low resistance of the drift region even when it is designed to support large voltages. The highest voltage that can be supported by a drift region is determined by the onset of impact ionization in the semiconductor with increasing electric field within the region. In the previous chapter, it was shown that the onset of impact ionization occurs at much larger electric fields in 4H-SiC when compared with silicon. The design of the drift region with this material is discussed in this chapter. It is demonstrated that the doping concentration of the drift region is several orders of magnitude larger in 4H-SiC devices when compared with silicon devices designed to support the same voltage. Furthermore, the width of the drift region for 4H-SiC is much smaller than that required for silicon devices.

Although the parallel-plane junction analysis is representative of the active region of power devices where current flow transpires, the maximum blocking voltage (highest value the device can support) can be limited by avalanche breakdown at its edges. The electric field in discrete power devices is invariably enhanced at its edges. All discrete power devices require an edge termination around the active area that is designed to improve the blocking voltage capability and make it approach the ideal value of the parallel-plane junction. Consequently, the edge termination design can limit the maximum voltage that can be

69

supported by the device. The design of edge terminations for SiC discrete power devices is described in this chapter. Modern edge terminations for 4H-SiC are capable of supporting close to the ideal parallel-plane breakdown voltage. In this case, the device breakdown voltage can occur at the cells in the active area. This is advantageous when the device is subjected to unclamped inductive load tests because the breakdown is spread over the active area rather than getting localized at the edges.

3.1 Parallel-Plane Breakdown

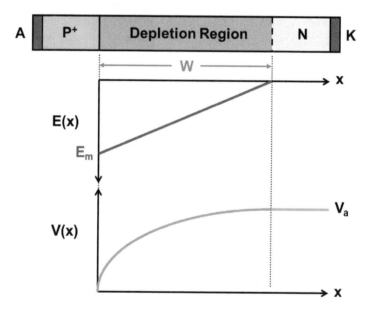

Fig. 3.1 Electric field and potential distribution for an abrupt parallel-plane P⁺N junction.

The analysis of a one-dimensional abrupt junction can be used to understand the design of the drift region within power devices[2]. The case of a P⁺/N junction is illustrated in Fig. 3.1 where the P⁺ side is assumed to be very highly doped so that the electric field supported within it can be neglected. This is referred to as a one-dimensional abrupt parallel-plane junction. When this junction is reverse-biased by the application of a positive bias to the cathode electrode (K), a depletion region is formed in the N-region as shown in the figure with the generation of a strong electric field within it that supports the voltage. The Poisson's equation for the N-region is then given by:

$$\frac{d^2V}{dx^2} = -\frac{dE}{dx} = -\frac{Q(x)}{\varepsilon_S} = -\frac{qN_D}{\varepsilon_S} \qquad [3.1]$$

where Q(x) is the charge within the depletion region due to the presence of ionized donors, ε_S is the dielectric constant for the semiconductor, q is the electron charge, and N_D is the donor concentration in the uniformly doped N-region.

Integration of the above equation with the boundary condition that the electric field must go to zero at the edge of the depletion region (i.e. at x = W) provides the electric field distribution:

$$E(x) = -\frac{qN_D}{\varepsilon_S}(W - x) \qquad [3.2]$$

The electric field has a maximum value of E_m at the P$^+$/N junction (x = 0) and decreases linearly to zero at x = W.

Integration of the electric field distribution through the depletion region provides the potential distribution:

$$V(x) = -\frac{qN_D}{\varepsilon_S}(Wx - \frac{x^2}{2}) \qquad [3.3]$$

This equation is obtained by using the boundary condition that the potential is zero at x = 0 within the P$^+$ region. The potential varies quadratically as illustrated in the figure. The thickness of the depletion region (W) is related to the applied reverse bias (V_a):

$$W = \sqrt{\frac{2\varepsilon_S V_a}{qN_D}} \qquad [3.4]$$

Using these equations, the maximum electric field at the junction can be obtained:

$$E_m = \sqrt{\frac{2qN_D V_a}{\varepsilon_S}} \qquad [3.5]$$

When the applied bias increases, the maximum electric field approaches values at which significant impact ionization begins to occur. The impact ionization coefficients for 4H-SiC and Si were compared in chapter 2 in Fig. 2.7.

The breakdown voltage is determined by the ionization integral becoming equal to unity[2]:

$$\int_0^W \alpha.dx = 1 \qquad [3.6]$$

where α is the impact ionization coefficient discussed in chapter 2. The exponential format for the impact ionization coefficients (see Eq. [2.10]) is not amenable to deriving simple analytical solutions for the breakdown voltage.

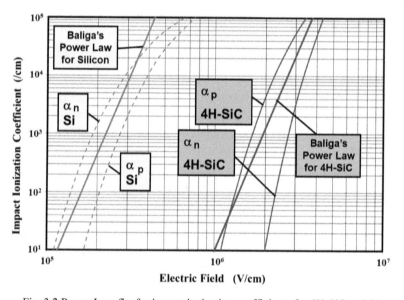

Fig. 3.2 Power Law fits for impact ionization coefficients for 4H-SiC and Si.

In order to obtain a closed form solution for the breakdown voltage, it is convenient to use a power law fit for the impact ionization coefficient in place of Chynoweth's Law[2]. For silicon, this was originally performed using the Fulop's power law formula:

$$\alpha_F(Si) = 1.8x10^{-35} E^7 \qquad [3.7]$$

However, this formula has been found to overestimate the breakdown voltages of actual devices[3]. The Baliga's power law for impact ionization coefficients in silicon, given by:

$$\alpha_B(Si) = 3.507 \, x 10^{-35} E^7 \qquad [3.8]$$

provides a good match between the analytically calculated breakdown voltages and those measured on silicon devices[3]. The impact ionization coefficient computed using Baliga's power law for silicon is compared with the measured impact ionization coefficients for holes and electrons in Fig. 3.2. The values obtained using the power law fall between the values for electrons and holes up to impact ionization coefficient values of 1 x 10^4 cm^{-1}.

Similarly, a Baliga's power law for the impact ionization coefficient in the case of 4H-SiC is given by:

$$\alpha_B(4H - SiC) = 1.0 \, x 10^{-41} E^7 \qquad [3.9]$$

This expression provides a good fit between the data for α_p and α_n reported by Konstantinov, et al,[4] for 4H-SiC as shown in Fig. 3.2. The breakdown voltages calculated for 4H-SiC devices using this power law are consistent with experimental results[5]. As mentioned in chapter 2, these values for the impact ionization coefficients may be enhanced by the presence of defects. Breakdown voltages larger than those obtained in this chapter by using the Konstantinov, et al data may be observed in defect free material. The breakdown voltages will then be consistent with calculation done using the Raghunathan/Baliga data shown in chapter 2.

The ionization integral can be solved by using the linear electric field distribution (Eq. [3.2]) with the above Baliga power law equations for the impact ionization coefficients. The analytical solution derived for the breakdown voltage for silicon[2] is:

$$BV_{PP}(Si) = 4.45 \, x 10^{13} N_D^{-3/4} \qquad [3.10]$$

The corresponding equation for 4H-SiC is:

$$BV_{PP}(4H-SiC) = 1.67 \, x 10^{15} N_D^{-3/4} \qquad [3.11]$$

The breakdown voltages for one-dimensional abrupt parallel-plane junctions obtained by using the analytical solutions are plotted in Fig. 3.3. For the same doping concentration, the breakdown voltage for 4H-SiC is 36.3 times larger than for silicon. For example, with a doping concentration of 1 x 10^{15} cm^{-3}, the breakdown voltage from the silicon case is 258 volts while that for 4H-SiC is 9382. From the power device design point of view, it is more important to compare the doping concentration in the drift region to achieve the same breakdown voltage that is required for an application. For the same breakdown voltage of 1000 volts, the doping concentrations in the drift region for the silicon and 4H-SiC one-dimensional parallel-plane junctions are 1.65 x 10^{14} cm^{-3} and 1.98 x 10^{16} cm^{-3}. In general, the doping concentrations in the drift region for the 4H-SiC one-dimensional parallel-plane junction is 120 times greater than that for silicon devices. This increase in doping concentration greatly decreases the resistance for the drift region in 4H-SiC discrete unipolar vertical devices as discussed in a later chapter.

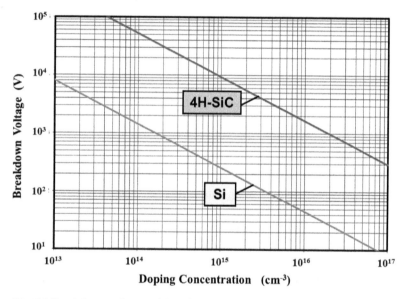

Fig. 3.3 Breakdown voltages of 4H-SiC abrupt parallel-plane junctions compared with the Si case.

The depletion width in the drift region reaches its largest value when it is supporting the breakdown voltage. An analytical expression for the maximum depletion can be derived by combining Eq. [3.4] with the equations for the breakdown voltage. The analytical equations for the case of silicon and 4H-SiC are:

$$W_{PP}(\text{Si}) = 2.404\,x10^{10}\,N_D^{-7/8} \qquad \text{[3.12]}$$

and

$$W_{PP}(4\text{H}-\text{SiC}) = 1.34\,x10^{11}\,N_D^{-7/8} \qquad \text{[3.13]}$$

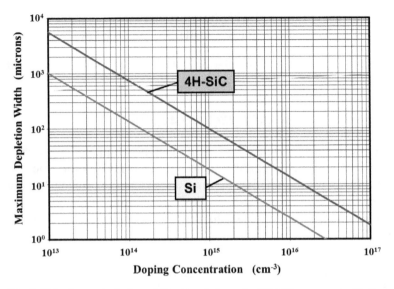

Fig. 3.4 Maximum depletion width at breakdown for 4H-SiC compared with the
Si case.

The maximum depletion layer width, reached at the onset of breakdown, predicted by these equations is shown in Fig. 3.4. As an example, with a doping concentration of 1×10^{15} cm^{-3}, the maximum depletion width for the silicon case is 18.3 μm while that for 4H-SiC is 100 μm, respectively. In general, for the same doping concentration, the maximum depletion width in 4H-SiC is 5.5x larger than that in silicon because it can sustain a much larger electric field. More importantly, for the same breakdown voltage, the depletion width in 4H-SiC is smaller than for a silicon device by a factor of 12 times because of the higher doping concentrations in the drift region. As an example, for the same breakdown voltage of 1000 volts, the maximum depletion width in the drift region for the silicon and 4H-SiC one-dimensional parallel-plane junctions are 18.3 μm and 7.37 μm. The smaller thickness of the drift region, in conjunction with the far larger doping concentration, results in an enormous reduction in the specific on-resistance of the drift region in 4H-SiC when compared with silicon as discussed in a later chapter.

Avalanche breakdown in semiconductors occurs when the ionization integral becomes equal to unity[2]. There is a corresponding peak electric field at the junction for each doping concentration in the drift region. This value is defined as the critical electric field (E_C) for breakdown. An analytical solution for the critical electric field can be derived by using Eq. [3.5] with the equations for the breakdown voltage. The critical electric fields for Si and 4H-SiC are given by:

$$E_C(Si) = 3.70 \, x 10^3 \, N_D^{1/8} \qquad \text{[3.14]}$$

and

$$E_C(4H-SiC) = 2.49 \, x 10^4 \, N_D^{1/8} \qquad \text{[3.15]}$$

The critical electric field for 4H-SiC can be compared with that for silicon using Fig. 3.5. For the same doping concentration, the critical electric fields for 4H-SiC is 6.62-times larger than for silicon. The larger critical electric field in 4H-SiC allows supporting high voltages with larger doping concentration in the drift region with a smaller depletion layer width.

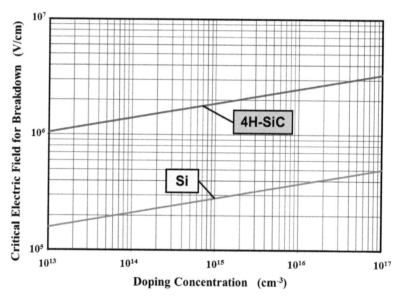

Fig. 3.5 Critical electric field for breakdown in 4H-SiC compared with the Si case.

It is worth highlighting that the critical electric field for breakdown is not a single value for any semiconductor material as often quoted in publications. It is a strong function of the doping concentration as shown by Eq. [3.14] and Eq. [3.15]. Consequently, when comparing semiconductor materials, it is important to use the critical electric field pertinent to the same breakdown voltage for all the materials.

3.2 Punch-Through Diode Breakdown

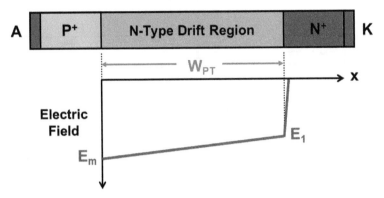

Fig. 3.6 Electric field distribution for the punch-through diode structure.

In the case of bipolar power devices, such as PiN rectifiers and asymmetric IGBTs, it is preferable to employ a punch-through drift region design to reduce its thickness[2]. The punch-through diode structure is illustrated in Fig. 3.6 with its electric field distribution at high reverse bias voltages. The electric field has a shallow slope in the drift region because it is designed with a low doping concentration. The electric field is truncated when the depletion region reaches the N^+ substrate due to its high doping concentration.

The breakdown voltage for the punch-through diode structure is give by[2]:

$$BV_{PT} = E_C W_{PT} - \frac{qN_D W_{PT}^2}{2\varepsilon_S}$$

[3.16]

The breakdown voltage for the case of silicon punch-through diodes is provided in Fig. 3.7. A 5 micron thick drift region can support about 100 volts for the silicon case. The breakdown voltage increases to 900 volts when the drift region thickness for the silicon punch-through diode is increased to 50 μm. The gradual reduction in breakdown voltage at lower doping levels shown in the figure does not occur in practice[6].

The breakdown voltage for the case of 4H-SiC punch-through diodes is provided in Fig. 3.8 for various values of drift region thickness. A 5 micron thick drift region can support about 800 volts in the case of 4H-SiC. The breakdown voltage increases to about 7,000 volts when the drift region thickness for the 4H-SiC diode is increased to 50 microns.

The much larger values than in the case of silicon are due to the greater critical electric field for breakdown in this material.

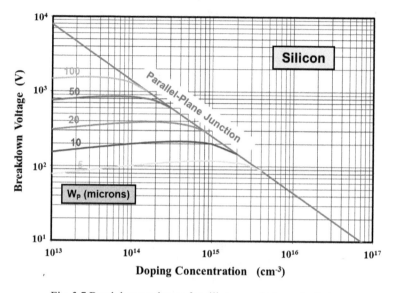

Fig. 3.7 Breakdown voltages for silicon punch-through diodes.

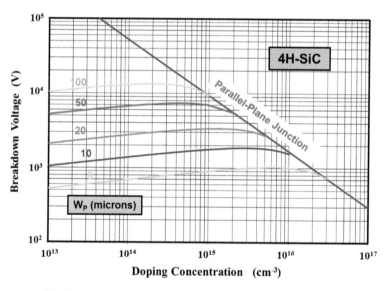

Fig. 3.8 Breakdown voltages for 4H-SiC punch-through diodes.

3.3 Open-Base Transistor Breakdown

Silicon carbide bipolar power devices like GTOs and IGBTs are usually fabricated using the asymmetrical structure[2] with the depletion layer designed to punch-through to a buffer layer located adjacent to the collector junction as illustrated in Fig. 3.10. The forward blocking capability of these devices is determined by the open-base transistor breakdown phenomenon[2]. The maximum blocking voltage occurs when the common base current gain of the wide base transistor becomes equal to unity. The common base current gain is determined by the product of the emitter injection efficiency, the base transport factor, and the multiplication factor. Using the avalanche breakdown criteria when the multiplication co-efficient becomes equal to infinity, as assumed in some papers, leads to significant errors in the design of the drift region for these structures. The multiplication coefficients is usually below 10 for the open-base transistor case.

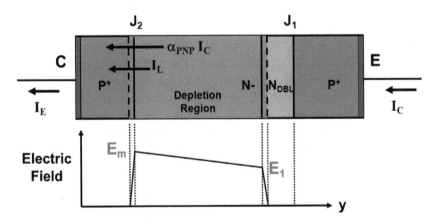

Fig. 3.9 Electric field distribution in the punch-through bipolar transistor structure.

The emitter injection efficiency is smaller than unity for the structure shown in Fig. 3.9 due to the high doping concentration (N_{DBL}) of the N-buffer layer. The emitter injection efficiency for the P^+ collector/N-buffer junction (J_1) can be obtained by using[2]:

$$\gamma_E = \frac{D_{pNBL} L_{nC} N_{AC}}{D_{pNBL} L_{nC} N_{AC} + D_{nC} W_{NBL} N_{DBL}}$$ [3.17]

where D_{pNBL} and D_{nC} are the diffusion coefficients for minority carriers in the N-buffer layer and P$^+$ collector regions; N_{AC} and L_{nC} are the doping concentration and diffusion length for minority carriers in the P$^+$ collector region; N_{DBL} and W_{NBL} are the doping concentration and width of the N-buffer layer. In determining the diffusion coefficients and the diffusion length, it is necessary to account for impact of the high doping concentrations in the P$^+$ collector region and N-buffer layer on the mobility. In addition, the lifetime within the highly doped P$^+$ collector region is reduced due to heavy doping effects, which shortens the diffusion length.

As shown in the figure, the electric field is truncated by the high doping concentration of the N-buffer layer making the un-depleted width of the NPN transistor base region equal to the width of the N-buffer layer if the depletion width in the buffer layer is assumed to be small. The base transport factor is then given by:

$$\alpha_T = \frac{1}{\cosh\left(W_{NBL} / L_{pNB}\right)} \qquad [3.18]$$

which is independent of the collector bias. Here, $L_{p,NB}$ is the diffusion length for holes in the N-buffer layer. The diffusion length for holes ($L_{p,NB}$) in the N-buffer layer depends upon the diffusion coefficient and the minority carrier lifetime in the N-buffer layer. The diffusion coefficient varies with the doping concentration in the N-buffer layer based upon the concentration dependence of the mobility. In addition, the minority carrier lifetime has been found to be dependent upon the doping concentration[7] in the case of silicon devices. Although this phenomenon has not been verified for silicon carbide, this scaling of the lifetime is commonly used when performing numerical analysis of silicon carbide devices. The effect can be modeled by using the relationship:

$$\frac{\tau_{LL}}{\tau_{p0}} = \frac{1}{1 + \left(N_D / N_{REF}\right)} \qquad [3.19]$$

where N_D is a doping concentration of the layer and N_{REF} is a reference doping concentration whose value will be assumed to be 5 x 10^{16} cm^{-3}.

The multiplication factor for a P-N junction is given by:

$$M = \frac{1}{1 - \left(V_A / BV_{PP}\right)^n} \qquad [3.20]$$

with a value of n = 6 for the case of a P^+/N junction. Here, V_A is the applied reverse bias and BV_{PP} is the avalanche breakdown voltage of the P-base/N-base junction *without the punch-through phenomenon*. In order to apply this equation to the punch-through case relevant to the asymmetric silicon carbide structure, it is necessary to relate the maximum electric field at the junction for the two cases[2]. The electric field at the interface between the lightly doped portion of the N-base region and the N-buffer layer is given by:

$$E_1 = E_m - \frac{qN_D W_N}{\varepsilon_S}$$ [3.21]

The voltage supported by the device is given by:

$$V_C = \left(\frac{E_m + E_1}{2} \right) W_N = E_m W_N - \frac{qN_D}{2\varepsilon_S} W_N^2$$ [3.22]

From this expression, the maximum electric field is given by:

$$E_m = \frac{V_C}{W_N} + \frac{qN_D W_N}{2\varepsilon_S}$$ [3.23]

The corresponding equation for the non-punch-through case is:

$$E_m = \sqrt{\frac{2qN_D V_{NPT}}{\varepsilon_S}}$$ [3.24]

Consequently, the non-punch-through voltage that determines the multiplication coefficient 'M' corresponding to the applied collector bias 'V_C' for the punch-through case is given by:

$$V_{NPT} = \frac{\varepsilon_S E_m^2}{2qN_D} = \frac{\varepsilon_S}{2qN_D} \left(\frac{V_C}{W_N} + \frac{qN_D W_N}{2\varepsilon_S} \right)^2$$ [3.25]

The multiplication coefficient for the asymmetric silicon carbide IGBT structure can be computed by using this non-punch-through voltage:

$$M = \frac{1}{1 - \left(V_{NPT} / BV_{PP} \right)^n}$$ [3.26]

The multiplication coefficient increases with increasing collector bias. The open-base transistor breakdown voltage (and the forward blocking capability of the punch-through transistor structure) is determined by the collector voltage at which the multiplication factor becomes equal to the reciprocal of the product of the base transport factor and the emitter injection efficiency.

The doping concentration of the N-buffer layer must be sufficiently large to prevent reach-through of the electric field to the P^+ collector region. Although the electric field at the interface between the N-base region and the N-buffer layer is slightly smaller than at the blocking junction (J_2), a worse case analysis can be done by assuming that the electric field at this interface is close to the critical electric field for breakdown in the drift region. The minimum charge in the N-buffer layer to prevent reach-through can be then obtained using:

$$N_{DBL}W_{NBL} = \frac{\varepsilon_S E_C}{q} \qquad [3.27]$$

Using a critical electric for breakdown in silicon carbide of 2×10^6 V/cm for a doping concentration of 1.5×10^{14} cm^{-3} in the N-base region, the minimum charge in the N-buffer layer to prevent reach-through for a silicon carbide punch-through transistor structure is found to be 1.07×10^{13} cm^{-2}. An N-buffer layer with doping concentration of 5×10^{16} cm^{-3} and thickness of 5 µm has a charge of 2.5×10^{13} cm^{-2} that satisfies this requirement.

The drift region thickness required to achieve various breakdown voltages for the 4H-SiC transistor punch-through structure calculated using the above equations is shown in Fig. 3.10. From this graph, it can concluded that the drift region thickness must be increased from 50 microns to 300 microns to achieve an increase in breakdown voltage from 5 kV to 25 kV. For this analysis, the structure was assumed to have a P^+ collector region with doping concentration of 1×10^{19} cm^{-3} and the buffer layer had a thickness of 5 µm with a doping concentration of 5×10^{16} cm^{-3}. The lifetime in the drift region was assumed to be 1 µs. The emitter injection efficiency computed using Eq. [3.21] is 0.971 by using these parameters. When the device is close to breakdown, the entire N-base region is depleted and the base transport factor computed by using Eq. [3.22] in this case is 0.903. Based up on Eq. [7.3], open-base transistor breakdown will then occur when the multiplication coefficient becomes equal to 1.14 for the above values for the injection efficiency and base transport factor.

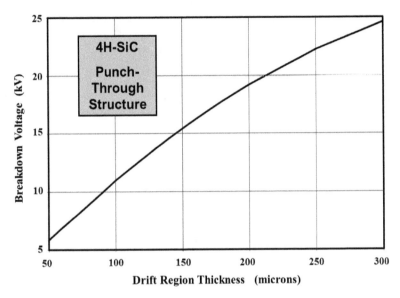

Fig. 3.10 Open base breakdown voltages for the 4H-SiC punch through transistor structures.

3.4 Silicon Carbide Device Edge Terminations

The parallel-plane breakdown voltage discussed in the previous section is considered to be the ideal value for breakdown because it represents the highest breakdown voltage that is achievable for a drift region with a particular doping concentration. In practical discrete devices with a vertical architecture, the breakdown voltage is reduced below the ideal value due to localized electric field enhancement at the periphery of the active area. The P-N junction in devices like power MOSFETs or metal-semiconductor junction in Schottky rectifiers cannot be extended to the scribe lanes used to separate the chips for packaging. The scribing or sawing operation produces severe damage in the semiconductor that can degrade the junctions. It is important to stop the depletion region at the junctions from extending into the scribe lanes. This is achieved by using an edge termination surrounding the active area of discrete power devices[2]. Edge terminations for 4H-SiC devices are reviewed in this section.

A variety of edge terminations have been created for silicon power devices[2]. For small discrete devices, it is commonplace to use floating field rings or the junction termination extension approach. The utilization of this concept to 4H-SiC devices was initially hampered by the lack of a technology for making P-N junctions by ion-implantation. Consequently, a unique approach was proposed and demonstrated for silicon carbide by amorphisation of the surface using argon ion-implantation to produce a highly resistive region at the periphery. The formation of floating field rings and JTE terminations has been widely practiced after improved technology for activation of ion-implants in 4H-SiC was developed.

For large discrete devices made from an entire silicon wafer, it is commonplace to use bevel edge terminations[2]. The bevel edge termination has recently been extended to small discrete devices fabricated from 4H-SiC by using a V-shaped dicing blade.

3.4.1 Unterminated Planar SiC Schottky Diode

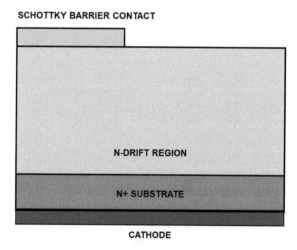

Fig. 3.11 The un-terminated Schottky diode structure.

The first high voltage (400 V) vertical Schottky barrier rectifiers were demonstrated at PSRC/NCSU from 6H-SiC in 1992 using a remarkably simple process of evaporating metal through a 'dot' mask onto a 6H-SiCe surface after appropriate cleaning[8]. This approach was later successfully demonstrated at PSRC for the fabrication of 1000-V Schottky rectifiers from 4H-SiC in 1995[9].

The unterminated Schottky barrier diode structure, illustrated in Fig. 3.11, contains a sharp metal edge at the periphery of the diode leading to electric field enhancement and reduction of the breakdown voltage. This phenomenon can be observed using the results of two-dimensional numerical simulations on a Schottky diode[10]. The diode was found to exhibit a breakdown voltage of 650 volts which is only 40 % of the parallel-plane breakdown voltage of 1670 volts. It is necessary to include an edge termination at the periphery of the Schottky contact to improve the breakdown voltage.

3.4.2 SiC Schottky Diode with Floating Metal Field Rings

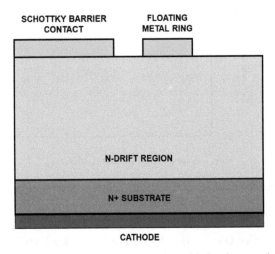

Fig. 3.12 Schottky diode edge termination with floating metal ring.

A simple method for reducing the electric field enhancement at the edge of Schottky diode without adding processing steps is by placement of floating metal field rings around the periphery of the diode[11] as illustrated in Fig. 3.12. This concept is similar to floating field rings produced in silicon devices by creating p-type regions in the n-drift region around the periphery of P-N junction diodes[2]. An optimum spacing of one-quarter of the maximum parallel-plane depletion width (W_{PP}) is predicted by analytical theory for a single floating field ring in agreement with empirical evidence in silicon devices[12].

A typical 4H-SiC Schottky rectifier with breakdown voltage of 1000 volts has a drift region with doping concentration of 2×10^{16} cm^{-3} (see Fig. 3.3). The maximum depletion width for this doping concentration is 7.3 µm. Consequently, the optimum spacing for the metal field ring should be about 2 µm. The measured breakdown voltage as a function of metal ring spacing[13] is shown in Fig. 3.13. The breakdown voltage increases when the spacing is made much larger and saturates at a value of 5 µm. This indicates that there is substantial charge at the surface of silicon carbide that spreads the depletion region.

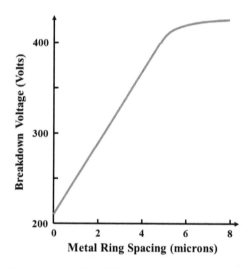

Fig. 3.13 Breakdown voltage of the Schottky diode edge termination with a single floating metal ring.

3.4.3 SiC Schottky Diode with Resistive Schottky Extension

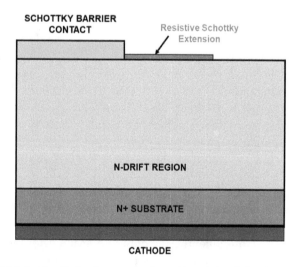

Fig. 3.14 Schottky diode edge termination with resistive Schottky extension.

The electric field at the edge of the Schottky contact can be reduced by spreading the potential along the surface. One of the methods that has been demonstrated to achieve this is by creating a resistive Schottky extension[12] as illustrated in Fig. 3.14. The resistive region must have a high sheet resistance in the range of 10^8 Ω/sq. This has been achieved by oxidation of a thin (50 angstrom) titanium film in air at 300 °C. An increase in the breakdown voltage from 150 to 500 volts was reported using this approach.

3.4.4 SiC Schottky Diode with Field Plate Edge Termination

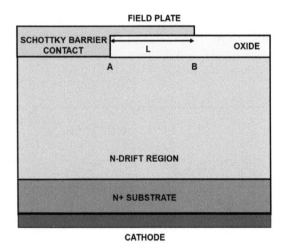

Fig. 3.15 Schottky diode structure with field plate termination.

The breakdown voltage for the planar Schottky diode can be significantly improved by using a field plate at its periphery to reduce the electric field at the metal edge[2]. This termination is illustrated in Fig. 3.15 with oxide as the dielectric. The depletion region spreads along the surface in the presence of the field plate reducing the potential crowding at point A. Numerical simulations have shown that the structure with the field plate had a breakdown voltage of 1300 volts compared with 650 volts for the un-terminated diode[12]. For the case of an oxide thickness of 1 μm, the ratio of the peak electric field at point A to that in the middle of the diode is reduced to 2.3x in comparison with a ratio of 2.7x for the un-terminated diode.

A further reduction of the electric field at the metal edge (point A) can be obtained by reducing the oxide thickness. For the case of an oxide thickness of 0.6 μm, the peak electric field at the metal corner is 2x of that in the middle. This allowed the breakdown voltage to increase to 1430 volts. A further reduction in oxide thickness to 0.2 μm leads to an even lower electric field at the metal corner. Unfortunately, the electric field at the field plate edge (point B) now becomes larger than at point A leading to a reduction of the breakdown voltage to 840 volts. This occurs because the field plate behaves like a cylindrical junction with a radius of curvature given by:

$$x_J = \left(\frac{\varepsilon_{SiC}}{\varepsilon_{OX}}\right) t_{OX} \approx 3t_{OX} \qquad [3.28]$$

The smaller effective radius of curvature at the edge of the field plate reduces the breakdown voltage in accordance with breakdown voltage of cylindrical junctions[14].

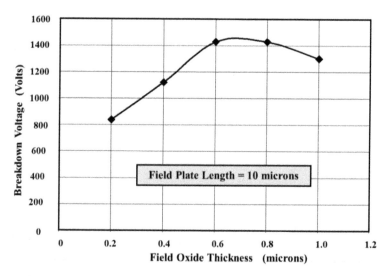

Fig. 3.16 Breakdown voltage of 4H-SiC Schottky diodes with field plates.

The variation of the breakdown voltage with field oxide thickness obtained using numerical solutions is plotted in Fig. 3.16. It is obvious that there is an optimum oxide thickness at which the breakdown voltage reaches a maximum value. It is also important to use a sufficient length (L) for the field plate as shown in Fig. 3.17. A length of 10 μm is adequate for the simulated case. In general, the field plate length must be made larger than the maximum depletion layer width for the underlying drift region doping concentration.

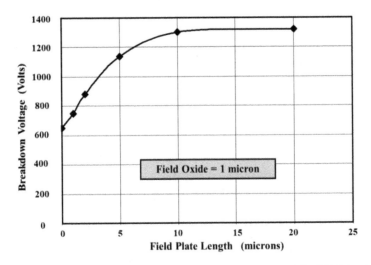

Fig. 3.17 Impact of field plate length on breakdown voltage of 4H-SiC Schottky Diodes.

Experimental results[15] on Schottky diodes made from p-type 6H-SiC with doping concentration of 1 x 10^{16} cm^{-3} display the trend shown in Fig. 3.17. The breakdown voltage of the diodes increased from 327 volts for the unterminated diode to 1000 volts for a diode with field plate using a 0.6 μm thick oxide. An important issue with the field plate edge termination is degraded reliability due to the high electric field produced in the oxide. The electric field in the oxide is related that in the silicon carbide by:

$$E_{OX} = \left(\frac{\varepsilon_{SiC}}{\varepsilon_{OX}} \right) E_{SiC} \simeq 3 E_{SiC} \qquad [3.29]$$

This equation predicts an electric field in the oxide of close to 10 MV/cm when the electric field in the silicon carbide reaches the critical electric field for breakdown (see Fig. 3.5). Such high electric fields have been known to produce a reliability problem in devices. Operating the field plate edge termination with an electric field of less than 3 MV/cm severely reduces the blocking voltage for the diode [16].

One variation of the basic field plate structure is to use a ramp oxide whose thickness increases away from the Schottky contact as shown in Fig. 3.18. This type of ramp profile can be created by using phosphosilicate glass and over etching the oxide with a photoresist mask[17]. Breakdown voltages close to the ideal parallel-plane value were reported for Schottky diodes fabricated from 6H-SiC. However, the electric field in the oxide is still well above the reliability limit[19]. Similar results have been obtained for Schottky diodes fabricated using 4H-SiC[18].

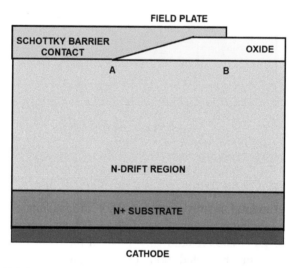

Fig. 3.18 Schottky diode structure with ramp oxide field plate termination.

Based up on Eq. [3.29], the electric field in the oxide can be reduced by using dielectrics with larger permittivity. This was first proposed for reducing the electric field in the gate oxide of power MOSFETs[19]. A field plate edge termination with aluminum nitride as the high-k dielectric with permittivity of 8.5 has been studied[20]. A thin silicon dioxide film was used below the AlN to improve the interface characteristics. The breakdown voltage was found to increase with increasing high-k dielectric thickness up to 0.6 μm similar to silicon dioxide case shown in Fig. 3.16 and then reduce beyond this thickness. The electric field in the high-k dielectric was calculated to be 2 MV/cm improving the oxide reliability. The breakdown voltage for the field plate termination with AlN as the dielectric was observed to be 1700 volts compared to 1100 volts with silicon dioxide as the dielectric. This is attributed to a reduced electric field at the edge of the Schottky metal (point A in Fig. 3.15) with the larger permittivity. Numerical simulations have also been performed for field plate structures with various high-k dielectrics[21]. It was found that increasing the permittivity to 25 by using Hafnium oxide improves the breakdown voltage.

3.4.5 SiC Schottky Diode Termination with Argon Implant

Since the breakdown voltage of the planar Schottky diode is limited by electric field enhancement at the edge of the metal, its breakdown voltage can be increased by spreading the potential along the surface. One effective method for achieving this is by creating a highly resistive layer along the surface as illustrated in Fig. 3.19. This was first demonstrated at PSRC by using 30 keV argon ion implantation around Schottky diodes in 6H-SiC to produce nearly ideal breakdown voltages[22] followed by its successful application to 4H-SiC[23]. The energy of the ion implant is chosen so that it does not penetrate the Schottky metal allowing retaining its good on-state characteristics. This allowed using the Schottky metal as the mask during the argon ion implantation. A remarkable increase in the breakdown voltage from 300 V to 1000 V was achieved with this technique. The breakdown voltage increases until it reaches the ideal value for an argon implant dose of 10^{16} cm^{-2}.

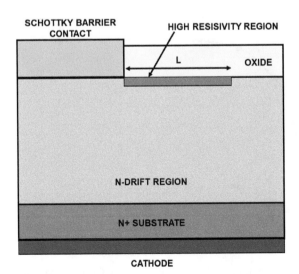

Fig. 3.19 Schottky diode edge termination with high resistivity extension.

The principle behind the approach is to utilize ion implantation to create damage in the silicon carbide lattice to produce deep levels in its band gap. This moves the Fermi level close to the center of the band gap within the implanted zone producing a high resistivity layer due to the large band gap of the semiconductor[24]. The presence of the deep level traps has been confirmed using Deep Level Transient Spectroscopy (DLTS) measurements. The damage can be created by using any implantation species (including dopants, such as Aluminum and Boron, without sufficient annealing to remove all the deep level defects) as subsequently reported by other groups[25,26].

The design of the argon implanted edge termination has been studied to determine its optimum length[27]. It was found that a length of 100 μm is adequate to achieve a breakdown voltage of 800 V for a 6H-SiC diode fabricated using an epitaxial layer doping concentration of 2 x 10^{16} cm^{-3} as shown in Fig. 3.20. An argon implant dose of 1 x 10^{15} cm^{-2} was used at the periphery of the Schottky diodes. The length of the implanted zone is about ten times the width of the depletion region at breakdown. The leakage current was found to increase linearly with the length of the implanted zone. It is therefore important to use a length just sufficient to achieve the parallel plane breakdown voltage. It has been found that the leakage current can be reduced by two-orders of magnitude with post implantation annealing at 600 °C[28].

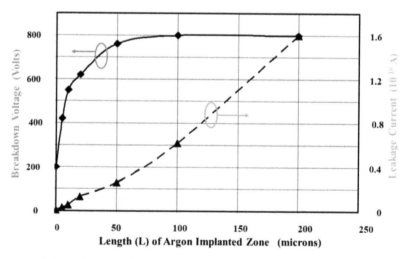

Fig. 3.20 Design of the high resistivity extension for the argon implanted edge termination.

3.5 Silicon Carbide P-N Junction Edge Terminations

The P-N junction is commonly used for the formation of a variety of power device structures. This type of structure is commonly used to make bipolar power diodes in silicon. Although the emphasis in this book is on unipolar devices due to their high performance characteristics when fabricated from 4H-SiC, even unipolar devices such as power MOSFETs require P-N junctions to support the blocking voltage within the active region. The P-N junction can also be used at the edges of these devices to reduce electric field crowding. Device edge terminations that utilize P-N junctions are discussed in this section.

3.5.1 Unterminated Planar Junction

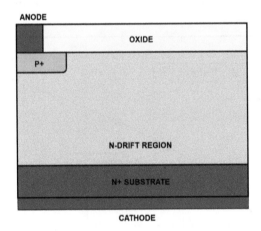

Fig. 3.21 Ion-implanted planar unterminated P-N junction in 4H-SiC.

One of the simplest edge terminations used for silicon power devices is the cylindrical junction. The breakdown voltage of this type of termination is well below that for the parallel-plane junction due to electric field enhancement at the corner of the cylindrical junction[2]. This behavior has been analytically modeled[16]. In silicon carbide, the dopants do not move during the ion implant annealing cycles despite the relatively high temperature because of their extremely low diffusion coefficients (see chapter 2). The ion-implanted junctions must therefore be modeled with very small characteristic diffusion lengths that are representative of the ion implant straggle. This type of planar edge termination is illustrated in Fig. 3.21 with an oxide passivation.

The unterminated P-N junction structure in 4H-SiC was analyzed by performing two-dimensional numerical simulations using a drift region doping concentration of 1×10^{16} cm^{-3} and thickness of 30 µm[12]. The depth of the P$^+$ region was varied to examine its impact on the breakdown voltage. The breakdown voltage of the structure was found to increase with increasing junction depth as shown in Fig. 3.22. For a shallow junction depth of 0.2 µm, the breakdown occurred at 400 volts. This is due to a significant enhancement in the electric field at the corner of the junction. This field enhancement was found to be reduced when the junction depth was increased to 0.9 µm leading to an increase in the breakdown voltage to 900 volts. These values are well below the breakdown voltage (1670 volts) for the ideal parallel plane junction. They are consistent with the measured breakdown voltages for nitrogen implanted N$^+$/P diodes formed in boron implanted 6H-SiC diodes[29].

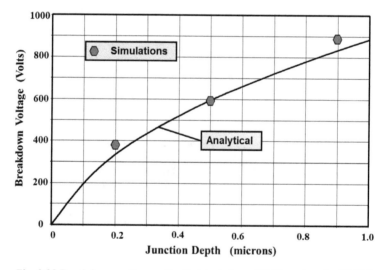

Fig. 3.22 Breakdown voltages of cylindrical planar P-N junctions in 4H-SiC.

The breakdown voltage of cylindrical junctions can be predicted by using the following analytical relationship[2]:

$$\frac{BV_{CYL}}{BV_{PP}} = \frac{1}{2}\left[\left(\frac{r_J}{W_{PP}}\right)^2 + 2\left(\frac{r_J}{W_{PP}}\right)^{6/7}\right].\ln\left[1 + 2\left(\frac{W_{PP}}{r_J}\right)^{8/7}\right] - \left(\frac{r_J}{W_{PP}}\right)^{6/7}$$

[3.30]

where r_J is the radius of curvature of the junction. The breakdown voltage calculated using this equation is shown in Fig. 3.22 by the solid line for the case of 4H-SiC with a doping concentration of 1×10^{16} cm^{-3}. The breakdown voltage obtained with the analytical formula are in reasonable agreement the two dimensional numerical simulations (shown by the symbols) even though the junction is not cylindrical in shape for the case of 4H-SiC.

3.5.2 Planar Junction with Field Plate

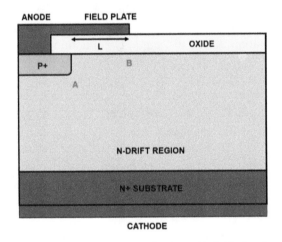

Fig. 3.23 Planar P-N junction edge termination with field plate for 4H-SiC.

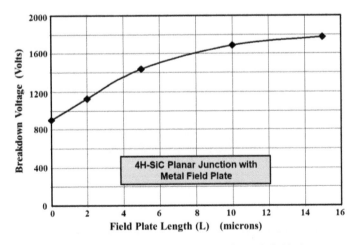

Fig. 3.24 Planar P-N junctions in 4H-SiC with field plate.

In the previous section, it was demonstrated that the breakdown voltage of a planar junction is limited by the enhanced electric field at the corner of the P-N junction (location A in Fig. 3.23 above). This electric field enhancement can be ameliorated by forming a field plate by extending the anode metal over the edge of the junction on top of the oxide. For silicon devices, the improvement in the breakdown voltage depends upon the length (L) of the field plate and the thickness of the oxide underneath the field plate[2]. Although this is also true in principle for the case of silicon carbide structures, an additional consideration is the much higher electric field within the oxide as discussed in section 3.4.3.

Two-dimensional numerical simulations of the planar junction with field plate were performed[12] using an N-type drift region with doping concentration of 1×10^{16} cm^{-3}. The junction depth was chosen as 0.9 μm. The addition of the field plate reduces the potential crowding at the junction by spreading the depletion region along the surface resulting in larger breakdown voltages. The increase in the breakdown voltage is shown in Fig. 3.24 with increasing length of the field plate. In these simulations, the oxide thickness was kept at 1 μm. The breakdown voltage can be increased two-fold with sufficient field plate length. A field plate length of 15 μm is adequate for this particular N-region doping concentration. The electric field at the edge of the field plate can become greater than that at the junction if the oxide thickness is reduced.

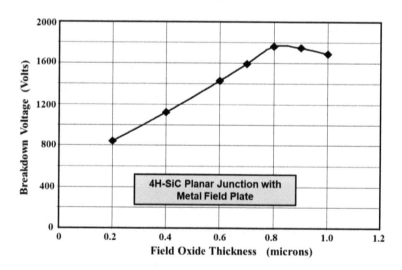

Fig. 3.25 Planar P-N junctions in 4H-SiC with field plate.

The impact of changing the field oxide thickness on the breakdown voltage is shown in Fig. 3.25. It can be seen that the breakdown voltage reaches a maximum value at a field oxide thickness of 0.8 μm. However, the change in breakdown voltage is small for larger oxide thickness values. These results indicate that a simple edge termination for 4H-SiC devices can be constructed using a P-N junction with a field plate extending over an oxide at the edges. The main advantage of this approach is that no additional masking or processing steps are required during device fabrication to prepare the edge termination.

Excellent breakdown voltages with low leakage currents were experimentally observed on 6H-SiC and 4H-SiC with both n-type and p-type drift regions by using field plates with either silicon dioxide or silicon nitride as the dielectric[30]. Breakdown voltages for 4H-SiC P-N diodes comparable to those for floating field rings were also reported using field plates with silicon dioxide[31].

3.5.3 Planar Junction Termination with Floating Field Rings

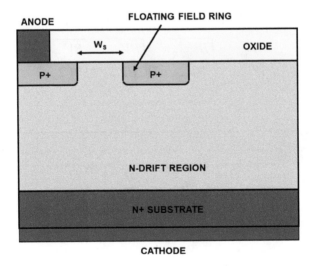

Fig. 3.26 Planar P-N junction edge termination with floating field ring.

The planar junction edge termination with a single floating field ring (FFR)[32] is shown in Fig. 3.26. This method for edge termination is commonly used in silicon devices to improve the breakdown voltages[2]. One of the advantages of this approach is that the floating field ring can be fabricated simultaneously with the main junction without adding process steps. The breakdown voltage of the termination depends upon the spacing (W_S) of the floating field ring from the main junction[2]. If the spacing is too large, the electric field at the edge of the main junction remains high leading to a breakdown voltage similar to the planar junction without the field ring. If the spacing is too small, a high electric field develops at the outer edge of the floating field ring leading to a breakdown voltage equal to that for a planar junction without the field ring. An optimum spacing is required to achieve an increase in the breakdown voltage. The breakdown voltage of a planar junction with a single floating field ring can be calculated using an analytical method[14]:

$$\frac{BV_{FFR} - BV_{CYL}}{BV_{PP}} = \left[0.5\left(\frac{r_J}{W_{PP}}\right)^2 - 0.96\left(\frac{r_J}{W_{PP}}\right)^{6/7} \right]$$

$$+1.92\left(\frac{r_J}{W_{PP}}\right)^{6/7} . \ln\left[1.386\left(\frac{W_{PP}}{r_J}\right)^{4/7}\right] \qquad \text{[3.31]}$$

with the optimum floating field ring spacing given by:

$$\frac{W_S}{W_{PP}} = \sqrt{\frac{BV_{FFR}}{BV_{PP}}} - \sqrt{\frac{BV_{FFR}}{BV_{PP}} - \frac{BV_{CY}}{BV_{PP}}} \qquad \text{[3.32]}$$

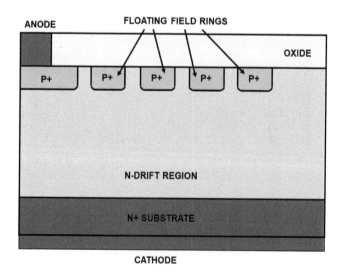

Fig. 3.27 Planar P-N junction edge termination with multiple floating field rings.

For the case of a drift region doping concentration of 1×10^{16} cm^{-3} and a junction depth of 0.9 μm, these equations predict an increase in the breakdown voltage from about 800 V to 1200 V for an optimum field ring spacing of 4.5 μm. An increase in the breakdown voltage has been experimentally observed for junctions fabricated in 4H-SiC with field ring spacing of 2-4 μm[33]. An optimum field ring spacing of 5 μm has also been reported for diodes with a breakdown voltage of 1600 volts[33], consistent with the predictions of the analytical model.

The planar junction edge termination with multiple floating field rings is shown in Fig. 3.27. The use of more floating rings allows the depletion region to spread further along the surface than with a single ring. The results of numerical simulations and experiments on 4H-SiC P-N junction diodes with up to 4 rings have been reported[34]. It was demonstrated that an optimized design with a distance between the rings increasing from 1.5 to 2.0 to 2.5 μm produces 85 % of the ideal breakdown voltage. A breakdown voltage of 1.2 kV was achieved in a 4H-SiC JBS diode by using an edge termination having 5 rings with an equal spacing of 3 μm[35]. Breakdown voltages of 70 % of the ideal value of 1800 V have been achieved by using 12 guard rings[36]. 10-kV diodes have been reported by using 102 floating field rings[37] distributed over a space of 900 μm for a drift region doped at 8×10^{14} cm^{-3}.

3.5.4 Planar Junction with Junction Termination Extension

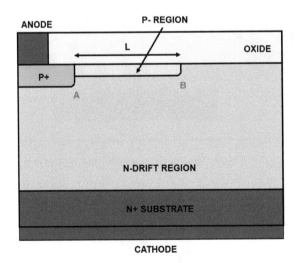

Fig. 3.28 Planar P-N junction diode with single zone junction termination extension.

For silicon devices, the breakdown voltage has been shown to be greatly improved by using a 'Junction Termination Extension (JTE)'[38]. This concept has also been applied to silicon carbide devices. The JTE structure, illustrated in Fig. 3.28, contains a P-type region formed at the periphery of a P$^+$/N junction. This lightly doped P-type region is usually formed by using ion implantation to precisely control the dopant charge within the layer. If the doping concentration in the P-type region is too high, the breakdown occurs at its edge (point B) at a lower breakdown voltage than the main junction due to its smaller radius of curvature. If the doping concentration is too low in the P-type region, it becomes completely depleted at low reverse bias voltages resulting in breakdown at the main junction (point A) at the same voltage as the un-terminated junction. However, with an optimum charge in the P-type region, such that it is completely depleted near the ideal breakdown voltage, the depletion region in the N-drift region spreads laterally so that the electric field at points A and B remain balanced and low in magnitude. This increases the breakdown voltage close to the ideal parallel-plane break-down voltage value for the N-drift region.

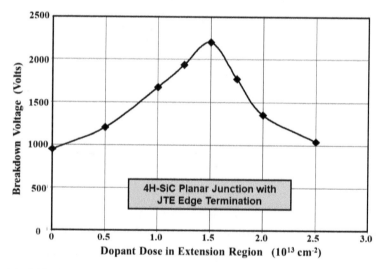

Fig. 3.29 Planar 4H-SiC diodes with single zone junction termination extension.

The optimum charge in the P-type region is:

$$Q = \varepsilon_S E_C \qquad\qquad [3.37]$$

which amounts to 1.72×10^{-6} C/cm^2 for a critical electric field of 2×10^6 V/cm for 4H-SiC. This is equivalent to a dopant dose of 1.1×10^{13} cm^{-2}, which is about 10 times larger than that used in silicon devices[2]. A more precise optimization of the dose can be performed by two-dimensional numerical simulations of the structure.

The results of the simulations[12], performed using an extension length of 10 μm, are summarized in Fig. 3.29 where the variation in breakdown voltage is plotted as a function of the dopant dose in the P-region. As in the case of silicon devices, there is an optimum dose at which the breakdown voltage has a maximum value. At lower doses, the breakdown voltage continues to occur at the main junction due to the peak in the electric field at point A. At higher doses, the breakdown voltage occurs at the edge of the extension due to the peak in the electric field at point B. The optimum dose obtained by using the numerical simulations is in agreement with that predicted by using the simple formula in Eq. [3.37]. The breakdown voltage obtained at the optimum dose is twice that for the un-terminated junction for this extension length of 10 μm.

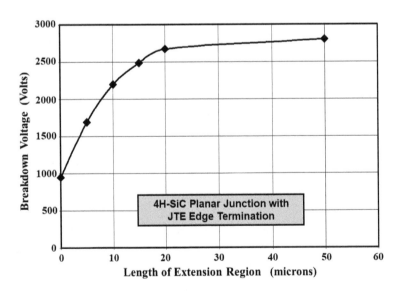

Fig. 3.30 Planar P-N junctions in 4H-SiC with junction termination extension.

The dependence of the breakdown voltage on the extension length is shown in Fig. 3.30 at the optimum dose in the extension. It can be seen that a breakdown voltage close to the parallel plane junction case can be obtained by using an extension length of 50 μm.

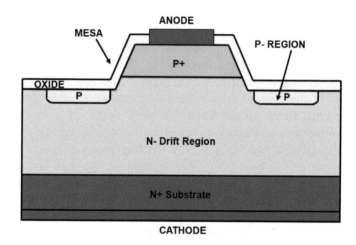

Fig. 3.31 Mesa P-N junction in 4H-SiC with junction termination extension.

This method for edge terminations has gained popularity due to its effectiveness in suppressing the edge breakdown for P-N junctions[39,40,41]. The optimum dose doe the single zone JTE region is just above 1 x 10^{13} cm^{-2} based on this work. In order to implement this technique it was necessary to develop methods for precisely controlling the P-type dopant dose in the extension. Although the dose can be controlled very well by using ion implantation, processes for the annealing and activation of P-type dopants (Boron and Aluminum) needed to be developed. In addition, the performance has been found to be sensitive to surface charge in the passivation as also reported for silicon devices. In the case of P-N diodes made by the growth of a P^{+} epitaxial layer on an N-drift region, the JTE termination can be created by first producing a mesa as shown in Fig. 3.31[42,43]. Diodes with a breakdown voltage of 10 kV were fabricated using an edge termination length of 200 μm and an optimum JTE dose of 1 x 10^{13} cm^{-2}.

3.5.5 Planar Junction with Two-Zone JTE

The fabrication of the JTE region requires precise control of the dose of the dopants. In silicon devices, this can be performed by using ion-implantation and annealing to achieve 100 % activation. The precise control of dopant concentration in 4H-SiC was initially difficult due to poor activation of dopants in ion implanted layers. Consequently, early work on creating JTE regions relied up on the epitaxial growth of the P-type region on the N-type drift region followed by etching mesas as illustrated in Fig. 3.32. Enhancements to the breakdown voltage were achieved using multiple zones with different dopant dose levels[38,44] achieved by etching steps in an epitaxially grown P-type layer with aluminum doping. The P-type layer was 0.7 μm thick with an aluminum concentration of 2 x 10^{18} cm^{-3}. A breakdown voltage of over 90 % of the ideal value was achieved by using etch depths of d_1 = 0.4 μm and d_2 = 0.04 μm. This method requires precise control and uniformity for the etch rate for 4H-SiC. The dose of the second zone is 10 % smaller than the first zone.

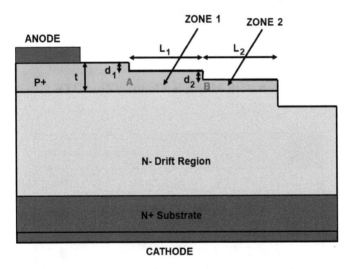

Fig. 3.32 Planar P-N junction diode with two zone mesa junction termination extension created by etching the epitaxially grown P$^+$ anode region.

After the development of annealing processes for ion implanted regions in 4H-SiC, it was possible to fabricate planar JTE edge termi-nations[45] as shown in Fig. 3.33. JTE zones of 65 μm in length were sufficient for 1.7 kV diodes. The dose for the first zone was 1 x 10^{14} cm^{-2} while that for the second zone was 10-times smaller. A breakdown voltage of over 90 % of the ideal value was obtained by using this approach. The leakage current was reduced significantly by using silicon dioxide as passivation on the surface.

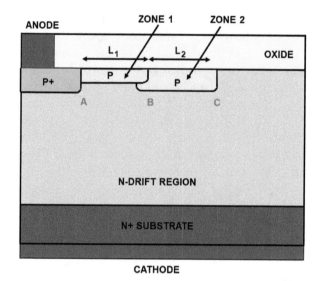

Fig. 3.33 Planar P-N junction diode with two zone junction termination extension.

3.5.6 Planar Junction with Multiple Floating Zone JTE

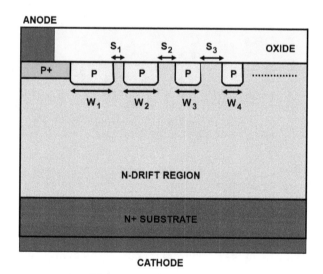

Fig. 3.34 Planar diode with multiple floating zone junction termination extension.

The multiple floating zone junction termination extension (MFZ-JTE)[46] concept utilizes floating rings with low doping concentrations as illustrated in Fig. 3.34. The zones are designed with decreasing widths (W_1, W_2, W_3,...) and increasing spacings (S_1, S_2, S_3,...). The widths of the zones are reduced by a factor of 1.02 while the spacing is increased by a factor of 1.02 to create a very gradual change in the net P-type charge along the surface. A breakdown voltage of 10-kV was achieved by using 36 and 72 zones with a dose of 2 x 10^{13} cm^{-2}. The advantages of this method are that a single photolithography step and ion-implant steps can be used to form the edge termination and that it has a wide tolerance in ion implant dose for the P-region. This concept has been analyzed using numerical simulations with a mesa etched P-N junction[47] and applied to fabrication of 21-kV 4H-SiC bipolar transistors[48].

3.5.7 Planar Junction with Ring Assisted JTE

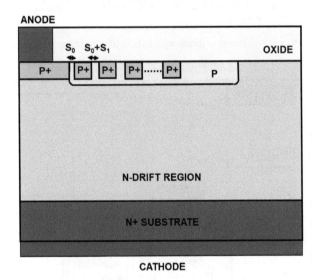

Fig. 3.35 Planar P-N junction diode with ring assisted junction termination extension.

The ring assisted (RA) junction termination extension (JTE) was created to reduce the sensitivity of the breakdown voltage to the ion implant dose used for the JTE region[49]. It consists of a JTE region with P$^+$ floating field rings (FFR) embedded inside it as illustrated in Fig. 3.35. This approach increases the breakdown voltage in the low dose range but there is still a sharp reduction in the breakdown voltage when the dose exceed a critical value as observed for the SZ JTE case. The spacing between the FFR must be optimized to achieve good performance.

3.5.8 Planar Junction with Hybrid Multiple Floating Zone JTE

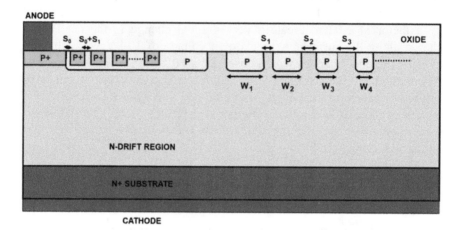

Fig. 3.35 Planar P-N junction diode with hybrid junction termination extension.

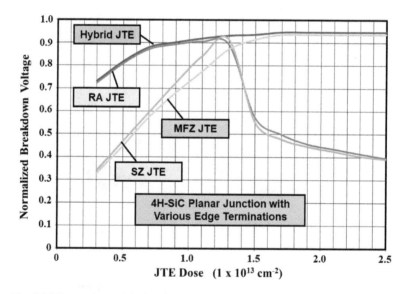

Fig. 3.36 Comparison of the breakdown voltages achieved for 4H-SiC P-N junction diodes by using various junction termination extension approaches.

The ring assisted (RA) JTE structure can be combined with the MFZ structure to form the termination shown in Fig. 3.35[50,51]. This terminated is called the hybrid JTE approach. The hybrid JTE approach produces a high breakdown voltage over a wide range of ion implant doses for the JTE region. This produces very little sensitivity to charge in the passivation dielectric and device processing after the JTE ion implant is performed. It can be used for a wide range of blocking voltage capability for 4H-SiC diode and transistors.

A comparison of the performance of the various JTE approaches is provided in Fig. 3.36. The single zone JTE requires a precise dose of 1.3×10^{13} cm^{-2} for the JTE region to obtain a high breakdown voltage. Presence of fixed oxide charge in the passivation layer or any loss of charge due to surface oxidation during device processing can change the dose producing large variations and reductions in the breakdown voltage[52]. The ring assisted JTE approach improves the breakdown voltage at lower doses of the JTE region but exhibits a sharp fall in breakdown voltage above a critical dose like the SZ-JTE. The multiple floating zone (MFZ) JTE approach prevents the rapid degradation of breakdown voltage at higher doses but behaves like a SZ JTE structure at low doses. In contrast, the hybrid JTE approach produces a high breakdown voltage over a very broad range of doses for the JTE region. It has been shown to be insensitive to the charge in the oxide and loss of charge in the JTE region due to thermal oxidation[54].

3.5.9 Orthogonal Bevel Edge Terminations

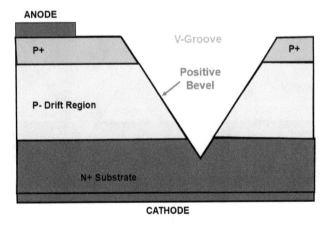

Fig. 3.37 Orthogonal positive bevel edge termination.

The use of bevels to terminate the edges of high voltage silicon power rectifiers and thyristors has been extensively used since the 1960s[2]. The positive bevel approach is based on removal of more semiconductor material from the lightly doped side of the P-N junction to spread the depletion layer over a larger distance. The resulting reduction in surface electric field has been shown to move the breakdown to the interior parallel-plane junctions allowing achieving 100 % of the ideal breakdown voltage. This approach was restricted to single devices made from an entire wafer because the terminations require tapering the wafer edges. The positive bevel was formed by using grit blasting with a nozzle oriented at an angle to the wafer surface while the wafer was rotated. The damage produced to the silicon surface by the grit blasting was removed by etching the silicon in acids.

The application of bevel edges to silicon carbide devices requires producing bevels for multiple devices with small areas on a single wafer. This has been achieved by performing orthogonal saw cuts on 4H-SiC wafers with a V-shaped blade[53]. The saw cut produces a positive bevel at the N$^+$ substrate-P drift region junction as illustrated in Fig. 3.37. The damage produced by the sawing operation must be removed by reactive ion etching. Three dimensional numerical simulations have demonstrated that the orthogonal positive bevels reduce the surface electric field at the corners to even below the low electric field along the edges. This allows obtaining close to ideal breakdown voltages.

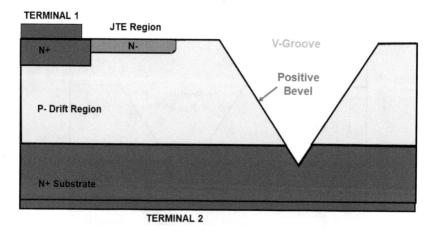

Fig. 3.38 Symmetric blocking bevel edge termination.

The orthogonal positive bevel is particularly suitable for making silicon carbide power devices with symmetric blocking voltage capability such as GTOs and IGBTs. Such devices are required for circuit breakers used in micro-grids to isolate faults. The symmetric blocking capability can be accomplished by using the structure shown in Fig. 3.38. Here, the forward blocking capability is obtained by using the JTE edge termination at the upper N^+/P drift region junction and the reverse blocking capability is achieved with the orthogonal positive bevel[54] for the lower N^+ substrate/P drift region junction.

3.5.10 Bevel Junction Termination Extension

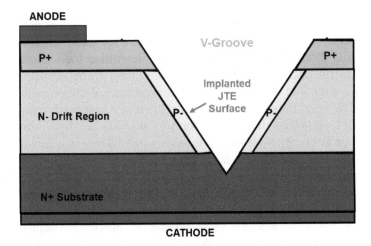

Fig. 3.39 Bevel junction termination extension.

The orthogonal positive bevel and JTE concepts have been combined to achieve the edge termination shown in Fig. 3.39. This bevel-JTE termination[55] was created by ion-implantation of aluminum to form the P- JTE region after forming the bevel by the sawing of the wafers and etching out the damage. A breakdown voltage of over 90 % of the ideal value was observed when the aluminum dose is 1 to 2 x 10^{13} cm^{-2}. Numerical simulations have shown that the breakdown voltage is reduced when the JTE dose is too high because of a high electric field developed at the junction between the P- region and the N^+ substrate. The breakdown voltage is also reduced when the JTE dose is too low because of a high electric field developed at the junction between the P^+ region and the N drift region. The termination works well for a broad range of bevel angles ranging from 30 to 60 degrees.

3.6 Summary

The design issues pertinent to obtaining a high breakdown voltage in 4H-SiC vertical discrete device structures have been reviewed in this chapter. As a bench mark, the breakdown voltage of the abrupt parallel plane junction has been analyzed for 4H-SiC using Baliga's power law equations for the impact ionization coefficients. These analytical formulae allow development of closed form analytical equations for the depletion layer width and critical electric field at breakdown. The breakdown voltage of open-base transistor structures with buffer layers is also provided for the design of 4H-SiC GTOs and IGBTs.

The breakdown voltage of practical devices is limited by the electric field crowding at their edges. Various edge termination methods for 4H-SiC diodes have been reviewed to determine their performance relative to the ideal parallel plane junction. The argon implanted high resistance zone and the junction extension using a P-region with a dose of 1-2 x 10^{13} cm^{-2} have been found to provide the best performance. The hybrid JTE approach has been found to provide the best breakdown voltages of above 95 % of the ideal value while having low sensitivity to charges in the passivation layer and to thermal oxidation after ion implantation of the JTE zone. This termination is very useful for 4H-SiC JBS diodes, power MOSFETs, and IGBTs. Unique orthogonal bevel edge terminations have been created by sawing the 4H-SiC wafers with a V-shaped blade to achieve high symmetric blocking voltages. This approach allows fabrication of symmetric blocking 4H-SiC IGBTs for AC circuit applications.

References

[1] B. J. Baliga, "The IGBT Device: Physics, Design, and Applications of the Insulated Gate Bipolar Transistor", Second Edition, Elsevier Press, Amsterdam, 2023.

[2] B. J. Baliga, "Fundamentals of Power Semiconductor Devices", Second Edition, Chapter 3, Springer-Science, New York, 2019.

[3] B. J. Baliga, "Advanced Power MOSFET Concepts", Springer-Science, New York, 2010.

[4] A. O. Konstantinov, et al, "Ionization Rates and Critical Electric Fields in 4H-SiC", Applied Physics Letters, Vol. 71, pp. 90, 1997.

[5] J. W. Palmour, et al, "Silicon Carbide for Power Devices", IEEE International Symposium on Power Semiconductor Devices and ICs, pp. 25-32, 1997.

[6] T. Kimoto and J. A. Cooper, "Fundamentals of Silicon Carbide Technology", p. 279, IEEE Press, 2014.

[7] B. J. Baliga and M. S. Adler, "Measurement of Carrier Lifetime Profiles in Diffused Layers of Semiconductors", IEEE Transactions on Electron Devices, Vol. ED-25, pp. 472-477, 1978.

[8] M. Bhatnagar, P. K. McLarty, and B. J. Baliga, "Silicon Carbide High Voltage (400V) Schottky Barrier Diodes", IEEE Electron Device Letters, Vol. 13, pp. 501-503, 1992.

[9] R. Raghunathan, D. Alok, and B. J. Baliga, "High Voltage 4H-SiC Schottky Barrier Diodes", IEEE Electron Device Letters, Vol. 16, pp. 226-227, 1995.

[10] B. J. Baliga, "Silicon Carbide Power Devices", World Scientific Press, Singapore, 2006.

[11] M. Bhatnagar, et al, "Edge Terminations for SiC High Voltage Schottky Rectifiers", IEEE International Symposium on Power Semiconductor Devices and ICs, pp. 89-94, 1993.

[12] B. J. Baliga, "Closed Form Analytical Solutions for the Breakdown Voltage of Planar Junctions Terminated with a Single Floating Field Ring", Solid State Electronics, Vol. 33, pp. 485-488, 1990.

[13] M. Bhatnagar, et al, "Edge Terminations for SiC High Voltage Schottky Rectifiers", International Symposium on Power Semiconductor Devices and ICs, pp. 89-94, 1993.

[14] B. J. Baliga and S. K. Ghandhi, "Analytical Solutions for the Breakdown Voltage of Abrupt Cylindrical and Spherical Junctions", Solid State Electronics, Vol. 19, pp. 739-744, 1976.

[15] M. C. Tarplee, et al, "Design Rules for Field Plate Edge Termination in SiC Schottky Diodes", IEEE Transactions on Electron Devices, Vol. 48, pp. 2659-2664, 2001.

[16] S. Hu and K. Sheng, "A Study of Oxide Reliability Limitation on different Field Plate based Termination Techniques for SiC Power Devices", International Power Electronics and Motion Control Conference, Vol. 2, pp. 868-872, 2004.

[17] G. Brezeanu, et al, "A Nearly Ideal SiC Schottky Barrier Device Edge Termination", International Semiconductor Conference, Vol. 1, pp. 183-186, 1999.

[18] G. Brezeanu, et al, "High Performance SiC Diodes based on an Efficient Planar Termination", International Semiconductor Conference, Vol. 1, pp. 27-36, 2003.

[19] S. Sridevan, P. K. McLarty, and B. J. Baliga, "Analysis of Gate Dielectrics for SiC Power UMOSFETs", IEEE International Symposium on Power Semiconductor Devices and ICs, pp. 153-156, 1997.

[20] A. S. Kumta, P. Rusli, and X. Jinghua, "Field-Plate-Terminated 4H-SiC Schottky Diodes using Al-Based High-k Dielectrics", IEEE Transactions on Electron Devices, Vol. 56, pp. 2925-2934, 2009.

[21] Y. Huang, et al, "Effects of Edge Termination using Dielectric Field Plates with Different Dielectric Constants, Thicknesses, and Bevel Angles", IEEE Applied Power Electronics Conference, pp. 2902-2906, 2014.

[22] D. Alok, B. J. Baliga, and P. K. McLarty, "A Simple Edge Termination for Silicon Carbide with Nearly Ideal Breakdown Voltage", IEEE Electron Device Letters, Vol. ED15, pp. 394-395, 1994.

[23] D. Alok, R. Raghunathan, and B. J. Baliga, "Planar Edge Termination for 4H-SiC Devices", IEEE Transactions on Electron Devices, Vol. 43, pp. 1315-1317, 1996.

[24] D. Alok, B. J. Baliga, M. Kothandaraman, and P. K. McLarty, "Argon Implanted SiC Device Edge Termination: Modeling, Analysis, and Experimental Results", Institute of Physics Conference Series, Vol. 142, pp. 565-568, 1996.

[25] A. Itoh, T. Kimoto, and H. Matsunami, "Excellent Reverse Blocking Characteristics of High Voltage 4H-SiC Schottky Rectifiers with Boron Implanted Edge Termination", IEEE Electron Device Letters, Vol. ED17, pp. 139-141, 1996.

[26] R. Weiss, L. Frey, and H. Ryssel, "Different Ion Implanted Edge Terminations for Schottky Diodes on SiC", IEEE International Ion Implantation Technology Conference, pp. 139-142, 2002.

[27] D. Alok and B. J. Baliga, "SiC Device Edge Termination using Finite Area Argon Implantation", IEEE Transactions on Electron Devices, Vol. 44, pp. 1013-1017, 1997.

[28] A. P. Knights, et al, "The Effect of Annealing on Argon Implanted Edge Terminations for 4H-SiC Schottky Diodes", MRS Symposium Proceedings, Vol. 572, pp. 129-134, 1999.

[29] P. M. Shenoy and B. J. Baliga, "Planar, High Voltage, Boron Implanted 6H-SiC P-N Junction Diodes", Institute of Physics Conference Series, Vol. 142, pp. 717-720, 1996.

[30] R. K. Chilukuri, P. Ananthanarayanan, V. Nagapudi, and B. J. Baliga, "High Voltage P-N Junction Diodes in Silicon Carbide using Field Plate Edge Termination", MRS Symposium Proceedings, Vol. 572, pp. 81-86, 1999.

[31] R. Singh and J. W. Palmour, "Planar Terminations in 4H-SiC Schottky Diodes with Low Leakage and High Yields", IEEE International Symposium on Power Semiconductor Devices and ICs, pp. 157-160, 1997.

[32] Y. C. Kao and E. D. Wolley, "High Voltage Planar P-N Junctions", Proceedings of the IEEE, Vol. 55, pp. 1409-1414, 1967.

[33] W. Bahng, et al, "Fabrication and Characterization of 4H-SiC pn Diode with Field Limiting Ring", Silicon Carbide and Related Materials – 2003, Materials Science Forum, Vol. 457-460, pp. 1013-1016, 2004.

[34] D. C. Sheridan, et al, "Simulation and Fabrication of High Voltage 4H-SiC Diodes with Multiple Floating Guard Ring Termination", Silicon Carbide and Related Materials – 2000, Materials Science Forum, Vol. 338-342, pp. 1339-1342, 2000.

[35] S-C. Kim, et al, "Fabrication Characteristics of 1.2kV SiC JBS Diode", IEEE International Conference on Microelectronics, pp. 181-184, 2008.

[36] X. Li, et al, "Theoretical and Experimental Study of 4H-SiC Junction Edge Termination", Silicon Carbide and Related Materials – 1999, Materials Science Forum, Vol. 338-342, pp. 1375-1378, 2000.

[37] S-H Ryu, et al, "10 kV, 5A 4H-SiC Power DMOSFET", IEEE International Symposium on Power Semiconductor Devices and ICs, pp. 1-4, 2006.

[38] V. A. K. Temple, "Junction Termination Extension: a New Technique for increasing Avalanche Breakdown Voltage and controlling Surface Electric Fields in P-N Junctions", IEEE International Electron Devices Meeting, Abstract 20.4, pp. 423-426, 1977.

[39] R. Rupp, et al, "Performance and Reliability Issues of SiC Schottky Diodes", Silicon Carbide and Related Materials – 1999, Materials Science Forum, Vol. 338-342, pp. 1167-1170, 2000.

[40] H. P. Felsl and G. Wachutka, "Performance of 4H-SiC Schottky Diodes with Al-Doped p-Guard-Ring Junction Termination at Reverse Bias", Silicon Carbide and Related Materials – 2001, Materials Science Forum, Vol. 389-393, pp. 1153-1156, 2002.

[41] C. Raynaud, et al, "Design, Fabrication, and Characterization of 5kV 4H-SiC P+ N Planar Bipolar Diodes protected by Junction Termination

Extension", Silicon Carbide and Related Materials – 2004, Materials Science Forum, Vol. 457-460, pp. 1033-1036, 2004.

[42] R. Singh, et al, "SiC Power Schottky and PiN Diodes", IEEE Transactions on Electron Devices, Vol. ED49, pp. 665-672, 2002.

[43] T. Hiyoshi, et al, "Simulation and Experimental Study on the Junction Termination Extension Structure for High-Voltage 4H-SiC PiN Diodes", IEEE Transactions on Electron Devices, Vol. 55, pp. 1841-1846, 2008.

[44] P. Alexandrov, et al, "High Performance C plus Al Co-implanted 500V 4H-SiC PiN Diode", Electronics Letters, Vol. 37, pp. 531-533, 2001.

[45] R. Perez, et al, "Planar Edge Termination Design and Technology Considerations for 1.7kV 4H-SiC PiN Diodes", IEEE Transactions on Electron Devices, Vol. 52, pp. 2309-2316, 2005.

[46] W. Sung, et al, "A New Edge Termination Technique for High Voltage Devices in 4H-SiC – Multiple Floating Zone Junction Termination Extension", IEEE Electron Device Letters, Vol. 32, pp. 880-882, 2011.

[47] G. Feng, J. Suda, and T. Kimoto, "Space-Modulated Junction Termination Extension for Ultrahigh-Voltage p-i-n Diodes in 4H-SiC", IEEE Transactions on Electron Devices, Vol. 59, pp. 414-418, 2012.

[48] H. Miyake, et al, "21-kV SiC BJTs with Space-Modulated Junction Termination Extension", IEEE Electron Device Letters, Vol. 33, pp. 1598-1600, 2012.

[49] K. Kinoshita, et al, "Guard Ring Assisted RESURF: A New Termination Structure Providing Stable and High Breakdown Voltage for SiC Power Devices", IEEE International Symposium on Power Semiconductor Devices and ICs, pp. 253-256, 2002.

[50] W. Sung and B. J. Baliga, "A Near Ideal Edge Termination Technique for 4500V 4H-SiC Devices: The Hybrid Junction Termination Extension", IEEE Electron Device Letters, Vol. 37, pp. 1609-1612, 2016.

[51] W. Sung and B. J. Baliga, "A Comparative Study 4500-V Edge Termination Techniques for SiC Devices", IEEE Trans. Electron Devices, Vol. 64, pp. 1647-1652, 2017.

[52] N. Yun and W. Sung, "A Comparative Study 4500-V Edge Termination Techniques for SiC Devices", IEEE Trans. Electron Devices, Vol. 69, pp. 3826-3832, 2022.

[53] X. Huang, et al, "Orthogonal Positive-Bevel Termination for Chip-Size SiC Reverse Blocking Devices", IEEE Electron Device Letters, Vol. 33, pp. 1592-1594, 2012.

[54] X. Huang, et al, "SiC Symmetric Blocking Terminations using Orthogonal Positive Bevel Termination and Junction Termination

Extension", IEEE International Symposium on Power Semiconductor Devices and ICs, pp. 179-182, 2013.

[55] W. Sung, et al, "Bevel Junction Termination Extension – A New Edge Termination Technique for 4H-SiC High-Voltage Devices", IEEE Electron Device Letters, Vol. 36, pp. 594-596, 2015.

Chapter 4

Ideal Specific On-Resistance

All unipolar power device structures, such as Schottky rectifiers and power MOSFETs, contain a drift region designed to support the high blocking voltages. The drift region is therefore an essential component of the device structure without which the power device could not sustain a high voltage in power electronic circuits. The rest of the device structure is required for control of the operating points of the device such as the on-state and blocking mode. This includes the gate structure, source and drain contacts, and substrates used for handling the device wafers during processing. The resistance of these components in the device structure must be minimized by design optimization. In addition, the current flow through the drift region is not uniform making its resistance larger than desired. The ultimate goal is to create a device whose on-resistance becomes close to that of the drift region. The drift region resistance with uniform current flow represents the lowest value that is achievable with traditional one-dimensional potential distribution. This parameter is consequently called the *ideal specific on-resistance* ($R_{on,sp}$).

Until the 1990s, power devices relied up on parallel-plane junctions with voltage supported across one-dimensional depletion regions. The solution of Poisson's equation for these drift regions indicates a triangular electric field distribution as shown in Fig. 3.1. In the 1990s, the concept of two-dimensional charge coupling was proposed to alter the electric field profile in the drift region to a more uniform distribution. It was demonstrated that the doping concentration in the drift region could be substantially increased with this approach leading to much lower specific on-resistance than possible with the one-dimensional case.

This chapter describes the electric field distribution for the conventional one-dimensional and charge-coupled two-dimensional cases. Using this information, the specific on-resistance for the conventional one-dimensional and charge-coupled two-dimensional cases is derived.

These analytical solutions are used to define the lowest possible specific on-resistance in silicon and 4H-SiC unipolar power devices. This information is important for a proper understanding of the limits of performance of power devices made from these materials. Actual power device structures can approach but not exceed this performance barrier.

4.1 Ideal Specific On-Resistance for One-Dimensional Case

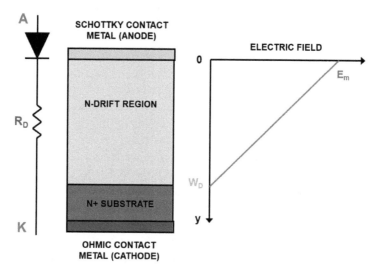

Fig. 4.1 The ideal drift region and its electric field distribution.

Most unipolar power devices contain a drift region which is designed to support the blocking voltage using a one-dimensional potential distribution. The doping concentration and thickness of the *ideal drift region* can be analyzed by assuming an abrupt junction profile with high doping concentration on one side and a low uniform doping concentration on the other side, while neglecting any junction curvature effects by assuming a parallel-plane configuration. This is applicable to vertical power MOSFET structures. The same electric field distribution is valid for the case of a Schottky rectifier illustrated in Fig. 4.1.

The solution of Poisson's equation leads to a triangular electric field distribution within a uniformly doped drift region, as previously discussed in chapter 3, with the slope of the electric field profile proportional to the doping concentration. The maximum voltage that can be supported by the drift region is determined by the maximum electric field (E_m) reaching the critical electric field (E_c) for breakdown for the semiconductor material. The critical electric field for breakdown and the doping concentration then determine the maximum depletion width (W_{PP}). The critical electric fields for Si and 4H-SiC were discussed in chapter 3.

It is convenient to define a specific on-resistance as the resistance for the case of an active area of 1 cm^2. This allows analysis of the power devices independent of any particular current rating that is decided by the size of chip. The specific resistance (resistance per unit area) of the ideal drift region is given by:

$$R_{on.sp} = \left(\frac{W_D}{q\mu_n N_D} \right) \qquad [4.1]$$

where W_D is the thickness of the drift region, N_D is the doping concentration of the drift region, μ_n is the electron mobility corresponding to this doping level, and q is the electron charge. Since this resistance was initially considered to be the lowest value achievable with silicon devices, it has historically been referred to as the *ideal specific on-resistance of the drift region*. As derived in chapter 3, the depletion width under breakdown conditions is given by:

$$W_{PP} = \frac{2BV}{E_C} \qquad [4.2]$$

where BV is the desired breakdown voltage. The doping concentration in the drift region required to obtain this breakdown voltage is given by:

$$N_D = \frac{\varepsilon_S E_C^2}{2q\,BV} \qquad [4.3]$$

Combining these relationships, the specific resistance of the ideal drift region is obtained:

$$R_{on-ideal} = \frac{4BV^2}{\varepsilon_S \mu_n E_C^3} \qquad [4.4]$$

This theoretical analysis, relating the specific on-resistance of unipolar power devices to the fundamental properties of the semiconductor material for the first time, was first published in a GE classified report[1] in 1979. It was eventually released for external publication in 1982[2].

The denominator of Eq. [4.4] is now commonly referred to as *Baliga's Figure of Merit (BFOM) for Power Devices*:

$$BFOM = \varepsilon_S \, \mu_n \, E_C^3 \qquad\qquad [4.5]$$

It is worth emphasizing that this FOM is applicable to unipolar power devices with triangular electric field distribution in the drift region. It is an indicator of the impact of the semiconductor material properties on the resistance of the drift region. Based on Eq. [4.4], the BFOM is given by:

$$BFOM = \frac{4BV^2}{R_{on-ideal}} \qquad\qquad [4.6]$$

It has become commonplace to take the measured breakdown voltage and specific on-resistance of fabricated SiC devices to compute the BFOM using Eq. [4.6] as a measure of approaching the ideal performance of the material.

Information on impact ionization coefficients and the critical electric field for breakdown in semiconductors was not available when the theoretical analysis was first published relating the power device drift region resistance to the properties of the semiconductor material in 1982[2]. It was therefore assumed that the critical electric field is proportional to the energy band gap allowing its substitution for comparison of semiconductors. The *initial Baliga's Figure of Merit (BFOM) proposed for Power Devices* was:

$$BFOM(i) = \varepsilon_S \, \mu_n \, E_G^3 \qquad\qquad [4.7]$$

This equation makes it apparent that a larger figure of merit is obtained when the energy band gap of the semiconductor becomes larger. This is the basis for development of power devices from wide band gap semiconductors.

The critical electric field for breakdown in many wide band gap semiconductors has now been measured allowing the use of the more accurate relationship given in Eq. [4.4]. The changes in the specific on-resistance for the drift region with critical electric field and mobility obtained by using this equation are shown in Fig. 4.2 for the case of a breakdown voltage of 1000 volts. The cases of mobility values of 1000, 2000, 4000, and 8000 cm²/V-s are used as examples. The specific on-resistance reduces rapidly with increasing critical electric field for breakdown due to the strong cubic dependence. It is also reduced when the mobility increases. In order to evaluate specific semiconductors, it is important to first determine the doping concentration for the drift region to obtain the breakdown voltage of 1000 volts. Using this doping concentration, the mobility and the critical electric field can be obtained as discussed in chapter 3. These values should then be applied to Eq. [4.4].

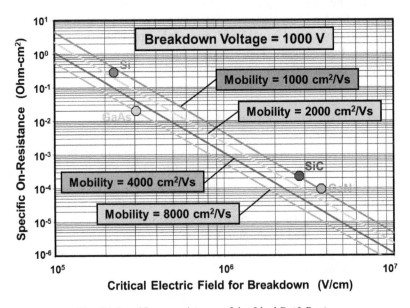

Fig. 4.2 Specific on-resistance of the *Ideal Drift Region*.

In the case of silicon, the specific on-resistance is very high as shown by the data point in blue in the figure. The dependence of the drift region resistance on the mobility (assumed to be for electrons here because in general they have higher mobility values than for holes) of the carriers favors semiconductors such as Gallium Arsenide whose electron mobility is 8000 cm[2]/V-s. Its specific on-resistance is about 20-times smaller than for silicon as indicated by the data point in Fig. 4.2. This significant improvement was pursed at GE in the 1980s resulting in successful fabrication of GaAs power Schottky rectifiers[3] and FETs[4,5]. These were the first power device structures demonstrated using wide band gap material because the band gap of GaAs is 1.4 eV compared with 1.1 eV for Si.

The strong (cubic) dependence of the on-resistance on the critical electric field for breakdown favors semiconductors with even wider band gap than GaAs. This can be achieved by ternary alloys such as GaAlAs[2]. The impact is even greater with 4H-SiC and GaN due to their larger band gaps of 3.26 and 3.44, respectively. The critical electric field for breakdown for 4H-SiC as determined by the impact ionization coefficients for holes and electrons was discussed in the chapter 3. The location of the specific on-resistances for 4H-SiC and GaN are shown in Fig. 4.2 by the red and green points. The specific on-resistance of the drift region for SiC and GaN is 100-times lower than that for GaAs. The specific on-resistances for 4H-SiC and GaN are 1000-times and 2000-times better than silicon. The practical realization of SiC power device structures is discussed in the rest of this book.

4.2 Ideal Specific On-Resistance for Silicon Carbide

The ideal specific on-resistance for the drift region in unipolar 4H-SiC power devices can be obtained by using Eq. [4.1] with the doping concentration and depletion layer width at breakdown derived in chapter 3. Due to the relatively high doping concentration for the drift region in 4H-SiC, it is important to include the dependence of mobility on doping level that was provided in chapter 2.

The doping concentration of the drift region can be related to the breakdown voltage by using Eq. [3.12]:

$$N_D = \frac{1.98 \times 10^{20}}{BV^{4/3}}$$ [4.8]

The depletion layer width can be related to the breakdown voltage by using Eq. [3.15]:

$$W_{PP} = 2.33 \times 10^{-7} BV^{7/6}$$ [4.9]

The ideal specific on-resistance for the drift region in 4H-SiC devices can be computed by using the above equations together with the doping dependence of mobility given by Eq. [2.22]. The results are shown in Fig. 4.3 for breakdown voltages from 100 to 100,000 volts. The case of silicon drift regions is included in this figure for comparison. A significant reduction in the specific on-resistance of drift regions is predicted by replacing silicon with 4H-SiC. The ratio of the specific on-resistance for silicon to that for 4H-SiC increases from 527 at a breakdown voltage of 100 volts to 1260 for breakdown voltage of 20,000 volts. The change in this ratio is due to the reduction of electron mobility in 4H-SiC at the higher doping levels predicted at the lower breakdown voltages.

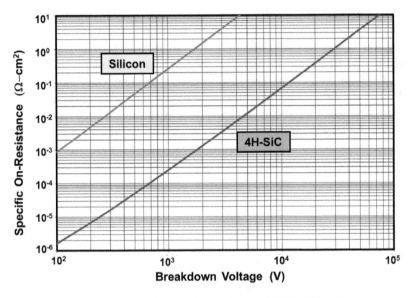

Fig. 4.3 Ideal specific on-resistance for the 4H-SiC drift region.

The ideal specific on-resistance for 4H-SiC at a breakdown voltage of 1000 V is 2.54 x 10^{-4} Ω-cm^2. Using these values in Eq. [4.6], the ideal BFOM is calculated to be 15.8 GW/cm^2. The performance of the fabricated devices should be made to approach close to this ideal value for the BFOM.

4.3 Ideal Specific On-Resistance for Charge Coupled Si Devices

The introduction of the two-dimensional charge-coupling concept has enabled reducing the specific on-resistance of the drift region for silicon devices to values well below that of the 'ideal specific on-resistance' given by Eq. [4.4]. The analysis of the specific on-resistance for the charge coupled devices is provide here. These silicon devices have been widely commercialized and serve as the new bench mark of performance that must be exceeded by the wide band gap semiconductor based power devices.

In the case of traditional silicon devices designed with one-dimensional potential distribution, the specific on-resistance of the devices becomes limited by the boundary set by the ideal specific on-resistance. An innovative approach to break this barrier was proposed based on using two-dimensional charge coupling. The first device concept was based up on using an electrode embedded inside an oxide coated trench etched into the drift region[6,7] to create the CC-MOSFET and GD-MOSFET structures. The second concept is based up on charge coupling between adjacent vertical pillars of N and P-type drift regions to create the COOLMOS structure[8].

4.3.1 Silicon GD-MOSFET Structure

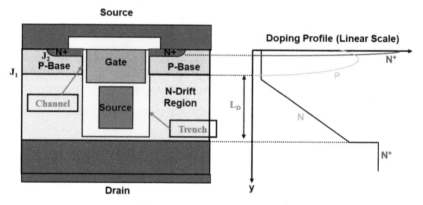

Fig. 4.4 GD-MOSFET structure with a linearly graded doping profile for the drift region.

The CC-MOSFET and GD-MOSFETs are discussed in detail in a previously published book[9]. The GD-MOSFET structure is illustrated in Fig. 4.4 with its doping profile. It was found that the electric field along the y-direction is not constant if a uniform doping concentration is used for the drift region[10]. A constant electric field along the y-direction can be achieved by using a linearly graded doping profile[7]. Only this case is analyzed here because it allows scaling the breakdown voltages to large values. The structure shown in Fig. 4.4 contains an electrode in the trench that is connected to the source electrode. This electrode produces the desired two-dimensional charge coupling to reduce the specific on-resistance. It also shields the gate electrode from the drain producing a very low drain-gate capacitance and charge[7]. This implementation has been commonly called the split-gate structure in the literature although this is a misnomer because the structure has only one gate electrode.

Without the application of a gate bias, a high voltage can be supported in the GD-MOSFET structure when a positive bias is applied to the drain. In this case, junction J_1 formed between the P-base region and the N-drift region becomes reverse biased. Simultaneously, the drain voltage is applied across the vertical MOS structure formed between the electrode in the deep trenches and the N-drift region. The MOS structure operates in the deep-depletion mode due to the presence of the reverse bias across junction J_1 between the P-base and the N-drift regions. Consequently, depletion regions are simultaneously formed across the horizontal junction J_1 and the vertical trench sidewall. This two-dimensional depletion alters the electric field distribution from the triangular shape observed in conventional parallel-plane junctions to a uniform distribution due to the linear doping profile. It allows supporting a required blocking voltage over a shorter vertical distance (L_D) which reduces the drift region resistance. In addition, the doping concentration in the drift region can be made far greater than that required for the one-dimensional case. This produces very substantial reduction of the specific on-resistance to well below the ideal specific on-resistance at any desired breakdown voltage.

Drain current flow in the GD-MOSFET structure is induced by the application of a positive bias to the gate electrode. This produces an inversion layer at the surface of the P-base region along the trench sidewalls. The threshold voltage for the power GD-MOSFET structure can be controlled by adjusting the dose for the boron ion-implantation for the P-base region to adjust its doping profile shown in Fig. 4.4. The inversion layer channel provides a path for transport of electrons from the source to the drain when a positive drain voltage is applied. After transport from the source region through the channel, the electrons enter the N-drift region and are then transported through the mesa region to the N^+ substrate. The resistance of the drift region is very low in the power GD-MOSFET structure due to the high doping concentration in the mesa region. The channel resistance in the power GD-MOSFET structure can be made very small by using a small cell pitch to achieve a high channel density.

The input capacitance and gate charge for power MOSFET structures must be reduced to enhance their switching performance. These device parameters are reduced for the GD-MOSFET structure by using a source connected electrode in the trenches adjacent to the drift region as illustrated in Fig. 4.4[10]. The connection to the source electrode embedded within the trench is made orthogonal to the cross-section shown in Fig. 4.4. The thickness of the oxide in the portion with the source electrode must be much larger than the gate oxide thickness because a high drain voltage is supported across it during the blocking mode[10].

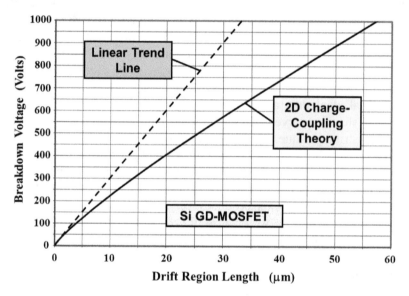

Fig. 4.5 Breakdown voltages for GD-MOSFET devices.

When the drain bias reaches the breakdown voltage, the maximum electric field in the semiconductor along the y-direction becomes equal to the critical electric field (E_{CU}) for breakdown of the semiconductor with uniform electric field profile. The critical electric field at which breakdown occurs can be derived for this field distribution by using the criterion that the ionization integral becomes unity at breakdown:

$$\int_0^{L_D} \alpha\,dx = 1 \qquad\qquad [4.10]$$

Using Baliga's formula for the impact ionization coefficient for silicon (see Eq. [3.8]), an expression for the critical electric field for the case of a uniform (or constant) electric field is obtained:

$$E_{CU} = 8.36 \times 10^4 \, L_D^{-1/7} \qquad\qquad \text{[4.11]}$$

where L_D is the length of the drift region as shown in Fig. 4.4. The breakdown voltage in this case is then given by:

$$BV = E_{CU} \, L_D = 8.36 \times 10^4 \, L_D^{6/7} \qquad\qquad \text{[4.12]}$$

by using Eq. [4.11].

    The breakdown voltage for two-dimensional charge-coupled devices with a uniform electric field increases non-linearly with increasing length of the drift region as shown in Fig. 4.5 by the solid line. Using the analytical model, the drift region lengths required to achieve breakdown voltages of 50, 100, 200, 500, and 1000 volts are predicted to be 1.74, 3.9, 8.8, 25.5, and 57.2 μm, respectively. Note that the drift region length for the power GD-MOSFET structure is the length of the source electrode within the trenches as indicated in Fig. 4.4 and not the trench depth because the two-dimensional charge coupling occurs only between the source electrode and the drift region.

    To compute the specific on-resistance for the power GD-MOSFET structure, it is necessary to derive a relationship for the doping profile in the drift region which will result in a uniform electric field profile in the y-direction for the two-dimensional structure[11]. Since the doping profile is optimized to achieve a uniform electric field along the y-direction, the voltage increases linearly with distance along the y-direction:

$$V(y) = E_Y \, y \qquad\qquad \text{[4.13]}$$

In the power GD-MOSFET structure, breakdown occurs by impact ionization at the middle of the mesa region (and not near the trench surface). At the on-set of breakdown, the electric field in the y-direction at the middle of the mesa region becomes equal to the critical electric field (E_{CU}) for breakdown in the uniform electric field case.

    The electric field is uniform in the oxide and varies linearly along the x-direction in the semiconductor because the doping concentration is constant along the x-direction[9]. The voltage at any depth in the drift region is then given by:

$$V(y) = V_{OX} + V_S = E_X \left[\frac{\varepsilon_{Si}}{\varepsilon_{OX}} t_{TOX} + \frac{W_M}{4} \right] \qquad\qquad \text{[4.14]}$$

where E_X is the electric field in the x-direction at the interface between the oxide and the semiconductor. Applying Gauss's Law at any depth in the drift region:

$$\varepsilon_{Si}\, E_X = qN_D\left(y\right)\frac{W_M}{2} \qquad [4.15]$$

The optimum doping profile to achieve a uniform electric field in the y-direction is obtained by combining the above relationships:

$$N_D\left(y\right) = \frac{2\varepsilon_{Si}E_{CU}}{qW_M\left[\dfrac{\varepsilon_{Si}}{\varepsilon_{OX}}t_{T,OX} + \dfrac{W_M}{4}\right]}\, y \qquad [4.16]$$

It can be seen that the predicted optimum doping profile has a linear distribution along the y-direction.

The gradient (or slope) of the optimum doping profile is given by:

$$G = \frac{2\varepsilon_{Si}E_{CU}}{qW_M\left[\dfrac{\varepsilon_{Si}}{\varepsilon_{OX}}t_{TOX} + \dfrac{W_M}{4}\right]} \qquad [4.17]$$

The optimum doping gradient is a function of the trench oxide thickness and the mesa width. In addition, the critical electric field is a function of the breakdown voltage. It is prudent to keep the maximum electric field in the trench oxide at less than 2×10^6 V/cm in order to avoid reliability problems. Based up on this criterion, the trench oxide thickness must be scaled with the desired blocking voltage capability. Using this electric field in the trench oxide, the trench oxide thicknesses for breakdown voltages of 50, 100, 200, 500, and 1000 V are found to be 2500, 5000, 7500, 10000 and 20000 Å, respectively. With these values, the optimum doping gradients predicted by the analytical model for breakdown voltages of 50, 100, 200, 500, and 1000 V are found to be 8.4, 4.04, 1.87, 0.66 and 0.30 $\times 10^{20}$ cm^{-4}, respectively, for a mesa width of 0.5 μm.

A larger optimum doping gradient is predicted for power GD-MOSFET structures with lower breakdown voltages. This is favorable for reducing the specific on-resistance of the drift region. Even in the case of power GD-MOSFET structures with larger breakdown voltages, the doping concentration is high in the vicinity of the N^+ substrate despite the smaller doping gradient because the drift region length is longer. As a typical example, the doping concentration for the power GD-MOSFET structure with breakdown voltage of 50 volts increases from 1 x 10^{16} cm^{-3} near the P-base/N-drift junction to 2 x 10^{17} cm^{-3} near the bottom of the trench. Such high doping concentrations are also required for the higher voltage power GD-MOSFET structures. These high doping levels result in very low specific on-resistance for the power GD-MOSFET structures.

The ideal specific on-resistance for the GD-MOSFET structure will be defined as the resistance contributed by only the drift region. In the mesa portion of the structure, the current density is uniform with a current density enhanced by the ratio of the cell pitch to the mesa width. The drift region resistance contribution from the mesa region can be computed by considering a small segment (dy) of the drift region at a depth y from the bottom of the gate electrode. The specific resistance of the drift region for the mesa portion is given by:

$$R_{on-ideal}(GDM) = \left(\frac{W_{Cell}}{W_M}\right)\int_0^{L_D} \rho_D(y)dy \qquad [4.18]$$

where the resistivity ρ_D is a function of the position in the drift region due to the graded doping profile. The resistivity of the drift region is given by:

$$\rho_D(y) = \frac{1}{q\mu_n(y)N_D(y)} \qquad [4.19]$$

The dependence of the electron mobility on the doping concentration must be taken into account when analyzing the drift region resistance in the power GD-MOSFET structure because the doping concentration exceeds 1 x 10^{16} cm^{-3}. The electron mobility is given by[12]:

$$\mu_n = \frac{5.1x10^{18} + 92\,N_D^{0.91}}{3.75x10^{15} + N_D^{0.91}} \qquad [4.20]$$

In order to simplify the analysis, the following approximation for the dependence of the electron mobility on doping concentration is adequate for the doping levels ranging between 1 x 10^{16} cm^{-3} and 3 x 10^{17} cm^{-3}:

$$\mu_n = \frac{5.1x10^{18}}{3.75x10^{15} + N_D^{0.91}} \qquad [4.21]$$

Using Eq. [4.19] and Eq. [4.21] in Eq. [4.18]:

$$R_{on-ideal}(GDM) = \left(\frac{W_{Cell}}{W_M}\right)\int_0^{L_D}\left[\frac{4.6 \times 10^{15}}{N_D(y)} + \frac{1.225}{N_D(y)^{0.09}}\right]dy \qquad [4.22]$$

For a linearly graded doping profile with a gradient G:

$$N_D(y) = N_0 + G y \qquad [4.23]$$

where N_0 is the initial doping concentration in the mesa region at the depth of the gate electrode. Integrating Eq. [4.22] with Eq. [4.23] yields:

$$R_{on-ideal}(GDM) = \left(\frac{W_{Cell}}{W_M}\right)\left\{\begin{array}{l}\dfrac{4.6 \times 10^{15}}{G}\ln\left(\dfrac{N_0 + GL_D}{N_0}\right) + \\[2ex] \dfrac{1.346}{G}\left[(N_0 + GL_D)^{0.91} - N_0^{0.91}\right]\end{array}\right\} \qquad [4.24]$$

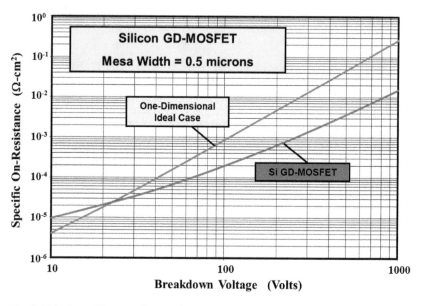

Fig. 4.6 Ideal specific on-resistance for the power GD-MOSFET structures compared with the one-dimensional case.

The specific on-resistance for the GD-MOSFET drift region obtained by using the analytical solution in Eq. [4.24] is shown in Fig. 4.6. A mesa width of 0.5 μm was assumed for these calculations. These values can be compared to those for the ideal specific on-resistance of the drift region for the one-dimensional potential distribution case in the figure. It can be observed that the lines cross at a breakdown voltage of 20 volts. The advantages of the GD-MOSFET structure become larger with increasing breakdown voltage. For the case of 1000 volt devices, the specific on-resistance for the GD-MOSFET case is 43-times smaller than that for the one-dimensional case. Silicon GD-MOSFET devices have been widely commercialized for applications. Consequently, it is important for the 4H-SiC devices to be competitive with not only conventional silicon devices but also those that utilize the charge coupling concept.

4.3.2 Silicon Super-Junction Structure

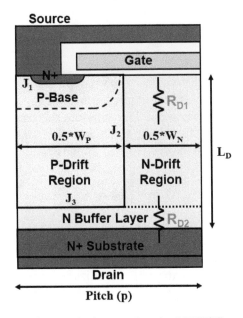

Fig. 4.7 Resistances in the super-junction MOSFET structure.

A cross-section of the super-junction (SJ) power MOSFET structure is shown in Fig. 4.7. The structure was first commercialized as the COOLMOS[TM] device by Infineon[8]. The drift region of this structure includes a vertical P-type column which produces a vertically oriented junction J_2. A much larger doping concentration can be employed in the drift region of the power SJ-MOSFET structure when compared with the conventional MOSFET structures. This enables a significant reduction of the specific on-resistance for devices capable of supporting high voltages.

The doping concentration in the drift region is determined by two-dimensional charge coupling for the power SJ-MOSFET structure. In order to achieve good charge coupling, the N-type and P-type drift regions must be completely depleted when the drain bias approaches the breakdown voltage. The electric field then becomes uniform along the y-direction in the N-type and P-type drift regions. The super-junction concept has been found to be particularly effective for devices with breakdown voltages between 500 and 1000 volts.

Based up on the depletion of the N-type and P-type drift regions when the electric field at junction J_2 becomes equal to the critical electric field (E_{CU}) for breakdown for the uniform electric field distribution case[9]:

$$Q_{Optimum} = qN_D \frac{W_N}{2} = \varepsilon_s E_{CU} = qN_A \frac{W_P}{2} \qquad [4.25]$$

where W_N and W_P are the widths of the N-type and P-type drift regions, respectively; N_D and N_A are the doping concentration of the N-type and P-type drift regions, respectively. This provides the criterion for choosing the dopant dose (product of doping concentration and thickness) in the N-drift region to achieve the desired two-dimensional charge coupling:

$$N_D W_N = N_A W_P = \frac{2\varepsilon_s E_{CU}}{q} \qquad [4.26]$$

An expression for the critical electric field for the case of a uniform (or constant) electric field can be derived (see Eq. [4.21] by using Baliga's formula for the impact ionization coefficient for silicon. The breakdown voltage for the two dimensional charge coupled device is then given by Eq. [4.12]. The breakdown voltage for devices with a uniform electric field is plotted in Fig. 4.5. A drift region length of 25 μm is required to achieve a breakdown voltage of 500 volts. According to the analytical model, the drift region length must be increased to 57 μm to obtain a breakdown voltage of 1000 volts.

Combining Eq. [4.11] and Eq. [4.12] with Eq. [4.26] yields:

$$N_D W_N = 1.106 \times 10^6 \frac{\varepsilon_S}{q} BV^{-1/6} \qquad \text{[4.27]}$$

The optimum dose predicted by this expression is plotted in Fig. 4.8 as a function of the breakdown voltage. It can be observed that the optimum dose decreases gradually with increasing breakdown voltage. The optimum dose for the N-type and P-type drift regions predicted by the analytical model is 2.54 x 10^{12} and 2.27 x 10^{12} cm^{-2} for breakdown voltages of 500 and 1000 volts, respectively.

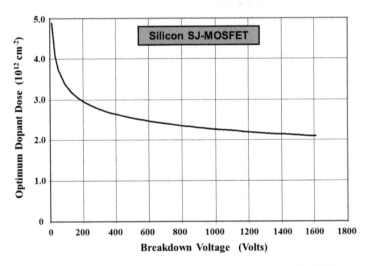

Fig. 4.8 Optimum drift region dose for Si super-junction MOSFETs.

The lowest possible specific on-resistance that can be achieved by using the super-junction concept can be obtained by neglecting the contributions from the channel, accumulation, and JFET regions, as well as the substrate and contacts, i.e. by analysis of only the drift region resistance. The drift region resistance can be analyzed with the two components R_{D1} for the N-type drift region and R_{D2} for the N-buffer layer that are shown in Fig. 4.7. For high voltage power SJ-MOSFET structures, the contribution from the N-buffer layer can be neglected because it is much smaller than the N-drift region contribution. The ideal specific on-resistance for the super-junction devices is then given by:

$$R_{on-ideal}(SJ) = R_{D1,sp} = \rho_{ND} L_D \left(\frac{W_{Cell}}{W_N} \right) = \frac{L_D}{q\mu_N N_D} \left(\frac{W_N + W_P}{W_N} \right) \qquad \text{[4.28]}$$

where ρ_{ND} is the resistivity of the N-type drift region. The length of the drift region can be related to the breakdown voltage of the super-junction device:

$$L_D = \frac{BV}{E_{CU}} \qquad [4.29]$$

because the electric field along the y-direction has a constant value equal to the critical electric for breakdown with uniform electric field in the case of super-junction devices. Using Eq. [4.26], the optimum doping concentration for super-junction devices is given by:

$$N_D = \frac{2\varepsilon_s E_{CU}}{qW_N} \qquad [4.30]$$

Combining the above relationships:

$$R_{on-ideal}(SJ) = \frac{BV}{\varepsilon_s \mu_N E_{CU}^2}\left(\frac{W_N + W_P}{2}\right) \qquad [4.31]$$

The critical electric field for breakdown with uniform electric field can be related to the breakdown voltage by using Eq. [4.11] and Eq. [4.12]:

$$R_{on-ideal}(SJ) = \frac{1.635 \times 10^{-12}\, BV^{4/3}\left(W_N + W_P\right)}{\varepsilon_s \mu_N} \qquad [4.32]$$

It is typical to use the same width for the P-type and N-type drift regions in super-junction devices. In this case, the ideal specific on-resistance for super-junction devices can be computed using:

$$R_{on-ideal}(SJ) = \frac{3.27 \times 10^{-12}\, BV^{4/3}\, W_N}{\varepsilon_s \mu_N} \qquad [4.33]$$

The ideal specific on-resistance for super-junction devices computed by using Eq. [4.33] is provided in Fig. 4.9 for the case of two widths for the N-type drift region under the assumption that the width of the P-type drift region has the same value. Since the optimum doping concentration is relatively high for these devices, the dependence of the mobility on doping concentration was included during this analysis. The ideal specific on-resistance for the drift region in one-dimensional devices as computed by using Baliga's power law for the impact ionization coefficients is also shown in Fig. 4.9 for comparison purposes. It can be observed from this figure that the specific on-resistance for the drift region of super-junction MOSFETs can be less than the ideal specific on-resistance for silicon devices. The range of breakdown voltages for which the performance of the super-junction devices is superior to that of the ideal one-dimensional structure becomes larger when the width of the N-drift region is reduced. For a breakdown voltage of 600 volts, the specific on-resistance for the drift region of super-junction device is 6.1-times smaller than that for the one-dimensional case. For a breakdown voltage of 1000 volts, the specific on-resistance for the drift region of super-junction device is 11.1-times smaller.

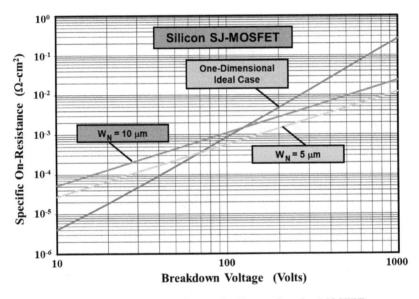

Fig. 4.9 Ideal specific on-resistance for Si super-junction MOSFETs.

From Fig. 4.9, it is apparent that there is a cross-over point (breakdown voltage) between the specific on-resistance for the super-junction and the ideal one-dimensional devices. The ideal specific on-resistance for the one-dimensional case is given by:

$$R_{ON,sp}(\text{Ideal 1D}) = \frac{1.181 \times 10^{-17} BV^{5/2}}{\varepsilon_S \mu_N} \qquad [4.34]$$

An analytical expression for cross-over point can be derived by equating the specific on-resistance for the one-dimensional case to the ideal specific on-resistance for the super-junction devices if the dependence of the mobility on doping concentration is neglected. The cross-over break-down voltage is then given by:

$$BV(Cross - Over) = 4.62 \times 10^4 \, W_N^{6/7} \qquad [4.35]$$

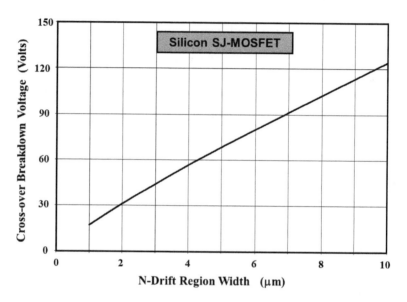

Fig. 4.10 Cross-over breakdown voltage for the Si super-junction devices.

The cross-over breakdown voltage computed using Eq. [4.35] is provided in Fig. 4.10. The cross-over breakdown voltage predicted by the above equation is in good agreement with the cross-over points in Fig. 4.9 indicating the assumption of a constant mobility is reasonable. It can be observed that the cross-over breakdown voltage increases with increasing width of the N-drift region. It is therefore advantageous to utilize small widths for the drift region to maximize the performance of the super-junction devices. However, the presence of a depletion region across the vertical junction (J₃) can create an increase in the on-resistance for super-junction devices[13]. This has an adverse impact on the specific on-resistance.

4.4 Silicon Carbide Super-Junction MOSFET

The ideal specific on-resistance of the drift region for 4H-SiC devices is 1000-times smaller than that for Si devices. This allows obtaining a low value for the specific on-resistance for breakdown voltages of up to 5000 V with 4H-SiC. It would be beneficial to apply the two-dimensional charge coupling concepts to reduce the specific on-resistance of the drift region of 4H-SiC devices with breakdown voltages above 5000 V. The GD-MOSFET structure shown in Fig. 4.4 cannot be adopted to 4H-SiC because of generation of very high electric fields in the oxide layer. However, the SJ-MOSFET structure shown in Fig. 4.7 can be adopted with development of suitable process technology.

The ideal specific on-resistance of the SJ-MOSFET structure for the case of 4H-SiC can be derived using the same theory used for the Si SJ devices in section 4.5.2. Eq. [4.31] can be applied to the case of 4H-SiC with appropriate values for the ε_S, μ_n, and E_{CU}.

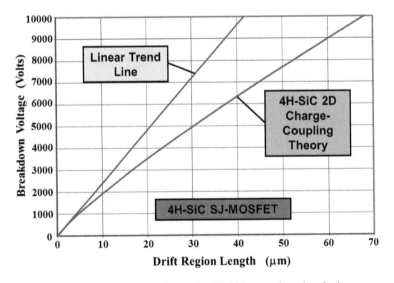

Fig. 4.11 Breakdown voltages for 4H-SiC super-junction devices.

An expression for the critical electric field for the case of a uniform (or constant) electric field can be derived using Baliga's formula for the impact ionization coefficient for 4H-SiC:

$$E_{CU}\left(4H - SiC\right) = 7.20 \times 10^5 \ L_D^{-1/7} \qquad [4.36]$$

The breakdown voltage in this case is then given by:

$$BV\left(4H-SiC\right)= E_{CU}\cdot L_{D} = 7.20 \; x \; 10^{5} \; L_{D}^{6/7} \qquad [4.37]$$

by using Eq. [4.36].

The breakdown voltage for two-dimensional charge-coupled 4H-SiC devices with a uniform electric field increases non-linearly with increasing length of the drift region as shown in Fig. 4.11 by the red line. Using the analytical model, the drift region lengths required to achieve breakdown voltages of 1000, 2000, 3000, 5000, and 10,000 V are predicted to be 4.6, 10.4, 16.7, 30.3, and 68.1 μm, respectively. These values are larger than follow the linear trend line shown in purple in the figure.

Combining Eq. [4.27] and Eq. [4.37], yields the optimum dose:

$$\left(N_{D}\cdot W_{N}\right)\left(4H-SiC\right)= \frac{2\epsilon_{S}E_{CU}}{q} = 7.32 \; x \; 10^{13} \; BV^{-1/6} \qquad [4.38]$$

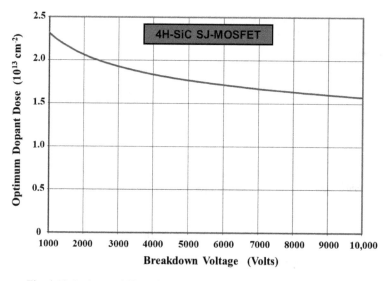

Fig. 4.12 Optimum drift region dose for 4H-SiC super-junction devices.

The optimum dose for 4H-SiC charge coupled devices predicted by this expression is plotted in Fig. 4.12 as a function of the breakdown voltage for the range of 1000 to 10,000 V. It can be observed that the optimum dose decreases gradually with increasing breakdown voltage. The optimum dose for the N-type and P-type drift regions predicted by the analytical model is 1.77 x 10^{13} and 1.57 x 10^{13} cm^{-2} for breakdown voltages of 5000 and 10,000 volts, respectively.

The lowest possible specific on-resistance that can be achieved by using the super-junction concept for 4H-SiC devices can be obtained by neglecting the contributions from the channel, accumulation, and JFET regions, as well as the substrate and contacts, i.e. by analysis of only the drift region resistance. The drift region resistance can be analyzed with the two components R_{D1} for the N-type drift region and R_{D2} for the N-buffer layer that are shown in Fig. 4.7. For high voltage 4H-SiC power SJ-MOSFET structures, the contribution from the N-buffer layer can be neglected because it is much smaller the N-drift region contribution. The ideal specific on-resistance for the 4H-SiC super-junction devices is then given by:

$$R_{on-ideal}(SJ) = R_{D1,sp} = \rho_{ND}L_D\left(\frac{W_{Cell}}{W_N}\right) = \frac{L_D}{q\mu_N N_D}\left(\frac{W_N + W_P}{W_N}\right) \qquad [4.39]$$

where ρ_{ND} is the resistivity of the N-type drift region. The length of the drift region can be related to the breakdown voltage of the super-junction device:

$$L_D = \frac{BV}{E_{CU}} \qquad [4.40]$$

because the electric field along the y-direction has a constant value equal to the critical electric for breakdown with uniform electric field in the case of super-junction devices. Using Eq. [4.26], the optimum doping concentration for super-junction devices is given by:

$$N_D = \frac{2\varepsilon_S E_{CU}}{qW_N} \qquad [4.41]$$

Combining the above relationships:

$$R_{on-ideal}(SJ) = \frac{BV}{\varepsilon_S \mu_N E_{CU}^2}\left(\frac{W_N + W_P}{2}\right) \qquad [4.42]$$

The relationship between the critical electric field for breakdown with uniform electric field for 4H-SiC and the breakdown voltage can be derived using Eq. [4.36] and Eq. [4.37]:

$$E_{CU}\left(4H-SiC\right)=6.82\,x\,10^{6}\ BV^{-1/6} \qquad \textbf{[4.43]}$$

Using this relationship in [4.42] yields:

$$R_{on-ideal}\left(4H-SiC\ SJ\right)=\frac{1.075\,x\,10^{-14}\ BV^{\frac{4}{3}}(W_{N}+W_{P})}{\varepsilon_{S}\mu_{N}} \qquad \textbf{[4.44]}$$

It is typical to use the same width for the P-type and N-type drift regions in super-junction devices. In this case, the ideal specific on-resistance for super-junction devices can be computed using:

$$R_{on-ideal}\left(4H-SiC\ SJ\right)=\frac{2.14\,x\,10^{-14}.\ BV^{\frac{4}{3}}.W_{N}}{\varepsilon_{S}\mu_{N}} \qquad \textbf{[4.45]}$$

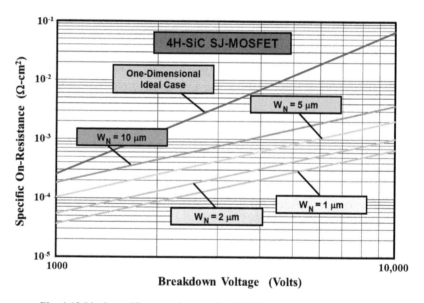

Fig. 4.13 Ideal specific on-resistance for 4H-SiC super-junction devices.

The ideal specific on-resistance for 4H-SiC super-junction devices computed by using Eq. [4.56] is provided in Fig. 4.13 for the case of four widths for the N-type drift region under the assumption that the width of the P-type drift region has the same value. Since the optimum doping concentration is relatively high for these devices, the dependence of the mobility on doping concentration was included during this analysis. The ideal specific on-resistance for the drift region in one-dimensional devices as computed by using Baliga's power law for the impact ionization coefficients for 4H-SiC is also shown in Fig. 4.13 for comparison purposes. It can be observed from this figure that the specific on-resistance for the drift region of super-junction MOSFETs can be much smaller than the ideal specific on-resistance for 4H-SiC devices. For the case of an N-drift region width of 10 μm, the specific on-resistance is reduced by a factor of 8, 12, and 18 times for breakdown voltages of 5000, 7000, and 10,000 V, respectively. The specific on-resistance for the 4H-SiC SJ device case becomes significantly smaller when the width of the N-drift region is reduced. It is reduced by a factor of 1.8, 5.3, and 5.4 times when the width is reduced from 10 μm to 5, 2, and 1 μm, respectively, for the 5000 V case.

4.5 Summary

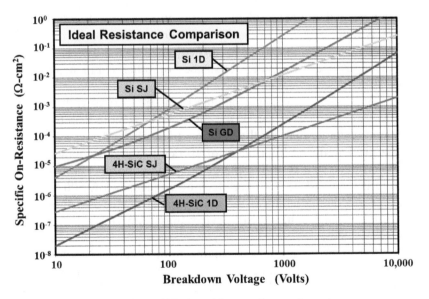

Fig. 4.14 Comparison of ideal specific on-resistance for various cases.

The ideal specific on-resistance for the drift region in power devices has been defined for one-dimensional (1D) potential distribution and related to the semiconductor material properties. This relationship indicates that semiconductors with wider band gaps, or more precisely semiconductors with larger critical electric fields for breakdown, will have substantially smaller drift region resistances. The improved performance that is achievable by replacing silicon with silicon carbide has been quantified.

The drift region resistance can be substantially reduced for silicon devices by taking advantage of two-dimensional charge coupling. The specific on-resistance of the silicon GD-MOSFET and SJ-MOSFET that utilize this principle has been provided in this chapter for comparison with the 4H-SiC devices. Recently, the application of the super-junction concept to 4H-SiC power MOSFET has been gaining interest to reduce the resistance of very high voltage devices. The resistance achievable with this approach has been analyzed.

The ideal specific on-resistance for various cases can be compared in Fig. 4.14 for breakdown voltages ranging from 10 to 10,000 volts. The Si and 4H-SiC super-junction devices were assumed to have N and P-type regions with a width of 5 μm here. The silicon devices have excellent performance for devices with breakdown voltages below 100 volts. They can be expected to continue to serve these low voltage applications. Although the ideal specific on-resistance for the 4H-SiC devices is much superior to that for the silicon structures at breakdown voltages below 100 volts, it is very difficult to exceed the performance of the silicon devices when the resistances of other components in the device structures are taken into account.

At breakdown voltages ranging from 100 to 1000 volts, the ideal specific on-resistance for the 1D 4H-SiC devices is more than two orders of magnitude better than for the traditional 1D silicon devices. However, this margin is reduced by a factor of 10 due to the development of the 2D silicon devices that utilize charge coupling concept. The best Si 2D structure is the GD-MOSFET for blocking voltages below 500 V. The Si 2D super-junction structure is the most popular device structure for the 600 – 1000 V range. The 4H-SiC devices must outperform these state-of-the-art Si devices.

For breakdown voltages ranging from 1000 to 10,000 volts, the 1D 4H-SiC devices offer much superior on-resistance performance compared to the Si devices. They will be discussed in subsequent chapters. The 2D super-junction 4H-SiC structure offers even further reduction of the specific on-resistance for breakdown voltages above 5000 V. The fabrication of such devices is challenging. Methods to create practical 2D super-junction 4H-SiC MOSFETs are discussed in a subsequent chapter.

References

[1] B. J. Baliga, "Optimum Semiconductors for High Voltage Vertical Channel Field Effect Transistors", GE Class 2 Technical Report No. 79CRD186, November 1979.

[2] B. J. Baliga, "Semiconductors for High Voltage Vertical Channel Field Effect Transistors", J. Applied Physics, Vol. 53, pp. 1759-1764, 1982.

[3] B. J. Baliga, et al, "Gallium Arsenide Schottky Power Rectifiers", IEEE Transactions on Electron Devices, Vol. ED-32, pp. 1130-1134, 1985.

[4] P. M. Campbell, et al, "150 Volt Vertical Channel GaAs FET", IEEE International Electron Devices Meeting, Abstract 10.4, pp. 258-260, 1982.

[5] P. M. Campbell, et al, "Trapezoidal Groove Schottky Gate Vertical Channel GaAs FET", IEEE International Electron Devices Meeting, Abstract 7.3, pp. 186-189, 1984.

[6] B. J. Baliga, "Vertical Field Effect Transistors having Improved Breakdown Voltage Capability and Low On-state Resistance", U.S. Patent # 5,637,898, Issued June 10, 1997.

[7] B. J. Baliga, "Trends in Power Discrete Devices", IEEE International Symposium on Power Semiconductor Devices and ICs, Abstract P-2, pp. 5-10, 1997.

[8] L. Lorenz, et al, "COOLMOS – A New Milestone in High Voltage Power MOS", IEEE International Symposium on Power Semiconductor Devices and ICs, Abstract P-1, pp. 3-10, 1999.

[9] B. J. Baliga, "Advanced Power MOSFET Concepts", Chapter 5, Springer-Science, New York, 2010.

[10] B. J. Baliga, "Power Semiconductor Devices having Improved High Frequency Switching and Breakdown Characteristics", U.S. Patent # 5,998,833, Issued December 7, 1999.

[11] S. Mahalingam and B. J. Baliga, "The Graded Doped Trench MOS Barrier Schottky Rectifier: a Low Forward Drop High Voltage Rectifier", Solid State Electronics, Vol. 43, pp. 1-9, 1999.

[12] B. J. Baliga, "Fundamentals of Power Semiconductor Devices", Second Edition, Springer-Science, 2019.

[13] D. Disney and G. Dolny, "JFET Depletion in Super-Junction Devices", IEEE International Symposium on Power Semiconductor Devices and ICs", pp. 157-160, 2008.

Chapter 5

Schottky Rectifiers

The main advantage of wide band gap semiconductors for power device applications is the very low resistance for their drift regions even when designed to support large voltages as discussed in the previous chapter. This favors the development of high voltage unipolar devices which have much superior switching speed than Si bipolar device structures. The Schottky rectifier, formed by making a rectifying contact been a metal and the semiconductor drift region, is an attractive unipolar device for power applications. In the case of silicon, the maximum breakdown voltage of Schottky rectifiers has been limited by the increase in the resistance of the drift region[1]. Commercially available silicon devices are generally rated at breakdown voltages of less than 100 volts. Novel silicon structures that utilize the charge-coupling concept have allowed extending the breakdown voltage to the 200 volt range[2,3].

Many applications described in chapter 1 require fast switching rectifiers with low on-state voltage drop that can also support over 500 volts. The much lower resistance of the drift region for 4H-SiC enables development of such Schottky rectifiers with high breakdown voltages. These devices offer fast switching speed and elimination of the large reverse recovery current observed in high voltage silicon P-i-N rectifiers. This reduces switching losses not only in the rectifier but also in the IGBTs used within the power circuits[4].

This chapter describes the characteristics of 4H-SiC Schottky rectifiers. Unique issues that relate to the 4H-SiC devices must be given special consideration. The much greater electric field in these semiconductors leads to larger Schottky barrier lowering with increasing reverse voltage when compared with silicon devices. The high doping level in the drift region leads to tunneling currents at the Schottky barrier that enhances the leakage current as well. Experimental results on relevant structures are provided to define the state of the development effort on 4H-SiC Schottky rectifiers.

The very rapid increase in the leakage current observed with increasing reverse bias voltage for 4H-SiC Schottky rectifiers is discussed in this chapter. This problem can be overcome by using the junction barrier controlled Schottky (JBS) rectifier, which is discussed in detail in the next chapter.

5.1 Schottky Rectifier Structure: Forward Conduction

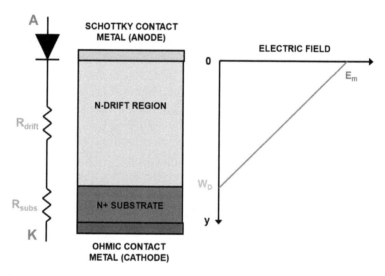

Fig. 5.1 Schottky rectifier structure and the electric field during reverse blocking.

The basic one-dimensional structure of the metal-semiconductor or Schottky rectifier structure is shown in Fig. 5.1 together with the electric field profile under reverse bias operation. The applied voltage is supported by the drift region with a triangular electric field distribution if the drift region doping is uniform. The maximum electric field (E_m) occurs at the metal contact. The device undergoes breakdown when this field becomes equal to the critical electric field as discussed in chapter 3.

An equation for the specific on-resistance of the drift region was derived in chapter 4:

$$R_{on-ideal} = \frac{4BV^2}{\varepsilon_S \mu_n E_C^3} \qquad [5.1]$$

The specific on-resistance of the drift region (R_{drift}) for 4H-SiC can be computed using this equation while accounting for the variation of the electron mobility with doping level. The ideal specific on-resistance for 4H-SiC is approximately 1000 times smaller than for silicon devices as discussed in chapter 4.

The on-state voltage drop for the Schottky rectifier at a forward current density J_F, including the substrate contribution (R_{subs}), is given by:

$$V_F = \frac{kT}{q}\ln\left(\frac{J_F}{J_S}\right) + \left(R_{drift} + R_{subs}\right)J_F \qquad [5.2]$$

where J_S is the saturation current density. In Eq. [5.2], the first term accounts for the voltage drop across the metal-semiconductor contact while the second term accounts for the voltage drop across the series resistances (shown as R_{drift} and R_{subs} in Fig. 5.1).

5.1.1 Saturation Current

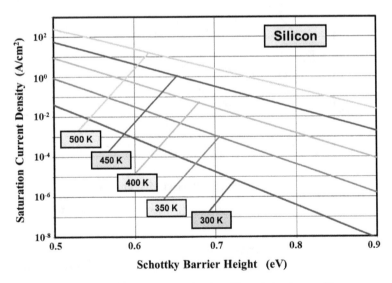

Fig. 5.2 Saturation current density for Silicon Schottky rectifiers.

The saturation current density (J_S) for the Schottky barrier is related to the Schottky barrier height (ϕ_b) by[1]:

$$J_S = AT^2 \exp\left(-\frac{q\phi_b}{kT}\right) \qquad\qquad [5.3]$$

where A is Richardson's constant. For silicon, the Richardson's constant is 110 A°K^{-2}cm^{-2} while that for 4H-SiC[5] have been calculated to be 146 and 24 A°K^{-2}cm^{-2}. Values in this range have been reported using measurements on Schottky contacts[5] made to SiC.

The saturation current density for silicon Schottky rectifiers is shown in Fig. 5.2 as a function of the barrier height for various values of the temperature. For a typical barrier height of 0.7 eV for the silicon devices, the saturation current density is 10^{-5} A/cm^2 at room temperature. It increases rapidly with reduction of the barrier height and increase in the temperature.

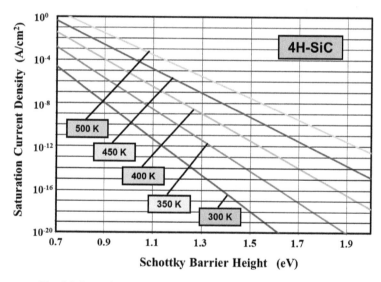

Fig. 5.3 Saturation current density for 4H-SiC Schottky rectifiers.

The saturation current density for 4H-SiC Schottky rectifiers is shown in Fig. 5.3 as a function of the barrier height for various values of the temperature. A larger value for the Schottky barrier height is possible for 4H-SiC due to its larger band gap than Si. The saturation current density is 10^{-15} A/cm^2 at room temperature for a barrier height of 1.3 eV for 4H-SiC. It increases rapidly with reduction of the barrier height and increase in temperature. The much smaller saturation current density for

4H-SiC when compared with silicon produces reduced leakage current in Schottky rectifiers, which allows their operation at higher temperatures.

5.1.2 On-State Characteristics

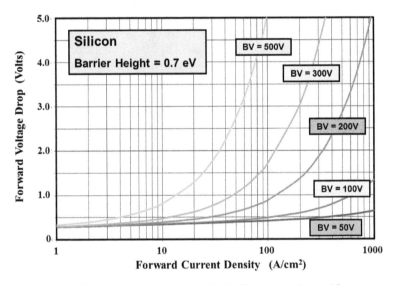

Fig. 5.4 Forward Characteristics of ideal silicon Schottky rectifiers.

The calculated forward conduction characteristics for ideal silicon Schottky rectifiers are shown in Fig. 5.4 for various breakdown voltages. The resistance contribution from the substrate was excluded from these characteristics. A Schottky barrier height of 0.7 eV was chosen because this is a typical value used in actual devices. It can be seen that the series resistance of the drift region does not adversely impact the on-state voltage drop for the device with breakdown voltage of 50 volts at a nominal on-state current density of 200 A/cm^2. However, the drift region resistance becomes significant when the breakdown voltage exceeds 100 volts. This has limited the application of silicon Schottky rectifiers to systems, such as switch-mode power supply circuits, operating at voltages below 100 V.

The significantly smaller resistance of the drift region enables scaling of the breakdown voltage of 4H-SiC Schottky rectifiers to much larger voltages typical of medium and high power electronic systems, such as those used for industrial and electric vehicle motor control. The forward characteristics of high voltage 4H-SiC Schottky rectifiers are shown in Fig. 5.5 for the case of a Schottky barrier height of 1.6 eV. This value was chosen because it is representative of nickel Schottky contacts commonly used for products. The N^+ substrate resistance was not included to obtain these ideal characteristics. It can be seen that the drift region resistance does not produce a significant increase in on-state voltage drop until the breakdown voltage exceeds 3000 volts. From these results, it can be concluded that 4H-SiC Schottky rectifiers are excellent companion diodes for Insulated Gate Bipolar Transistors (IGBTs) in medium and high power electronic systems. Their fast switching speed and absence of reverse recovery current can reduce power losses and improve the efficiency in motor control applications[4].

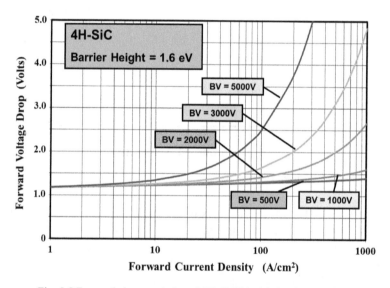

Fig. 5.5 Forward characteristics of 4H-SiC ideal Schottky rectifiers.

All practical Schottky rectifiers are fabricated by the growth of a thin epitaxial layer on a highly doped N^+ substrate that is sufficiently thick for handling the wafers in process equipment during device fabrication. It is important to include the resistance associated with the thick, highly doped N^+ substrate because this is comparable to that for the drift region in many instances. The specific resistance of the N^+ substrate can be determined by taking the product of its resistivity and thickness. For silicon, N^+ substrates with resistivity of 1 mΩ-cm are available. The specific resistance contributed by the N^+ substrate is 2 x 10^{-5} Ω-cm^2 for a substrate thickness of 200 μm. The impact of adding this substrate resistance on the forward characteristics for silicon Schottky rectifiers is shown in Fig. 5.6 for the cases of breakdown voltages of 50 and 100 volts. It can be concluded that the impact is very small in this case.

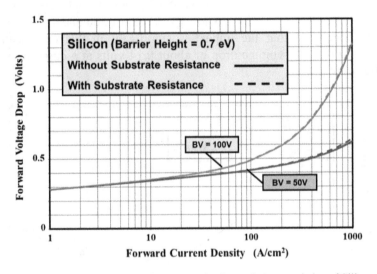

Fig. 5.6 Impact of substrate resistance on the forward characteristics of Silicon Schottky rectifiers.

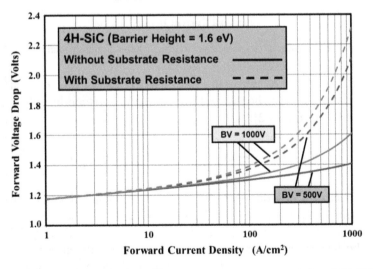

Fig. 5.7 Impact of substrate resistance on the forward characteristics of 4H-SiC Schottky rectifiers.

The available resistivity of the 4H-SiC N⁺ substrates is sub-stantially larger. The substrate resistance contribution is 7 x 10⁻⁴ Ω-cm² for the 4H-SiC N⁺ substrates with a typical resistivity of 0.02 Ω-cm and thickness of 350 microns. The impact of adding this substrate resistance on the forward characteristics for 4H-SiC Schottky rectifiers is shown in Fig. 5.7 for the cases of breakdown voltages of 500 and 1000 volts. It can be concluded that the impact is significant in this case with an increase in on-state voltage drop of about 0.14 volts at a current density of 200 A/cm².

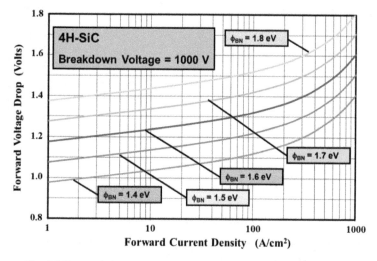

Fig. 5.8 Forward characteristics of 4H-SiC 1000-V Schottky rectifiers.

The effect of changing the barrier height on the on-state characteristics of the Schottky rectifier can be understood by substitution of Eq. [5.3] into Eq. [5.2]:

$$V_F = \phi_B + \frac{kT}{q} \ln\left(\frac{J_F}{AT^2}\right) + \left(R_{drift} + R_{subs}\right).J_F \qquad [5.4]$$

It then becomes obvious that the on-state characteristics will shift to higher values in proportion to the increase in the barrier height.

The changes in the forward characteristics for the cases of 4H-SiC Schottky rectifiers are illustrated in Fig. 5.8 for the case of a break-down voltage of 1000 volts. The substrate resistance was not included in these plots. The curves are shifted along the y-axis when the barrier height is altered.

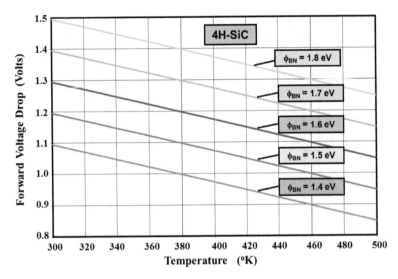

Fig. 5.9 Temperature dependence of on-state voltage drop for 4H-SiC Schottky Rectifiers.

The on-state voltage drop for the Schottky rectifiers reduces with increasing temperature. This is in accordance with Eq. [5.4] because the second term has a negative value. This reduction in on-state voltage drop at an current density of 100 A/cm^2 is shown in Fig. 5.9 for the case 4H-SiC devices. The contribution from the substrate and drift regions was not included in these plots. This behavior can lead to current localization with hot spots that can damage the devices. This problem does not occur in practice due to the power loss contribution from the leakage current discussed in the next section.

5.2 Schottky Rectifier Structure: Reverse Blocking

The voltage is supported across the drift region with the maximum electric field located at the metal-semiconductor contact as shown in Fig. 5.1 when a negative bias is applied to the anode of the Schottky rectifier. The potential energy band diagram under reverse blocking conditions is illustrated in Fig. 5.10. The reverse bias voltage is supported across a depletion region. The conduction band becomes narrow in width at the metal-semiconductor interface in wide band gap semiconductors due to the relatively high doing concentration in the drift region and the high electric fields in these materials. This can lead to tunneling of electrons through the barrier producing a current component not observed in silicon devices. The thermionic emission current transport mechanism that is dominant for Si Schottky rectifiers[1] is still a significant component in the 4H-SiC rectifiers.

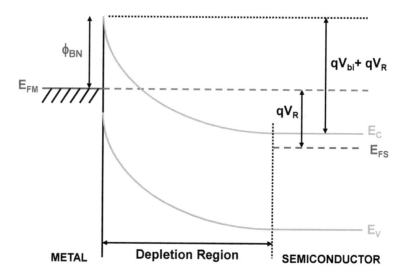

Fig. 5.10 Energy band diagram for reverse biased Schottky power rectifier.

5.2.1 Thermionic Emission Current

According to thermionic emission theory, the leakage current is independent of the reverse bias voltage as determined by the saturation current given in Eq. [5.3][1]. The saturation current for 4H-SiC calculated by using this equation was shown in Fig. 5.3 for various temperatures. In comparison with silicon, it is possible to obtain a much larger barrier height in 4H-SiC metal-semiconductor contacts due to its larger band gap. Consequently, it is possible to achieve very low saturation current density, and hence leakage current, in 4H-SiC by using a Schottky barrier height of 1.6 eV. However, it is preferable to use a lower barrier height to obtain a smaller on-state voltage drop as shown in Fig. 5.9. For 4H-SiC Schottky rectifiers with blocking voltage above 500 volts, a good compromise occurs for a barrier height of 1.6 eV. This can be achieved by using Nickel as the Schottky contact metal as discussed in section 2.15.4. A lower barrier height of about 1.1 eV can be obtained by using Titanium as the contact metal.

5.2.2 Schottky Barrier Lowering

In silicon Schottky rectifiers, it is well established that the leakage current is exacerbated by the Schottky barrier lowering phenomenon[1]. The barrier lowering is determined by the electric field at the metal-semiconductor interface:

$$\Delta\phi_B = \sqrt{\frac{qE_m}{4\pi\varepsilon_S}} \qquad [5.5]$$

where E_m is the maximum electric field located at the metal-semiconductor interface. For a one-dimensional structure, the maximum electric field is related to the applied reverse bias voltage (V_R) by:

$$E_m = \sqrt{\frac{2qN_D}{\varepsilon_S}(V_R + V_{bi})} \qquad [5.6]$$

In addition, it is necessary to include the effect of pre-avalanche multiplication on the leakage current[6]. The multiplication coefficient (M) can be determined from the maximum electric field at the metal-semiconductor contact:

$$M = \left\{1 - 1.52\left[1 - \exp\left(-\frac{4.33x10^{-24}E_m^{4.93}W_D}{6}\right)\right]\right\}^{-1} \qquad [5.7]$$

where W_D is the depletion layer width. Commercially available silicon devices exhibit an order of magnitude increase in leakage current from low reverse bias voltages to the rated voltage (about 80 percent of the breakdown voltage) due to these phenomena.

As discussed in chapter 4, the low specific on-resistance of the drift region in 4H-SiC devices is associated with the much larger electric field in the material before the on-set of impact ionization. The large electric field leads to much greater Schottky barrier lowering in 4H-SiC Schottky rectifiers than in silicon devices. This is illustrated in Fig. 5.11 for the case of a drift region doping level of 1×10^{16} cm^{-3}. It is worth pointing out the 4H-SiC devices have much larger breakdown voltages than the silicon device for this doping concentration. The horizontal axis is the reverse voltage normalized to the breakdown voltage for each semiconductor material. It can be seen that the barrier lowering is three times greater in 4H-SiC at the breakdown voltage when compared with

Si. This enhances the increase in leakage current as the reverse bias voltage is increased.

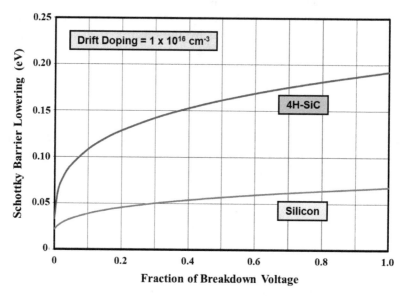

Fig. 5.11 Schottky barrier lowering for 4H-SiC Schottky rectifiers compared with the Si case.

5.2.3 Tunneling Current

The leakage current for 4H-SiC and GaN Schottky rectifiers increases much more rapidly with reverse bias than for silicon devices due to the enhanced Schottky barrier lowering. However, even this effect is insufficient to account the extremely rapid increase in leakage current with reverse bias voltage observed in actual devices. In order to explain this more rapid increase in leakage current, it is necessary to include the field emission (or tunneling) component of the leakage current[7].

The thermionic field emission model for the tunneling current leads to a barrier lowering effect proportional to the square of the electric field at the metal-semiconductor interface. When combined with the thermionic emission model, the leakage current density can be written as:

$$J_S = AT^2 \exp\left(-\frac{q\phi_b}{kT}\right) . \exp\left(\frac{q\Delta\phi_b}{kT}\right) . \exp\left(C_T E_m^2\right) \qquad \text{[5.8]}$$

where C_T is a tunneling coefficient. A tunneling coefficient of 8 x 10^{-13} cm^2/V^2 for 4H-SiC was found to yield an increase in leakage current by six orders of magnitude consistent with the behavior observed in the literature[1].

5.2.4 Leakage Current

The enhanced Schottky barrier lowering in silicon carbide devices leads to a more rapid increase in leakage current with increasing reverse bias as shown in Fig. 5.12 for the case of a 1000-V device with a barrier height of 1.1 eV. The saturation current density (no barrier lowering case) and the results of computation with only Schottky barrier lowering are shown in the figure for comparison. It is worth emphasizing that the leakage current is increased beyond the saturation current level even at zero bias due to the presence of electric field at the contact due to the built-in potential. The leakage current is predicted by the model given by Eq. [5.8] to increase by five orders of magnitude when the reverse voltage approaches the breakdown voltage. The Schottky barrier lowering effect produces an increase by three-orders of magnitude as shown in the figure. Both the Schottky barrier lowering effect and the tunneling effect can be mitigated by using the JBS rectifier structure discussed in the next chapter.

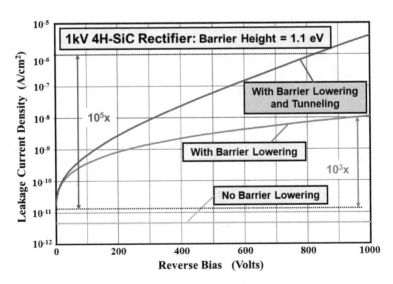

Fig. 5.12 Leakage current density for a 1000 V 4H-SiC Schottky rectifier with barrier height of 1.1 eV.

5.3 4H-SiC Vertical Diode Experimental Results

The first high voltage Schottky rectifiers with low on-state voltage drop and excellent switching behavior were reported by using 6H-SiC material[8] by using Platinum as the Schottky contact metal. These devices had a breakdown voltage of 400-V without any edge termination. The breakdown voltage was later improved to 1000-V by using an argon ion plant at the periphery of the diodes[9]. These devices had a low on-state voltage drop of 1.1 volts at an on-state current density of 100 A/cm^2 and showed no reverse recovery current, which is a major problem for Si P-i-N rectifiers. It was found that the leakage current increased by about 5 orders of magnitude with increase in reverse bias voltage consistent with the theoretical prediction in the previous section. Similar results were later demonstrated for Schottky rectifiers fabricated at using 4H-SiC[10] by using Titanium as the Schottky contact metal. These diodes had an on-state voltage drop of less than 1.1 volts at an on-state current density of 100 A/cm^2. It was found that the leakage current for these Schottky diodes also increased by about 5 orders of magnitude with increase in reverse bias voltage. Similar results were subsequently reported by other groups[11,12,13,14].

Schottky rectifiers with higher breakdown voltages have been developed over the years due to the low specific on-resistance of the drift region in 4H-SiC. Devices with breakdown voltages of 1.5 – 2.5 kV were reported from 4H-SiC in 1999[15] with on-state voltage drop of 2.4 volts at an on-state current density of 100 A/cm^2. Schottky rectifiers with breakdown voltage of 4-kV were reported[16] using 50 μm thick epitaxial layers with a high on-state voltage drop of over 6 volts an on-state current density of 100 A/cm^2. 4H-SiC based Schottky rectifiers with breakdown voltage of 4.9-kV were reported[17] in 2000 using 50 μm thick epitaxial layers with a doping concentration of 7 x 10^{14} cm^{-3}. These diodes used a 100 μm wide boron-implanted edge termination. They also had a high on-state voltage drop of 2.4 volts at an on-state current density of 25 A/cm^2. Rectifiers were fabricated using Molybdenum Schottky contacts on 4H-SiC with a breakdown voltage of 4.15-kV[18]. These diodes used a 3-zone JTE edge termination to achieve the breakdown voltage within 90 % of the ideal value. The on-state voltage drop for these diodes was good at 1.89 volts at an on-state current density of 100 A/cm^2. All of these Schottky diodes exhibited an increase in leakage current by 5 orders of magnitude with increasing reverse bias voltage.

5.4 Summary

The physics of operation of the 4H-SiC and GaN Schottky rectifiers is similar to that of silicon devices in the forward conduction direction. The low specific on-resistance for the drift region for these materials allows development of devices with very high breakdown voltages compared with silicon devices. However, the reverse leakage current in 4H-SiC Schottky rectifiers is significantly enhanced by the larger Schottky barrier lowering effect and thermionic field emission (or tunneling) current at high reverse bias voltages. This is due to the much larger electric field in the 4H-SiC drift regions when compared with silicon in the blocking mode. Fortunately, the availability of larger Schottky barrier heights for metal contacts on 4H-SiC, at the expense of an increased on-state voltage drop, allows reducing the absolute values for the leakage currents to a level where the reverse bias power dissipation is below the forward bias power dissipation enabling stable operation in circuits.

A better approach is to shield the Schottky contact from the high electric field developed in the 4H-SiC drift region as discussed in the next chapter. This is achieved by using the JBS structure for 4H-SiC.

References

[1] B. J. Baliga, "Fundamentals of Power Semiconductor Devices", Second Edition, Springer-Science, 2019.

[2] B. J. Baliga, "Schottky Barrier Rectifiers and Methods of Forming the Same", U.S. Patent 5,612,567, March 18, 1997.

[3] B. J. Baliga, "The Future of Power Semiconductor Technology", Proceedings of the IEEE, Vol. 89, pp. 822-832, 2001.

[4] B. J. Baliga, "Power Semiconductor Devices for Variable Frequency Drives", Proceedings of the IEEE, Vol. 82, pp. 1112-1122, 1994.

[5] A. Itoh, T. Kimoto, and H. Matsunami, "High Performance of High Voltage 4H-SiC Schottky Barrier Diodes", IEEE Electron Device Letters, Vol. 16, pp. 280-282, 1995.

[6] S. L. Tu and B. J. Baliga, "On the Reverse Blocking Characteristics of Schottky Power Diodes", IEEE Transactions on Electron Devices, Vol. 39, pp. 2813-2814, 1992.

[7] T. Hatakeyama and T. Shinohe, "Reverse Characteristics of a 4H-SiC Schottky Barrier Diode", Silicon Carbide and Related Materials – 2001, Material Science Forum, Vol. 389-393, pp. 1169-1172, 2002.

[8] M. Bhatnagar, P. K. McLarty, and B. J. Baliga, "Silicon Carbide High Voltage (400V) Schottky Barrier Diodes", IEEE Electron Device Letters, Vol. EDL-13, pp. 501-503, 1992.

[9] D. Alok, B. J. Baliga, and P. K. McLarty, "A Simple Edge Termination for Silicon Carbide with Nearly Ideal Breakdown Voltage", IEEE Electron Device Letters, Vol. EDL-15, pp. 394-395, 1994.

[10] R. Raghunathan, D. Alok, and B. J. Baliga, "High Voltage 4H-SiC Schottky Barrier Diodes", IEEE Electron Device Letters, Vol. EDL-16, pp. 226-227, 1995.

[11] A. Itoh, T. Kimoto, and H. Matsunami, "Efficient Power Schottky Rectifiers of 4H-SiC", IEEE International Symposium on Power Semiconductor Devices and ICs, pp. 101-106, 1995.

[12] A. Itoh, T. Kimoto, and H. Matsunami, "Excellent Reverse Blocking Characteristics of High-Voltage 4H-SiC Schottky Rectifiers with Boron-Implanted Edge Termination", IEEE Electron Device Letters, Vol. 17, pp. 139-141, 1996.

[13] K. J. Schoen, et al, "Design Considerations and Experimental Analysis of High Voltage SiC Schottky Barrier Rectifiers", IEEE Transactions on Electron Devices, Vol. 45, pp. 1595-1604, 1998.

[14] V. Saxena, et al, "High-Voltage Ni and Pt SiC Schottky Diodes utilizing Metal Field Plate Terminations", IEEE Transactions on Electron Devices, Vol. 46, pp. 456-464, 1999.

[15] R. K. Chilukuri and B. J. Baliga, "High Voltage Ni/4H-SiC Schottky Rectifiers", IEEE International Symposium on Power Semiconductor Devices and ICs, pp. 161-164, 1999.

[16] H. M. McGlothlin, et al, "4 kV Silicon Carbide Schottky Diodes for High Frequency Switching Applications", IEEE Device Research Conference, pp. 42-43, 1999.

[17] R. Singh, et al, "SiC Power Schottky and PiN Diodes", IEEE Transactions on Electron Devices, Vol. 49, pp. 665-672, 2002.

[18] T. Nakamura, et al, "A 4.15 kV 9.07 mΩ-cm^2 4H-SiC Schottky Barrier Diode using Mo Contact Annealed at High Temperature", IEEE Electron Device Letters, Vol. 26, pp. 99-101, 2005.

Chapter 6

Shielded Schottky Rectifiers

It has been traditional to trade-off the on-state (or conduction) power loss against the reverse blocking power loss by optimizing the Schottky barrier height in silicon Schottky rectifiers. As the Schottky barrier height is reduced, the on-state voltage drop decreases producing a smaller conduction power loss. At the same time, the smaller barrier height produces an increase in the leakage current leading to larger reverse blocking power loss. It has been demonstrated that the power loss can be minimized by reducing the Schottky barrier height. However, the maximum operating temperature becomes smaller[1].

The optimization procedure is exacerbated by the rapid increase in the leakage current with increasing reverse bias voltage due to the Schottky barrier lowering phenomenon in silicon devices. The first method proposed to ameliorate the barrier lowering effect in vertical silicon Schottky rectifiers utilized shielding by incorporation of a P-N junction[2,3]. Since the basic concept was to create a potential barrier to shield the Schottky contact against high electric fields generated in the semiconductor by using closely spaced P^+ regions around the contact, this structure was named the *'Junction-Barrier controlled Schottky (JBS) rectifier'*. In the JBS rectifier, the on-state current was designed to flow in the un-depleted gaps between the P^+ regions when the diode is forward biased to preserve unipolar operation. In addition to reducing the leakage current, the presence of the P^+ regions was also shown to enhance the ruggedness of the diodes. Detailed optimization of the silicon JBS rectifier characteristics was achieved with sub-micron dimensions between the P^+ regions[4].

Subsequently, a novel silicon structure that utilizes the charge-coupling concept was proposed to reduce the resistance in the drift region[5]. Since these structures utilized an electrode embedded within an oxide coated trench region that surrounds the metal-semiconductor contact, this structure was named the *'Trench MOS Barrier controlled*

Schottky (TMBS) rectifier'. The performance of this structure was further enhanced by using a graded doping profile to create a device named the *'Graded-Doped Trench MOS Barrier controlled Schottky (GD-TMBS) rectifier'*[6]. This has allowed extending the breakdown voltage of silicon Schottky rectifiers to the 200 volt range[7,8]. Commercial products using this concept are now sold under the TMBS name[9].

Yet another method proposed to create a potential barrier under the Schottky contact for Si Schottky rectifiers was the utilization of a second metal-semiconductor contact with large barrier height surrounding the main Schottky contact with a low barrier height[10]. Since a stronger potential barrier could be created by locating the high barrier metal with a trench, this structure was named the *'Trench Schottky Barrier controlled Schottky (TSBS) rectifier'*.

In the previous chapter it was demonstrated that the increase in leakage current with reverse bias voltage is much stronger for the Schottky rectifiers made from 4H-SiC material. This is due to a larger Schottky barrier lowering effect associated with the larger electric field in silicon carbide drift regions and the onset of field emission (or tunneling) current. It is therefore obvious that the methods proposed to suppress the electric field at the Schottky contact in silicon diodes will have even greater utility in SiC rectifiers.

This chapter discusses the application of shielding techniques to reduce the electric field at the metal-semiconductor contact in SiC Schottky rectifiers. It is demonstrated that the JBS and TSBS concepts can be extended to SiC to achieve significant improvement in performance. However, the TMBS and GD-TMBS approaches are not appropriate for these semiconductors because of the high electric field generated in the oxide leading to its rupture or unreliable operation. This problem may be overcome using high-k dielectrics instead of silicon dioxide. Experimental results on relevant structures are provided to define the state of the development effort on shielded SiC Schottky rectifiers.

6.1 Junction Barrier Schottky (JBS) Rectifier

The Junction Barrier controlled Schottky (JBS) rectifier structure for 4H-SiC is illustrated in Fig. 6.1. It consists of a P^+ region placed around the Schottky contact to generate a potential barrier under the metal-semiconductor contact in the reverse blocking mode. Unlike the Si case, the P-N junctions in SiC do not take a cylindrical shape due to the negligible diffusion of the dopants in SiC. The ion-implantation process for the P-type dopant (typically Aluminum) creates a vertical junction profile. However, it has recently been shown that ion implant straggle plays an important role in determining the JBS diode characteristics as discussed later in this chapter[11]. The junction takes a rectangular profile as opposed to a cylindrical shape in silicon devices. This shape is preferable for creating a potential barrier below the Schottky contact to suppress the electric field at the contact.

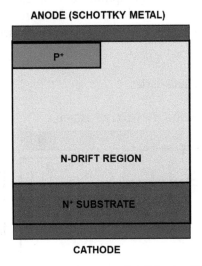

Fig. 6.1 Silicon carbide Junction Barrier controlled Schottky (JBS) rectifier structure.

The space between the P^+ regions is chosen so that there is an un-depleted region below the Schottky contact to enable unipolar conduction through the structure in the on-state. The voltage drop across the diode is not sufficient to forward bias the P-N junction during normal on-state operation. Low voltage silicon devices operate with on-state voltage drops around 0.4 volts which is well below the 0.7 volts needed for inducing strong injection across the P-N junction. The margin is even larger for 4H-SiC due to its much larger band gap. Typical SiC Schottky rectifiers have on-state voltage drops of less than 1.5 volts due to the low specific resistance of the drift region. This is well below the 3 volts required to induce injection from the P-N junction. Consequently, the JBS concept is well suited for development of SiC structures with very high breakdown voltages. Moreover, the P-N junctions are beneficial for obtaining better surge current handling capability as discussed later in the chapter.

The P⁺ region is usually formed by ion-implantation of P-type dopants using a mask with appropriate spacing to leave room for the Schottky contact. For processing convenience, the same metal layer is used to make an ohmic contact to the highly doped P⁺ region as well as to make the Schottky barrier contact to the N-drift region. This requires a unique process for simultaneously forming of an ohmic contact to the P⁺ region and a Schottky contact to the N-drift region. The space between the P⁺ regions must be optimized to obtain the best compromise between the on-state voltage drop, which increases as the space is reduced, and the leakage current, which decreases as the space is reduced.

6.1.1 On-State Characteristics

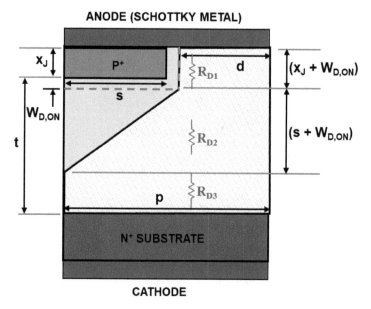

Fig. 6.2 On-state current flow pattern in the 4H-SiC JBS Rectifier Structure.

The current flow path in the 4H-SiC JBS rectifier can be modelled using the green shaded area shown in Fig. 6.2. In this model, it is assumed that the current through the Schottky contact flows only within the un-depleted portion with dimension 'd' under the Schottky contact.

Consequently, the current density at the Schottky contact (J_{FS}) is related to the cell (or cathode) current density (J_{FC}) by:

$$J_{FS} = \left(\frac{p}{d}\right) J_{FC} \qquad [6.1]$$

where p is the cell pitch. The dimension 'd' is determined by the cell pitch (p), the size of the P^+ region ion-implant window (s), and the on-state depletion width ($W_{D,ON}$):

$$d = p - s - W_{D,ON} \qquad [6.2]$$

In deriving this equation, it has been assumed that there is no straggle in the ion-implant. The impact of ion implant straggle is discussed later in the chapter.

It can be observed from Fig. 6.2 that the presence of the P^+ region degrades the on-state current flow path. The lithography used for device fabrication should minimize the size of the P^+ region (dimension 's' in Fig. 6.2). The current density at the Schottky contact can be enhanced by a factor of two or more depending up on the relative size of s and pitch p. This must be taken into account when computing the voltage drop across the Schottky contact by using J_{FS} and not J_{FC}:

$$V_{FS} = \phi_B + \frac{kT}{q} \ln\left(\frac{J_{FS}}{AT^2}\right) \qquad [6.3]$$

where ϕ_B is the Schottky barrier height, k is Boltzmann's constant, T is the absolute temperature, q is the electron charge, and A is Richardson's constant.

The current flows through the un-depleted portion of the drift region after leaving the Schottky contact. In the model, it is assumed that the current flows through a region with a uniform width 'd' until it reaches the bottom of the depletion region and then spreads to the entire cell pitch (p) at a 45 degree spreading angle. The current paths overlap at a distance (s + $W_{D,ON}$) from the bottom of the depletion region. The current then flows through a uniform cross-sectional area.

The net resistance to current flow can be calculated by adding the resistance of the three segments. The resistance of the first segment of uniform width 'd' is given by:

$$R_{D1} = \frac{\rho_D.(x_J + W_{D,ON})}{d.Z}$$ [6.4]

where ρ_D is the resistivity of the drift region, and Z is the length of the cell orthogonal to the cross-section shown in Fig. 6.2. The resistance of the second segment is given by:

$$R_{D2} = \frac{\rho_D}{Z} \ln\left(\frac{p}{d}\right)$$ [6.5]

The resistance of the third segment with a uniform cross-section of width p is given by:

$$R_{D3} = \frac{\rho_D.(t - s - 2W_{D,ON})}{p.Z}$$ [6.6]

The specific resistance for the drift region can be calculated by multiplying the total cell drift region resistance (R_{D1} + R_{D2} + R_{D3}) by the cell-area (p.Z):

$$R_{sp,drift} = \frac{\rho_D.p.(x_J + W_{D,ON})}{d} + \rho_D.p.\ln\left(\frac{p}{d}\right) + \rho_D.(t - s - 2W_{D,ON})$$

[6.7]

In addition, it is important to include the resistance associated with the thick, highly doped N^+ substrate because this is substantially larger than for silicon devices. The specific resistance of the N^+ substrate can be determined by taking the product of its resistivity and thickness. For 4H-SiC, the lowest available resistivity for N^+ substrates is 20 mΩ-cm. If the thickness of the substrate is 350 microns, the specific resistance contributed by the N^+ substrate is 7 x 10^{-4} Ω-cm². Manufacturers thin the N^+ substrate after doing the top side process steps to reduce its resistance.

The on-state voltage drop for the JBS rectifier at a forward cell current density J_{FC}, including the substrate contribution, is then given by:

$$V_F = \phi_B + \frac{kT}{q} \ln\left(\frac{J_{FS}}{AT^2}\right) + \left(R_{sp,drift} + R_{sp,subs}\right).J_{FC}$$ [6.8]

The depletion layer width for silicon carbide is also substantially larger than for silicon due to the larger built-in potential. However, these

structures operate at a relatively larger on-state voltage drop of over
1 volt. Consequently, when computing the on-state voltage drop using
the above equation, it is satisfactory to make the approximation that the
depletion layer width can be computed by subtracting an on-state voltage
drop of 1.5 volts from a built-in potential (V_{bi}) of about 3.2 volts for the
P-N junction:

$$W_{D,ON} = \sqrt{\frac{2\varepsilon_S\left(V_{bi}-1.5\right)}{qN_D}}$$ [6.9]

Alternately, an iterative process can be used to account for the true on-
state voltage drop given by Eq. [6.8] in Eq. [6.9]. Due to the abrupt
junctions formed in silicon carbide by the ion implant process, it is
appropriate to assume that the entire depletion occurs on the lightly
doped N-side of the junction. For a 4H-SiC JBS rectifier fabricated using
a doping concentration of 2×10^{16} cm^{-3}, corresponding to a breakdown
voltage of about 1000 V, the zero bias depletion width is about 0.4 µm.
Based upon this, it can be concluded that it is important to take the
depletion width into account during the design of the cell dimension d for
SiC JBS rectifiers.

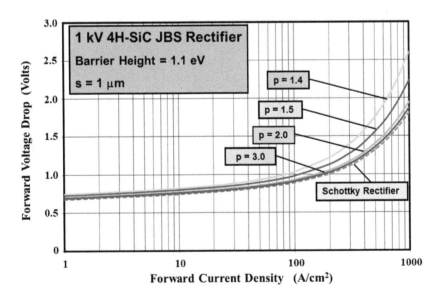

Fig. 6.3 Forward characteristics of 1-kV 4H-SiC JBS rectifiers for case of a Schottky
barrier height of 1.1 eV with various cell pitch values in µm.

        4H-SiC JBS rectifiers are commonly fabricated using either Ni
or Ti as the Schottky barrier metal contacts. The Schottky barrier height
for the case of Ni is 1.6 eV on 4H-SiC while it is 1.1 eV for the case
of Ti[12]. The forward characteristics of 1-kV 4H-SiC JBS rectifiers
calculated using the above analytical model with a Schottky barrier
heights of 1.1 eV corresponding to the Ti barrier case are shown in Fig.
6.3. The cell pitch (p) was used as a variable because it determines the
space d when the P^+ region width s is kept constant at a value of 1 μm. A
junction depth of 1 μm was used with a drift region thickness of 10 μm
below the junction to support the 1000 volts. The doping concentration
of the drift region was 2×10^{16} cm^{-3}. In comparison with the Schottky
rectifier characteristics (shown by the blue dashed lines in the figure), the
increase in on-state voltage drop at a forward current density of 200
A/cm^2 is small (less than 0.1 volts) as long as the cell pitch is more than
1.5 μm. This cell pitch is sufficient to obtain substantial reduction of the
electric field at the metal-semiconductor contact as shown in the next
section. A low on-state voltage drop of 1.05 V at a current density of 200
A/cm2 is predicted by the model for a cell pitch of 2 μm. This is superior
to values for fast switching Si P-i-N rectifiers with the same voltage
rating.

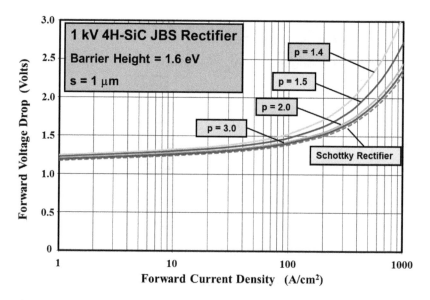

Fig. 6.4 Forward characteristics of 1-kV 4H-SiC JBS rectifiers for case of a Schottky
barrier height of 1.6 eV with various cell pitch values in μm.

The forward characteristics of 1-kV 4H-SiC JBS rectifiers, calculated for the same structure using the above analytical model with a Schottky barrier height of 1.6 eV corresponding to the Ni barrier case, are shown in Fig. 6.4 with the cell pitch (p) as a parameter. The larger barrier height increases the on-state voltage drop. In comparison with the Schottky rectifier characteristics (shown by the blue dashed line in the figure), the increase in on-state voltage drop at a forward current density of 200 A/cm^2 is small (less than 0.1 volts) as long as the cell pitch is more than 1.5 μm. The on-state voltage drop is 1.55 V for the case of a cell pitch of 2 μm. The leakage current density is greatly reduced by using this larger barrier height.

6.1.2 Reverse Leakage Current

The leakage current in the SiC JBS rectifier can be calculated by firstly taking into account the smaller Schottky contact area in the JBS rectifier cell. Secondly, it is necessary to include Schottky barrier lowering while accounting for the smaller electric field at the Schottky contact due to shielding by the P-N junction. Thirdly, the thermionic field emission current must be included while accounting for the smaller electric field at the Schottky contact due to shielding by the P-N junction.

After making these adjustments, the leakage current for the SiC JBS rectifier can be calculated by using:

$$J_L = \left(\frac{p-s}{p}\right) AT^2 \exp\left(-\frac{q\phi_b}{kT}\right).\exp\left(\frac{q\Delta\phi_{bJBS}}{kT}\right).\exp\left(C_T E_{JBS}^2\right) \quad \text{[6.10]}$$

where C_T is a tunneling coefficient (8 x 10^{-13} cm^2/V^2 for 4H-SiC). In contrast to the Schottky rectifier, the barrier lowering for the JBS rectifier is determined by the reduced electric field E_{JBS} at the Schottky contact:

$$\Delta\phi_{bJBS} = \sqrt{\frac{qE_{JBS}}{4\pi\varepsilon_S}} \quad \text{[6.11]}$$

The electric field at the Schottky contact in the JBS rectifier varies with distance away from the P-N junction. The highest electric field is observed at the middle of the Schottky contact (right hand edge of cell shown in Fig. 6.1) with a progressively smaller value closer to the P-N junction. When developing an analytical model with a worst case scenario, it is prudent to use the electric field at the middle of the contact to compute the leakage current.

The electric field at the metal-semiconductor interface in the middle of the contact increases with the applied reverse bias voltage as in the case of the Schottky rectifier until the depletion regions from the adjacent P-N junctions produce a potential barrier under the Schottky contact. A potential barrier is established by the P-N junctions after depletion of the drift region below the Schottky contact at the pinch-off voltage. The pinch-off voltage (V_P) can be obtained from the device cell parameters:

$$V_P = \frac{qN_D}{2\varepsilon_S}(p-s)^2 - V_{bi} \qquad [6.12]$$

It is worth pointing out that the built-in potential for 4H-SiC is much larger than for silicon. Although the potential barrier begins to form after the reverse bias exceeds the pinch-off voltage, the electric field continues to rise at the Schottky contact due to encroachment of the potential to the Schottky contact. This problem is less acute for the silicon carbide structure than in the silicon JBS rectifier because of the rectangular shape of the P-N junction in 4H-SiC. In order to analyze the impact of this on the reverse leakage current, the electric field E_{JBS} can be related to the reverse bias voltage by:

$$E_{JBS} = \sqrt{\frac{2qN_D}{\varepsilon_S}(\alpha V_R + V_{bi})} \qquad [6.13]$$

where α is a coefficient used to account for the build-up in the electric field after pinch-off.

Due to the two-dimensional nature of the P-N junction in the JBS rectifier structure, it is difficult to derive an analytical expression for alpha (α). However, the value for alpha (α) for 4H-SiC has been related to the aspect ratio of the structure[13] by using numerical simulations:

$$\alpha(4H-SiC) = e^{-5.75*(AR)} \qquad [6.14]$$

with the aspect ratio defined as:

$$(AR) = \frac{x_J}{2(p-s)} \qquad [6.15]$$

For a junction depth of 1 μm, the aspect ratio is 0.5 for a pitch of 2.0 μm if s is 1 μm. This results in an alpha (α) value of only 0.0564 which implies a greatly reduced electric field according to Eq. [6.13].

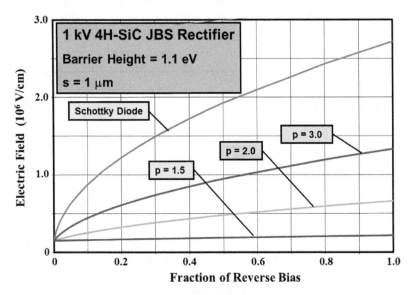

Fig. 6.5 Electric field at the Schottky contact for 1 kV 4H-SiC JBS Rectifiers with various cell pitch values in μm.

As an example, consider the case of the 1-kV SiC JBS rectifier discussed in the previous section with a junction depth of 1 μm and a P⁺ region with dimension 's' of 1 μm. The reduction of the electric field at the Schottky contact can be predicted by calculating values for alpha (α) as given by Eq. [6.14]. The alpha (α) values for a pitch of 1.5, 2.0, and 3.0 μm are 0.00318, 0.0564, and 0.2375, respectively. The electric field at the middle of the Schottky contact in the SiC JBS rectifier structure obtained by using these values for alpha (α) are plotted in Fig. 6.5. An alpha (α) of unity corresponds to the Schottky rectifier structure with no shielding. It can be observed that substantial reduction of the electric field at the Schottky contact is obtained as the pitch is reduced. Even for a pitch of 2 μm, which results in an on-state characteristic close to that of the Schottky diode as shown in Fig. 6.3 and 6.4, the electric field at the Schottky contact is reduced to only 6.6×10^5 V/cm at 100 % of the breakdown voltage compared with 2.7×10^6 V/cm for the Schottky diode.

The Schottky barrier lowering due to the reduction of the electric field at the Schottky contact in the 4H-SiC JBS structure is shown in Fig. 6.6 for the case of the 1-kV device. Without the shielding by the P-N junction, a barrier lowering of 0.20 eV occurs in the Schottky rectifier at close to the breakdown voltage. The barrier lowering is reduced to 0.10 eV with a cell pitch of 2 μm in the SiC JBS rectifier structure.

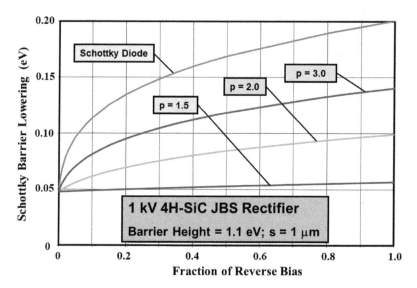

Fig. 6.6 Schottky barrier lowering in 1 kV 4H-SiC JBS Rectifiers with various cell pitch values in μm.

As discussed in the previous chapter, the large Schottky barrier lowering for 4H-SiC, in conjunction with the thermionic field emission current and tunneling current, results in an increase in leakage current by five-orders of magnitude when the voltage increases to the breakdown voltage. The leakage current is greatly reduced by the shielding in the 4H-SiC JBS rectifier structure as shown in Fig. 6.7. For the 4H-SiC JBS rectifier structure with pitch of 2.0 μm and an implant window s of 1 μm, the Schottky contact area is reduced to 50 percent of the cell area. This results in a proportionate reduction of leakage current at low reverse bias voltages. More importantly, the suppression of the electric field at the Schottky contact, by the presence of the P-N junction, greatly reduces the rate of increase in leakage current with increasing reverse bias. The reverse leakage increases by only one order of magnitude when the reverse bias is increased to the breakdown voltage. The net effect is a reduction in leakage current density by a factor of 13,000x at the break-down voltage when compared with the Schottky diode. This example demonstrates that a very large improvement in reverse power dissipation can be achieved with the SiC Schottky rectifiers with a very small increase in the on-state voltage drop by adopting the JBS concept.

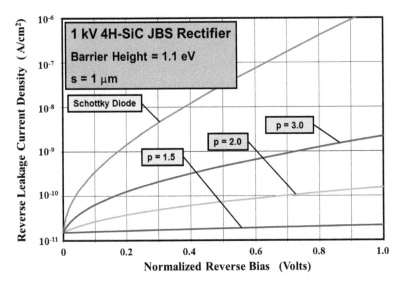

Fig. 6.7 Reverse leakage current for 1 kV 4H-SiC JBS Rectifiers various cell pitch values in μm.

All commercially available SiC power Schottky rectifiers utilize the JBS structure. The leakage current density predicted for the SiC JBS rectifier with a pitch of 2 μm is very low in magnitude (only 10^{-10} A/cm^2) at room temperature even with the lower barrier height of 1.1 eV. The leakage current in practical devices is determined by currents associated with the edge termination and package. However, the leakage current produced at the Schottky contact in the JBS rectifier can be observed at elevated temperatures[11].

6.1.3 Experimental Results

The first high voltage silicon carbide JBS rectifiers were reported in 1997 after the evolution of adequate technology for ion-implantation and activation of P-type dopants[14,15]. These structures were sometimes erroneously labeled as Merged PN Schottky (MPS) rectifiers[14]. The MPS concept was originally proposed for improving the performance of high voltage silicon rectifiers[16]. In the MPS concept, the P-N junction is used to inject minority carriers into the drift region and modulate (reduce) the resistance in series with the Schottky contact. When compared to PiN rectifiers, the MPS structure has been found to contain a smaller stored charge leading to an improved trade-off between on-state voltage drop and reverse recovery characteristics for silicon rectifiers. As already pointed out, the very low resistance in the drift region of high voltage silicon carbide rectifiers does not warrant the modulation of its conductivity with the injection of minority carriers that degrade the switching performance. It is therefore appropriate to use the JBS nomenclature for the high voltage silicon carbide structures rather than the MPS moniker. However, these JBS rectifiers can operate in the MPS mode at surge current levels. This is beneficial for reducing the power losses for creating a more rugged operation.

In the first JBS rectifiers[15] with breakdown voltage of 700 volts achieved by using 9 μm thick epitaxial layers with doping level of 3 x 10^{15} cm^{-3}, the addition of the P^{+} regions to the Schottky contact was found to result in an improvement in the breakdown voltage and leakage current. In spite of a reduction of the electric field at the titanium Schottky contact consistent with that shown in Fig. 6.5, the reduction of the leakage current was only by two orders of magnitude. However, the increase in the on-state voltage drop was small, similar to that shown in Fig. 6.3. Subsequently, the breakdown voltage of the JBS rectifier was extended to 2.8 kV[17] by using 27 μm thick epitaxial layers with doping concentration of 3 x 10^{15} cm^{-3}. The on-state voltage drop for these JBS diodes was 2.0 volts versus 1.8 volts observed for the Schottky diodes. In this study, the leakage current for the Schottky diode was reported to increase with reverse voltage by a factor of 10^{6} while that for the JBS diode increased by only a factor of 10^{3}.

Subsequent work[18,19] on JBS rectifiers confirmed the benefits of using the junction barrier concept for reducing the leakage current. In addition, it was found that the surge current capability of the diodes was enhanced when compared with Schottky diodes. In Schottky rectifiers, the on-state voltage drop becomes extremely large ($\sim$ 30 volts) under surge current levels (current density above 1000 A/cm^{2}) leading to the observation of destructive failures. In contrast, the injection of minority carriers at applied voltages above 3.5 volts in the JBS rectifier (MPS mode) enables reduction of the on-state voltage drop under surge current levels preventing destructive failures. Further, unlike Schottky rectifiers, the JBS rectifiers were found to exhibit a positive temperature coefficient for the on-state voltage drop at a current density of 100 A/cm^2. Thus, the increased resistance created by the P$^+$ regions in the JBS rectifiers had the benefit of compensating for the reduction in voltage drop across the Schottky contact with increasing temperature.

Excellent 4H-SiC JBS rectifiers with breakdown voltage of 1400 V were reported in 2002 by using linear and honeycombed P$^+$ grid structures[20]. Ion implantation of aluminum was used to form the P$^+$ regions and the Schottky contact was made using Ti/Pt/Au. The on-state voltage drop for the 4H-SiC JBS rectifiers was about 1.2 volts at an on-state current density of 100 A/cm^2, which is close to the predictions of the analytical model in the previous section. The reverse recovery current for these diodes was found to be much smaller than for silicon P-i-N rectifiers resulting in improved efficiency for DC-DC converters.

The breakdown voltage of the JBS rectifier was extended[21] to 4.3 kV using a 30 μm thick drift layer with doping concentration of 2 x 10^{15} cm^{-3}. The leakage current for these diodes was reported to increase by 3 orders of magnitude with reverse bias when compared with 6 orders of magnitude for the Schottky diode. For this reduced doping concentration, an optimum spacing of 9 μm between the P$^+$ regions was observed to provide the best characteristics.

JBS rectifiers manufactured from 4H-SiC were reported in 2006 with much better ruggedness than previous Schottky rectifier products[22]. The operation of the JBS diodes in the MPS mode was shown to reduce power losses and improve the ability to operate at surge current levels.

3.5 kV JBS rectifiers fabricated using epitaxial layers with 1.5 x 10^{15} cm^{-3} doping and thickness of 31 μm were reported in 2007[23]. These devices could operate at up to 300 °C with increase in leakage current by only 10x up to the full blocking voltage. An increase in the reverse recovery charge by a factor of 10x was observed from 30 °C to 200 °C.

The blocking voltage capability of 4H-SiC JBS rectifiers was extended to 10-kV by using epitaxial layers with 6 x 10^{14} cm^{-3} doping and thickness of 120 μm[24]. These diodes were operated an on-state current density of 20 A/cm^2 to obtain an on-state voltage drop of 4 volts. The P$^+$ grid was fabricated using aluminum ion implants and Nickel was used as the Schottky contact. The leakage current for the diodes increased by three-orders of magnitude with increasing reverse bias voltage indicating shielding of the Schottky contact.

When the spacing between the P$^+$ grid regions in the 4H-SiC JBS rectifiers is reduced, it becomes important to include the impact of lateral straggle of the aluminum ion-implants. Monte-Carlo simulations of the lateral extension of aluminum ions indicates a spread of about 0.2 μm from the mask edges[25]. This phenomenon is important when optimizing the 4H-SiC JBS rectifier structure.

The characteristics of 10 kV 4H-SiC JBS rectifiers with Ti and Ni Schottky barrier contacts were found to be strongly influenced by lateral straggle of the aluminum implant[26]. The knee voltage for the Ti contact increased from 0.9 V to 1.5 V due to the reduction of space between the P-N junctions created by the implant straggle. This occurred even for diodes with enhanced doping between the P-N junctions using an additional N-type implant. The JBS diodes had a high on-state voltage drop of 5 V at a current density of 40 A/cm^2. The authors ascribe the impact of the lateral straggle on the low doping concentration (7 x 10^{14} cm^{-3}) of the drift region.

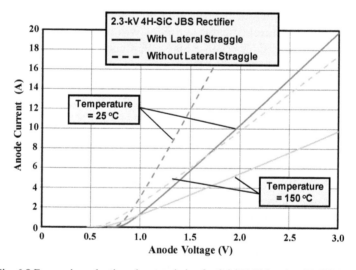

Fig. 6.8 Forward conduction characteristics for 2.3 kV Ti-barrier 4H-SiC JBS Rectifiers computed with and without ion implant straggle of the Al ions.

However, the importance of ion implant straggle on SiC JBS diodes has also been demonstrated for 2.3 kV devices in 2020[11]. These devices were fabricated n-type epitaxial layers with a 10-times larger doping concentration of 6 x 10^{15} cm^{-3} than the 10 kV devices; and a thickness of 17 μm. The device cells had a pitch (p) of 2 μm and P$^+$ region width (s) of 1 μm. The knee voltage for the Ti Schottky barrier diodes was 0.9 V as expected but the series resistance was larger than expected. The analytically modelled forward and reverse characteristics are shown in Fig. 6.8 and 6.9 for the cases with and without including an ion implant straggle of 0.35 μm. A significant increase in the series resistance of the JBS diode is observed after accounting for the straggle in Fig. 6.8. The straggle narrows the space between the P-N junctions decreasing the dimension d in Fig. 6.2, which increase the resistance components RD1 and RD2. The on-state voltage drop is increased by about 0.3 V. The analytically modelled forward conduction characteristics are in agreement with experimental results only after the straggle is taken into account. The ion implant straggle also impacts the reverse leakage current as shown in Fig. 6.9. It is reduced by a factor of about 5x when the straggle is taken into account. The analytically modelled leakage currents are in agreement with the experimental data only after straggle is taken into account.

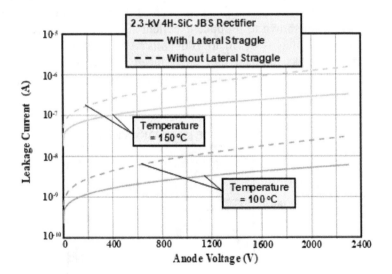

Fig. 6.9 Reverse blocking characteristics for 2.3 kV 4H-SiC JBS Rectifiers computed with and without ion implant straggle of the Al ions.

In conclusion, the JBS concept has been found to be very valuable for reducing the leakage current in 4H-SiC Schottky rectifiers with a modest increase in the on-state voltage drop. All the products available from manufacturers rely up on the JBS structure to achieve low leakage current and ruggedness. It has allowed commercialization of 4H-SiC Schottky power diodes with blocking voltages ranging from 600 to

3300 V by 2020. Even higher blocking voltage, perhaps up to 10 kV, commercial diodes may be feasible.

6.2 Trench MOS Barrier Schottky (TMBS) Rectifier

The Trench MOS barrier Schottky Rectifier (TMBS) structure, shown in Fig. 6.10, was originally proposed for silicon Schottky rectifiers[5,27] to achieve charge coupling between the electrode in the trench and the dopant charge in the drift region. The charge coupling allows for very high doping concentration in the drift region while maintaining a breakdown voltage above the theoretically predicted values for one-dimensional parallel plane junctions[13]. The high drift region doping reduces the series resistance of the drift region resulting in low on-state voltage drop for Schottky rectifiers with higher breakdown voltages. This concept, particularly when enhanced with a linearly graded doping profile[6,7], has been shown to produce excellent silicon Schottky rectifiers with breakdown voltages of 50 to 100 volts[28]. In addition, the electric field at the Schottky contact can be reduced by the formation of a potential barrier due to extension of the depletion region from the sidewalls of the trench.

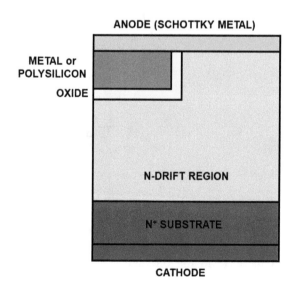

Fig. 6.10 Trench MOS Barrier controlled Schottky (TMBS) rectifier structure.

Recently, there have been attempts to apply the TMBS concept to silicon carbide Schottky rectifiers[29,30]. This approach is misdirected because of two problems. Firstly, the doping concentration in the drift region for high voltage silicon carbide structures is very high when compared with silicon as shown earlier. It is therefore unnecessary to utilize charge coupling to enhance the doping unless the operating voltages are above 5000 volts. Secondly, the electric field within the silicon carbide drift regions is an order of magnitude larger than within silicon devices. This creates an equally higher electric field inside the oxide used for the TMBS structure. The oxide can consequently be subjected to field strengths that induce failure by rupture. For these reason, the TMBS structure is not discussed in detail in this book. Detailed analysis can be found in a previous book[31].

6.3 Trench Schottky Barrier Schottky (TSBS) Rectifier

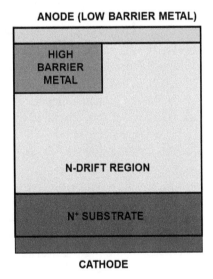

ANODE (LOW BARRIER METAL)

HIGH
BARRIER
METAL

N-DRIFT REGION

N⁺ SUBSTRATE

CATHODE

Fig. 6.11 Trench Schottky Barrier controlled Schottky (TSBS) rectifier structure.

It has been demonstrated in the section 6.1.2 that reducing the electric field at the metal-semiconductor contact by P-N junction shielding suppresses leakage current at high voltages. The potential barrier that must be created under the Schottky contact for the shielding can also be produced by using another Schottky contact placed adjacent to the main

Schottky contact. The second Schottky contact must have a larger barrier height than the main Schottky contact so that the leakage current from this contact is small despite the high electric field at its interface with the semiconductor. In addition, it is preferable to locate the high barrier height metal contact within a trench surrounding the main low barrier metal Schottky contact as illustrated in Fig. 6.11. The trench architecture enhances the potential barrier under the main Schottky contact in comparison with a planar structure.

All of the above features were first proposed for improvement of Schottky barrier rectifiers in a patent[10] issued in 1993. This patent describes devices with a high barrier metal located in trenches etched around the main low barrier metal Schottky contact with various geometries, such a stripes or cellular configurations. A simple method for fabrication of the device was also described. It consists of depositing the low barrier metal and patterning it to expose areas for etching the trenches. The trenches are then formed using the metal as the masking layer. The high barrier metal is then deposited into the trenches and over the low barrier metal to complete the cell structure. The TSBS concept was not pursued for silicon devices due to the success of the JBS and TMBS concepts. However, it was initially suitable for silicon carbide devices because it eliminated the need for formation of P-N junctions which require very high temperature anneals that can degrade the semi-conductor surface. Due to the large band gap of silicon carbide, it is possible to produce high barrier Schottky contacts by using metals such as Nickel in conjunction with low barrier main Schottky contacts such as Titanium. Detailed analysis of the 4H-SiC TSBS is available in a previously book[30].

The TSBS concept for improving the performance of silicon carbide Schottky rectifiers was first simultaneously explored at PSRC[32,33] and Purdue University[34]. Titanium was used as the main Schottky contact metal due to its relatively low barrier height (1.1 eV) on 4H-SiC while Nickel was used in the trenches as the high barrier height (1.6 eV) metal. A breakdown voltage of 400 volts was observed when using this approach on an epitaxial layer with doping concentration of 3×10^{15} cm^{-3} and thickness of 13 μm[35]. This was far below the capability of the material and compares poorly with 1720 volts observed for the planar nickel Schottky rectifier. The analysis discussed in the previous section indicates that this breakdown problem is not endemic to the TSBS structure but may be related to the chip design and layout. However, a reduction of the leakage current by a factor of 75x was observed confirming the ability of the TSBS concept in mitigating the barrier lowering and tunneling currents from the main Schottky contact. In addition, the on-state characteristics were found to be similar to those for a planar Titanium Schottky contact as expected.

A reduction of leakage current by a factor of 30x has also been reported by using the planar TSBS structure (i.e. zero trench depth) with little impact on the forward characteristics[36]. The smaller improvement in the leakage current when compared with the trench structure is consistent with the smaller potential barrier. The breakdown voltages of these diodes were also far below the capability of the underlying drift region due to absence of adequate edge termination.

The JBS concept was successfully implemented in 4H-SiC devices once ion implantation and annealing of p-type dopants such as aluminum and boron in 4H-SiC was optimized. Since the JBS concept produces superior performance to the TSBS concept, further development of the TSBS concept has become unnecessary.

6.4 Summary

The JBS rectifier concept was first proposed for improving the trade-off between on-state voltage drop and leakage current for silicon Schottky rectifiers. This idea has been widely adopted for 4H-SiC Schottky rectifiers because the larger electric field in the drift region for this material produces much greater Schottky barrier lowering and creates tunneling induced leakage current as well. It is demonstrated in this chapter that a significant improvement in the leakage current of SiC Schottky rectifiers can be achieved by shielding the Schottky contact against high electric fields generated in the semiconductor. The analysis shows that JBS structures are very effective in reducing leakage current without significant degradation of the forward characteristics. The JBS concept has been widely adopted for commercialization of 4H-SiC Schottky diodes.

References

[1] B. J. Baliga, "Fundamentals of Power Semiconductor Devices", Second Edition, Springer-Science, 2019.

[2] B. J. Baliga, "The Pinch Rectifier: A Low Forward Drop High Speed Power Diode", IEEE Electron Device Letters, Vol. 5, pp. 194-196, 1984.

[3] B. J. Baliga, "Pinch Rectifier", U. S. Patent 4,641,174, Issued February 3, 1987.

[4] M. Mehrotra and B. J. Baliga, "Very Low Forward Drop JBS Rectifiers Fabricated using Sub-micron Technology", IEEE Transactions on Electron Devices, Vol. 41, pp. 1655-1660, 1994.

[5] M. Mehrotra and B. J. Baliga, "Schottky Barrier Rectifier with MOS Trench", U. S. Patent 5,365,102, Issued November 15, 1994.

[6] B. J. Baliga, "Schottky Barrier Rectifiers and Methods of Forming the Same", U.S. Patent 5,612,567, March 18, 1997.

[7] S. Mahalingam and B. J. Baliga, "The Graded Doped Trench MOS Barrier Schottky Rectifiers", Solid State Electronics, Vol. 43, pp. 1-9, 1999.

[8] B. J. Baliga, "The Future of Power Semiconductor Technology", Proceedings of the IEEE, Vol. 89, pp. 822-832, 2001.

[9] https://www.vishay.com/docs/89098/tmbs.pdf.

[10] L. Tu and B. J. Baliga, "Schottky Barrier Rectifier including Schottky Barrier regions of Differing Barrier Heights", U. S. Patent 5,262,668, November 16, 1993.

[11] A. Agarwal, K. Han, and B. J. Baliga, "2.3-kV, 5-A 4H-SiC Ti and Ni JBS Rectifiers manufactured in Commercial Foundry: Impact of Implant Lateral Straggle", IEEE Workshop on Wide Bandgap Power Devices and Applications, pp. P1-P6, 2020.

[12] T. Kimoto and J. A. Cooper, "Fundamentals of Silicon Carbide Technology", pp. 253, John Wiley, New York, 2014.

[13] B. J. Baliga, "Advanced Power Rectifier Concepts", Springer-Science, 2009.

[14] R. Held, N. Kaminski and E. Niemann, "SiC Merged p-n/Schottky Rectifiers for High Voltage Applications", Silicon Carbide and Related Materials – 1997, Material Science Forum, Vol. 264-268, pp. 1057-1060, 1998.

[15] F. Dahlquist, et al, "Junction Barrier Schottky Diodes in 4H-SiC and 6H-SiC", Silicon Carbide and Related Materials – 1997, Material Science Forum, Vol. 264-268, pp. 1061-1064, 1998.

[16] B. J. Baliga, "Analysis of a High Voltage Merged PiN/Schottky (MPS) Rectifier", IEEE Electron Device Letters, Vol. 8, pp. 407-409, 1987.

[17] F. Dahlquist, et al, "A 2.8kV JBS Diode with Low Leakage", Silicon Carbide and Related Materials – 1999, Material Science Forum, Vol. 338-342, pp. 1179-1182, 2000.

[18] D. Peters, et al, "Comparison of 4H-SiC pn, Pinch, and Schottky Diodes for the 3kV Range", Silicon Carbide and Related Materials – 2001, Material Science Forum, Vol. 389-393, pp. 1125-1128, 2002.

[19] F. Dahlquist, H. Lendenmann and M. Ostling, "A JBS Diode with controlled Forward Temperature Coefficient and Surge Current Capability", Silicon Carbide and Related Materials – 2001, Material Science Forum, Vol. 389-393, pp. 1129-1132, 2002.

[20] R. Singh, et al, "High Power 4H-SiC JBS Rectifiers", IEEE Transactions on Electron Devices, Vol. 49, pp. 2054-2063, 2002.

[21] J. Wu, et al, "4,308V, 20.9 mO-cm2 4H-SiC MPS Diodes Based on a 30 micron Drift Layer", Silicon Carbide and Related Materials – 2003, Material Science Forum, Vol. 457-460, pp. 1109-1112, 2004.

[22] R. Rupp, et al, "2nd Generation" SiC Schottky Diodes", IEEE International Symposium on Power Semiconductor Devices and ICs, pp. 1-4, 2006.

[23] P. Brosselard, et al, "High Temperature behavior of 3.5 kV 4H-SiC JBS Diodes", IEEE International Symposium on Power Semiconductor Devices and ICs, pp. 285-288, 2007.

[24] B. A. Hull, "Performance and Stability of Large Area 4H-SiC 10-kV Junction Barrier Schottky Rectifiers", IEEE Transactions on Electron Devices, Vol. 55, pp. 1864-1870, 2008.

[25] K. Mochizuki, et al, "Influence of Lateral Spreading of Implanted Aluminum Ions and Implantation-Induced Defects on Forward Current-Voltage Characteristics of 4H-SiC Junction Barrier Schottky Diodes", IEEE Transactions on Electron Devices, Vol. 56, pp. 992-997, 2009.

[26] J. Lynch, N. Yun, and W. Sung, "Design Considerations for High Voltage SiC Power Devices: An Experimental Investigation into Channel Pinching of 10kV SiC Junction Barrier Schottky (JBS) Diodes", IEEE International Symposium on Power Semiconductor Devices and ICs, pp. 223-226, 2019.

[27] M. Mehrotra and B. J. Baliga, "The Trench MOS Barrier Schottky Rectifier", IEEE International Electron Devices Meeting, Abstract 28.2.1, pp. 675-678, 1993.

[28] S. Mahalingam and B. J. Baliga, "A Low Forward Drop High Voltage Trench MOS Barrier Schottky Rectifier with Linearly Graded Doping

Profile", IEEE International Symposium on Power Semiconductor Devices and ICs, Paper 10.1, pp. 187-190, 1998.

[29] V. Khemka, V. Ananthan, and T. P. Chow, "A 4H-SiC Trench MOS Barrier Schottky (TMBS) Rectifier", IEEE International Symposium on Power Semiconductor Devices and ICs, pp. 165-168, 1999.

[30] Q. Zhang, M. Madangarli, and T. S. Sudarshan, "SiC Planar MOS-Schottky Diode", Solid State Electronics, Vol. 45, pp. 1085-1089, 2001.

[31] B. J. Baliga, "Silicon Carbide Power Devices", World Scientific Press, Singapore, 2005.

[32] M. Praveen, S. Mahalingam, and B. J. Baliga, "Silicon Carbide Dual Metal Schottky Rectifiers", PSRC Technical Working Group Meeting, Report TW-97-002-C, 1997

[33] B. J. Baliga, "High Voltage Silicon Carbide Devices", Material Research Society Symposium Proceedings, Vol. 512, pp. 77-88, 1998.

[34] K. J. Schoen, et al, "A Dual Metal Trench Schottky Pinch-Rectifier in 4H-SiC", IEEE Electron Device Letters, Vol. 19, pp. 97-99, 1998.

[35] F. Roccaforte, et al, "Silicon Carbide Pinch Rectifiers using a Dual-Metal Ti-NiSi Schottky Barrier", IEEE Transactions on Electron Devices, Vol. 50, pp. 1741-1747, 2003.

[36] F. Roccaforte, et al, "Silicon Carbide Pinch Rectifiers using a Dual-Metal Ti-NiSi Schottky Barrier", IEEE Transactions on Electron Devices, Vol. 50, pp. 1741-1747, 2003.

Chapter 7

P-i-N Rectifiers

Inverters for adjustable speed motor drives use silicon IGBTs with silicon P-i-N rectifiers as anti-parallel diodes[1]. These rectifiers have blocking voltages ranging from 300 volts to 5000 volts. In a P-i-N rectifier, the reverse blocking voltage is supported across a depletion region formed with a P-N junction structure. The voltage is primarily supported within the n-type drift region with the properties of the p-type region optimized for good on-state current flow. Any given reverse blocking voltage can be supported across a thinner drift region by utilizing the punch-through design[1]. Since it is beneficial to use a low doping concentration for the n-type drift region in this design, it is referred to as an i-region (implying that the drift region is intrinsic in nature). The silicon P-i-N rectifiers that are designed to support large voltages rely upon the high level injection of minority carriers into the drift region. This phenomenon greatly reduces the resistance of the thick, very lightly doped drift region necessary to support high voltages in silicon. Consequently, the on-state current flow is not constrained by the low doping concentration in the drift region. A reduction of the thickness of the drift region, by utilizing the punch-through design, is beneficial for decreasing the on-state voltage drop.

In the case of silicon carbide rectifiers, the drift region doping level is relatively large and its thickness is much smaller than for silicon devices to achieve very high breakdown voltages as discussed in chapter 3. This enables the design of 4H-SiC based Schottky rectifiers with reverse blocking capability of at least 5000 volts with low on-state voltage drop as shown in the previous chapters. Due to the inherent fast switching capability of Schottky rectifiers, 4H-SiC JBS rectifiers have already displaced silicon P-i-N rectifiers for many motor drive applications with reverse blocking capability of up to 5000 volts[2].

The 4H-SiC P-i-N rectifiers are of therefore of interest only for applications that require blocking voltage of 10-kV and higher. Their performance is discussed in this chapter. Their reverse recovery behavior is shown to be quite different than the Si devices.

7.1 P-i-N Rectifier Structure

The reverse blocking voltage capability for the P-i-N rectifier is achieved using a punch-through drift region design[1]. In this case, the drift region has a low doping concentration to make the electric field as uniform as possible across the drift region to minimize the thickness. The thickness of the drift region is chosen to achieve the desired reverse breakdown voltage. The breakdown voltage of the punch-through design was discussed in section 3.2.

The on-state current flow in the P-i-N rectifier is governed by three current transport mechanisms: (a) at very low current levels, the current transport is dominated by the recombination process within the space charge layer of the P-N junction – referred to as the *recombination current*; (b) at low current levels, the current transport is dominated by the diffusion of minority carriers injected into the drift region – referred to as the *diffusion current*; and (c) at high current levels, the current transport is dictated by the presence of a high concentration of both electrons and holes in the drift region – referred to as *high-level injection current*. These current transport phenomena are discussed in detail in the textbook[1]. At the on-state operating current levels, current flow in the P-i-N rectifier is governed by the third process with injection of mobile carriers with concentrations far greater than the background doping concentration of the drift region. Only this process is considered in this chapter.

7.2 Reverse Blocking

The reverse blocking capability for the P-i-N rectifier is governed by Eq. [3.16]. As discussed in chapter 3, the thickness of the drift region in the P-i-N rectifier can reduced by using this approach. The lowest doping concentration in the drift (or i-region) is determined by technological considerations. It is relatively low ($\sim 1 \times 10^{12}$ cm^{-3}) for Si diodes fabricated from neutron-transmutation-doped bulk wafers. The doping concentration of the drift region for 4H-SiC diodes is much larger ($\sim 1 \times$

10^{14} cm^{-3}). This has a significant impact of the diode performance as discuss below.

7.2.1 Silicon 10-kV Device

The example of a 10-kV design will be analyzed in this chapter for making a comparison of 4H-SiC and silicon devices. The lowest doping concentration feasible for silicon devices is 1 x 10^{12} cm^{-3}. Using this value, the drift region thickness is found to be 908 μm to achieve a reverse breakdown voltage of 10-kV.

7.2.2 4H-SiC 10-kV Device

In the case of 4H-SiC, the lowest doping concentration that is feasible is 1 x 10^{14} cm^{-3}. Using this value, the drift region thickness is found to be 75 μm to achieve a reverse breakdown voltage of 10-kV. The large reduction in drift region thickness produces a reduction in the stored charge within the device. This in turn improves the reverse recovery as shown in this chapter.

7.3 On-State Stored Charge

P-i-N rectifiers operate at on-state current density in excess of 10 A/cm^2 and typically at 100 A/cm^2. At these levels, the drift region operates under high level injection conditions. The physics of operation under high level injection conditions is discussed in detail in the textbook[1].

7.3.1 High Level Injection Physics

The N-drift region in the P-i-N rectifier must be lightly doped in order to support high voltages in the reverse blocking mode. When the forward bias applied to the rectifier increases, the injected minority carrier concentration also increases in the drift region until it ultimately exceeds the background doping concentration (N_D) in the drift region. This is defined as *high level injection*. The carrier distribution in the drift region under high-level injection conditions is given by[1]:

$$n(x) = p(x) = \frac{\tau_{HL} J_{ON}}{2qL_a} \left[\frac{\cosh(x/L_a)}{\sinh(d/L_a)} - \frac{\sinh(x/L_a)}{B\cosh(d/L_a)} \right] \qquad [7.1]$$

where J_{ON} is the on-state current density, τ_{HL} is the high-level lifetime in the drift region, q is the charge for the electron, and 2d is the width of the drift region, and L_a is the ambipolar diffusion length, The parameter B is given by:

$$B = \frac{\left(\mu_n + \mu_p\right)}{\left(\mu_n - \mu_p\right)} \qquad [7.2]$$

where μ_n and μ_p are the mobility for electrons and holes, respectively. The carrier distribution described by Eq. [7.1] is illustrated in Fig. 7.1.

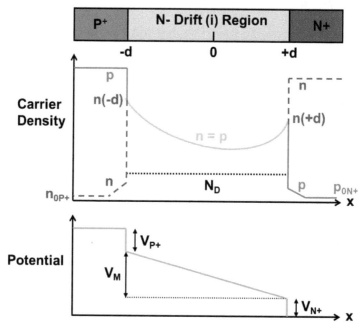

Fig. 7.1 Carrier and potential distribution under high-level injection conditions for a P-i-N rectifier.

The average carrier density injected in the drift region can be deduced from charge control considerations[1]. Under steady-state conditions, the current flow in the P-i-N rectifier can be related to sustaining the recombination of holes and electrons within the drift region if the recombination within the end-regions is neglected. The average carrier density in the drift region is then given by:

$$n_a = \frac{J_T \tau_{HL}}{2qd} \qquad [7.3]$$

From this relationship, it can be concluded that the average carrier density in the drift region will increase with the on-state current density and decrease with reduction of the lifetime.

The stored charge in the drift region can be obtained by multiplying the average carrier concentration and the thickness of the drift region:

$$Q_S = 2qdn_a = J_{ON}\tau_{HL} \qquad [7.4]$$

From this relationship, it is clear that the stored charge can be reduced by decreasing the lifetime.

7.3.2 High Level Injected Carriers: Silicon

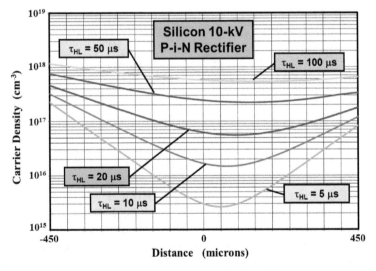

Fig. 7.2 Carrier distribution under high-level injection conditions for a 10-kV silicon P-i-N Rectifier with various high-level lifetime values.

The injected carrier profile for the 10-kV silicon P-i-N rectifier can be calculated by using Eq. [7.1]. The value for B for silicon is 2.14. The results obtained by using various high-level lifetime values are shown in Fig. 7.2 for the case of an on-state current density of 100 A/cm². In all cases, the injected concentration of holes and electrons is far greater than the doping concentration (1×10^{12} cm^{-3}) in the drift region. The lifetime values were chosen to maintain a reasonable on-state voltage drop as discussed later. The carrier distribution has a minimum close to the center of the drift region.

The stored charge in the drift region for the 10-kV silicon P-i-N rectifier can be computed using Eq. [7.4]. It has the values shown in Table 7.1. The stored charge in the silicon 10-kV Pi-N rectifier is large due to the large high level-lifetime values required to maintain a reasonable on-state voltage drop. This results in very large reverse recovery time and slow switching speed for the silicon 10-kV P-i-N rectifier as discussed later.

High Level Lifetime (microseconds)	Stored Charge (Coulombs/cm2)
100	1×10^{-2}
50	5×10^{-3}
20	2×10^{-3}
10	1×10^{-3}
5	5×10^{-4}

Table 7.1 Stored charge in a 10-kV silicon P-i-N rectifier.

7.3.3 High Level Injected Carriers: 4H-SiC

The injected carrier profile for the 10-kV 4H-SiC P-i-N rectifier can also be calculated by using Eq. [7.1]. The value for B for 4H-SiC is 1.235. The results obtained by using various high-level lifetime values are shown in Fig. 7.3 for the case of an on-state current density of 100 A/cm^2. In all cases, the injected concentration of holes and electrons is far greater than the doping concentration (1×10^{14} cm^{-3}) in the drift region. The lifetime values were chosen to maintain a reasonable on-state voltage drop as discussed later.

The stored charge in the drift region for the 10-kV 4H-SiC P-i-N rectifier can be computed using Eq. [7.4]. It has the values shown in Table 7.2. The stored charge in the 4H-SiC 10-kV Pi-N rectifier is much smaller than that in the 10-kV silicon P-i-N rectifier due to the smaller high level-lifetime values required to maintain a reasonable on-state voltage drop. This results in very small reverse recovery time and fast switching speed for the 4H-SiC10-kV P-i-N rectifier as discussed later.

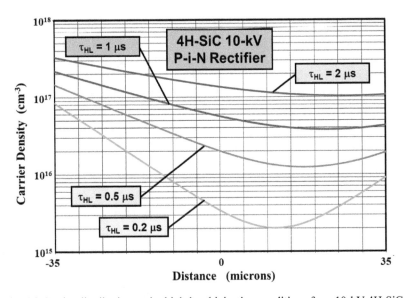

Fig. 7.3 Carrier distribution under high-level injection conditions for a 10-kV 4H-SiC P-i-N Rectifier with various high-level lifetime values.

High Level Lifetime (microseconds)	Stored Charge (Coulombs/cm2)
2	2e-4
1	1e-4
0.5	5e-5
0.2	2e-5

Table 7.2 Stored charge in a 10-kV 4H-SiC P-i-N rectifier.

7.4 On-State Voltage Drop

The on-state voltage drop for a P-i-N rectifier can be derived from the carrier distribution profile[1]. It is given by:

$$V_{ON} = \frac{2kT}{q} \ln\left[\frac{J_T d}{2qD_a n_i F(d/L_a)}\right]$$ [7.5]

In this expression, the function $F(d/L_a)$ is strongly dependent on the high-level lifetime because the ambipolar diffusion length L_a depends up on this parameter. It can be calculated using the expressions in the textbook[1]. It has a maximum value of 0.35 when d/L_a becomes equal to unity for Si. It has a maximum value of 0.59 when d/L_a becomes equal to 1.2 for 4H-SiC. Consequently, the lowest on-state voltage drop occurs when the high-level lifetime is chosen so that the ambipolar diffusion length becomes close to half the width of the drift region.

7.4.1 Silicon 10-kV Device

The calculated on-state voltage drop at an on-state current density of 100 A/cm^2 for silicon 10-kV P-i-N rectifiers with a drift region width of 908 μm are shown in Fig. 7.4 when the high-level lifetime is changed. As expected, the on-state voltage drop exhibits a minimum at a (d/L_a) ratio of unity and increases rapidly when the (d/L_a) ratio exceeds 3. The cases of high level-lifetimes of 5, 10, 20, 50, and 100 μs are indicated on the figure to relate the on-state voltage drop and the stored charge.

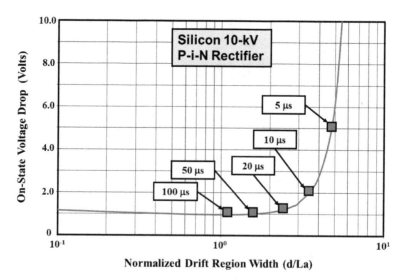

Fig. 7.4 On-state voltage drops of 10-kV silicon P-i-N rectifiers with changes in the high-level lifetime.

7.4.2 4H-SiC 10-kV Device

The calculated on-state voltage drops at an on-state current density of 100 A/cm2 for 4H-SiC 10-kV P-i-N rectifiers with a drift region width of 75 μm are shown in Fig. 7.5 when the high-level lifetime is changed. The on-state voltage drop exhibits a minimum at a (d/L_a) ratio of 1.2 and increases rapidly when the (d/L_a) ratio exceeds 3. The on-state voltage drop for the 4H-SiC P-i-N rectifier is 3 times larger than for the silicon device at small vales for the d/L_a ratio due to its larger bandgap. The cases of high level-lifetime of 0.2, 0.5, 1, and 2 μs are indicated on the figure to relate the on-state voltage drop and the stored charge. The on-state voltage drop remains low even for these very small high-level lifetime values due to the small thickness of the drift region in the 4H-SiC device. For example, the on-state voltage drop for the 4H-SiC P-i-N rectifier is only 3.9 volts even when the lifetime is reduced to 0.2 micro-seconds. This is superior to the Si 10 kV P-i-N rectifier with a lifetime of 5 μs. Comparing the numbers given in Tables 7.1 and 7.2 for these lifetime cases, the stored charge in the 4H-SiC P-i-N rectifier is 25-times smaller making its switching performance much superior. Even better performance can be achieved by adopting the MPS structure as discussed in the next chapter.

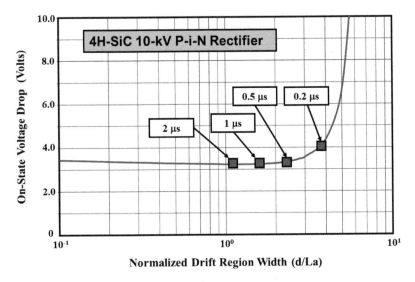

Fig. 7.5 On-state voltage drops of 10-kV 4H-SiC P-i-N rectifiers with changes in the high-level lifetime.

7.5 Reverse Recovery

Power rectifiers control the direction of current flow in circuits used in various power conditioning applications. They operate for part of the time in the on-state when the bias applied to the anode is positive and for the rest of the time in the blocking state when the bias applied to the anode is negative. During each operating cycle, the diode must be rapidly switched between these states to minimize power losses. Much greater power losses are incurred when the diode switches from the on-state to the reverse blocking state than when it is turned on. The stored charge within the drift region of the power rectifier produced by the on-state current flow must be removed before it is able to support high voltages[1]. This produces a large reverse current for a short time duration. This phenomenon is referred to as *reverse recovery*.

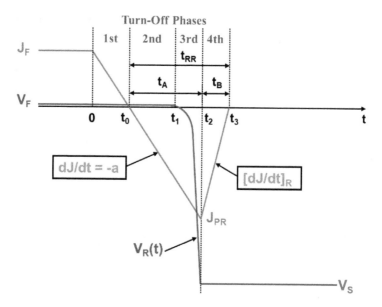

Fig. 7.6 Anode current and voltage waveforms for the P-i-N Rectifier during the reverse recovery process.

It is common-place to use power rectifiers with an *inductive load* in power electronic circuits. In this case, the current reduces at a constant ramp rate ('a') as illustrated in Fig. 7.6 until the diode is able to support voltage. Consequently, a large *peak reverse recovery current* (J_{PR}) occurs due to the stored charge followed by the reduction of the current to zero.

The power rectifier remains in its forward biased mode with a low on-state voltage drop until time t_1. The voltage across the diode then rapidly increases to the supply voltage with the rectifier operating in its reverse bias mode. The current flowing through the rectifier in the reverse direction reaches a maximum value (J_{PR}) at time t_2 when the reverse voltage becomes equal to the reverse bias supply voltage (V_S).

The simultaneous presence of a high current and voltage produces large instantaneous power dissipation in the power rectifier. The peak reverse recovery current also flows through the power switch that is controlling the switching event. This increases the power losses in the transistor[1]. In the case of typical motor control PWM circuits that utilize IGBTs as power switches, a large reverse recovery current can trigger latch-up failure that can destroy both the transistor and the rectifier. It is therefore desirable to reduce the magnitude of the peak reverse recovery current and the time duration of the recovery transient. This time duration is referred to as the *reverse recovery time* (t_{rr}).

An analytical model for the reverse recovery process for the turn-off of a P-i-N rectifier under a constant rate of change of the current (*current ramp-rate*) was created by assuming that the concentration of the free carriers in the drift region can be linearized[1]. The time t_0 at which the current crosses zero is given by:

$$t_0 = \frac{J_F}{a} \qquad [7.6]$$

The second phase of the turn-off process occurs from the time t_0 at which the current crosses zero up to the time t_1 when the P$^+$/N junction can begin to support voltage. This time is given by[1]:

$$t_1 = \frac{J_F}{a} \sqrt{\frac{L_a}{(Kd - L_a)} + 1} \qquad [7.7]$$

where

$$K = \left[\frac{\cosh(-d/L_a)}{\sinh(d/L_a)} - \frac{\sinh(-d/L_a)}{B\cosh(d/L_a)} \right] \qquad [7.8]$$

During the third phase of the turn-off transient, the P-i-N rectifier begins to support an increasing voltage. This requires the formation of a space-charge region $W_{SC}(t)$ at the P$^+$/N junction that expands with time. The expansion of the space-charge region is achieved by further extraction of the stored charge in the drift region resulting in the reverse current continuing to increase after time t_1. The growth of the reverse bias voltage across the P-i-N rectifier can be analytically modeled under the assumption that the sweep out of the stored charge is occurring at an approximately constant current.

The evolution of the space charge region is given by[1]:

$$W_{SC}(t) = \frac{a}{2qn_a}\left(t^2 - t_1^2\right) - \frac{J_{ON}}{qn_a}\left(t - t_1\right) \qquad [7.9]$$

The voltage supported across this space-charge region can be obtained by solving Poisson's equation:

$$V_R(t) = \frac{q\left[N_D + p(t)\right]}{2\varepsilon_S} W_{SC}(t)^2 \qquad [7.10]$$

This expression, in conjunction with Eq. [7.9] for the expansion of the space-charge width, indicates a rapid rise in the voltage supported by the P-i-N rectifier after time t_1. The end of the third phase occurs when the reverse bias across the P-i-N rectifier becomes equal to the supply voltage (V_S). Using this value in Eq. [7.10] together with Eq. [7.9], the time t_2 (and hence J_{PR}) can be obtained.

During the fourth phase of the turn-off process, the reverse current rapidly reduces at approximately a constant rate as illustrated in Fig. 7.6 while the voltage supported by the P-i-N rectifier remains constant at the supply voltage. The stored charge within the drift region after the end of the third phase is removed during this time. The equations for obtaining time t_B are provided in the textbook[1].

7.5.1 Silicon 10-kV Device

The reverse recovery waveforms for the 10-kV silicon P-i-N rectifier are discussed here for the case of a ramp rate of 2×10^7 A/cm²-s. The voltage waveforms calculated using the analytical solutions are shown in Fig. 7.7 for the case of a high level lifetimes of 5, 10, 20, 50, and 100 µs. The voltages rises more rapidly when the lifetime is reduced. This phase ends when the device supports the supply voltage V_S of 6000 V in the figure with a red dashed line.

The reverse recovery current waveforms obtained using the analytical models are shown in Fig. 7.8 for the various values of lifetime. The peak reverse recovery current occurs at the end of the third phase.

The peak reverse recovery current densities predicted by the analytical model are 90, 120, 160, 230, and 310 A/cm^2 for lifetime values of 5, 10, 20, 50, and 100 μs, respectively. The reverse recovery time (t_{RR}) increases from 11 to 16 to 23 to 39 to 55 μs as the high level lifetime is increased from 5 to 10 to 20 to 50 to 100 μs. These very long reverse recovery times limit the maximum operating frequency for the 10-kV silicon rectifier as discussed later.

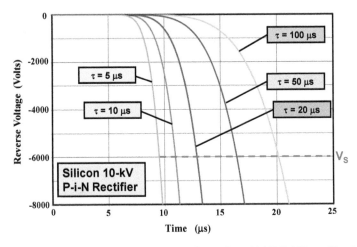

Fig. 7.7 Analytically calculated voltage waveforms for a 10 kV P-i-N rectifier during the reverse recovery process for various lifetime values.

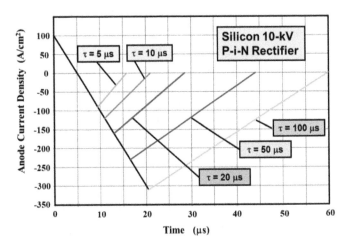

Fig. 7.8 Analytically calculated current waveforms for a 10 kV silicon P-i-N rectifier during the reverse recovery process using various lifetime values.

7.5.2 4H-SiC 10-kV Device

The reverse recovery waveforms for the 10-kV 4H-SiC P-i-N rectifier are discussed here. The same ramp rate of 2×10^7 A/cm^2-s was used here for comparison with the silicon 10 kV P-i-N rectifier. The 4H-SiC P-i-N rectifier does not behave the same way as the silicon diode because of the much thinner drift layer and reduced stored charge. The first two phases for turn-off are the same as for the silicon device. However, during the third phase, the space charge region expands through the entire drift layer even before the anode voltage reaches the supply voltage. Consequently, the end of the third phase is defined by the time at which the space charge layer becomes equal to the thickness (2d) of the drift region. After this, the voltage rises very rapidly to the supply voltage.

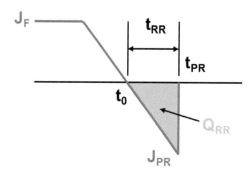

Fig. 7.9 Reverse recovery current waveform for 4H-SiC P-i-N rectifier.

    A simple model can be created to define the end of the third phase for the 4H-SiC P-i-N rectifier by assuming that all the stored charge in the drift region is removed during the reverse recovery time (t_{RR}). The reverse recovery waveform for the current in this case is illustrated in Fig. 7.9. There is an abrupt reduction in the current after the peak because all the stored charge in the drift region has been removed.

    The charge removed during reverse recovery is given by:

$$Q_{RR} = \frac{1}{2} J_{PR} t_{PR} \qquad \text{[7.11]}$$

The peak reverse recovery current is related to the ramp rate by:

$$J_{PR} = a t_{PR} \qquad \text{[7.12]}$$

Combining these relationships with Eq. [7.4] for the stored charge in the drift region yields:

$$t_{RR} = \sqrt{\frac{2\tau_{HL} J_{ON}}{a}}$$

[7.13]

and

$$J_{PR} = \sqrt{2a\tau_{HL} J_{ON}}$$

[7.14]

These expressions allow obtaining the peak reverse recovery current and reverse recovery times for the 4H-SiC P-i-N rectifier.

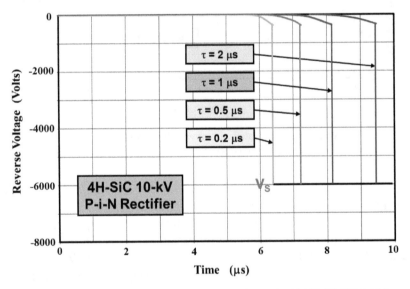

Fig. 7.10 Analytically computed voltage waveforms for 10 kV 4H-SiC P-i-N rectifiers during the reverse recovery process for various lifetime values.

Based up on the above model, the voltage waveforms calculated for the 4H-SiC 10-kV rectifier, with a drift region doping concentration of 10^{14} cm^{-3}, using the analytical solutions with a ramp rate of 2 x 10^{7} A/cm^2-s, are shown in Fig. 7.10 for the case of a high level lifetimes of 5, 10, 20, 50, and 100 μs. The voltages rises at an earlier time when the lifetime is reduced. For all the cases, the abrupt rise in voltage occurs when it reaches a value of less than 500 volts well below the supply voltage of 6 kV. This is due to the space charge region reaching a width of 70 μm, the total width of the i-region for the 4H-SiC 10 kV rectifier case, when the anode voltage reaches 500 V.

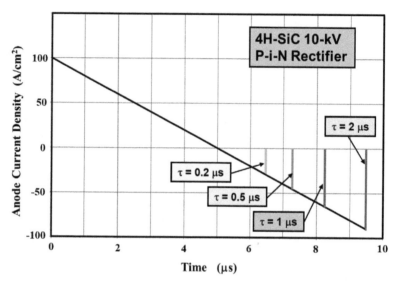

Fig. 7.11 Analytically calculated current waveforms for 10 kV 4H-SiC P-i-N rectifiers during the reverse recovery process using various lifetime values.

The reverse recovery current waveforms obtained using the analytical model for the 4H-SiC P-i-N rectifier are shown in Fig. 7.11 for the various values of lifetime. The peak reverse recovery current occurs at the end of the third phase. The peak reverse recovery current densities predicted by the analytical model are 28.3, 44.7, 63.2, and 89.4 A/cm^2 for lifetime values of 0.2, 0.5, 1, and 2 μs, respectively. The reverse recovery time (t_{RR}) increases from 1.4 to 2.2 to 3.2 to 4.5 μs as the high level lifetime is increased from 0.2 to 0.5 to 1 to 2 μs. These very short reverse recovery times allow the 4H-SiC 10-kV P-i-N rectifier to operate at higher frequencies as discussed later. However, the abrupt (or snappy) reverse recovery of the current is a potential problem because it creates large voltages across stray inductances in power circuits and oscillations in the current.

7.6 4H-SiC 10 kV P-i-N Rectifier Trade-Off Curves

For power system applications, it is desirable to reduce the total power dissipation produced in the rectifiers to maximize the power conversion efficiency. This also reduces the heat generated within the power devices maintaining a lower junction temperature which is desirable to prevent thermal runaway and reliability problems. In the previous sections, it was demonstrated that the peak reverse recovery current and the turn-off time can be reduced by reducing the minority carrier lifetime in the drift region of the P-i-N rectifier structure. This enables reduction of the power losses during the switching transient. However, the on-state voltage drop in a P-i-N rectifier increases when the minority carrier lifetime is reduced, which produces an increase in the power dissipation during on-state current flow. To minimize the power dissipation, it is common-place to perform a trade-off between on-state and switching power losses for power P-i-N rectifiers by developing trade-off curves.

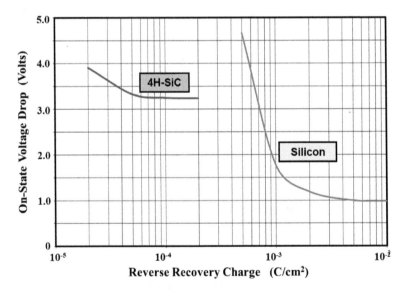

Fig. 7.12 Trade-off curves for the 10-kV P-i-N rectifiers using reverse recovery charge.

One type of the trade-off curve for a power P-i-N rectifier can be generated by plotting the on-state voltage drop against the reverse recovery charge. These trade-off curves for the 10-kV silicon and 4H-SiC P-i-N rectifiers are shown in Fig. 7.12. The reverse recovery charge is equal to the stored charge in the drift region for the 4H-SiC rectifier because all the stored charge is removed during expansion of the space region. The trade-off curves cross when the stored charge in the silicon rectifier is reduced below 7 x 10^{-4} C/cm^2.

Another commonly used trade-off curve for a power P-i-N rectifier can be generated by plotting the on-state voltage drop against the reverse recovery time. These trade-off curves for the 10-kV silicon and 4H-SiC P-i-R rectifiers are shown in Fig. 7.13. The trade-off curves cross when the reverse recovery time in the silicon rectifier is reduced below 15 μs. From this figure, it can be concluded that the 4H-SiC 10-kV P-i-N rectifier can be operated at a much higher frequency than the silicon device.

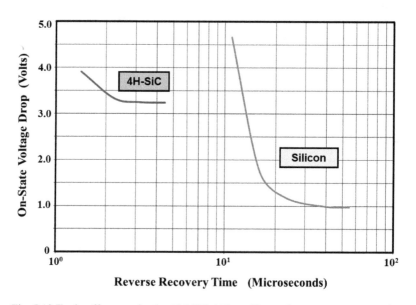

Fig. 7.13 Trade-off curves for the 10-kV P-i-N rectifiers using reverse recovery time.

7.7 4H-SiC 10 kV PiN Rectifier Maximum Operating Frequency

The P-i-N rectifiers are often used in power circuits operated with pulse width modulation signals. It is beneficial to use a higher frequency for the PWM signal to improve the quality of the synthesized AC-waveforms in variable frequency motor drives. The reverse recovery of the power rectifier must be over well before end of each on-off switching event. Based up on this a maximum operating frequency for the power rectifier can be defined by the reverse recovery time becoming one-twentieth of the period of the PWM signal:

$$f_{MAX} = \frac{1}{\left[20 * t_{RR}\right]}$$ [7.15]

Using this criterion, the maximum operating frequency for the silicon 10-kV P-i-N rectifier is found to be only 3 kHz in the case of a lifetime of 10 μs which yields a reverse recovery time of 16 μs. In contrast, the maximum operating frequency for the 4H-SiC 10-kV P-i-N rectifier is found to be 35 kHz in the case of a lifetime of 0.2 μs which yields a reverse recovery time of 1.4 μs.

7.8 4H-SiC P-i-N Rectifier Experimental Results

Many groups have worked on the development of high voltage P-i-N rectifiers over the years. In early studies, the quality of the P^+ region was poor due to problems with achieving a high doping concentration[3]. The best results were obtained by epitaxial growth of the anode followed by etching steps to create the edge termination[4]. More recently, the anode has been formed by ion implantation of Al or B or both dopants. The forward characteristic of implanted junction diodes was found to be sensitive to the junction depth and activation process[5]. The on-state voltage drop of a 4H-SiC diode fabricated using 100 μm thick drift region with doping concentration of 1-3 x 10^{14} cm^{-3} has been reported[3] at 7.1 V for a current density of 100 A/cm^2. These diodes had a breakdown voltage of 8.6 kV. This is significantly worse than that obtained by the numerical simulations despite the reported lifetime in the diodes being about 2 μs. The high on-state voltage drop can be partly attributed to the high contact resistance to the anode.

The on-state voltage drop of diodes formed by co-implantation of aluminum, carbon, and boron to create the anode region[6] has been reported to be about 4.7 V at room temperature. These diodes, fabricated using a 40 μm thick drift region with doping concentration of 1 x 10^{15} cm^{-3}, had a breakdown voltage of about 4.5 kV. The on-state voltage drop was found to reduce with increasing temperature at a current density of 100 A/cm^2. This was attributed to a reduction in the contact resistance to the anode region. The lifetime extracted from the reverse recovery measurements was about 21 ns. These results confirm the conclusion that fast switching PiN rectifiers can be developed from 4H-SiC.

By making improvements to the epitaxial growth process, 4H-SiC power rectifiers with blocking voltage of up to 20 k V were reported in 2004[7]. This required continuous growth of a 100 μm thick drift layer with doping concentration of 2 x 10^{14} cm^{-3} followed by the anode layer of 2 μm in thickness and doping concentration of 8 x 10^{18} cm^{-3}. The 10-kV 4H-SiC P-i-N rectifier had an on-state voltage drop of only 3.9 V at an on-state current density of 100 A/cm^2. The reverse recovery time for these diodes was 0.2 μs with a peak reverse recovery current equal to the on-state current density. The diode yield was greatly improved by reduction of basal plane dislocations.

The use of carbon implantation and thermal oxidation to improve the lifetime in the drift region of P-i-N rectifiers was reported in 2012[8]. A 120 μm thick epitaxial layer with doping concentration of 7 x 10^{13} cm-3 was grown for a targeted breakdown voltage of 18.5 kV. An on-state voltage drop of only 4 V at an on-state current density of 100 A/cm^2 was achieved. The reverse recovery time was reported to be only 0.1 μs with the peak reverse current equal to the on-state current level. However, these tests were performed at a low supply voltage of 200 V.

The reverse recovery behavior of 4H-SiC 6.5 kV, 1 kA P-i-N rectifiers has been compared with those of silicon diodes for medium voltage converter applications[9,10]. The 6 kV 4H-SiC diodes had an on-state voltage drop of 3.42 V at 100 A/cm^2. The 4H-SiC diode module was constructed using 3.5 mm x 3.5 mm diode chips with an anode area of 7.1 mm^2. The on-state characteristics of the silicon and 4H-SiC P-i-N rectifiers crossed at a current density of 40 A/cm^2 and on-voltage of 3.5 V. The 4H-SiC devices had superior on-state voltage drop above this current density. The reverse recovery current and time for the 4H-SiC rectifiers was demonstrated to be far better than the silicon diodes. However, it was found that the 4H-SiC rectifiers exhibit a snappy reverse recovery which produces severe ringing. This is consistent with the model in section 7.5.2.

A record high 21.7 kV breakdown voltage was reported for a 4H-SiC diode in 2012[11]. A space-modulated JTE edge termination was employed to achieve a breakdown voltage within 81 % of the ideal breakdown voltage of the 186 μm thick epitaxial layer with doping concentration of 2.3 x 10^{14} cm^{-3}. The on-state voltage drop for the diodes was 9.34 V at an on-state current density of 50 A/cm^2.

The performance of a 6.5 kV 100 A 4H-SiC P-i-N rectifier has been reported with a mesa edge termination containing the MFZ-JTE concept[12]. The P^+ anode regions were epitaxially grown on top of the epitaxially grown n-type drift region with thickness of 55 μm and doping concentration of 1 x 10^{15} cm^{-3}. The diode active area was 4.6 mm x 4.6 mm (0.211 cm^2). The on-state voltage drop was 3.2 V at an on-state current density of 100 A/cm^2, which corresponds to an on-state current of 20 A. The peak reverse recovery current was 10 A with a reverse recovery time of 0.17 μs at 25 °C. The peak reverse recovery current increased to 25 A with a reverse recovery time of 0.26 μs at 175 °C.

7.9 4H-SiC P-i-N Rectifier Forward Bias Instability

An unusual increase in on-state voltage drop after forward current flow through the 4H-SiC power P-N junction diodes for long periods of time, called the *bipolar degradation phenomenon*, has been reported[13]. The mechanism for this phenomenon[14] is: (a) electron-hole recombination occurring in the i-region of the diode provides energy to the 4H-SiC lattice allowing the basal plane dislocations (BPDs) to create stacking faults; (b) the stacking fault traps electrons becoming negatively charged; (c) the injection of electrons from the cathode is inhibited by the negative charge in the vicinity of the stacking faults; (d) the electron-hole injected concentration near the stacking faults is greatly reduced suppressing current flow through these regions; (e) the loss of current carrying area increases the current density over the rest of the device area; and (f) the increased current density results in the observed rise in on-state voltage drop. The creation and propagation of the stacking fault from the bottom of the epitaxial layer near the cathode junction towards the P-N junction at the top of the device has been observed using light emission images[12]. The lifetime is not reduced by this phenomenon nor is the leakage current degraded[15].

The bipolar degradation phenomenon is unacceptable for utilization of 4H-SiC P-i-N rectifiers in power electronic circuits. It can be suppressed by elimination of the basal plane dislocations with better epitaxial growth technology for 4H-SiC.

7.10 Summary

The physics of operation of the SiC P-i-N rectifiers has been shown to be similar to that used to describe silicon devices. High level injection in the drift region enables modulating its conductivity to reduce the on-state voltage drop. Due to the much smaller width of the drift region required to obtain a given breakdown voltage when compared with Si devices, a far smaller lifetime can be used in 4H-SiC devices. This is favorable for reducing switching losses. However, the large band gap of 4H-SiC results in a large on-state voltage drop of 3 to 4 volts. Consequently, 4H-SiC P-i-N rectifiers are superior to 4H-SiC Schottky rectifiers only when the blocking voltage exceeds 10 kV. 4H-SiC P-i-N diodes with breakdown voltage of 21.7 kV have been fabricated and characterized.

References

[1] B. J. Baliga, "Fundamentals of Power Semiconductor Devices", Springer Scientific, Second Edition, New York, 2019.

[2] B. J. Baliga, "Advanced Power Rectifier Concepts", Springer-Science, New York, 2009.

[3] R. Singh, "Silicon Carbide Bipolar Power Devices – Potentials and Limits", MRS Symposium Proceedings, Vol. 640, pp. H4.2.1-H4.2.12, 2001.

[4] Y. Sugawara, K. Asano, R. Singh, and J. W. Palmour", "6.2 kV 4H-SiC pin Diode with Low Forward Voltage Drop", Silicon Carbide and Related Materials – 1999, Material Science Forum, Vol. 338-342, pp. 1371-1374, 2000.

[5] R. K. Chilukuri, P. Ananthanarayanan, V. Nagapudi, and B. J. Baliga, "High Voltage P-N Junction Diodes in Silicon Carbide using Field Plate Edge Termination", MRS Symposium Proceedings, Vol. 572, pp. 81-86, 1999.

[6] J. B. Fedison, et al, "Al/C/B Co-implanted High Voltage 4H-SiC PiN Junction Rectifiers", Silicon Carbide and Related Materials – 1999, Material Science Forum, Vol. 338-342, pp. 1367-1370, 2000.

[7] M. K. Das, et al, "High Power, Drift-Free 4H-SiC PIN Diodes", International Journal of High Speed Electronics and Systems, Vol. 14, pp. 860-864, 2004.

[8] K. Nakayama, et al, "Characteristics of a 4H-SiC PiN Diode with Carbon Implantation/Thermal Oxidation", IEEE Transactions on Electron Devices, Vol. 59, pp. 895-901, 2012.

[9] F. Filsccker, R. Alvarez, and S. Bernet, "Comparison of 6.5 kV Silicon and SiC Diodes", IEEE Energy Conversion Congress and Exhibition, pp. 2261-2267, 2012.

[10] F. Filsecker, R. Alvarez, and S. Bernet, "Characterization of a New 6.5 kV 1000 A SiC Diode for Medium Voltage Converters", IEEE Energy Conversion Congress and Exhibition, pp. 2253-2260, 2012.

[11] H. Niwa, et al, "Breakdown Characteristics of 12-20 kV class 4H-SiC PiN Diodes with Improved Junction Termination Structure", IEEE International Symposium on Power Semiconductor Devices and ICs, pp. 381-384, 2012.

[12] M. Tao, et al, "Design, Fabrication and Characterization of 6.5kV/ 100A 4H-SiC PiN power rectifier", IEEE Workshop on Wide Bandgap Power Devices and Applications, pp. 228-231, 2021.

[13] R. Singh, "Reliability and Performance Limitations in SiC Power Devices", Microelectronics Reliability, Vol. 46, pp. 713-730, 2006.

[14] M. K. Das, et al, "Ultra High Power 10 kV, 50 A SiC PiN Diodes", IEEE International Symposium on Power Semiconductor Devices and ICs, pp. 159-162, 2005.

[15] P. Brosselard, et al, "The Effect of the Temperature on the Bipolar Degradation of 3.3 kV 4H-SiC PiN Diodes", IEEE International Symposium on Power Semiconductor Devices and ICs, pp. 237-240, 2008.

Chapter 8

MPS Rectifiers

In the previous chapter, it was shown that the reverse recovery transient in a P-i-N rectifier produces large power dissipation in the diodes and the switching transistors. The reverse recovery transient was shown to be related to the presence of stored charge in the drift region during on-state current flow. The MPS rectifier structure was proposed to reduce the stored charge within silicon power rectifiers[1] in the 1980s by merging the physics of the P-i-N rectifier and the Schottky rectifier. The 4H-SiC MPS rectifier structure is illustrated in Fig. 8.1. It has the same form as the 4H-SiC JBS rectifier with a thick N-drift region to support higher voltage. However, the physics of operation of the MPS rectifier is different due to injection from the P-N junction during on-state operation.

ANODE (SCHOTTKY METAL)

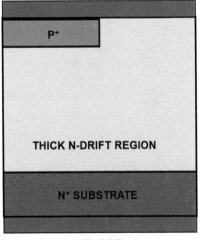

CATHODE

Fig. 8.1 The 4H-SiC MPS rectifier structure.

In the MPS structure, the drift region is designed using the same criteria as used for P-i-N rectifiers in order to support the desired reverse blocking voltage. The device structure contains a P-N junction over a portion under the metal contact and a Schottky contact for the remaining portion. It is convenient to utilize the same metal layer for making an ohmic contact to the P$^+$ region and a Schottky contact to the N- drift region.

8.1 Device Physics

As shown in Fig. 8.1, the P-i-N rectifier and Schottky rectifier are located in close proximity in the MPS rectifier structure allowing the mingling of the physics of operation of both devices. The space between the P-N junctions in the MPS rectifier structure is designed so that it is pinched off at a relatively small reverse bias voltage. After the depletion of the space between the P-N junctions, a potential barrier is formed under the Schottky metal which screens the contact from the reverse bias applied to the cathode terminal. The electric field at the Schottky contact can be greatly reduced in the MPS rectifier when compared with the normal Schottky rectifier by judicious choice of the space between the P-N junctions. This allows suppression of the Schottky barrier lowering reducing the leakage current in silicon devices well below that for Schottky rectifiers. An even greater reduction of the leakage current can be achieved for silicon carbide devices due to suppression of the thermionic field emission current. Consequently, it is possible to achieve good reverse blocking characteristics in the MPS rectifier structure. This behavior is the same as discussed for the JBS rectifier in the previous chapter.

In the JBS rectifier, on-state current flow occurs only via the Schottky contact with no current flow across the P-N junction to maintain unipolar operation. In contrast, the on-state current flow in the MPS rectifier occurs via the P-N junction and the Schottky contact. At low on-state bias levels applied to the cathode, current transport via the Schottky contact is favored due to the larger potential required for the injection of holes into the drift region from the P-N junction. However, this current flow is limited by the large resistance of the un-modulated drift region which has a low doping concentration and large thickness as required to achieve a high reverse blocking voltage capability. As the forward bias voltage is increased, the P-N junction begins to inject a significant concentration of holes into the drift region. The drift region then operates under high-level injection conditions as in the case of the P-i-N rectifier. Since the resistance of the drift region is reduced by conductivity modulation, a large current flow can occur via the Schottky contact in the MPS rectifier structure. This allows on-state current flow with an on-state voltage drop that can be smaller than that for the P-i-N rectifier which is a remarkable outcome.

The carrier concentration at the Schottky contact remains low in the MPS rectifier because it does not inject a significant concentration of minority carriers into the drift region. The resulting carrier profile is superior to that observed in the P-i-N rectifier in terms of charge removal during the turn-off transient. The MPS rectifier exhibits a smaller peak reverse recovery current and charge leading to reduced switching power loss. Moreover, the trade-off between the on-state voltage drop and reverse recovery power loss can be generated by changing the relative area of the P-N junction and Schottky contact in the MPS rectifier structure. A further refinement of the trade-off curve can be achieved by using the lifetime control techniques commonly used for the P-i-N rectifier.

8.2 On-State Characteristics

The MPS rectifier operates like the JBS rectifier at low current levels because there is insufficient voltage to produce injection from the P-N junction. The P-N junction begins to inject holes into the drift region at on-state current densities. The hole concentration then exceeds the doping concentration resulting in operation under high-level injection conditions like in a P-i-N rectifier. The resulting modulation of the conductivity of the drift layer allows efficient current flow via the Schottky contact with a lower on-state voltage drop than a P-i-N rectifier. The MPS rectifier has excellent surge current handling capability due to strong injection from the P-N junction at the very high current densities.

8.2.1 Low Forward Bias Conditions

The N-drift region in the MPS rectifier must be lightly doped in order to support a high voltage in the reverse blocking mode. At small forward bias voltages, the voltage across the P-N junction produces low-level injection of holes into the N-type drift region. There is no conductivity modulation of the drift region at these small forward bias voltages. The resistance of the drift region is therefore determined by the doping concentration. Current transport through the MPS rectifier occurs by the thermionic emission process at the Schottky contact followed by current flow through the drift region. The high resistance of the drift region in MPS rectifiers designed to support large reverse bias voltages initially limits the current transport. The MPS rectifier characteristics resemble those of a JBS rectifier at these small forward bias voltages.

The forward conduction i-v characteristics of the MPS rectifier can be analytically modeled as a metal-semiconductor (Schottky) contact with the series resistance of the drift region. In the analytical model, it is important to include the impact of the larger current density at the Schottky contact when compared with the cathode current density because the P-N junction occupies a portion of the upper surface area. The current constriction in the region between the P-N junctions and current spreading from this region into the drift region enhances the series resistance. This resistance can be modeled as previous performed for the JBS rectifier. Unlike for the JPS rectifiers, the P-N junction depth is a very small fraction of the drift region thickness in the case of the MPS rectifiers because they are designed to support large voltages. The drift region resistance in the MPS rectifier is quite close to the one-dimensional resistance of the drift region. In order to keep this resistance as small as possible, it is preferable to employ a non-punch-through design for the drift region. This is possible for the 4H-SiC devices due to relatively high doping concentrations in the drift region even for devices with large blocking voltages.

Due to the large thickness of the drift region in relation to the junction depth and the width of the window used for the P$^+$ diffusions in the MPS rectifier structure, the current path in the drift region will invariably overlap before reaching the N$^+$ substrate. The current flow pattern was illustrated in Fig. 6.2 with the shaded area. In the 4H-SiC MPS rectifier structure, the thickness of the drift region (t in Fig. 6.2) is much larger than that for the 4H-SiC JBS rectifier due to larger blocking voltages.

The current density at the Schottky contact (J_{FS}) is enhanced due to the presence of the P$^+$ region and the depletion layer at the P-N junction. This increases the voltage drop across the Schottky contact. The current through the Schottky contact flows only within the un-depleted portion (with dimension 'd') of the drift region at the top surface.

Consequently, the current density at the Schottky contact (J_{FS}) is related to the cell (or cathode) current density (J_{FC}) by:

$$J_{FS} = \left(\frac{p}{d}\right) J_{FC} \qquad [8.1]$$

where p is the cell pitch. The dimension 'd' is determined by the cell pitch (p), the size of the P^+ ion-implant window (2s), and the on-state depletion width ($W_{D,ON}$):

$$d = p - s - W_{D,ON} \qquad [8.2]$$

Depending up on the lithography used for device fabrication to minimize the size (dimension 's') of the P^+ region, the current density at the Schottky contact can be considerably enhanced. This must be taken into account when computing the voltage drop across the Schottky contact given by:

$$V_{FS} = \phi_B + \frac{kT}{q}\ln\left(\frac{J_{FS}}{AT^2}\right) \qquad [8.3]$$

The specific resistance for the drift region can be calculated by using Eq. [6.7] derived for the JBS rectifier:

$$R_{sp,drift} = \frac{\rho_D \cdot p \cdot (x_J + W_{D,ON})}{d} + \rho_D \cdot p \cdot \ln\left(\frac{p}{d}\right) + \rho_D \cdot (t - s - x_J - 2W_{D,ON})$$
$$[8.4]$$

The on-state voltage drop for the 4H-SiC MBS rectifier at a small forward bias (< 3 V), including the substrate contribution, is then given by:

$$V_F = \phi_B + \frac{kT}{q}\ln\left(\frac{J_{FS}}{AT^2}\right) + (R_{sp,drift} + R_{sp,subs})J_{FC} \qquad [8.5]$$

When computing the on-state voltage drop using this equation, it is satisfactory to make the approximation that the depletion layer width can be computed by subtracting the on-state voltage drop from the built-in potential of the P-N junction.

8.2.2 High Level Injection Conditions

When the forward bias applied to the 4H-SiC MPS rectifier increases, the injected minority carrier concentration from the P-N junction also increases in the drift region until it ultimately exceeds the background doping concentration (N_D) in the drift region resulting in *high level injection*. After the injected hole concentration in the drift region becomes much greater than the background doping concentration, charge neutrality requires that the concentrations for electrons and holes become equal:

$$n(x) = p(x) \qquad\qquad [8.6]$$

The large concentration of free carriers reduces the resistance of the drift region resulting in *conductivity modulation* of the drift region. As in the case of the P-i-N rectifier, conductivity modulation of the drift region is beneficial for allowing the transport of a high current density through lightly doped drift regions with a low on-state voltage drop.

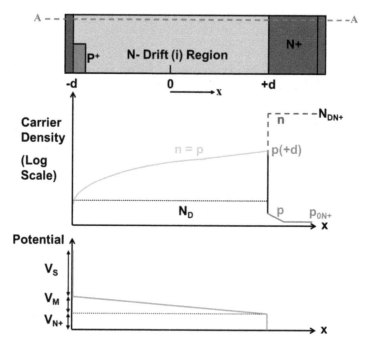

Fig. 8.2 Carrier and potential distribution under high-level injection conditions for the 4H-SiC MPS rectifier.

The carrier distribution within the drift region for the 4H-SiC MPS rectifier is different from that observed for the P-i-N rectifier because of the presence of the Schottky contact. The carrier distribution $p(x)$ can be obtained by solving the continuity equation for holes in the N-region[2]:

$$\frac{d^2p}{dx^2} - \frac{p}{L_a^2} = 0 \qquad [8.7]$$

where L_a is the ambipolar diffusion length given by:

$$L_a = \sqrt{D_a \tau_{HL}} \qquad [8.8]$$

The general solution for the carrier concentration governed by Eq. [8.7] is given by:

$$p(x) = A \cosh\left(\frac{x}{L_a}\right) + B \sinh\left(\frac{x}{L_a}\right) \qquad [8.9]$$

with the constants A and B determined by the boundary conditions for the N-drift region.

For the 4H-SiC MPS rectifier, it is appropriate to solve for the carrier profile along the path indicated by the dashed line marked 'A-A' in Fig. 8.2 which is located through the Schottky contact. At the interface between the N-drift region and the N^+ cathode region (located at $x = +d$ in Fig. 8.2), the total current flow occurs exclusively by electron transport:

$$J_{FC} = J_n(+d) \qquad [8.10]$$

and

$$J_p(+d) = 0 \qquad [8.11]$$

Using these equations:

$$J_{FC} = 2qD_n \left(\frac{dp}{dx}\right)_{x=+d} \qquad [8.12]$$

The second boundary condition occurs at the junction between the N-drift region and the Schottky contact (located at $x = -d$ in Fig. 8.2). Here, the hole concentration becomes zero due to negligible injection at the Schottky contact:

$$p(-d) = 0 \qquad\qquad [8.13]$$

The above boundary conditions can be used to obtain the constants A and B in Eq. [8.13]:

$$A = -\frac{L_a J_{FC}}{2qD_n}\left[\frac{\sinh(-d/L_a)}{\cosh\left(-d/L_a\right)\cosh\left(d/L_a\right)-\sinh(-d/L_a)\sinh\left(d/L_a\right)}\right]$$

[8.14]

$$B = -\frac{L_a J_{FC}}{2qD_n}\left[\frac{\cosh(-d/L_a)}{\cosh\left(-d/L_a\right)\cosh\left(d/L_a\right)-\sinh\left(-d/L_a\right)\sinh\left(d/L_a\right)}\right]$$

[8.15]

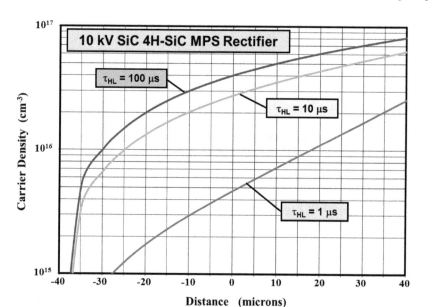

Fig. 8.3 Carrier distribution under high-level injection conditions for the 10 kV SiC MPS rectifier with various high-level lifetime values.

Using these constants in Eq. [8.9] and simplifying the expression yields:

$$p(x) = n(x) = \frac{L_a J_{FC}}{2qD_n}\frac{\sinh\left[(x+d)/L_a\right]}{\cosh\left[2d/L_a\right]}$$

[8.16]

The carrier distribution described by this equation was schematically illustrated in Fig. 8.2. It has a maximum value at the interface between the drift region and the N^+ substrate with a magnitude of:

$$p(+d) = p_M = \frac{L_a J_{FC}}{2qD_n} \frac{\sinh[2d/L_a]}{\cosh[2d/L_a]} = \frac{L_a J_{FC}}{2qD_n} \tanh\left(\frac{2d}{L_a}\right) \qquad [8.17]$$

and reduces monotonically when proceeding towards the Schottky contact in the negative x direction. The concentration becomes equal to zero at the Schottky contact as required to satisfy the boundary condition used to derive the expression.

For the case of the 10 kV 4H-SiC MPS rectifier, the drift region has a thickness of 80 μm and doping concentration of 5×10^{14} cm^{-3}. The carrier distributions calculated at an on-state current density of 100 A/cm^2 by using Eq. [8.16] and Eq. [8.17] are shown in Fig. 8.3 for the case of three values for the high-level lifetime for this 10-kV 4H-SiC MPS rectifier. The largest concentrations for the electrons and holes in the drift region occur at its boundary with the N^+ end-region. The carrier concentration at this boundary decreases when the lifetime is reduced. It has a magnitude of 8.2×10^{16} cm^{-3} for a high lifetime of 100 μs, 6.3×10^{16} cm^{-3} for a moderate lifetime of 10 μs, and 2.6×10^{16} cm^{-3} for a low lifetime of 1 μs. When the lifetime is reduced to 1 μs, the analytical model predicts that the entire drift region is not conductivity modulated as shown in Fig. 8.3. However, such low lifetime values are not necessary in the case of the 4H-SiC MPS rectifier as shown later in the chapter. The carrier profiles for the higher lifetime cases are close to linear in shape.

8.2.3 On-State Voltage Drop

At low on-state current density levels, the on-state characteristics for the silicon carbide MPS rectifier will resemble those for the Schottky rectifier with an enhanced current density at the Schottky contact. At larger current levels with high-level injection in the drift region, the on-state voltage drop for the silicon carbide MPS rectifier can be obtained by summing the voltage drops along the path marked 'A-A' in Fig. 8.2 through the Schottky contact. The total voltage drop along this path consists of the voltage drop across the Schottky contact (V_{FS}), the voltage drop across the drift region (middle region voltage V_M), and the voltage drop at the interface with the N^+ substrate (V_{N+}) as shown at the bottom of Fig. 8.2:

$$V_{ON} = V_{FS} + V_M + V_{N+}$$

[8.18]

The voltage drop across the Schottky contact is given by:

$$V_{FS} = \phi_{BN} + \frac{kT}{q} \ln\left(\frac{J_{FS}}{AT^2}\right)$$

[8.19]

where the current density at the Schottky contact (J_{FS}) is related to the cell or cathode current density by Eq. [8.1]. The voltage drop in the drift (middle) region with inclusion of recombination is given by[2]:

$$V_M = \left\{ \frac{4D_n}{(\mu_n + \mu_p)} \left[\frac{(d/L_a)}{\tanh(2d/L_a)} \right] - \frac{kT}{2q} \right\} \ln\left(\frac{2d}{x_J}\right)$$

[8.20]

The voltage drop across the interface between the drift region and the N^+ substrate is given by:

$$V_{N+} = \frac{kT}{q} \ln\left[\frac{p_M}{N_D}\right] = \frac{kT}{q} \ln\left[\frac{J_{FC}L_a \tanh(2d/L_a)}{2qD_nN_D}\right]$$

[8.21]

by using Eq. [8.17]. The on-state voltage drop for the MPS rectifier can be computed by utilizing the three components discussed above:

$$V_{ON} = \phi_{BN} + \frac{kT}{q} \ln\left(\frac{J_{FC}p}{AT^2d}\right)$$

$$+ \left\{ \frac{4D_n}{(\mu_n + \mu_p)} \left[\frac{(d/L_a)}{\tanh(2d/L_a)} \right] - \frac{kT}{2q} \right\} \ln\left(\frac{2d}{x_J}\right)$$

$$+ \frac{kT}{q} \ln\left[\frac{J_{FC}L_a \tanh(2d/L_a)}{2qD_nN_D}\right]$$

[8.22]

The on-state voltage drop for the MPS rectifier is a function of the lifetime in the drift region because the middle region and N/N^+ interface voltage drops change with lifetime.

As an example, consider the case of a 4H-SiC MPS rectifier with a drift region doping concentration of 5×10^{14} cm^{-3} and thickness of 80 μm capable of supporting 10,000 volts in the reverse blocking mode. The variation of the on-state voltage drop with high-level lifetime in the drift region for this case as predicted by the analytical model is provided in Fig. 8.4 for the case of a Schottky barrier height of 2.95 eV. This high barrier height was chosen to allow the P-N junction to become forward biased and produce the desired injection of minority carriers into the drift region. It can be observed that the on-state voltage drop begins to increase when the lifetime is reduced below 10 μs. This is due to the relatively low diffusion length for holes in silicon carbide. The three components of the on-state voltage drop are also shown in the figure. The voltage drop at the Schottky contact is independent of the lifetime. Due to the large Schottky barrier height used in the analytical model, this contribution to the on-state voltage drop is large. The voltage drop at the N/N$^+$ interface increases slightly when the lifetime becomes larger than 1 μs but makes only a small contribution to the total on-state voltage drop. The most significant increase in the voltage drop occurs for the middle region when the lifetime is reduced below 10 μs. It is therefore necessary to achieve lifetime values approaching 10 μs to obtain a low on-state voltage drop in the 10 kV 4H-SiC MPS rectifier. The on-state voltage drop of the 10 kV 4H-SiC MPS rectifier is found to be just under 3 volts for a drift region lifetime of 10 μs. This is remarkable because it is less than the on-state voltage drop for a 4H-SiC P-i-N rectifier.

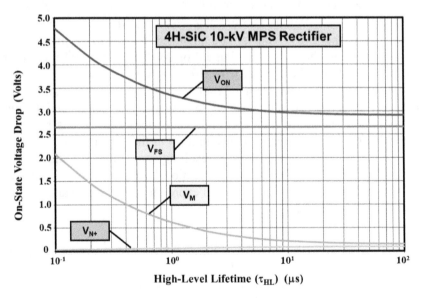

Fig. 8.4 Voltage drops in the 10 kV 4H-SiC MPS rectifier.

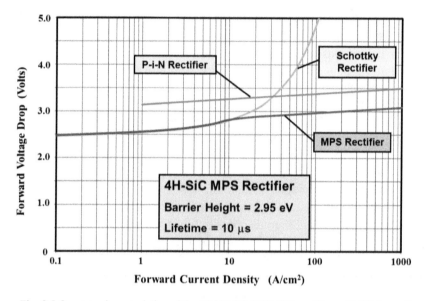

Fig. 8.5 On-state characteristics of the 10 kV 4H-SiC MPS rectifier with lifetime of
10 μs in the drift region.

The analytically modelled on-state characteristic for the 10 kV
4H-SiC MPS rectifier is shown in Fig. 8.5 for the case of a lifetime of
10 μs in the drift region. The on-state characteristics for the Schottky
rectifier and the P-iN rectifier are included for comparison. At low
current densities, the on-state voltage drop for the 4H-SiC MPS rectifier
resembles that for the Schottky rectifier, as observed in Fig. 8.5 for
current density up to 10 A/cm². At larger on-state current densities, the
injected carrier density in the drift region exceeds the background doping
concentration leading to high level injection conditions. In this mode of
operation, the injected carrier concentration in the drift region increases
in proportion to the current density resulting in a constant voltage drop
across the drift region for the analytical model without recombination in
the N⁺ end region. From Eq. [8.22], an expression for the on-state current
density can be derived:

$$J_{FC} = \sqrt{\frac{2qAT^2 D_n N_D}{p} \frac{(d/L_a)}{\tanh(2d/L_a)}} e^{-\frac{q(\phi_{BN}+V_M)}{2kT}} e^{\frac{qV_{ON}}{2kT}} \qquad [8.23]$$

The current flow is observed to become proportional to (qV_ON/2kT),
similar to that observed for the P-i-N rectifier under high-level injection

conditions, as observed in Fig. 8.5. It is worth pointing out that the on-state voltage drop for the MPS rectifier is lower than that for the P-i-N rectifier by about 0.4 V in this example.

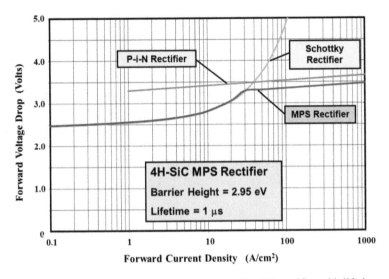

Fig. 8.6 On-state characteristics of the 10 kV 4H-SiC MPS rectifier with lifetime of 1 μs in the drift region.

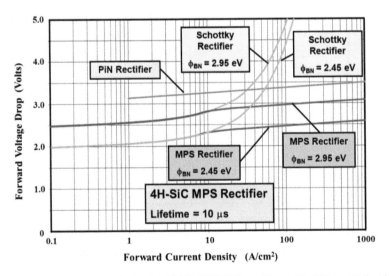

Fig. 8.7 On-state characteristics for 10 kV SiC MPS rectifiers with different Schottky barrier heights.

The impact of reducing the lifetime to 1 μs in the drift region on the on-state characteristics for the 10 kV 4H-SiC MPS rectifier is shown in Fig. 8.6. The on-state voltage drop for the 4H-SiC MPS rectifier increases by more than that for the P-i-N rectifier making its on-state voltage drop closer to that for the P-i-N rectifier. However, the stored charge in the 4H-SiC MPS rectifier is smaller making its switching performance superior to that for the P-i-N rectifier as shown later in the chapter.

The on-state voltage drop for the 4H-SiC MPS rectifier is also dependent on the barrier height of the Schottky metal. According to the analytical model in Eq. [8.22], a reduction in the on-state voltage drop of the silicon carbide MPS rectifier can be achieved by reducing the barrier height. This is illustrated in Fig. 8.7 where the characteristics of devices with two barrier heights are compared. The analytical model predicts a decrease in on-state voltage drop that is equal to the reduction of the barrier height.

8.3 Reverse Blocking

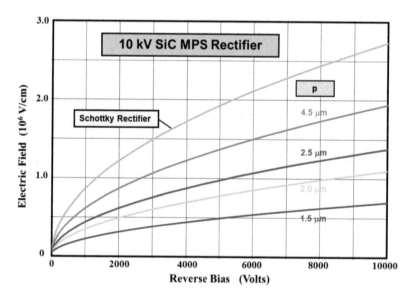

Fig. 8.8 Electric field at the Schottky contact for 10 kV 4H-SiC MPS Rectifiers with various values for cell pitch p.

The reverse blocking characteristics for the MPS rectifier can be modelled by using the same approach as described for the JBS rectifiers in chapter 6. The leakage current in the MPS rectifiers is low due to suppression of the Schottky barrier lowering and tunneling by the shielding provided to the Schottky contacts by the P-N junctions.

As an example, consider the case of the 10-kV SiC MPS rectifier discussed in the previous section with a junction depth of 1 μm and a P^+ region with dimension 's' of 1 μm. The doping concentration of N-drift region is 8 x 10^{14} cm^{-3}. The reduction of the electric field at the Schottky contact can be predicted by calculating values for alpha as given by Eq. [6.14]. The alpha values for a pitch (p) of 4.5, 2.5, 2.0, and 1.5 μm are 0.506, 0.256, 0.163, and 0.0655, respectively. The electric field at the middle of the Schottky contact in the SiC JBS rectifier structure obtained by using these values for alpha are plotted in Fig. 8.8. An alpha value of unity corresponds to the Schottky rectifier structure with no shielding. It can be observed that substantial reduction of the electric field at the Schottky contact is obtained as the pitch is reduced. For a pitch of 2.5 μm, the electric field at the Schottky contact is reduced to only 1.35 x 10^6 V/cm at 100 % of the breakdown voltage compared with 2.7 x 10^6 V/cm for the Schottky diode.

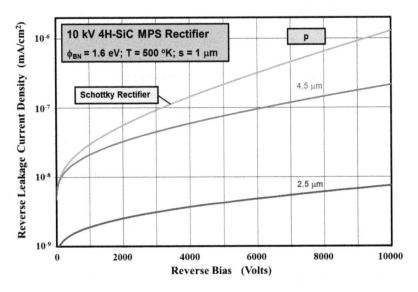

Fig. 8.9. Reverse leakage current for 10 kV 4H-SiC MPS Rectifiers with various values for cell pitch p.

The large Schottky barrier lowering for 4H-SiC, in conjunction with the thermionic field emission current and tunneling current, results in an increase in leakage current by 2-orders of magnitude when the voltage increases to the breakdown voltage in the case of the 10 kV Schottky rectifier as shown in Fig. 8.9. This increase is not as severe as in the case of diodes with lower blocking voltages (e.g. 1200 V) because of the smaller electric fields in the case of the 10 kV diode. The leakage current is greatly reduced by the shielding in the 4H-SiC JBS rectifier structure as shown in Fig. 8.9. For the 4H-SiC JBS rectifier structure with pitch of 2.5 μm and an implant window s of 1 μm, the Schottky contact area is reduced to 60 percent of the cell area. This results in a proportionate reduction of leakage current at low reverse bias voltages. More importantly, the suppression of the electric field at the Schottky contact, by the presence of the P-N junction, greatly reduces the rate of increase in leakage current with increasing reverse bias. The reverse leakage increases by only one order of magnitude when the reverse bias is increased to the breakdown voltage. This example demonstrates that a very large improvement in reverse power dissipation can be achieved with the 4H-SiC MPS structure.

8.4 Switching Performance

Power rectifiers operate for part of the time in the on-state when the bias applied to the anode is positive and for the rest of the time in the blocking state when the bias applied to the anode is negative. During each operating cycle, the diode must be rapidly switched between these states to minimize power losses. Much greater power losses are incurred when the diode switches from the on-state to the reverse blocking state than when it is turned on. The presence of a large concentration of free carriers in the drift region during on-state current flow is responsible for the low on-state voltage drop of high voltage P-i-N and MPS rectifiers. The stored charge within the drift region of the power rectifier produced by the on-state current flow must be removed before it is able to support high voltages. This produces a large reverse current for a short time duration. This phenomenon is referred to as *reverse recovery*. The peak reverse recovery current and reverse recovery time for the MPS rectifier are analyzed in this section.

8.4.1 Stored Charge

It is instructive to compare the stored charge in the 4H-SiC MPS rectifier structure with that in a 4H-SiC P-i-N rectifier because this provides a relative measure of the energy loss that will occur during the turn-off transient. In the case of the P-i-N rectifier, the drift region has almost a uniform (average) carrier concentration given by Eq. [7.3]. In contrast, the carrier distribution in the MPS rectifier has a triangular shape with a maximum value at the interface between the drift region and N^+ substrate.

The stored charge for the MPS rectifier is given by:

$$Q_S = \frac{1}{2} q p_M (2d) = \frac{q d L_a J_{FC}}{2 D_n} \tanh\left(\frac{2d}{L_a}\right) \qquad [8.24]$$

For a lifetime of 10 µs in the drift region, the maximum carrier concentration is found to be 6.3×10^{16} cm^{-3} at an on-state current density of 100 A/cm^2. The total stored charge in the drift region of the 4H-SiC MPS rectifier is then found to be 40 µC/cm^2. The stored charge in the 4H-SiC MPS rectifier is 2.5-times smaller than for the 4H-SiC P-i-N rectifier with a lifetime of 1 µs in the drift region. Moreover, the carrier concentration for the MPS rectifier is zero at the P-N junction during on-state operation. This allows the device to begin supporting a reverse voltage much faster than in the case of the P-i-N rectifier which shortens the reverse recovery process making the peak reverse recovery current of the MPS rectifier much smaller than that of the P-i-N rectifier.

8.4.2 Reverse Recovery: Highly Doped Drift Layer

As discussed previously in chapter 6, it is common-place to use power rectifiers with an *inductive load*. In this case the current reduces at a constant ramp rate ('a') when the rectifier is switched from the on-state to the blocking state as illustrated in Fig. 8.10. A large *peak reverse recovery current* (J_{PR}) occurs due to the stored charge followed by the reduction of the current to zero. In the case of the P-i-N rectifier, the device remains in its forward biased mode with a low on-state voltage drop even after the current reverses direction as illustrated in Fig. 7.6 due to the high minority carrier concentration at the junction in the initial on-state. Until the minority carrier concentration reduces to zero (at time t_1 in Fig. 7.6), the junction is unable to support a reverse blocking voltage.

The voltage across the diode then rapidly increases to the supply voltage with the rectifier operating in its reverse bias mode. The current flowing through the rectifier in the reverse direction reaches a maximum value (J_{PR}) (at time t_2 in Fig. 7.6) when the reverse voltage becomes equal to the reverse bias supply voltage (V_S).

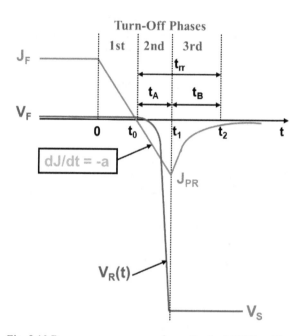

Fig. 8.10 Reverse recovery waveforms for the MPS Rectifier.

In the case of the MPS rectifier, the carrier concentration at the Schottky contact is zero in the on-state making the carrier concentration at the junction also close to zero. Consequently, this device is able to support a reverse blocking voltage immediately after the current reverses direction as illustrated in Fig. 8.10. The voltage across the diode then rapidly increases to the supply voltage with the rectifier operating in its reverse bias mode. The current flowing through the rectifier in the reverse direction reaches a maximum value (J_{PR}) at time t_1 in Fig. 8.10 when the reverse voltage becomes equal to the reverse bias supply voltage (V_S). After this time, the remaining stored charge in the drift region is removed by the diffusion of carriers into the N^+ cathode and the space charge region.

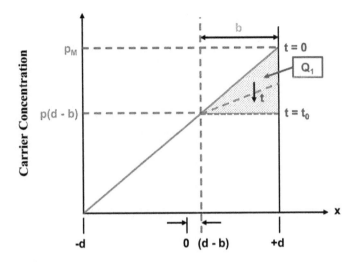

Fig. 8.11 Carrier distribution profiles in the MPS rectifier during the first phase of the reverse recovery process.

An analytical model for the reverse recovery process for the turn-off of the MPS rectifier under a constant rate of change of the current (*current ramp-rate*) can be created[2] by assuming that the initial concentration of the free carriers in the drift region can be linearized as illustrated in Fig. 8.11. As shown in the figure, the initial carrier distribution established by the on-state current flow is linear with the concentration increasing from zero at $x = -d$ to the concentration of p_M at $x = +d$:

$$p(x) = n(x) = \left(\frac{x+d}{2d}\right) p_M \qquad [8.25]$$

The hole and electron concentrations in the drift region can be assumed to be equal in the on-state and during the turn-off transient because of charge neutrality. In the case of finite lifetime in the drift region, the maximum carrier concentration p_M is given by Eq. [8.17].

During the first phase of the turn-off process, the current flow reduces from the on-state current density to zero. Since the current flow remains in the forward direction, the Schottky contact and the P-N junction remain in forward bias during this time interval. The hole and electron concentrations remain close to zero at the Schottky contact and the P-N junction to satisfy the boundary conditions at the Schottky contact (as in the case of the on-state analysis). However, electrons are extracted from the cathode side during this time interval. The current flowing at the cathode due to the diffusion of electrons is given by:

$$J = 2qD_n \left(\frac{dn}{dx}\right)_{x=+d}$$

[8.26]

If the carrier distribution during the first phase is linearized as illustrated in Fig. 8.11, the slope of the carrier profile near the cathode is given by:

$$\left(\frac{dn}{dx}\right)_{x=+d} = \left(\frac{dp}{dx}\right)_{x=+d} = \frac{J(t)}{2qD_n} = \frac{J_{ON} - at}{2qD_n}$$

[8.27]

where 'a' is the current ramp rate. At the end of the first phase (time t_0 in Fig. 8.10), the current becomes equal to zero leading to a zero slope for the carrier profile as illustrated in Fig. 8.11. As in the case of the turn-off analysis for the P-i-N rectifier, it will be assumed that the carrier profile pivots around a fixed point located at a distance 'b' from the interface between the drift region and the N^+ substrate[1].

The distance 'b' in Fig. 8.11 can be obtained by relating the charge Q_1 removed during the first phase to the current flow. Note that the x-values are defined from the center of the drift region as shown in Fig. 8.11. The hole concentration at x = (d - b) can be assumed to remain the same as during the on-state operation if recombination is neglected during the turn-off transient. This assumption is justified because the turn-off time is much shorter than the lifetime in the drift region. The change in the stored charge within the drift region during the first phase can be obtained from the purple shaded area, indicated by Q_1, in the figure:

$$Q_1 = \frac{qb}{2}\left[p_M - p(d-b)\right]$$

[8.28]

Using Eq. [8.25] for the initial carrier profile, the hole concentration at x = (d − b) is given by:

$$p(d-b) = \left(\frac{2d-b}{2d}\right)p_M$$

[8.29]

Substituting this into Eq. [8.28] yields:

$$Q_1 = \frac{qp_M}{4d}b^2$$

[8.30]

According to the charge control principle, this charge can be related the current flow during the turn-off transient from t = 0 to t = t_0:

$$Q_1 = \int_0^{t_0} J(t)\,dt = \int_0^{t_0} (J_{ON} - at)\,dt = J_{ON}t_0 - \frac{at_0^2}{2} = \frac{J_{ON}^2}{2a} \qquad [8.31]$$

because the time t_0 at which the current crosses zero is given by:

$$t_0 = \frac{J_F}{a} \qquad [8.32]$$

Combining the above relationships:

$$b = \sqrt{\frac{2d}{qap_M}} J_{ON} \qquad [8.33]$$

The distance 'b' can therefore be calculated from the on-state current density and the ramp rate 'a'.

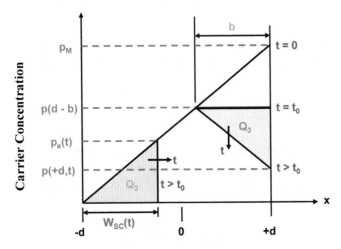

Fig. 8.12 Carrier distribution profiles in the MPS rectifier during the second phase of the reverse recovery process.

Once the current density becomes negative at the start of the second phase of the turn-off process, the MPS rectifier immediately begins to support a reverse voltage as illustrated in Fig. 8.10 with the formation of a space-charge region $W_{SC}(t)$ at the P^+/N junction that expands with time as illustrated in Fig. 8.12. The expansion of the space-charge region is achieved by extraction of the stored charge in the drift region in the vicinity of the junction resulting in the reverse current continuing to increase after time t_0. It can be assumed that the initial hole distribution in the vicinity of the junction does not change during the second phase of the turn-off process in the conductivity modulated portion of the N-base region because the lifetime in the drift region is much greater than the switching time interval. Consequently, the concentration of holes at the edge of the space-charge region (p_e) increases during the turn-off process as the space-charge width increases:

$$p_e(t) = p_M \left[\frac{W_{SC}(t)}{2d} \right]$$ [8.34]

According to the charge-control principle, the charge removed by the expansion of the space-charge layer must equal the charge removed due to collector current flow:

$$J(t) = q p_e(t) \frac{dW_{SC}(t)}{dt} = q p_M \left[\frac{W_{SC}(t)}{2d} \right] \frac{dW_{SC}(t)}{dt}$$ [8.35]

by using Eq. [8.34]. The collector current density increases linearly at the ramp rate during the second phase of the turn-off process. Consequently:

$$q p_M \left[\frac{W_{SC}(t)}{2d} \right] \frac{dW_{SC}(t)}{dt} = at$$ [8.36]

where 'a' is the ramp rate. Integrating this equation and applying the boundary condition of zero width for the space-charge layer at time zero provides the solution for the evolution of the space-charge region width with time:

$$W_{SC}(t) = \sqrt{\frac{2da}{q p_M}} t$$ [8.37]

According to this analysis, the space-charge layer expands towards the right-hand-side at a constant rate as indicated by the horizontal time arrow in Fig. 8.12.

The collector voltage supported by the MPS rectifier structure is related to the space charge layer width by:

$$V_R(t) = \frac{q(N_D + p_{SC})W_{SC}^2(t)}{2\varepsilon_S} = \left(\frac{N_D + p_{SC}}{p_M}\right)\left(\frac{da}{\varepsilon_S}\right)t^2 \qquad [8.38]$$

where p_{SC} is the hole concentration in the space-charge region. This indicates a rapid rise in voltage as a square of the time after the current crosses zero. The hole concentration in the space-charge layer (p_{SC}) can be related to the collector current density under the assumption that the carriers are moving at the saturated drift velocity for holes in the space-charge layer:

$$p_{SC}(t) = \frac{J_R(t)}{qv_{sat,p}} \qquad [8.39]$$

In the MPS rectifier, the hole concentration in the space-charge region increases during the voltage rise-time because the current density is increasing.

The end of the second phase of the turn-off process occurs when the collector voltages reaches the reverse bias supply voltage (V_S). This time interval (t_A in Fig. 8.10) can be obtained by making the reverse bias voltage equal to the supply voltage in Eq. [8.38]:

$$t_A = \sqrt{\frac{\varepsilon_S p_M V_S}{ad(N_D + p_{SC})}} \qquad [8.40]$$

According to the analytical model, the voltage rise-time is proportional to the square root of the reverse bias supply voltage and inversely proportional to square root of the ramp time.

The width of the space-charge layer at the end of the voltage transient can be obtained by using the collector supply voltage:

$$W_{SC}(t_A) = \sqrt{\frac{2\varepsilon_S V_{CS}}{q(N_D + p_{SC})}} \qquad [8.41]$$

The width of the space-charge layer at the end of the second phase depends upon the reverse bias supply voltage and the peak reverse recovery current (via p_{SC}).

Since the end of the second phase occurs when the reverse bias across the MPS rectifier becomes equal to the supply voltage (V_S):

$$t_1 = t_0 + t_A = t_0 + \sqrt{\frac{\varepsilon_S p_M V_S}{ad(N_D + p_{SC})}} \qquad [8.42]$$

The hole concentration (p_{SC}) in the space charge layer is a function of time because of the increasing reverse current density. However, its magnitude is typically much smaller than the doping concentration (N_D) in the drift region for 4H-SiC devices. Consequently, the time (t_1) at which the peak reverse recovery current occurs can be computed using:

$$t_1 = \frac{J_{ON}}{a} + \sqrt{\frac{\varepsilon_S p_M V_S}{ad N_D}} \qquad [8.43]$$

This expression indicates that the time for the end of the second phase is reduced with increasing ramp rate and increased with increasing reverse bias supply voltage. The time taken to reach the peak reverse recovery current after the current crosses zero is defined in Fig. 8.10 as t_A. Using this value of time, the peak reverse recovery current can be obtained:

$$J_{PR} = at_A = \sqrt{\frac{a\varepsilon_S p_M V_S}{d(N_D + p_{SC})}} \qquad [8.44]$$

Based upon this expression, it can be concluded that the peak reverse recovery current will increase with increasing ramp rate and increasing reverse bias supply voltage.

Consider the case of a 10 kV 4H-SiC MPS rectifier that is turned off from an on-state current density of 200 A/cm^2 at a ramp rate of 3 x 10^8 A/cm^2-s. It has a drift region thickness of 80 μm, doping concentration of 8 x 10^{14} cm^{-3}, and high-level lifetime of 10 μs. During the reverse recovery transient, the space charge layer width expands to 80 μm when the reverse voltage reaches 5167 V. Consequently, there is no storage charge left in the drift region when the voltage reaches the supply voltage of 6000 V at 1.45 μs as shown in Fig. 8.14. The diode current then rapidly drops to zero as shown in Fig. 8.15. The peak reverse recovery current density (JPR) is 235 A/cm^2, which is close to the on-state current density.

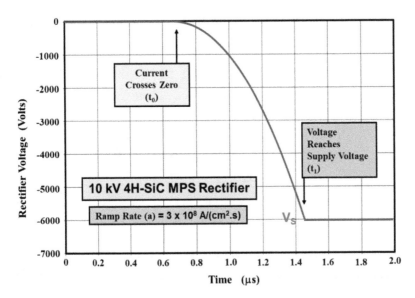

Fig. 8.14 Analytically calculated reverse recovery voltage waveform for the 10 kV
4H-SiC MPS rectifier structure.

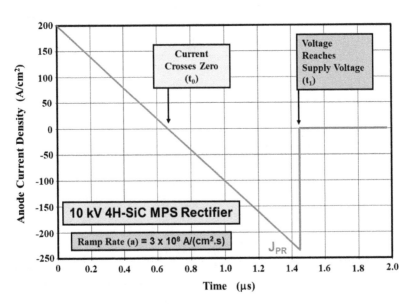

Fig. 8.15 Analytically calculated reverse recovery current waveform for the 10 kV
4H-SiC MPS rectifier structure.

8.4.3 Reverse Recovery: Lightly Doped Drift Layer

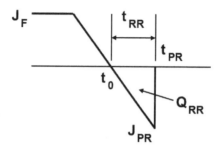

Fig. 8.16 Reverse recovery waveform for the 10 kV 4H-SiC MPS rectifier structure with lightly doped drift layer.

As discussed in chapter 7 for the 4H-SiC P-i-N rectifier, all the stored charge in the drift region can be removed by the space charge layer well before the voltage reaches the supply voltage if the doping concentration in the drift region is small. This will also occurs for the 4H-SiC MPS rectifier. A simple model for the turn-off can be created for this case by assuming that the charge removed during the reverse recovery is equal to the stored charge. In this model, the current abruptly drops to zero after it reaches the peak value as shown in Fig. 8.16 because all the stored charge has been removed at this time.

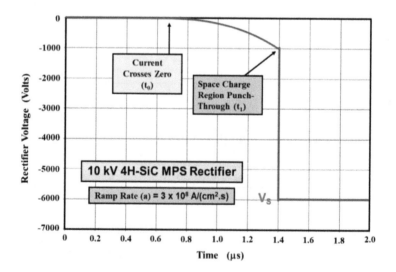

Fig. 8.17 Analytically calculated reverse recovery voltage waveform for the 10 kV 4H-SiC MPS rectifier structure with low drift region doping.

The charge removed by the reverse recovery current flow is given by:

$$Q_{RR} = \frac{1}{2} J_{PR} t_{RR} = \frac{1}{2} a t_{RR}^2 \qquad [8.45]$$

Equating this to the stored charge in the drift region of the MPS rectifier is given by Eq. [8.24] yields:

$$t_{RR} = \sqrt{\frac{2 q d p_M}{a}} = \sqrt{\frac{d L_a J_{FC}}{a D_n} \tanh\left(\frac{2d}{L_a}\right)} \qquad [8.46]$$

and

$$J_{PR} = \sqrt{2 q a d p_M} = \sqrt{\frac{a d L_a J_{FC}}{D_n} \tanh\left(\frac{2d}{L_a}\right)} \qquad [8.47]$$

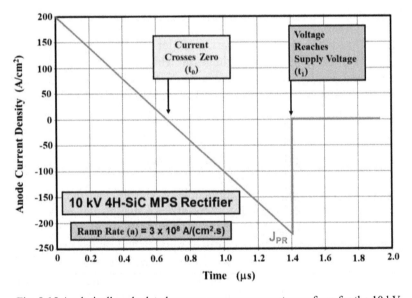

Fig. 8.15 Analytically calculated reverse recovery current waveform for the 10 kV 4H-SiC MPS rectifier structure with low drift region doping.

The reverse recovery waveforms for the 10 kV 4H-SiC MPS rectifier with a low drift region doping concentration of 1×10^{14} cm^{-3} with a lifetime of 10 μs are shown in Fig. 8.17 and 8.18. A ramp rate of 3×10^8 A/cm^2-s was used. In the MPS rectifier, the space charge region now spans the entire drift region at a low reverse bias of 1000 volts. The voltage then rapidly increases to the supply voltage (V_S) of 6000 V. The time t_{RR} at which this occurs is 1.4 μs according to Eq. [8.46] and the peak reverse recovery current J_{PR} calculated using Eq. [8.47] is 220 A/cm^2.

8.5 4H-SiC MPS Rectifier with Low Schottky Barrier Height

In the previous sections, a large barrier height of 2.95 eV was used to illustrate the operating principles of the 4H-SiC MPS rectifier structure. In practice, the metals used as Schottky contacts for 4H-SiC SiC have a barrier height of 1.9 eV at most (reported for Platinum). When the barrier height is reduced, it becomes more difficult to forward bias the P-N junction in the MPS rectifier suppressing the injection of holes into the drift region. This produces a snap-back in the on-state characteristics[2]. This problem can be overcome by making the width of the Schottky contact very small in the 4H-SiC MPS rectifier structure. With a sufficiently small width, the P-N junction depletion width can be sufficient to create a potential barrier under the Schottky contact even at zero bias. This raises the voltage at which current begins to flow through the Schottky contact which is equivalent to increasing the barrier height. Excellent on-state characteristics can be derived by using this design approach[2].

8.6 4H-SiC MPS Rectifier: Experimental Results

Since the MPS concept is only applicable to 4H-SiC rectifiers with very high blocking voltage capability, there are not many relevant papers in the literature on the device. However, 4H-SiC MPS rectifiers with 10-kV blocking voltage capability were designed and fabricated at the FREEDM Systems Center using a drift region with doping concentration of 2.7 x 10^{14} cm^{-3} and thickness of 100 μm^3. P-i-N and JBS rectifiers were simultaneously fabricated for comparison. The JBS rectifiers had a large spacing of 4 μm between the P-N junctions compared with only 2 μm for the MPS rectifiers. The MPS rectifiers had two designs: a linear cell and a hexagonal cell. The on-state voltage drop for the linear MPS design was very close to that for the P-i-N rectifier at 125 °C with a value of 4.2 V at an on-state current density of 30 A/cm^2. In comparison, the JBS rectifier had a much higher on-state voltage drop of 8.7 V. The leakage current for the JBS rectifier was found to be very high, while that for the MPS rectifiers was close to that for P-i-N rectifiers. The reverse recovery charge for the MPS was found to be 60 % of that measured for the P-i-N rectifier and only 10 % greater than that for the JBS rectifier. These results demonstrate that the 10-kV 4H-SiC MPS rectifier provides a significantly better switching performance when compared with P-i-N rectifiers without higher on-state voltage drop.

The MPS mode of operation has been observed in 4H-SiC JBS rectifiers with low blocking voltages under surge current levels and at elevated temperatures. It has been found that the P-N junctions in the JBS rectifiers begin to inject carriers into the drift region at surge current levels (50x of the on-state current density). This reduces their on-state voltage drop when compared with Schottky rectifiers greatly reducing the power dissipation[4]. The Schottky diodes were destroyed while the MPS rectifiers could survive the surge current pulse.

The stored charge in 10 kV 4H-SiC MPS rectifiers has been shown to increase at a slower pace with increasing temperature compared with P-i-N rectifiers[5] while its on-state voltage drop increased at the same pace as the P-i-N rectifier. Consequently, the trade-off curve between on-state voltage drop and reverse recovery charge became even superior with increasing temperature.

8.7 Summary

The physics of operation of the MPS rectifier has been analyzed in this chapter. Analytical expressions have been derived for the on-state and blocking state, as well as the reverse recovery transients. At on-state current levels, the injected minority carrier density in the drift region exceeds the relatively low doping concentration required to achieve high breakdown voltages. This high level injection in the drift region modulates its conductivity producing a reduction in the on-state voltage drop. Unlike the P-i-N rectifier, the carrier concentration at the junction is close to zero with a maximum value at the interface between the drift region and the N^+ cathode region. The on-state voltage drop for the MPS rectifier can be smaller than that for the P-i-N rectifier due to the presence of the Schottky contact with a lower barrier for current flow when compared with the P-N junction.

The MPS rectifier can support a large voltage in the reverse blocking mode by appropriate choice of the doping concentration and thickness of the drift region. The leakage current in the reverse direction is larger than that for the P-i-N rectifier due to the thermionic current across the Schottky contact. However, this current can be made small by using a large Schottky barrier height and a small area for the Schottky contact.

As in the case of the P-i-N rectifier, the switching of the MPS rectifier from the on-state to the reverse blocking state is accompanied by a significant current flow in the reverse direction. However, the peak reverse recovery current and reverse recovery time are smaller than those observed in the P-i-N rectifier. The reverse recovery charge for the MPS rectifier is much smaller than that for the P-i-N rectifier. This reduces switching losses in the rectifier and the switches in the power circuits. The performance of the MPS rectifier relative to the P-i-N rectifier has been found to improve with increasing temperature.

Since a lifetime control process has not matured for silicon carbide bipolar devices, the MPS structure offers an elegant approach to producing high voltage power rectifiers with low on-state voltage as well as much smaller reverse recovery power losses. In addition, the current density flowing through the P-N junction in the silicon carbide MPS rectifier is low because it is a small fraction of on-state current density. This reduced current density at the P-N junction in the silicon carbide MPS rectifier structure suppresses the highly undesirable increase in on-state voltage drop observed during prolonged on-state operation at high current density of silicon carbide P-i-N rectifiers[6].

References

[1] B. J. Baliga, "Analysis of the High-Voltage Merged P-i-N/Schottky (MPS) Rectifier", IEEE Electron Device Letters, Vol. EDL-8, pp. 407-409, 1987.

[2] B. J. Baliga, "Advanced Power Rectifier Concepts", Chapter 7, Springer-Science, New York, 2009.

[3] E. R. Van Brunt, "Development of Optimal 4H-SiC Bipolar Power Diodes for High Voltage High-Frequency Applications", NCSU Ph.D. Thesis, 2012.

[4] B. Heinze, et al, "Surge Current Ruggedness of Silicon Carbide Schottky and Merged-PiN-Schottky Diodes" IEEE International Symposium on Power Semiconductor Devices and ICs, Paper WB-P-6, pp. 245-248, 2008.

[5] Y. Jiang, et al, "10kV 4H-SiC MPS Diodes for High Temperature Application", IEEE International Symposium on Power Semiconductor Devices and ICs, pp. 43-46, 2016.

[6] A. Hefner, et al, "Recent Advances in High-Voltage, High-Frequency, Silicon-Carbide Power Devices", IEEE 41st Industrial Application Society Conference, Vol. 1, pp. 330-337, 2006.

Chapter 9

Junction Field Effect Transistors

The main advantage of wide band gap semiconductor based unipolar power devices is the very low specific on-resistance of the drift region even when the device is designed to support large voltages. This favors the development of high voltage unipolar devices which have much superior switching speed than silicon bipolar devices such as IGBTs. At early stages of SiC power device development, the inversion layer mobility in the channel of the power MOSFET structure was found to be very low precluding their development. The *Junction Field Effect Transistor (JFET)* and the *Metal Semiconductor Field Effect Transistor (MESFET)* fabricated from SiC were therefore considered potential candidates as unipolar switches for power applications. These structures have also been called *Static Induction Transistors*[1]. In the case of silicon, the maximum breakdown voltage of JFETs was limited by the increase in the resistance of the drift region[2]. This limitation does not apply to silicon carbide due to the much larger doping concentration within the drift region for high voltage structures. However, as in the case of silicon structures, the normally-on behavior of the high voltage JFETs has been found to be a serious impediment to circuit applications. When powering up any electronic system, it is impossible to ensure that the gate voltage required to block current flow in the JFET is provided to the structure prior to the incidence of the drain voltage on the structure. This situation can result in shoot-through currents between the power rails resulting in destructive failure of the devices. This has discouraged the use of normally-on devices in power electronic applications.

The invention of the *Baliga Pair* circuit configuration[3,4,5] enabled achieving a normally-off power switch function with a high speed integral diode that is ideally suitable for H-bridge applications. The Baliga-Pair utilizes a high voltage normally-on silicon carbide JFET or MESFET with a low blocking voltage silicon power MOSFET connected in series with its source terminal to achieve a normally-off function. This configuration is discussed in detail in the next chapter because of commercial products that utilize the idea.

This chapter reviews the basic principles of operation of the vertical Junction (or Metal-Semiconductor) Field Effect Transistor. These structures must be designed to deplete the channel region by application of a reverse bias voltage to the gate-source junction. To prevent current flow through the device, a potential barrier for electron transport must be created in the channel to suppress electron transport even under large drain bias voltages. Concurrently, the channel must remain un-depleted (preferably at zero gate bias) to allow on-state current flow with low on-state resistance. Unique issues that relate to the wide band gap of silicon carbide must be given special consideration. Experimental results on relevant structures are provided to define the state of the development effort on high voltage silicon carbide JFETs and MESFETs.

9.1 Trench Junction (Metal-Semiconductor) FET Structure

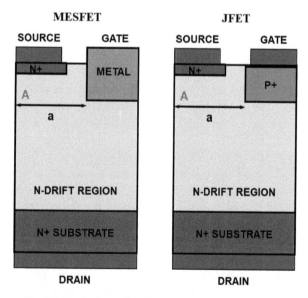

Fig. 9.1 Vertical trench MESFET and JFET structures.

The basic structure of the vertical trench Junction Field Effect Transistor (JFET) and the trench Metal-Semiconductor Field Effect Transistor

(MESFET) are shown in Fig. 9.1. The structures contain a drift region (usually N-type) between the drain and the source regions designed to support the desired maximum operating voltage. As discussed in detail later in the chapter, the drift region must be capable of supporting the sum of the drain bias and the reverse gate bias potentials without undergoing breakdown. This increases the specific on-resistance of the drift region for a particular drain blocking voltage capability. This increase can be kept to a minimum by achieving high blocking gain, defined as the ratio of the drain to gate voltage in the blocking mode.

To prevent current flow under forward blocking conditions, a gate region must be incorporated in the drift region. A P-N junction gate region is used for the JFET structure and a Schottky (metal-semiconductor) contact is used for the MESFET structure. In order to produce a strong potential barrier for suppressing the transport of electrons between the drain and the source in the blocking state, it is preferable to create a gate with vertical sidewalls. For the JFET structure, this can be achieved by utilizing multiple P-type ion implants with increasing energy using a common mask edge. For the MESFET structure, a trench is etched with vertical sidewalls followed by the selective deposition of the Schottky barrier gate metal to fill the trench.

When a negative bias is applied to the gate electrode with source as reference terminal, a depletion layer extends from the gate into the drift region. With sufficient gate bias, the entire space between the gate regions becomes depleted. The gate bias required to deplete the space between the gate regions is referred to as the *pinch-off voltage*. At a gate bias above the pinch-off voltage, a potential barrier forms under the source region at location A. This barrier suppresses the transport of electrons between the drain and the source. However, the potential barrier is reduced with application of the drain bias. Consequently, as the drain bias increases, drain current flow commences at voltages well below the breakdown voltage capability of the drift region. It is possible to support a larger drain bias voltage before the observation of drain current flow with a larger gate bias because a larger potential barrier is created.

The spacing between the gate regions is usually designed to be more than twice the zero bias depletion width. Consequently, an un-depleted portion of the drift region remains under the source region at zero gate bias. Current flow between the drain and source occurs through this region with the amount limited by the resistance of the channel region (between the gates) and the drift region below the gate. A large un-depleted region is favored for reducing the on-resistance but this reduces the magnitude of the potential barrier when the device operates in the forward blocking mode. Thus, a trade-off between the on-state resistance and blocking characteristics must be made when designing these structures.

9.1.1 Forward Blocking

Since the operating principles for the MESFET and JFET structures are similar, these names will be used interchangeably in this chapter. In a normally-on device structure, an un-depleted portion of the channel exists at zero gate bias. Drain current flow can therefore occur via this un-depleted region at zero gate bias. The forward blocking capability in the JFET structure is achieved by creating a potential barrier in the channel between the gate regions by applying a reverse bias to the gate region. At a gate bias above the pinch-off voltage, the channel becomes completely depleted. As the gate bias is increased above the pinch-off voltage, the potential barrier increases in magnitude. Current transport between the drain and source is suppressed because electrons must overcome the potential barrier. As the drain voltage is increased, the potential barrier reduces allowing injection of electrons over it.

    An exponential increase in the drain current is observed in the JFET structure with increasing drain bias with 'triode-like' characteristics. This behavior can be described by[6]:

$$J_D = \frac{qD_nN_D}{L}\sqrt{\frac{q}{\pi kT}(\alpha V_G - \beta V_D)}\exp\left\{-\left[\frac{q}{kT}(\alpha V_G - \beta V_D)\right]\right\} \quad \text{[9.1]}$$

where α and β are constants that depend upon the gate geometry. In this equation, D_n is the diffusion coefficient for electrons, N_D is the doping concentration in the drift region, L is the gate length (in the direction of current flow), q is the charge of the electron, k is Boltzmann's constant, T is the absolute temperature, V_G is the gate bias voltage and V_D is the drain bias voltage. The exponential variation of drain current predicted by Eq. [9.1] with variation of gate and drain bias has been observed in silicon vertical channel JFETs[7].

    The JFET structure can exhibit a normally-off behavior up to a limited drain voltage if the space between the gate regions in the JFET structure is reduced so that it becomes completely depleted by the zero bias depletion width. This type of design will exhibit purely triode-like characteristics. On the other hand, if the space between the gate regions is larger than the maximum depletion width at breakdown for the drift region, the structure will exhibit purely pentode-like characteristics. If the space between the gate regions falls between these extremes, the device will exhibit a mixed triode-pentode like characteristics. High voltage normally-on JFETs are usually designed to operate in this mixed triode-pentode mode to obtain a good compromise between low on-state resistance and high blocking voltage capability.

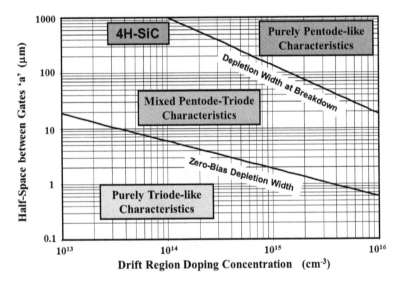

Fig. 9.2 Design space for high voltage 4H-SiC JFETs.

The design space for vertical high voltage JFETs is bounded by the depletion widths at breakdown and the zero-bias depletion width. These boundaries are shown in Fig. 9.2 for the case of 4H-SiC devices. For any given doping concentration, a much larger spacing between the gates is required for 4H-SiC devices than silicon devices due to the bigger depletion width at breakdown. In general, a greater latitude exists for the design of 4H-SiC devices to optimize the characteristics.

A good compromise between achieving a low on-state resistance and a good blocking voltage capability for high voltage JFETs requires designing the channel to operate in the mixed pentode-triode regime indicated in Fig. 9.2. At low drain current levels and high drain voltages, these devices exhibit triode-like characteristics. In this mode, it is useful to define a DC blocking gain (G_{DC}) as the ratio of the drain voltage to the gate voltage at a specified leakage current level. A differential blocking gain (G_{AC}) can also be defined as the increase in drain voltage, at a specified leakage current level, for an increase in the gate voltage by 1 volt. From Eq. [9.1], it can be shown that:

$$G_{AC} = \frac{dV_D}{dV_G} = \frac{\alpha}{\beta}$$

[9.2]

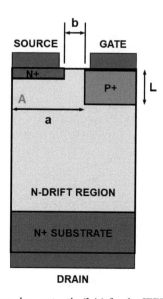

Fig. 9.3 Channel aspect ratio (L/a) for the JFET structures.

The parameters α and β are dependent upon the channel aspect ratio. The channel aspect ratio is defined as the ratio of the length of the gate (dimension 'L' in Fig. 9.3) in the direction of current flow and the space between the gate regions (dimension 'a' in Fig. 9.3). A large aspect ratio favors obtaining a high blocking gain, which is beneficial for reducing the gate voltage required to block high drain voltages. Theoretical analysis[8] and empirical observations[9] on high voltage silicon JFETs indicate that the blocking gain can be described by:

$$G_{DC} = \frac{V_D}{V_G} = A.\exp\left(B\frac{L}{a} \right)$$

[9.3]

where A and B are constants. Since the gate junction must support the sum of the negative gate bias voltage and the applied positive drain voltage, the drift region parameters must be chosen to account for the finite blocking gain.

The largest drain voltage that can be supported by the JFET structure before the on-set of significant current flow is determined by several factors. Firstly, it is limited by the intrinsic breakdown voltage capability of the drift region as determined by the doping concentration and thickness. The breakdown voltage can be obtained by using the graphs and equations provided in chapter 3. Secondly, the maximum drain voltage that can be supported without significant current flow can be limited by the applied gate bias and the blocking gain of the structure. In addition, the largest gate bias that can be applied is limited by the on-set of breakdown between the gate and the source regions. The break-down voltage between the gate and the source regions is determined by the depletion layer punch-through from the gate junction to the highly doped N^+ source region. Since the space between these regions must be kept small in order to obtain a high channel aspect ratio leading to high blocking gain, the electric field between the gate and source regions can be assumed to be uniform. Under this approximation, the gate-source breakdown voltage can be calculated using:

$$BV_{GS} = b . E_C \qquad [9.4]$$

where 'b' is the space between the gate and the source as shown in Fig. 9.3 and E_C is the critical electric field for breakdown. Fortunately, the critical electric field for breakdown in 4H-SiC is large allowing high gate-source breakdown voltages in spite of using small gate-source spacing.

9.1.2 On-State Resistance

The on-state current flow pattern at low drain bias voltages for the normally-on JFET design with mixed Pentode-Triode mode of operation is indicated in Fig. 9.4 by the green shaded area. The current flows from the source through a uniform cross section between the gate regions with a width (d) determined by the space between the gate regions (a) and the zero-bias depletion width (W_0). The current then spreads at a 45 degree angle into the drift region to a depth of 's' under the gate region, and then becomes uniform throughout the cross-section. This current flow pattern can be used to model the on-state resistance:

$$R_{on,sp} = \rho_D \left(L + W_0 \right) \left(\frac{p}{d} \right) + \rho_D \left(\frac{p(s+W_0)}{p-2d} \right) \ln \left(\frac{p}{2d} \right)$$
$$+ \rho_D \left(t - s \right)$$

[9.5]

where W_0 is the zero bias depletion width.

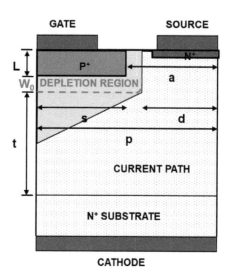

Fig. 9.4 On-state current flow pattern in the 4H-SiC JFET structure.

The specific on-resistance of the JFET can be much larger than the ideal specific on-resistance for any particular blocking voltage capability of the JFET structure. Firstly, this is because the drift region must support the sum of the gate and drain bias voltages. Secondly, it is increased by the contributions from the channel region and the spreading resistance. These contributions become more significant as the space between the gates is reduced. Thus, a compromise must be made between obtaining a low specific on-state resistance and a high blocking gain.

When a negative gate voltage is applied to reverse bias the gate junction, the depletion region extends further into the channel producing an increase in the on-resistance. Further, if the drain voltage becomes comparable to the gate bias voltage, the depletion width at the bottom of the channel on the drain side becomes larger (as determined by V_{GS} plus V_{DS}). This alters the current flow pattern as illustrated in Fig. 9.5. Under the assumption of a field independent mobility and by using the gradual channel approximation, the drain current is determined by[2]:

$$I_D = 2a\rho_D \frac{Z}{L}\left\{ V_{Dch} - \frac{2}{3a}\left(\frac{2\varepsilon_S}{qN_D}\right)^{1/2}\left[\left(V_{Dch}+V_G+V_{bi}\right)^{3/2} - \left(V_G+V_{bi}\right)^{3/2}\right]\right\}$$

[9.6]

where Z is the length of the device in the direction orthogonal to the cross-section, and V_{Dch} is the drain voltage at the bottom edge of the channel.

The basic I-V characteristics determined by this equation can be described using three segments. In the first segment, the drain voltage is much smaller than the gate bias voltage. This is referred to as the *linear region* because the drain current increases proportionally with the drain voltage. In this case, the channel resistance increases with reverse gate voltage as given by:

$$R_{ch} = \rho_D \frac{L}{2Z}\left[a - \sqrt{\frac{2\varepsilon_S}{qN_D}\left(V_{GS}+V_{bi}\right)}\right]$$

[9.7]

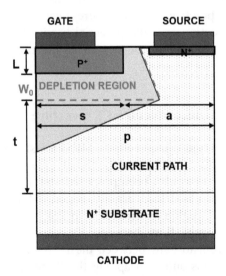

Fig. 9.5 Current flow pattern at larger V_{DS} for the JFET structure.

In the second segment, the drain voltage is comparable to the gate voltage. This produces a non-linear characteristic with the resistance increasing with increasing drain bias. Eventually, the entire space between the gate regions becomes depleted at a certain drain bias. This condition is described by:

$$V_P = \left(V_{Dch} + V_{GS} + V_{bi}\right) = \frac{qN_Da^2}{2\varepsilon_S} \qquad [9.8]$$

with V_P defined as the pinch-off voltage. The drain voltage, at which channel pinch-off occurs, decreases linearly with increasing gate voltage.

In the third segment, the drain current becomes constant because the channel is completely pinched off. The saturated drain current is given by[2]:

$$I_D = 2a\rho_D \frac{Z}{L}\left\{\frac{qN_Da^2}{6\varepsilon_S} - \left(V_{GS} + V_{bi}\right) + \frac{2}{3a}\left(\frac{2\varepsilon_S}{qN_D}\right)^{1/2}\left[\left(V_G + V_{bi}\right)^{3/2}\right]\right\}$$

$$[9.9]$$

A family of drain current-voltage curves is formed with the saturated drain current decreasing with increasing negative gate voltage. Although these equations predict a constant drain current beyond the channel pinch-off point, in practice, the drain current can increase after pinch-off due to electron injection over the potential barrier formed at the bottom of the channel. This phenomenon leads to the mixed Pentode-Triode characteristics.

9.2 Planar Metal-Semiconductor FET Structure

An elegant high voltage silicon carbide MESFET structure that utilizes a planar gate architecture (in place of the trench gate structure discussed in the previous section) has also been proposed and demonstrated[10]. In this device structure, a sub-surface heavily doped P-type region is placed below the N+ source region as illustrated in Fig. 9.6. The P+ region acts as a barrier to current flow between the source and drain regions restricting the current to gaps between the P+ regions. A gate region is placed over these gaps and overlapping the P+ region to enable control over the transport of current between the drain and source regions. In general, the gate can be constructed as a Metal-Semiconductor contact (to form a MESFET structure), a P-N Junction (to form a JFET structure) or as a Metal-Oxide-Semiconductor sandwich (to form a MOSFET structure). The MESFET structure will be discussed in detail in this section. The operation of the JFET structure is similar but requires taking into account the larger built-in potential of the gate P-N junction. The MOSFET structure is discussed in a subsequent chapter.

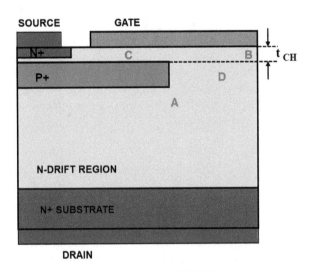

Fig. 9.6 The planar gate MESFET structure.

The sub-surface P$^+$ region in the planar gate MESFET structure can be either connected to the gate or to the source region. If the P$^+$ region is electrically connected to the gate electrode, it collaborates with the metal-semiconductor contact to constrict current flow from the source to the drain region. However, when the gate is reverse biased, a low gate-source breakdown voltage can occur due to the close vertical proximity of the N$^+$ source region and the sub-surface P$^+$ region. It is therefore preferable to connect the P$^+$ region to the source electrode. During the fabrication of the MESFET structure, this can be achieved by interruption of the N$^+$ region in the orthogonal direction to the cross-section shown in Fig. 9.6 and placing a P$^+$ contact region from the surface down to the sub-surface P$^+$ region in these gaps. This approach avoids a potential breakdown problem between the N$^+$ source and P$^+$ sub-surface regions. However, the breakdown voltage between the gate and source electrodes can now occur due to depletion region reach-through from the gate contact to the underlying P$^+$ region. Fortunately, relatively small reverse gate bias voltages are required in the planar MESFET to achieve high drain blocking voltages. The low gate-source breakdown voltage as a result of reach-through is therefore not a serious limitation with proper design of the structure.

The sub-surface P$^+$ region in the planar MESFET structure can be created by using ion-implantation of boron or aluminum with the appropriate energy[11]. Alternately, the sub-surface P$^+$ region can be formed by growth of an N-type epitaxial layer over a P$^+$ region formed in the drift region by lower energy ion-implantation[12]. In either case, the thickness of the N-type region between the gate and the sub-surface P$^+$ region must be sufficient to prevent complete depletion at zero gate bias. The doping concentration of the N-type region located between the gate and the sub-surface P$^+$ region can be increased above that for the N-type drift region if necessary by ion-implantation of nitrogen or during its epitaxial growth.

9.2.1 Forward Blocking

As previously described in this chapter, the forward blocking regime of operation for the MESFET structure is achieved by creating a potential barrier for transport of electrons between the source and drain region by the application of a reverse gate bias. In the planar MESFET structure, this potential barrier is formed in the channel (at location 'C' shown in Fig. 9.6). If the thickness of the channel (shown as t_{CH} in Fig. 9.6) is narrow, a potential barrier can be formed with relatively low reverse gate bias voltages. In addition, the planar MESFET structure contains a second JFET region formed between the adjacent P$^+$ regions (at location 'D' shown in Fig. 9.6). When the drain bias exceeds the pinch-off voltage for this JFET region, the potential at the surface under the gate becomes isolated from the potential applied at the drain electrode. Consequently, the channel potential barrier is shielded from the drain voltage enabling the support of high drain voltages without the on-set of drain current flow. These features favor producing a very high blocking gain with low reverse gate bias voltages.

9.2.2 On-State Resistance

The planar MESFET can be designed to contain an un-depleted channel region at zero gate bias. Current can then flow between the source and drain regions through the channel and the gap between the P$^+$ regions down to the N-type drift region. The resistance of these regions must be included in the analysis of the total on-state resistance of the structure.

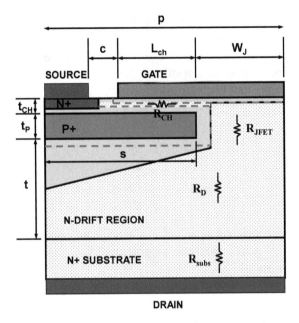

Fig. 9.7 Resistances in a planar gate MESFET structure.

The total specific on-resistance is given by:

$$R_{on,sp} = R_{CH} + R_{JFET} + R_D + R_{subs} \qquad [9.10]$$

where R_{CH} is the channel resistance, R_{JFET} is the resistance of the JFET region, R_D is the resistance of the drift region after taking into account current spreading from the JFET region, and R_{subs} is the resistance of the N^+ substrate. These resistances can be analytically modeled by using the current flow pattern indicated by the green shaded regions in Fig. 9.7. In this figure, the depletion region boundaries have also been shown using red dashed lines. The drain current flows through a channel region with a small cross-section before entering the JFET region. The current spreads into the drift region from the JFET region at a 45 degree angle and then becomes uniform. The dimension 'c' in Fig. 9.7 is decided by alignment tolerances used during device fabrication. A typical value of 0.5 μm has been assumed for the analysis in this chapter.

The channel resistance is given by:

$$R_{CH} = \frac{\rho_D (L_{CH} + \alpha W_P) p}{(t_{CH} - W_G - W_P)} \qquad [9.11]$$

where t_{CH} and L_{CH} are the channel thickness and length as shown in Fig. 7.28. In this equation, α is a factor that accounts for current spreading from the channel into the JFET region at their intersection. W_G and W_P are the zero-bias depletion widths at the gate contact and P^+ regions, respectively. They can be determined using:

$$W_G = \sqrt{\frac{2\varepsilon_S V_{biG}}{qN_D}}$$
[9.12]

$$W_P = \sqrt{\frac{2\varepsilon_S V_{biP}}{qN_D}}$$
[9.13]

where the built-in potential V_{biG} for a metal-semiconductor gate contact is typically 1 V while the built-in potential V_{biP} for the P^+ junction is typically 3.3 V for 4H-SiC.

The JFET region resistance is given by:

$$R_{JFET} = \rho_D \left(t_{CH} + t_P - W_G \right) \left(\frac{p}{W_J - W_P} \right)$$
[9.14]

where p is the cell pitch. The drift region spreading resistance can be obtained by using:

$$R_D = \rho_D \left(\frac{2p}{W_J - W_P} \right) \ln \left(\frac{2p}{W_J - W_P} \right) + \rho_D \left(t - s - W_P \right)$$
[9.15]

where t is the thickness of the drift region below the P^+ region and s is the width of the P^+ region.

The contribution to the resistance from the N^+ substrate is given by:

$$R_{subs} = \rho_{subs} . t_{subs}$$
[9.16]

where ρ_{subs} and t_{subs} are the resistivity and thickness of the substrate, respectively. A typical value for this contribution is 7×10^{-4} Ω-cm^2.

Using the analytical expressions, it is possible to model the change in specific on-resistance with alterations of the cell design parameters. The specific on-resistance is most sensitive to variations of the channel length (L_{CH}) and thickness (t_{CH}), as well as the width of the JFET region (W_J). The variation of the specific on-resistance with increasing channel length is shown in Fig. 9.8 and Fig. 9.9 for cases of channel thickness of 1 and 1.2 µm, respectively, for a 3.3 kV MESFET device. It can be seen that increasing the channel thickness reduces the specific on-resistance and its dependence on the channel length. Increasing the JFET width to 1 µm improves the on-resistance significantly.

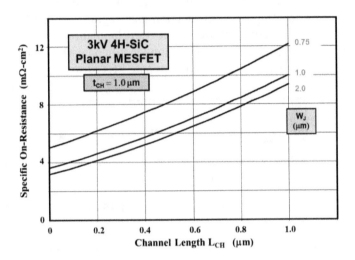

Fig. 9.8 Analytically calculated on-resistance for a 3 kV 4H-SiC planar MESFET for channel thickness of 1.0 µm.

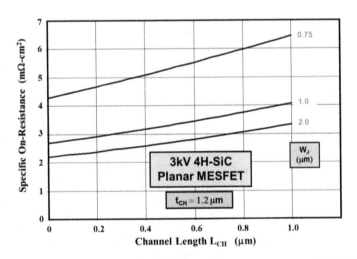

Fig. 9.9 Analytically calculated on-resistance for a 4H-SiC planar MESFET for channel thickness of 1.2 µm.

9.3 4H-SiC Experimental Results: Trench Gate Structures

Several approaches can be taken to construct a vertical FET structure that utilizes a potential barrier induced by a gate bias along the vertical path. The gate region in the device can be formed by using ion implantation of P-type dopants to form a JFET structure or by placing a metal contact within a trench etched between the source regions to form a MESFET structure or by forming a hetero-junction gate region within the trench to form a HJFET structure. Prior to the development of a process for formation of heavily doped P-type regions in silicon carbide, it was more practical to construct the hetero-junction gate FET structure.

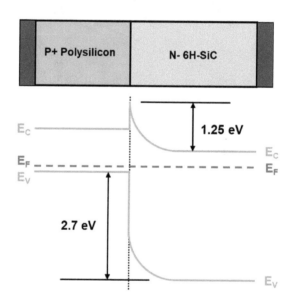

Fig. 9.10 P⁺ polysilicon/N- 6H-SiC hetero-junction band structure.

The formation of a hetero-junction between P-type polysilicon and N-type 6H-SiC was first demonstrated at PSRC in 1996[13]. The band structure for the interface between P⁺ Polysilicon and N-type 6H-SiC is shown in Fig. 9.10. Good rectification was experimentally confirmed at this hetero-junction[14] allowing consideration of this junction for the gate region in a HJFET structure, shown in Fig. 9.11. The fabrication process for this structure is simple because the polysilicon gate material can be deposited into the trenches and planarized due to the good selectivity between it and SiC during reactive-ion-etching. The HJFET structure

was analyzed in detail in 1996[15] followed by experimental demonstration[16] of a structure with the P$^+$ polysilicon located within trenches
etched between the source regions. Although some gate control was
observed, the performance of the structure was poor due to the bad
quality of the surface within the trenches after etching.

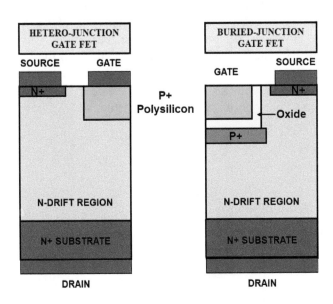

Fig. 9.11 Novel vertical trench gate SiC FET structures.

A trench JFET structure, also illustrated in Fig. 9.11, with a
MOS sidewall has been proposed and demonstrated[17]. This structure
requires ion implantation of the P$^+$ region at the bottom of the trenches
after they have been etched. Since the authors masked the P$^+$ implant, the
process is difficult to implement due to the poor topology for patterning
photoresist in the presence of 1 μm deep trenches. In addition, it is not
clear that the P-type implant will not occur on the trench sidewalls, an
effect disregarded by the authors. The authors deposited an oxide after
the P$^+$ implant and then refilled the trench with polysilicon to create
an MOS-structure on the trench sidewalls. The process described by
the authors precludes making contact to the P$^+$ gate regions along the
trenches. Since the contact to the P$^+$ gate regions must be located at
the periphery of the device, the structure would have poor switching
characteristics due to the very high resistance of the P$^+$ fingers
orthogonal to the cross-section. The authors report obtaining a specific

on-resistance of 5 mΩ-cm^2 for a device that is able to block 600 V using a reverse gate bias of -30 V.

The vertical JFET structure can also be fabricated using ion implantation to form the P$^+$ gate region. In order to obtain a good channel aspect ratio, it is necessary to resort to very high energy (1.3 MeV) aluminum implants to form the P$^+$ gate regions[18]. The authors obtained a blocking voltage of 2000 V with a reverse gate bias of -50 V (blocking gain of 40). However, the on-resistance for the devices was very high unless a positive gate bias of 2.5 V was applied. With the positive gate bias, the gate depletion region was reduced allowing drain current flow through the channel with a specific on-resistance of 70 mΩ-cm^2. These values indicate poor optimization of the structure which had a very large cell pitch of 32 μm.

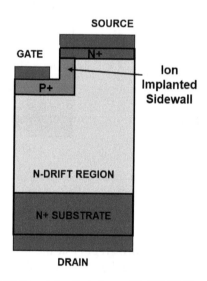

Fig. 9.12 Trench-implanted gate 4H-SiC JFET structure.

The 4H-SiC JFET shown in Fig. 9.12 was developed by etching vertical trenches followed by ion implantation of the sidewalls to create the P$^+$ gate regions[19]. A blocking voltage of 1650 V was obtained using a gate bias of -18 V (blocking gain of 92) if the channel width is made 0.7 μm. A specific on-resistance of 1.88 mΩ-cm^2 was measured by using a forward gate bias of 3 V. This results in gate current flow corresponding to the bipolar mode of operation for JFETs. The current gain under these conditions was 100. The on-resistance is very high without the forward bias on the gate.

The JFET structure shown in Fig. 9.12 can also be designed to operate as a normally-off device[20] if the width of the channel is reduced to 0.63 μm. These devices were operated in the bipolar-mode with a gate bias of 5 V resulting in a current gain of only 10. The difficulties of controlling the width of the trench and the need for bipolar mode of operation makes this type of structure unattractive.

A vertical channel JFET structure has also been developed by ion-implantation of the gate P-regions to obtain a 2 μm channel length[21]. The device structure is similar to that shown in Fig. 9.1 with a recessed gate contact. The devices could support 1680 V using a gate bias of -24 V corresponding to a blocking gain of 70. A specific on-resistance of 5.3 mΩ-cm^2 was measured by using a forward gate bias of 2.5 V. The current gain under these conditions was 16,800. The on-resistance is very high without the forward bias on the gate. The work was extended[22] to achieve a blocking voltage of 2055 V. Attempts to make the device normally-off by the same authors was found to be problematic because the space between the junction had to be reduced to only 0.38 μm leading to very high specific on-resistance[23]. However, a 9 kV normally-on JFET was successfully demonstrated by the authors using e-beam lithography[24]. The device could actually block only 3190 V with a gate bias of -32 V, a blocking gain of 100. A specific on-resistance of 104 mΩ-cm^2 was measured at zero gate bias.

The commercialization of the vertical channel JFET structure was attempted by SemiSouth in 2009. Although the company was unsuccessful, the device structure has been described and characterized more recently[25]. The structure has the cross-section shown in Fig. 9.1 with a drift region doping concentration of 7 x 10^{15} cm^{-3} and thickness of 12 μm. The 2.1 μm deep trenches were etched followed by a three-step aluminum ion implantation process to form vertically walled P$^+$ gate regions with a space of 0.55 μm between them. The channel length produced by the process, including the P$^+$ region formed at the bottom of the trenches, was about 3 μm. The datasheet for the SJEP120R100 product states a blocking voltage of 1.2 kV at zero gate bias. The normally-off JFET has an on-resistance of 80 mΩ at a gate bias of 3 V. It is worth pointing out that the gate junction can start injection holes into the drift region if bias much above this voltage. In fact, a gate current of 220 mA is stated at V_{GS} = 3 V. The resistance increases to 270 mΩ at 150 °C. The gate-drain capacitance (C_{GD}) and charge (Q_{GD}) for the device are 97 pF and 24 nC, respectively. The calculated high frequency figures of merit for the device are (HFFOM) [$R_{on,sp}$*$C_{GD,sp}$] and [$R_{on,sp}$*$Q_{GD,sp}$]

are then 7760 mΩ-pF and 1920 mΩ-nC, respectively. These values are inferior to modern 4H-SiC power MOSFETs described in a later chapter.

Vertical channel JFET devices have also been examined from the commercialization standpoint by United Silicon carbide, Inc. (USCi)[26]. The specific on-resistance ($R_{on,sp}$) for Gen-1 1.2 kV 4H-SiC JFETs with 3.3 μm cell pitch was 3 mΩ-cm^2, similar to that for 4H-SiC power MOSFETs. The $R_{on,sp}$ was reduced to 1.4 mΩ-cm^2 in Gen-3 devices by thinning the substrates and decreasing the cell pitch to 1 μm. The devices blocked 1740 V with a gate bias of -10 V. It is noteworthy that the leakage current increases by 5-orders of magnitude with increasing voltage[27]. These devices are ideally used to form the Baliga-Pair or Cascode topology discussed in the next chapter. The USCi 1.2 kV implementation increased the on-resistance from 75 mΩ for the 4H-SiC JFET to 80 mΩ for the Baliga-Pair. The Baliga-Pair was found to have excellent switching performance up to 200 °C. These devices are commercially available. As an example, the datasheet for the UJ3N120070K3S product has a blocking voltage of 1.2 kV for a gate bias of – 20 V. This normally-on JFET device has an on-resistance of 70 mΩ at zero gate bias. The gate-drain capacitance (C_{GD}) and charge (Q_{GD}) for the device are 40 pF and 63 nC, respectively. The calculated high frequency figures of merit for the device are (HFFOM) [$R_{on,sp}*C_{GD,sp}$] and [$R_{on,sp}*Q_{GD,sp}$] are then 2800 mΩ-pF and 4410 mΩ-nC, respectively. These values are inferior to modern 4H-SiC power MOSFETs described in a later chapter.

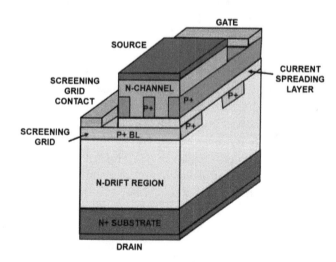

Fig. 9.13 4H-SiC JFET structure with screening grid.

A 4H-SiC JFET structure with reduced gate-drain capacitance (C_{GD}) was fabricated by using a screening grid located below the gate controlled channel region[28]. The device structure is illustrated in Fig. 9.13. It contains a P^+ screening grid on top of the n-drift region which is connected to a screening grid contact held at source potential. An n-type current spreading layer is grown on top of the screening grid followed by the n-type channel layer in which the P^+ gate grid is formed. A normally-off JFET with blocking voltage of 1300 V was achieved by using 1.5 μm space between the P^+ gate regions. The device a threshold voltage of 1 V and a specific on-resistance of 6.1 mΩ-cm^2 at a gate bias of 5 V. The specific gate-drain capacitance ($C_{GD,sp}$) was 235 pF/cm^2. The high frequency figure of merit (HFFOM) [$R_{on,sp}*C_{GD,sp}$] is then 1430 mΩ-pF. This value is competitive with modern 4H-SiC power MOSFETs described in a later chapter.

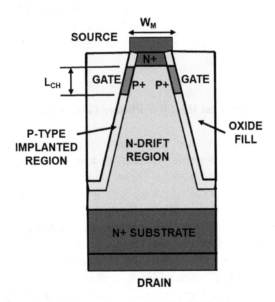

Fig. 9.14 Super-junction 4H-SiC JFET structure.

A super-junction 4H-SiC JFET structure was reported in 2020/2021 with the charge coupling achieved by ion-implantation of a p-type region on the sidewalls of trenches etched into a n-type drift region with sloping sidewalls[29] as illustrated in Fig. 9.14. Devices were fabricated on 9 μm thick epitaxial layers with doping concentration of 3 x 10^{16} cm^{-3}. Numerical simulations indicated an optimum mesa width

(W_M) of 1.6 μm and p-region doping of 2.6 x 10^{17} cm^{-3}. The fabricated devices had a threshold voltage of – 3 V. The blocking voltage of the device was 1000 V at a gate bias of – 15 V with a relatively high leakage current. A specific on-resistance of 1.3 mΩ-cm^2 was reported at a gate bias of 2 V. It increased to 4 mΩ-cm^2 at zero gate bias. No data on capacitances and gate charge were provided in this paper.

A superjunction 4H-SiC JFET was also reported in 2022 with vertically walled trenches[30]. This structure was fabricated using tilted ion-implantation of the sidewall with aluminum to form the p-type charge coupling layer. The fabricated devices had normally-off behavior for a mesa width (W_M) of 1.4 μm but showed normally-on characteristics for W_M of 1.6 μm and larger. The specific on-resistance for the 1.4 μm mesa device was 3.64 mΩ-cm^2 at a gate bias of 3 V and reduced to 0.85 mΩ-cm^2 at a gate bias of 3 V for a mesa width of 2 μm. The threshold voltage shifted from 0 V to – 15 V when the mesa width was increased from 1.4 to 2 μm. The devices blocked 1000 V with a gate bias of – 25 V for the 1.8 μm mesa width case. No data on capacitances and gate charge were provided in this paper.

9.4 4H-SiC Experimental Results: Planar Gate Structures

The planar gate FET structure was originally proposed and patented in 1996 with either a metal-semiconductor, or a junction, or an MOS gate region[10]. These structures have a lateral channel whose thickness and doping level can be controlled to achieve good blocking gain and on-state resistance in the vertical JFET structure. The sub-surface P$^+$ region can be formed by using ion-implantation with appropriate energy to locate the junction below the surface so as to create an un-depleted N-type channel region. An alternative approach is to grow an N-type epitaxial layer over the P$^+$ regions implanted into a substrate to create the N-type channel region. Experimental results on the lateral channel, vertical (planar) MESFET/JFET structures are discussed here.

The first planar MESFET structures were successfully fabricated at PSRC in 1996-97 by performing 380 keV boron ion-implants to form the sub-surface P$^+$ region[11]. Devices were fabricated from both 6H-SiC and 4H-SiC as the starting material with doping concentration of about 2 x 10^{16} cm^{-3}. The energy for the boron implants was chosen to locate the center of the P$^+$ region at about 0.5 μm below the surface[31]. An additional N-type nitrogen implant was used in the channel region to enhance its doping to produce normally-on devices. Contact to the sub-surface P^+ region was made by additional boron implants at lower energy in selective regions within the cell structure. The devices were found to exhibit a specific on-resistance of about 12 mΩ-cm^2 and had poor gate–drain breakdown voltage of about 50 volts.

Planar-gate 4H-SiC JFET structures that were fabricated at PSRC in 1996-97 using the same process conditions described with much better blocking capability[32]. In these devices, the P^+ gate region was formed by using a shallow 10 keV boron implant. The 4H-SiC planar JFETs fabricated using an N-type channel implant with a dose of 1-2 x 10^{13} cm^{-2} exhibited a specific on-resistance of 11-14 mΩ-cm^2. The devices were able to block a drain bias of 1100 V with a negative gate bias of 40 V, a very good blocking gain of 27.5. Excellent gate controlled pentode-like characteristics with drain current saturation was observed in the devices up to the breakdown voltage with a drain current density of 250 A/cm^2.

Lateral channel, vertical JFET structures, fabricated by epitaxial growth of an N-type layer over a P^+ region implanted into the drift region, have been reported by several groups. The first such devices were reported[12] in 1999 by using epitaxial layers capable of supporting 600 V and 1200 V. By growing an epitaxial layer with doping concentration of about 2 x 10^{16} cm^{-3} with a thickness of 2.5 μm over the sub-surface P^+ region, the devices were able to support a gate bias of more than 10 V above a channel pinch-off voltage of 40 V. This was sufficient to allow blocking a drain bias of 1200 V. The specific on-resistance for the devices was 18, 25, and 40 mΩ-cm^2 for devices capable of supporting 550, 800, and 950 V, respectively. The performance of these structures was subsequently improved[33] to a blocking voltage of 1800 V with a specific on-resistance of 24.5 mΩ-cm^2.

A comprehensive study of various gate structural options for 10-kV 4H-SiC normally-on vertical 4H-SiC JFETs with a lateral channel region was reported in 2012[34]. Four basic lateral channel JFET structures that were analyzed and fabricated are illustrated in Fig. 9.15. In the SG-JFET structure, the P^+ buried layer is connected to the source region and only the P^+ top layer is used as the gate. In the SBG-JFET structure, the P^+ buried layer and the P^+ top regions are both used as the gate. In the BG-JFET structure, the P^+ top layer is connected to the source and only the P^+ buried layer is used as the gate. In the DG-JFET structure, the P^+ top gate region does not overlap the gap between the P^+ buried layers.

The above structures were optimized by varying the length of the lateral channel (L_{CH}) and the gap between the P$^+$ buried layers (W_J) shown in Fig. 9.7. Devices were fabricated using 120 μm thick drift layers with doping concentration of 9 x 10^{14} cm^{-3} on N$^+$ substrates to achieve a measured breakdown voltage of 9.4 kV using a gate bias of -18 V. This corresponds to a blocking gain of over 500 which is essential to achieve such high blocking voltages. Such high blocking gains can only be achieved by using the lateral channel configuration. A minimum specific on-resistance of 130 mΩ-cm^2 was observed at a gap of 3.5 μm between the P$^+$ buried layers. The measured specific-on resistance is only 2-times larger than the ideal specific on-resistance for a 10-kV 4H-SiC device.

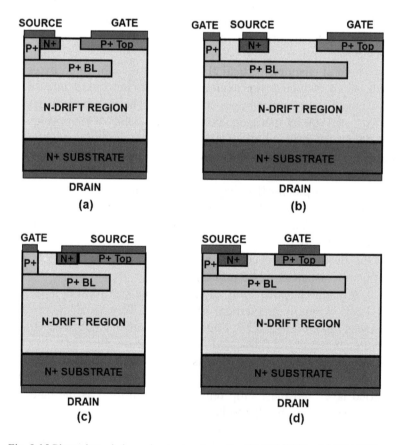

Fig. 9.15 Planar lateral channel gate structures for 4H-SiC JFETs: (a) SG-JFET; (b) SBG-JFET; (c) BG-JFET; and (d) DG-JFET

The lateral channel approach can also be used to make normally-off vertical JFET structures if the channel is fully depleted at zero gate bias. A 4H-SiC normally-off JFET, named SEJFET[35], was reported with a blocking voltage of 5.5 kV in 2001. This device has the same structure as shown in Fig. 9.15(b) with both the top and buried P^+ layers used for the gate. Pentode-like characteristics were observed by using positive gate bias voltages up to 2.6 volts. A specific on-resistance of 218 mΩ-cm^2 was obtained at a positive gate bias of 2.6 volts. This value is about 15-times larger than the ideal specific on-resistance for 4H-SiC. It was reported that the specific on-resistance reduced to 69 mΩ-cm^2 at a positive gate bias of 5 volts[36].

A normally-off vertical 4H-SiC JFET structure with the structure shown in Fig. 9.15(d) was reported with a blocking voltage of 1900 V at zero gate bias in 2002[37]. Pentode-like characteristics were observed by using positive gate bias voltages up to 4 V. A specific on-resistance of 19.6 mΩ-cm^2 was obtained at a positive gate bias of 4 V.

9.5 Summary

The physics of operation of the normally-on and normally-off vertical JFET/MESFET structure has been described in this chapter. The devices exhibit mixed triode-pentode like characteristics. The channel for these devices can be oriented along the vertical drain current flow path by using a trench gate architecture. Alternately, a lateral channel can be formed by introducing a sub-surface P^+ region below a planar gate design. The planar devices have been successfully made using either a deep P^+ ion implantation step into the N-drift region or by growth of an N-type epitaxial layer above a previously implanted P^+ region in the N-type drift region. Both methods have resulted in devices with low specific on-resistance and good gate controlled current saturation capability with relatively low reverse gate bias voltages. These devices are suitable for utilization in the *Baliga-Pair* configuration discussed in the next chapter.

References

[1] J. Nishizawa, T. Terasaki, and J. Shibata, "Field Effect Transistor versus Analog Transistor (Static Induction Transistor)", IEEE Transactions on Electron Devices, Vol. ED22, pp. 185-197, 1975.

[2] B. J. Baliga, "Modern Power Devices", John Wiley and Sons, 1987.

[3] B. J. Baliga, "Silicon Carbide Switching Device with Rectifying Gate", U. S. Patent 5,396,085, Issued March 7, 1995.

[4] B. J. Baliga, "Power Semiconductor Devices", Chapter 7, pp. 418-420, 1996.

[5] B. J. Baliga, "Silicon Carbide Power Devices", Chapter 8, pp. 199-219, 2005.

[6] P. Plotka and B. Wilamowski, "Interpretation of Exponential type Drain Characteristics of the Static Induction Transistor", Solid State Electronics, Vol. 23, pp. 693-694, 1980.

[7] B. J. Baliga, "A Power Junction Gate Field Effect Transistor Structure with High Blocking Gain", IEEE Transactions on Electron Devices, Vol. 27, pp. 368-373, 1980.

[8] X. C. Kun, "Calculation of Amplification Factor of Static Induction Transistors", IEE Proceedings, Vol. 131, pp. 87-93, 1984.

[9] B. J. Baliga, "High Voltage Junction Gate Field Effect Transistor with Recessed Gates", IEEE Transactions on Electron Devices, Vol. 29, pp. 1560-1570, 1982.

[10] B. J. Baliga, "Silicon Carbide Semiconductor Devices having Buried Silicon Carbide Conduction Barrier Layers Therein", U. S. Patent 5,543,637, Issued August 6, 1996.

[11] P. Shenoy and B. J. Baliga, "The Planar Lateral Channel SiC MESFET", PSRC Technical Report TR-97-038, 1997.

[12] H. Mitlehner, et al, "Dynamic Characteristics of High Voltage 4H-SiC Vertical JFETs", IEEE International Symposium on Power Semiconductor Devices and ICs, Abstract 11.1, pp. 339-342, 1999.

[13] P. M. Shenoy and B. J. Baliga, "High Voltage P+ Polysilicon/N- 6H-SiC Heterojunction Diodes", PSRC Technical Report TR-96-050, 1996.

[14] P. M. Shenoy and B. J. Baliga, "High Voltage P+ Polysilicon/N- 6H-SiC Heterojunction Diodes", Electronics Letters, Vol. 33, pp. 1086-1087, 1997.

[15] B. Vijay, K. Makeshwar, P. M. Shenoy, and B. J. Baliga, "Analysis of a High Voltage Heterojunction Gate SiC Field Effect Transistor", PSRC Technical Report TR-96-049, 1996.

[16] P. M. Shenoy, V. Bantval, M. Kothandaraman, and B. J. Baliga, "A Novel P$^+$ Polysilicon/N- SiC Heterojunction Trench Gate Vertical FET", IEEE International Symposium on Power Semiconductor Devices and ICs, pp. 365-368, 1997.

[17] R. N. Gupta, H. R. Chang, E. Hanna, and C. Bui, "A 600 V SiC Trench JFET". Silicon Carbide and Related Materials – 2001, Material Science Forum, Vol. 389-393, pp. 1219-1222, 2002.

[18] H. Onose, et al, "2 kV 4H-SiC Junction FETs", Silicon Carbide and Related Materials – 2001, Material Science Forum, Vol. 389-393, pp. 1227-1230, 2002.

[19] Y. Li, P. Alexandrov, and J. H. Zhao, "1.88-mΩ.cm2 1650-V Normally-on 4H-SiC TI-JFET", IEEE Transactions on Electron Devices, Vol. 55, pp. 1880-1886, 2008.

[20] J. H. Zhao, et al, "4H-SiC Normally-Off Vertical JFET with High Current Density", IEEE Electron Device Letters, Vol. 24, pp. 463-465, 2003.

[21] V. Veliadis, et al, "A 1680-V, 54-A Normally-On 4H-SiC JFET with 0.143-cm^2 Active Area", IEEE Electron Device Letters, Vol. 29, pp. 1132-1134, 2008.

[22] V. Veliadis, et al, "A 2055-V, 24-A Normally-On 4H-SiC JFET with 6.8-mm^2 Active Area", IEEE Electron Device Letters, Vol. 29, pp. 1325-1327, 2008.

[23] V. Veliadis, et al, "Investigation of the Suitability of 1200-V Normally-Off Recessed Implanted Gate SiC VJFETs for Efficient Power Switching Applications", IEEE Electron Device Letters, Vol. 30, pp. 736-738, 2009.

[24] V. Veliadis, et al, "A 9-kV Normally-On Vertical Channel SiC JFET for Unipolar Operation", IEEE Electron Device Letters, Vol. 31, pp. 470-472, 2010.

[25] K. Shile, R. Gharbi, and , M. B. Karoui, "Dynamic Characteristics of Normally-OFF Silicon Carbide JFET", IEEE Int. Conf. on Signal, Control and Communication, pp. 101-106, 2021.

[26] A. Bhalla, et al, "The Outlook for SiC Vertical JFET Technology", IEEE Workshop on Wide Bandgap Power Devices and Applications, pp. 40-43, 2013.

[27] X. Li, et al, "Study of SiC Vertical JFET Behavior during Unclamped Inductive Switching", IEEE Applied Power Electronics Conf., pp. 2588-2592, 2014.

[28] K. Yano, et al, "Experimental Demonstration of SiC Screen Grid Vertical JFET (SiC-SGVJFET) having a Ultra-Low C_{rss}", IEEE International Symposium on Power Semiconductor Devices and ICs, pp. 487-490, 2016.

[29] H. Wang, et al, "4H-SiC Super-Junction JFET: Design and Experimental Demonstration", IEEE Electron Device Letters, Vol. 41, pp. 445-448, 2020.

[30] C. Wang, et al, "Characterization and Analysis of 4H-SiC Super-Junction JFETs Fabricated by Sidewall Implantation", IEEE Trans. Electron Devices, Vol. 69, pp. 2543-2551, 2022.

[31] M. S. Janson, et al, "Range distributions of Implanted Ions in Silicon Carbide", Silicon Carbide and Related Materials – 2001, Material Science Forum, Vol. 389-393, pp. 779-782, 2002.

[32] P. Shenoy and B. J. Baliga, "A Planar Lateral Channel SiC Vertical High Power JFET", PSRC Technical Report TR-97-036, 1997.

[33] P. Friedrichs, et al, "Static and Dynamic Characteristics of 4H-SiC JFETs Designed for Different Blocking Categories", Silicon Carbide and Related Materials – 1999, Material Science Forum, Vol. 338-342, pp. 1243-1246, 2000.

[34] W. Sung, et al, "A Comparative Study of Gate Structures for 9.4-kV 4H-SiC Normally-on Vertical JFETs", IEEE Transactions on Electron Devices, Vol. 59, pp. 2417-2423, 2012.

[35] K. Asano, et al, "5.5kV Normally-off Low RonS 4H-SiC SEJFET", IEEE International Symposium on Power Semiconductor Devices and ICs, Paper 1.1, pp. 23-26, 2001.

[36] K. Asano, et al, "5kV 4H-SiC SEJFET with Low RonS of 69 mΩcm^2", IEEE International Symposium on Power Semiconductor Devices and ICs, pp. 61-64, 2002.

[37] J.H. Zhao, et al, "A Novel High-Voltage Normally-Off 4H-SiC Vertical JFET", Material Science Forum, Vol. 389-393, pp. 1223-1226, 2002.

Chapter 10

The Baliga-Pair (Cascode) Configuration

The ability to produce a high quality interface between silicon carbide and a suitable gate dielectric material was a significant challenge in the 1990s[1]. A large density of charge in the thermally grown oxide and at its interface with SiC caused threshold voltage shifts and degraded the inversion layer mobility. To compound the problem, the conventional silicon power MOSFET structure could not provide the full benefits of the high breakdown field strength of the SiC material because of reliability and rupture problems associated with the enhanced electric field in the gate oxide. The SiC JFET structure, discussed in chapter 9, eliminates the above issues because it does not rely on an MOS structure. This makes it easier from a development standpoint. However, the best on-resistance for the high voltage JFET is obtained when it has a normally-on characteristic which is not acceptable for power electronic circuits.

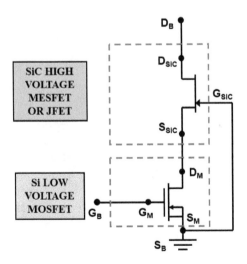

Fig. 10.1 The *Baliga-Pair* power switch configuration.

In order to overcome these problems, it was proposed in a patent[2] that a normally-on SiC high voltage JFET/MESFET be used together with a low voltage Si MOSFET to create a configuration with all of the desired features for a high quality power switch. The basic idea that is illustrated in Fig. 10.1 was shown in the patent as Fig. 5. It consists of a high voltage SiC JFET or MESFET structure with its source electrode connected to the drain electrode of a low voltage Si power MOSFET. An important feature of configuration is that the gate of the SiC device is connected to the source of the Si power MOSFET which serves as the ground or reference terminal in the Baliga-Pair configuration. Gate signals applied to the Baliga-Pair at terminal G_B are exclusively applied to the gate G_M of the Si power MOSFET. The drain of the SiC device is connected to the load in power circuits as would be done with the drain of silicon power MOSFETs. The Baliga-Pair is therefore a three-terminal power switch like a power MOSFET from the power circuit applications view point.

The third independent claim of the patent[2] states: *A three terminal gate controlled semiconductor switching device, comprising: an insulated-gate field effect transistor having an insulated gate electrode, a first source region and a first drain region; a rectifying-gate field effect transistor having a gate electrode, a second source region and a second drain region, wherein said gate electrode and said second source region are electrically connected to said first source region and first drain region, respectively; a drain contact electrically connected to said second drain region; a source contact electrically connected to said first source region; and wherein said rectifying-gate field effect transistor comprises a MESFET.* The fifth claim extends this configuration to include JFETs. These claims can be seen to cover any type of MESFET structures including GaN HEMT devices.

In an analogy to the *Darlington-Pair* configuration[3] commonly used for power control applications, it was suggested[4] that the proposed combination of devices be named the *Baliga-Pair* configuration. The idea was first presented in 1995 at the Conference on Silicon Carbide and Related Devices[5] held in Kyoto, Japan. A detailed discussion of the operating principles and characteristics of the Baliga-Pair were provided in a textbook published in 1996[6]. The Baliga-Pair configuration is a three-terminal power switch with an MOS-input interface provided by the silicon power MOSFET and high blocking voltage capability provided by the SiC JFET/MESFET.

The same circuit configuration was subsequently called the Cascode circuit[7] with the acknowledgement that it was first disclosed in a textbook in 1996[6]. The term cascode is a misnomer because it was originally coined to describe a two-stage triode vacuum tube amplifier with a second triode serving a load to achieve superior stability[8]. This distinction was apparent to the U.S. patent examiner who recognized that the Baliga-Pair circuit was novel and distinct from prior art allowing the patent claims to be issued.

This chapter discusses the operating principles of the Baliga-Pair configuration. It is demonstrated that a Si power MOSFET with low breakdown voltage rating (and hence low specific on-resistance) can be used to control a high voltage, normally-on SiC JFET/MESFET structure. This enables supporting large voltages within the SiC FET while allowing control of the composite switch with signals applied to the MOS gate electrode of the Si MOSFET. The same type of simple, low cost, integrated control circuits used for Si power MOSFETs and IGBTs can therefore be utilized for the Baliga-Pair configuration. Since both devices in the configuration are unipolar devices, the Baliga-Pair has very fast switching speed and excellent safe-operating-area. In concert with the low on-resistance for both the FETs, the fast switching speed results in very low overall power dissipation in applications[9]. In addition, this configuration contains an excellent fly-back diode allowing replacement of not only the IGBT but also the fly-back rectifier that is usually connected across it in H-bridge power circuits. From this stand-point, it is preferable to use the SiC MESFET structure due to lower on state voltage drop of the Schottky diode used as its gate.

10.1 The *Baliga-Pair* Configuration

The Baliga-Pair configuration consists of a low breakdown voltage Si MOSFET and a normally-on, high voltage SiC JFET/MESFET connected together as shown in Fig. 10.2. Any of the trench gate or planar gate JFET/MESFET structures discussed in the previous chapter can be used to provide the high blocking voltage capability. It is important that the SiC FET structure be designed for normally-on operation with a low specific on-resistance. It is also necessary for the SiC FET to be able to block the drain bias voltage with a gate bias less than the breakdown voltage of the Si power MOSFET.

The Si power MOSFET can be either a planar DMOS structure or a trench-gate UMOS structure to provide low specific on-resistance. The source of the SiC FET is connected to the drain of the Si power MOSFET. Note that the gate of the SiC FET is connected directly to the reference or ground terminal. The path formed between the drain and the gate contact of the SiC FET creates the fly-back diode. The composite switch is controlled by the signal applied to the gate of the Si power MOSFET. It is preferable to use a Si power MOSFET with low (< 30-V) breakdown voltage because of its excellent low on-resistance and fast switching capability.

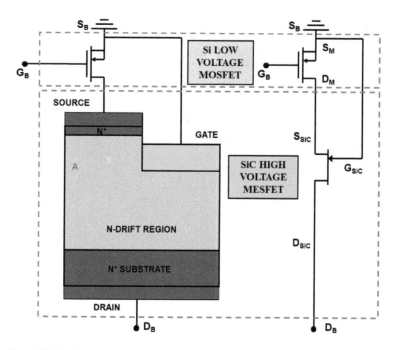

Fig. 10.2 The *Baliga-Pair* power switch with a SiC MESFET and Si MOSFET.

10.1.1 Voltage Blocking Mode

The Baliga-Pair switch can block current flow when the gate of the Si power MOSFET is shorted to ground by the external drive circuit. With zero gate bias, the Si power MOSFET supports any bias applied to its drain terminal (D_M) with low leakage current until the voltage exceeds its breakdown voltage. Consequently, at lower voltages applied to the drain terminal (D_B) of the Baliga-Pair switch, the voltage is supported across the Si power MOSFET because the SiC JFET is operating in its normally-on mode. However, as the voltage at the drain (D_M) of the Si power MOSFET increases, an equal positive voltage develops at the source (S_{SiC}) of the SiC FET. Since the gate (G_{SiC}) of the SiC FET is connected to the ground terminal, this produces a reverse bias across the gate-source junction of the SiC FET. Consequently, a depletion layer extends from the gate contact/junction into the channel of the SiC FET. When the depletion region pinches off the channel at location A in Fig. 10.2, further increase in the bias applied to the drain (D_B) of the composite switch is supported across the SiC FET. Since the potential at the source of the SiC FET is then isolated from the drain bias applied to the SiC FET, the voltage across the Si power MOSFET is also clamped to a value close to the pinch-off voltage of the SiC FET. This feature enables utilization of a Si power MOSFET with a low breakdown voltage. Such Si power MOSFETs have very low specific on-resistance with a mature technology available for their production. From this point of view, it is desirable to utilize Si power MOSFETs with breakdown voltages of below 30 volts.

For the Baliga-Pair switch designed to support a drain bias of 3000 volts, the ability to utilize a Si power MOSFET with a breakdown voltage of 30 V requires designing the SiC FET structure so that the channel is pinched-off at a gate bias of below 20 volts. Thus, the DC blocking gain of the SiC FET should be in excess of 150. This is feasible for both the trench-gate and planar gate architectures for SiC FETs discussed in the previous chapter. As pointed out in that chapter, much larger blocking gains could be achieved with the planar MESFET structure making it an attractive choice for use in the Baliga-Pair switch.

10.1.2 Forward Conduction Mode

The Baliga-Pair switch shown in Fig. 10.2 can be turned-on by application of a positive gate bias to the gate (G_B). This voltage is also applied to the gate (G_M) of the Si power MOSFET. The Si power MOSFET operates with a low on-resistance when the gate bias is well above its threshold voltage. Under these conditions, any voltage applied to the drain terminal (D_B) produces current flow through the normally-on SiC FET and the Si MOSFET. Due to the low specific on-resistance of both structures, the total on-resistance of the Baliga-Pair switch is also very small:

$$R_{on}(Baliga - Pair) = R_{on}(SiliconMOSFET) + R_{on}(SiCFET) \quad \text{[10.1]}$$

Depending up on the size of the two devices, an on-resistance of less than 10 mΩ-cm^2 is feasible even when the switch is designed to support 3000 volts. This indicates that the Baliga-Pair configuration will have an on-state voltage drop of about 1 V with a nominal on-state current density of 100 A/cm^2 flowing through the devices. This is well below typical values of around 4 V for a Si IGBT designed to support such high voltages.

10.1.3 Current Saturation Mode

One of the reasons for the success of the Si power MOSFET and IGBT in power electronics applications is the gate controlled current saturation capability of these devices. This feature enables controlling the rate of rise of current is power circuits by tailoring the input gate voltage waveform rather than by utilizing snubbers that are required for devices like gate turn-off thyristors. In addition, current saturation is essential for survival of short-circuit conditions where the device must limit the current.

The current saturation capability is inherent in the Baliga-Pair switch. If the gate voltage applied to the Baliga-Pair switch is reduced to near the threshold voltage of the Si MOSFET, it will enter its current saturation mode when the drain bias increases. This produces a constant current through both the Si MOSFET and the SiC FET while the drain bias applied to the composite switch increases. At lower drain bias voltages applied to the drain terminal (D_B), the voltage is supported across the Si power MOSFET. As this voltage increases, the channel in the SiC FET gets pinched-off and further voltage is then supported by the SiC FET. Under these bias conditions, both the devices sustain current flow while supporting voltage. The level of the current flowing through the devices is determined by the Si power MOSFET as controlled by the applied gate bias. In this sense, the Baliga-Pair switch behaves like a Si power MOSFET from the point of view of the external circuit on both the input and output side. This feature makes the configuration attractive for use in power electronic systems because the existing circuit topologies can be used. The safe-operating-area of the Baliga-Pair switch is mainly determined by the SiC FET because it supports a majority of the applied drain voltage. The excellent breakdown strength, thermal conductivity, and wide band gap of silicon carbide ensure good safe-operating-area for the FET structures.

10.1.4 Switching Characteristics

The transition between the on and off modes for the Baliga-Pair switch is controlled by the applied gate bias to the Si power MOSFET. During turn-on and turn-off, the gate bias must charge and discharge the capacitance of the Si power MOSFET. Since Si power MOSFETs are extensively used for high frequency power conversion, their input capacitance and gate charge have been optimized by the industry[10]. The switching speed of the Baliga-Pair is consequently very high because of the availability of Si power MOSFETs designed for high frequency applications. The main limitations to the switching speed of the Baliga-Pair switch is related to parasitic inductances in the package that could produce high voltage spikes. The Si power MOSFET chip can be directly soldered to the source electrode of the SiC FET to reduce the inductance.

10.1.5 Fly-Back Diode

The Baliga-Pair switch contains an inherent high quality fly-back rectifier. When the drain bias is reversed to a negative value, the gate-drain contact/junction of the SiC FET becomes forward biased. Since the gate of the SiC FET is directly connected to the ground terminal, current can flow through this path when the drain voltage is negative in polarity. From this stand-point, it is preferable to use a metal-semiconductor contact for the gate rather than a P-N junction. The Schottky gate contact provides for a lower on-state voltage drop by proper choice of the work-function for the gate contact. In addition, the Schottky contact has no significant reverse recovery current. This greatly reduces switching losses in both the rectifier and the FETs[9]. Thus, the Baliga-Pair configuration replaces not just the power switch (such as the IGBT or GTO) in applications but also the power rectifier that is normally used across the switch.

Another path for current flow in the Baliga-Pair configuration in the reverse direction is via the body diode of the Si power MOSFET and the channel of the SiC JFET/MESFET. This diode has a low on-state voltage drop corresponding to that for a Si P-i-N rectifier. The reverse recovery for the body diode of the Si MOSFET can be improved by electron irradiation[11].

10.2 Numerical Simulation Results

The results of numerical simulations of the Baliga-Pair switch have been described in detail in previous books[12,13]. The reader is encouraged to read these books for additional knowledge about the operation of this configuration. The switching waveforms are very similar to those observed for SiC power MOSFETs. It has been experimentally verified that the Baliga-Pair switch can be driven with a commercially available MOSFET driver chip[14]. This makes the Baliga-Pair switch an attractive option for replacing Si IGBTs to reduce power losses.

10.3 Experimental Results

The attractive features of the Baliga-Pair switch have been acknowledged by many research groups. The Baliga-Pair switch was referred to as the Cascode arrangement in 1999[7] with the acknowledgement that it was originally proposed and published in 1996[6]. The switching behavior of the Cascode arrangement was reported[15] by using a planar SiC JFET structure with a 50 volt Si power MOSFET. The authors compared the performance of SiC JFETs with the gate formed using the buried sub-surface P^+ region with a JFET fabricated using a gate formed on the upper surface (similar to the structure discussed in the previous chapter). It was found that the buried gate device had inferior switching performance due to the high resistance in the buried P^+ regions. The turn-off time was limited by the R-C charging time-constant for the buried P^+ regions. In addition, the slow response of this JFET structure resulted in the Si power MOSFET being driven into avalanche breakdown. These problems were not observed for the surface gate device.

In a subsequent paper[16], the authors stated: *"SiCED favors a combination of a silicon switch and a vertical, normally-on SiC junction field effect transistor"*. Their analysis concluded that the Baliga-Pair switch is useful up to at least the 4.5 kV range. The excellent performance of the Baliga-Pair switch has also been confirmed by using numerical simulations and compared with the performance of a SiC power MOSFET structure[17]. The authors, who called this a Cascade Configuration, found that the turn-off time for the Baliga-Pair switch was half that for the SiC power MOSFET due to the smaller Miller capacitance.

The utility of the reverse conduction path[18] for the Baliga-Pair switch was reported using 1200-V SiC vertical trench JFET devices. It was demonstrated that the reverse conduction occurs via both paths discussed in section 10.1.5. Switching in a totem-pole circuit demonstrated that the Baliga-Pair switch can be operated without an additional anti-parallel diode as usually required for Si power MOSFETs and IGBTs.

It has been found that the switching speed of the SiC/Si cascode circuit is very fast resulting in high [dV/dt] transients. The [dV/dt] can be reduced by (a) using a larger gate drive resistance as in the case of Si power MOSFETs and IGBTs[19]; (b) by connecting a capacitor between the drain of the SiC JFET and the gate of the Si power MOSFET; or (c) by connecting an R-C circuit between the drain of the SiC JFET and the gate of the SiC JFET. In all the cases, the energy loss during turn-on and turn-off switching events increases approximately inversely as the reduction of the [dV/dt].

Similarly, the [dV/dt] during switching was found to be dependent on the output capacitance of the Si power MOSFET and could be reduced by adding additional capacitance between its drain and source[20]. This method also results in an increase in the turn-off energy loss. In comparison with 1200-V trench-gate IGBTs, it was found that the SiC JFET/Si MOSFET cascode circuit has very similar power losses during switching.

The switching behavior of the 4H-SiC normally-on JFET/Si power MOSFET cascode configuration has been studied in detail[21]. The turn-on and turn-off switching transients were found to be similar to those for Si power MOSFETs. A boost converter with efficiency of 98 % was constructed at a switching frequency of 100 kHz using these devices.

Excellent turn-on and turn-off switching waveforms were also demonstrated for the 600-V 4H-SiC normally-on JFET/Si power MOSFET cascode configuration[22]. However, the very fast switching transients produced an EMI problem. The [dV/dt] could be reduced using a gate resistor but with significant increase in switching power loss. The losses could be reduced by 45 % by adding a resistor in series with the gate of the SiC JFET and reducing the gate resistor. This is because of the large transconductance of the SiC JFET.

An alternate cascade approach that makes use of a p-channel Si MOSFET has also been reported[23]. Here, the gate of the SiC JFET is not connected to ground. Instead an antiparallel diode is used across both the Si p-channel MOSFET and the SiC JFET. Double pulse switching tests performed with these devices on the low and high side showed high turn-on current spikes produced by the capacitances of the diode in the high side switch.

10.4 SiC JFET Super-Cascode

The Baliga-Pair switch has been extended to operation at higher voltages by using the 'super-cascode' concept[24]. In this approach, a single low voltage Si power MOSFET is used with multiple high voltage SiC JFETs connected in series to support a larger blocking voltage. A voltage clamping diode is required across each of the SiC JFETs as shown in Fig. 10.3 to achieve proper voltage sharing. The implementation used SiC JFET fabricated using drift regions with thickness of 35 μm and doping of 2 x 10^{15} cm^{-3}. Each SiC JFET could block 4 kV and had a specific on-resistance of 45 mΩ-cm^2. The devices used in the stack had an active area of 0.013 cm^2 corresponding to a device on-resistance of about 4 Ω. An 8 kV super-cascode was obtained by connecting 4 SiC JFETs in series.

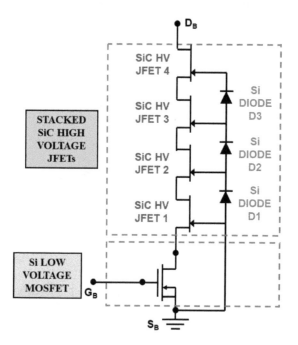

Fig. 10.3 The *Baliga-Pair* super-cascode configuration.

When the Si power MOSFET is turned-on by its gate bias, the voltage drop across is small. This makes source voltage of the SiC JFET 1 low resulting it operating in its on-state as in the Baliga-Pair switch. Since SiC JFET operates in the on-state, the voltage of source of SiC JFET 2 is also low and it operates in the on-state. The same holds true for SiC JFET 3 and SiC JFET 4. The entire stack of devices operate in the on-state allowing the super-cascode to operate in its on-state.

When the Si power MOSFET is turned-off and positive bias is applied to the drain (D_B) of the super-cascode, the drain voltage of the Si MOSFET first increases to the pinch-off voltage of the SiC JFET 1. SiC JFET 1 then begins to support high voltages as in the Baliga-Pair switch. This increase the voltage at the source of SiC JFET 2 until it pinches off because its gate is connected via diode D1 to ground. SiC JFET 2 then begins to support high voltages. This process continues with SiC JFET 3 and SiC JFET 4. Each Si diode is designed with the blocking voltage of 2 kV to achieve the total blocking voltage of 8 kV. The diodes must be rated to handle avalanche breakdown during switching. Relatively long turn-on and turn-off transient times were observed for the super-cascode stack due to the charging of the capacitances of the diodes.

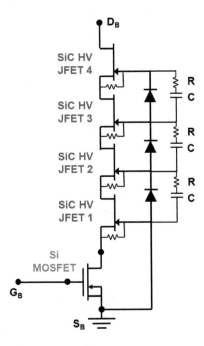

Fig. 10.4 Second super-cascode configuration with RC balancing network.

An improved super-cascode was created by adding R-C balancing circuits to each of the SiC JFETs as shown in Fig. 10.4[25]. Voltage balancing during switching is achieved by the charge in the capacitors. In addition, a resistor is placed between the gate and source of each SiC JFET to accommodate the variation in leakage current of individual devices. During switching of the super-cascode, sequential turn-on of the stacked JFET devices can produce over-voltages. The R-C network is added to mitigate this problem. The capacitors are chosen to ensure voltage balancing, while the resistors suppress voltage oscillations. For a super-cascode with 6 SiC JFETs, a switching transient with 50 ns voltage rise time was observed. The fall time was about 100 ns.

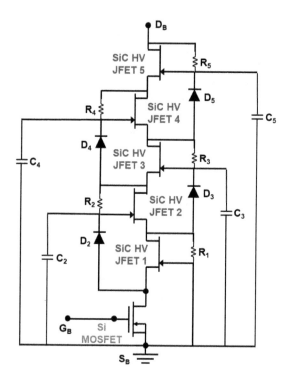

Fig. 10.5 Third super-cascode configuration with RC balancing network.

Another super-cascode implementation is shown in Fig. 10.5 with a network of diodes, resistors and capacitors for producing proper voltage sharing when the device is switching[26]. The diodes serve the same function as the previous cases to obtain voltage sharing between the JFETs in the blocking mode. The resistors are used to provide leakage currents for the diodes to establish stable avalanche breakdown. Switching measurements with three 1.2 kV SiC JFETs controlled by the Si MOSFET demonstrated good voltage sharing between the JFETs with a supply voltage of 2.4 kV. The turn-on (E_{on}) and turn-off (E_{off}) energy losses were 4 and 0.73 mJ, respectively, for a supply voltage of 2 kV and current of 30 A. The on-resistance of the super-cascode switch was 226 mΩ at a gate bias of 10 V. The authors subsequently reported a 4.5 kV 40 A module in 2017 using 5 JFETs in series[27]. The device had an on-resistance of 71 mΩ at a gate bias of 12 V. The gate-drain capacitance (C_{GD}) was 3 pF. The calculated high-frequency figure-of-merit HFFOM[R_{on}*C_{GD}] is 213 mΩ-pF, which is very good compared with SiC power MOSFETs. The module has a built-in body diode with low on-state voltage drop, while it's reverse recovery behavior is like the P-i-N diode.

The design challenges for the super-cascode switch have been reviewed[28]. Since the diodes undergo avalanche breakdown during each switching event, they are susceptible to failure due to stray inductance in the DC power loop. This problem can be mitigated by shifting the avalanche energy from the Si diodes to the SiC JFETs. A 10 kΩ resistor was added in series with each diode to limit the current flow when it is operating under avalanche breakdown.

A comprehensive comparison of various balancing networks for the super-cascode switch implementation has been performed[29]. The pros and cons with each case have been defined.

10.5 SiC Baliga-Pair Applications

The performance of the SiC Baliga-Pair in a typical boost converter has been compared with a SiC power MOSFET[30]. The Baliga-Pair switch was constructed using a SemiSouth 1.2 kV, 85 mΩ product with a 30 V, 7.5 mΩ IRF Si power MOSFET. The switching losses for the Baliga-Pair switch was 28 % larger than the stand-alone SiC JFET in the continuous-conduction-mode (CCM) mode with higher efficiency. However, the efficiency for the Baliga-Pair was better than the stand-alone SiC JFET for the discontinuous-conduction-mode (DCM) mode.

Avalanche ruggedness is an important metric for power switches used with inductive loads[31]. The unclamped inductive switching (UIS) capability of the Baliga-Pair switch has been explored[32] to assess this capability. The test were performed using an USCi Cascode device UJ3C065080K3S that has a blocking voltage of 650 V and on-resistance of 80 mΩ. During the avalanche interval, the cascode switch showed a dip in voltage from 850 to 750 V. The authors' analysis ascribes this to a high resistance (1000 Ω) between the gate of the JFET and the source of the Si MOSFET although this seems highly unlikely for co-packaged SiC and Si chips. Despite this dip, the avalanche capability of the USCI Cascode switch was satisfactory.

Another performance metric for power switches from an applications stand point is the short-circuit (SC) capability[31]. The SC withstand time for a 650 V SiC Baliga-Pair switch has been compared with SiC planar and trench gate MOSFETs[33]. The tests were performed using an USCi Cascode product UJ3C065080K3S that has a blocking voltage of 650 V and on-resistance of 80 mΩ. The SC tests were conducted at a supply voltage of 400 V. The device exhibited a peak SC current of 150 A and failed after 5 μs with a short circuit between drain and source. In contrast, the planar-gate SiC power MOSFET with the same die size also failed after a SC time of 5 μs. The SC energy density for the Baliga-Pair switch was 8.7 J/cm^2, the same as for the SiC planar MOSFET.

The performance of the Baliga-Pair switch has been compared with that for SiC power MOSFETs for electric vehicle drives[34,35]. The USCi Cascode product UJ3C065080K3S with a blocking voltage of 650 V and on-resistance of 80 mΩ was used. It was compared with a 650 V SiC trench MOSFET product SCT3060AL from ROHM, and a 900 V SiC planar MOSFET product C3M0065090D from Wolfspeed. According to the authors the Cascode product has the lowest specific on-resistance of 3 mΩ-cm^2 compared with 4.5 mΩ-cm^2 and 5.5 mΩ-cm^2 for the planar and trench SiC power MOSFETs. A 300-kW, 3-phase, 2-level, voltage source inverter for the electric vehicle drivetrain was analyzed by simulations. A SiC JBS diode was assumed to be connected across all the switches to reduce reverse recovery losses. The lowest power losses were observed for the Cascode product in the NEDC EV drive cycle, with 1.5x larger losses in the SiC planar power MOSFET and 2x larger losses in the SiC trench power MOSFET.

The SiC Baliga-Pair offers an alternative to the SiC power MOSFET for many applications. One of its main attributes is the absence of reliability concerns related to the gate oxide in SiC power MOSFETs. Several companies have developed products with this approach.

10.6 Summary

It has been demonstrated that the Baliga-Pair configuration creates an ideal power switch for high voltage power electronic applications. It can be used in the same manner as IGBTs packaged with anti-parallel rectifiers without alterations of the gate drive. The packaging of this combination of two FETs is similar to that for the two chips (IGBT and flyback diode) currently used because the Baliga-Pair contains an inherent fly-back rectifier. Until the development of reliable silicon carbide power MOSFETs with low specific on-resistance, the Baliga-Pair offered the only commercially viable near term option for high power electronic systems. However, many companies continue to offer the Baliga-Pair based products with high voltage SiC JFETs.

References

[1] B. J. Baliga, "Critical Nature of Oxide/Interface Quality for SiC Power Devices", Microelectronics Engineering, Vol. 28, pp. 177-184, 1995.

[2] B. J. Baliga, "Silicon Carbide Switching Device with Rectifying Gate", U. S. Patent 5,396,085, Issued March 7, 1995.

[3] S. Darlington, "Semiconductor Signal Translating Device", U. S. Patent 2,663,806, Issued December 22, 1953.

[4] P. M. McLarty, Private Communication, 1995.

[5] B. J. Baliga, "Prospects for Development of SiC Power Devices", Silicon Carbide and Related Materials – 1995, Institute of Physics Conference Series, Vol. 142, pp. 1-6, 1996.

[6] B. J. Baliga, "Power Semiconductor Devices", pp. 418-420, PWS Publishing Company, 1996.

[7] P. Friedrichs, et al, "Static and Dynamic Characteristics of 4H-SiC JFETs Designed for Different Blocking Categories", Silicon Carbide and Related Materials – 1999, Material Science Forum, Vol. 338-342, pp. 1243-1246, 2000.

[8] "Cascode", en.wikipedia.org/wiki/Cascode.

[9] B. J. Baliga, "Power Semiconductor Devices for Variable-Frequency Drives", Proceeding of the IEEE, Vol. 82, pp. 1112-1122, 1994.

[10] B. J. Baliga and D. Alok, "Paradigm Shift in Planar Power MOSFET Technology", Power Electronics Technology Magazine, pp. 24-32, November 2003.

[11] B. J. Baliga and J. P. Walden, "Improving the Reverse Recovery of Power MOSFET Integral Diodes by Electron Irradiation", Solid-State Electronics, Vol. 26, pp. 1133-1141, 1983.

[12] B. J. Baliga, "Silicon Carbide Power Devices", World Scientific Publishers, Singapore, 2005.

[13] B. J. Baliga, "Fundamentals of Power Semiconductor Devices", Second Edition, Springer-Science, New York, 2019.

[14] R. Xie, Y. Shi, and H. Li, "Study of 1200 V SiC JFET Cascode Device", IEEE Workshop on Wide Bandgap Power Devices and Applications", pp. 316-320, 2017.

[15] H. Mitlehner, et al, "Dynamic Characteristics of High Voltage 4H-SiC Vertical JFETs", IEEE International Symposium on Power Semiconductor Devices and ICs, Abstract 11.1, pp. 339-342, 1999.

[16] P. Friedrichs, et al, "Application-Oriented Unipolar Switching SiC Devices", Silicon Carbide and Related Materials – 2001, Material Science Forum, Vol. 389-393, pp. 1185-1190, 2002.

[17] A. Mihaila, et al, "Static and Dynamic Behavior of SiC JFET/Si MOSFET Cascade Configuration for High-Performance Power Switches", Silicon Carbide and Related Materials – 2001, Material Science Forum, Vol. 389-393, pp. 1239-1242, 2002.

[18] D. C. Sheridan, et al, "Reverse conduction properties of Vertical SiC Trench JFETs", IEEE International Symposium on Power Semiconductor Devices and ICs, pp. 385-388, 2012.

[19] D. Aggeler, et al, "DV/Dt Control Methods for the SiC JFET/Si MOSFET Cascode", IEEE Tran. Power Electronics, Vol. 28, pp. 4074-4082, 2013.

[20] R. Pittini, Z. Zhang, and M. A. E. Andersen, "SiC JFET Cascode Loss Dependence on the MOSFET Output Capacitance and Performance Comparison with Trench IGBTs", IEEE Applied Power Electronics Conference, pp. 1287-1293, 2013.

[21] A. Rodriquez, et al, "Switching Performance Comparison of the SiC JFET and SiC JFET/Si MOSFET Cascode Configuration", IEEE Tran. Power Electronics, Vol. 29, pp. 2428-2440, 2014.

[22] H. Shimizu, et al, "Controllability of Switching Speed and Loss for SiC JFET/Si MOSFET Cascode with External Gate Resistor", IEEE International Symposium on Power Semiconductor Devices and ICs, pp. 221-224, 2014.

[23] V. Baliga, et al, "Device Characterization and Performance of a 1200V/45A SiC JFET Module", IEEE Energy Conversion Congress and Exposition, pp. 273-278, 2013.

[24] P. Friedrichs, et al, "Stacked high voltage switch based on Sic VJFETs", IEEE International Symposium on Power Semiconductor Devices and ICs, pp. 139-142, 2003.

[25] J. Biela, et al, "Balancing Circuit for a 5-kV/50-ns Pulsed-Power Switch Based on SiC-JFET Super Cascode", IEEE Tran. Plasma Science, Vol. 40, pp. 2554-2560, 2012.

[26] X. Li, et al, "Series-Connection of SiC Normally-on JFETs", IEEE International Symposium on Power Semiconductor Devices and ICs, pp. 221-224, 2015.

[27] X. Li, et al, "Medium Voltage Power Module Based on SiC JFETs", IEEE Applied Power Electronics Conf., pp. 3033-3037, 2017.

[28] B. Gao, et al, "6.5kV SiC JFET-based Super Cascode Power Module with High Avalanche Energy Handling Capability", IEEE Workshop on Wide Bandgap Power Devices and Applications", pp. 319-322, 2018.

[29] L. Gill, et al, "A Comparative Study of SiC JFET Super-Cascode Topologies", IEEE Energy Conversion Congress and Exposition, pp. 1741-1748, 2021.

[30] A. R. Alonso, et al, "Switching Performance Comparison of the SiC JFET and SiC JFET/Si MOSFET Cascode Configuration", IEEE Tran. Power Electronics, Vol. 29, pp. 2428-2440, 2014.

[31] B. J. Baliga, "Fundamentals of Power Semiconductor Devices", Second Edition, Springer-Science, New York, 2019.

[32] N. S. Agbo, et al, "Characterization of Unclamped Inductive Switching in SiC Cascode JFETs", IEEE Int. Conf. on Power Electronics, Drives, and Machines, pp. P1-P6, 2020.

[33] E. Bashar, et al, "Comparison of Short Circuit Failure Modes in SiC Planar MOSFETs, SiC Trench MOSFETs and SiC Cascode JFETs", IEEE Workshop on Wide Bandgap Power Devices and Applications, pp. 384-388, 2021.

[34] R. Wu, et al, "The Potential of SiC Cascode JFETs in Electric Vehicle Traction Inverters", IEEE Tran. Transportation Electrification, Vol. 5, pp. 1349-1359, 2019.

[35] R. Wu, et al, "Fast Switching SiC Cascode JFETs for EV Traction Inverters", IEEE Applied Power Electronics Conf., pp. 3489-3496, 2020.

Chapter 11

Planar-Gate Power MOSFETs

The planar-gate power MOSFET was the first commercially successful unipolar switch developed using silicon technology[1] once the issues related to the metal-oxide-semiconductor interface had been resolved for CMOS technology. In order to reduce cost, the channel in these devices was created by the double diffusion (or D-MOS) process. In the DMOS process, the P-base and N^+ source regions are formed by ion implantations masked by a common edge defined by a refractory polysilicon gate electrode. A drive-in cycle is used after each ion implantation step to move the P-N junction in the lateral direction under the gate electrode. The separation between the N^+/P-base junction and the P-base/N-drift junction under the gate electrode defines the channel. Consequently, the channel length can be reduced to sub-micron dimensions without the need for high resolution lithography. This approach served the industry quite well from the 1970s into the 1990s with silicon planar power MOSFETs still available today for power electronic applications. In the 1990s, the industry borrowed the trench technology originally developed for DRAMs to introduce the UMOSFET structure for commercial applications[2]. This was important for the reduction of the channel and JFET resistance components in the planar MOSFET structure designed for lower (< 30 volts) voltage applications. This UMOSFET structure has also been explored for silicon carbide as described in a subsequent chapter.

In silicon power MOSFETs, the on-resistance becomes dominated by the resistance of the drift region when the breakdown voltage exceeds 200 volts[2]. At high breakdown voltages, the specific on-resistance for these devices becomes greater than 10^{-2} Ω-cm^2 leading to an on-state voltage drop of more than 1 V at a typical on-state current density of 100 A/cm^2. For this reason, the Insulated Gate Bipolar Transistor (IGBT) was developed in the 1980s to serve medium and high power systems[2]. The superior performance of the IGBT in high voltage

287

applications relegated the silicon MOSFETs to applications with operating voltages below 100 volts. Novel super-junction devices that utilize the charge-coupling concept have allowed extending the breakdown voltage of silicon power MOSFETs to the 600 volt range[3]. However, their specific on-resistance is still quite large limiting their use to high operating frequencies where switching losses dominate. The poor reverse recovery performance of the body diode of these super-junction Si MOSFETs can produce large switching losses.

In principle, the much lower resistance of the drift region in silicon carbide devices should enable development of power MOSFETs with very high breakdown voltages. These devices offer not only fast switching speed but also superior safe operating area when compared to high voltage silicon IGBTs. This allows reduction of both the switching loss and conduction loss components in power circuits[4]. However, the power MOSFET structures developed in silicon cannot be simply copied to form high performance SiC devices. Firstly, the lack of significant diffusion of dopants in SiC prevents the use of the silicon DMOS process. Secondly, a high electric field occurs in the gate oxide of the SiC MOSFET exceeding its rupture strength leading to catastrophic failure of devices in the blocking mode at high voltages. Thirdly, the P-base doping concentration becomes an order of magnitude smaller than for the Si case. This creates a P-base reach-through problems that can drastically reduce the blocking voltage. Fourthly, when compared with silicon, the smaller band offset between the conduction band of SiC and silicon dioxide can produce injection of hot carriers into the oxide leading to instability during operation. In addition, the quality of the oxide-semiconductor interface for SiC must be improved to allow good control over the threshold voltage and the channel mobility.

This chapter begins with a review of the basic principles of operation of the SiC planar power MOSFET structure. A SiC planar power MOSFET structure formed by staggering the ion implantation of the P-base and N^+ source regions to create the channel is then described. Next, the problem of exacerbation of reach-through breakdown in SiC is considered. Based upon fundamental considerations, the difference between the threshold voltage for silicon and SiC structures is analyzed. The relatively high doping concentrations and large channel lengths required to prevent reach-through are shown to be serious limitations to obtaining low specific on-resistance in these devices. In addition, the much larger electric field in the drift region for SiC devices is shown to lead to a high electric field in the gate oxide. Structures designed to reduce the electric field at the gate oxide by using a shielding region are therefore essential to realization of practical SiC planar-gate MOSFETs even after the MOS interface quality is improved. These structures are described and analyzed next in the chapter.

The operating frequency of power electronic circuits is being increased when replacing Si IGBTs with SiC power MOSFETs to take advantage of their unipolar operating physics. The use of higher frequencies in the power circuit enables reduction of the size, weight, and cost of passive elements such as inductors and filters that provide benefits which offset the higher cost of SiC power MOSFETs. Efforts to create SiC planar-gate MOSFETs with improved high frequency performance are therefore described in the chapter.

Replacement of Si IGBTs in motor drive applications, such as electric vehicles, with SiC power MOSFETs requires demonstration of good short-circuit (SC) withstand capability. Structural alterations to improve the SC withstand time are described in the chapter together with the trade-off in increased on-resistance. A novel SC improvement concept, called the BaSIC topology, is described for enhancing SC capability and preventing failure of SiC power MOSFETs under repetitive SC events.

Experimental results on relevant structures is then reviewed to define the state of the development effort on these devices. Commercial planar-gate SiC power MOSFETs are available with blocking voltage ratings of 600, 900, 1200, and 1700 V. Significant effort is underway to extend the blocking voltage rating to 3300 V and beyond.

11.1 Planar-Gate SiC Power MOSFET Structure

The basic structure of the SiC planar power MOSFET is shown in Fig. 11.1 together with the location of the ion implantation mask edges. In recognition of the low diffusion coefficients for dopants in silicon carbide, it was proposed[5] that the P-base and N^+ source ion implantations be staggered by using photoresist masks rather that be defined by the gate edge. This approach with staggered P-base and N^+ source implants was subsequently used to fabricate high voltage devices[6]. These devices have been called DIMOSFETs because of the Double-Implant process used for their fabrication. The measured performance of these structures is discussed at the end of the chapter.

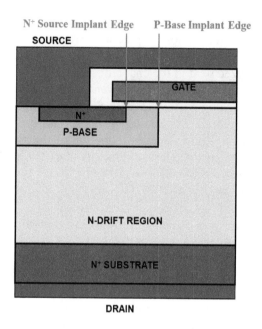

Fig. 11.1 The SiC planar power MOSFET structure.

11.1.1 Reach-Through Problem

The voltage is supported by a depletion region formed on both sides of the P-base/N-drift junction during the forward blocking mode of the SiC planar power MOSFET structure. The maximum blocking voltage can be determined by the electric field at this junction becoming equal to the critical electric field for breakdown if the parasitic $N^+/P/N$ bipolar transistor is completely suppressed. This suppression is accomplished by short-circuiting the N^+ source and P-base regions using the source metal as shown on the upper left hand side of the cross-section in Fig. 11.1. However, a large leakage current can occur when the depletion region in the P-base region reaches-through to the N^+ source region. This reach-through phenomenon will then limit the blocking voltage. The doping concentration and thickness of the P-base region must be designed to prevent the reach-through phenomenon from limiting the breakdown voltage.

Limitation of the blocking voltage for power MOSFETs due to reach-through of the P-base region is a well-known design consideration for silicon power MOSFETs[2]. The problem of reach-through is exacerbated for SiC devices due to the high doping concentration of the

N-type drift region and the higher electric field at the P-N junction. The applied drain voltage is supported by the N-drift region and the P-base region with a triangular electric field distribution as shown in Fig. 11.2 if the doping is uniform on both sides.

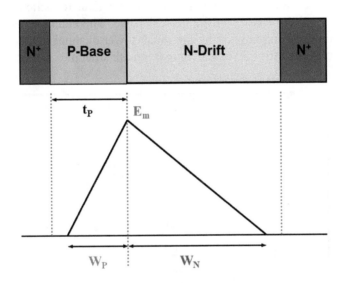

Fig. 11.2 Electric field reach-through in the P-base region of a SiC power MOSFET structure.

The maximum electric field occurs at the P-base/N-drift junction. The depletion width on the P-base side is related to the maximum electric field by:

$$W_P = \frac{\varepsilon_S E_m}{qN_A} \qquad [11.1]$$

where N_A is the doping concentration in the P-base region. The minimum P-base thickness required to prevent reach-though limited breakdown can be obtained by assuming that the maximum electric field at the P-base/N-drift junction reaches the critical electric field for breakdown when the P-base region is completely depleted:

$$t_P = \frac{\varepsilon_S E_C}{qN_A} \qquad [11.2]$$

where E_C is the critical electric field for breakdown in the semiconductor.

The calculated minimum P-base thickness for 4H-SiC power MOSFETs is compared with that for silicon devices in Fig. 11.3. At any given P-base doping concentration, the thickness for 4H-SiC is about six times larger than for silicon. This implies that the minimum channel length required for SiC devices is much larger than for silicon devices resulting in a big increase in the on-resistance. The enhancement of the on-resistance is compounded by the much lower channel inversion layer mobility observed for SiC when compared with silicon.

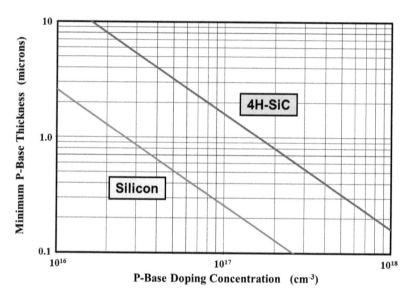

Fig. 11.3 Comparison of minimum P-base thickness to prevent reach-through breakdown in 4H-SiC and Si power MOSFETs.

The minimum thickness of the P-base region required to prevent reach-through breakdown decreases with increasing doping concentration as shown in Fig. 11.3. The typical P-base doping concentration for silicon power MOSFETs is 1×10^{17} cm^{-3} to obtain a threshold voltage between 1 and 5 volts for a gate oxide thickness of 500 to 1000 Å. At this doping level, the P-base thickness can be reduced to 0.5 μm without reach-through limiting the breakdown voltage. In contrast, it is necessary to increase the P-base doping concentration to above 4×10^{17} cm^{-3} for 4H-SiC to prevent reach-through with a 0.5 μm P-base thickness. This larger doping concentration makes the threshold voltage very large for 4H-SiC devices as discussed later in the chapter.

The P-base reach-through problem can be overcome by using a shielding region as discussed in the next section. The shielding region also allows achieving reasonable threshold voltages and preventing gate oxide reliability problems.

11.2 Shielded SiC Planar Power MOSFET

In the previous section, it was demonstrated that the conventional Si planar power DMOSFET structure cannot be utilized for SiC devices due to a P-base reach-through problem. This issue can be addressed by shielding the channel from the high electric field developed in the drift region. The concept of shielding of the channel region was first proposed at PSRC in the early 1990s with a U.S. patent issued in 1996[7]. The shielding was accomplished by formation of either a P^+ shielding region under the channel or by creating a high resistivity conduction barrier region under the channel with argon ion implantation.

This section begins with a review of the basic principles of operation of the shielded planar MOSFET structure. The impact of shielding on ameliorating the reach-through breakdown in SiC planar-gate power MOSFETs is described. This shielding approach has also been used very effectively for improvement of even Si low voltage planar power MOSFETs[8]. The P^+ shielding region also allows creating a SiC planar-gate power MOSFET with an N-base region where an accumulation channel region is formed to turn-on the device. Electrons in the accumulation-channel have a larger mobility than in inversion layers due to reduced band-bending at the SiC surface. This concept was met with skepticism when first proposed because of the assumption that an un-depleted N-type region is formed under the gate leading to a normally-on device. The accumulation-channel 4H-SiC MOSFETs are actually normally-off enhancement-mode structures.

The results of two-dimensional numerical simulations of the shielded planar-gate 4H-SiC power MOSFET structure are included in this section to demonstrate that the shielding concept also enables reduction of the electric field developed in the gate oxide leading to the possibility to fully utilize the breakdown field strength of the underlying semiconductor drift region. They are used to show the formation of a potential barrier for electrons in the channel for the accumulation-mode devices. The shielded accumulation-mode MOSFET structure (named the ACCUFET) discussed in this section has the most promising characteristics for the development of planar-gate power MOSFETs from 4H-SiC.

11.2.1 Shielded Planar-Device Structure

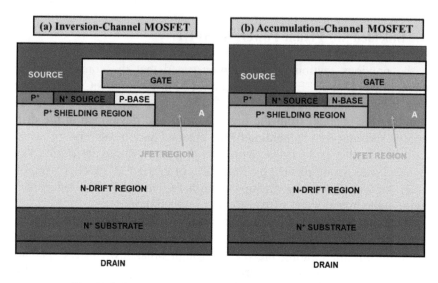

Fig. 11.4 Shielded planar-gate SiC power MOSFET structures.

The basic structures of the shielded SiC planar power MOSFET are shown in Fig. 11.4 with either P-base or N-Base region. The structure with the P-base region creates an inversion-mode MOSFET, while the structure with the N-base region creates an accumulation-mode MOSFET. A deep P^+ shielding region has been incorporated into both of these structures. In the case of the structure with the inversion layer channel, the P^+ shielding region extends under both the N^+ source region as well as under the P-base region. It could also extend beyond the edge of the P-base region. In the case of the structure with the accumulation layer channel, the P^+ shielding region extends under the N^+ source region and the N-base region located under the gate. This N-base region can be formed using an uncompensated portion of the N-type drift region or it can be created by adding N-type dopants near the upper surface with ion implantation or epitaxial growth to independently control its thickness and doping concentration.

The gap between the P^+ shielding regions is optimized to obtain a low specific on-resistance while simultaneously shielding the gate oxide interface from the high electric field in the drift region. In both of the structures shown in Fig. 11.4, a potential barrier is formed at location A after the JFET region becomes depleted by the applied drain bias in the blocking mode. This barrier prevents the electric field from becoming large at the gate oxide interface. The potential barrier also prevents reach-through breakdown in the P-base region even if it has a low doping concentration to achieve desired threshold voltages.

Both of the device structures in Fig. 11.4 are normally-off or enhancement-mode devices with a positive threshold voltage. When a positive gate drive voltage is applied, an inversion layer or accumulation layer channel is formed in the structures enabling the conduction of drain current with a low specific on-resistance. The higher electron mobility in the accumulation layers reduces the channel resistance contribution bringing down the specific on-resistance of the power MOSFET.

11.2.2 Blocking Mode

In the forward blocking mode of the shielded 4H-SiC planar-gate power MOSFET structure, the voltage is supported by a depletion region formed on both sides of the P^+ shielding region/N-drift junction. The maximum blocking voltage can be determined by the electric field at this junction becoming equal to the critical electric field for breakdown if the parasitic $N^+/P/N$ bipolar transistor is completely suppressed. This suppression is accomplished by short-circuiting the N^+ source and P^+ regions using the source metal as shown on the upper left hand side of the cross-section. This short circuit can be accomplished at a location orthogonal to the cell cross-section. This eliminates the P^+ contact region in cell allowing shrinking the cell pitch to reduce of the specific on-resistance. If the doping concentration of the P^+ region is high (e.g. 1 x 10^{18} cm^{-3}), the reach-through breakdown problem discussed in the previous chapter is completely eliminated. In addition, the high doping concentration in the P^+ region promotes the depletion of the JFET region at lower drain voltages providing enhanced shielding of the channel and gate oxide.

With the shielding provided by the P^+ region, the minimum P-base thickness for 4H-SiC power MOSFETs is no longer constrained by the reach-through limitation discussed in the previous section. This enables reducing the channel length below the values associated with any particular doping concentration of the P-base region that were shown in Fig. 11.3. The P-base doping concentration can be decreased to allow achieving the threshold voltage as discussed later in the chapter. The smaller channel length and threshold voltage provide the benefits of reducing the channel resistance contribution.

In the case of the accumulation-mode planar-gate 4H-SiC power MOSFET structure, the presence of the sub-surface P^+ shielding region under the N-base region creates a P-N junction. The built-in potential of the P-N junction is sufficient to *completely deplete* the N-base region if its doping concentration and thickness are appropriately chosen. A potential barrier is then formed in the N-base region that cuts-off the flow of electrons from the N^+ source region to the JFET region at zero gate bias. This enables *normally-off operation* of the accumulation-mode planar-gate 4H-SiC power MOSFET. The channel potential barrier does not have to have a large magnitude because the depletion of the JFET region screens the channel from the drain bias. It is worth pointing out that this mode of operation is fundamentally different than that of buried channel MOS devices[9]. Buried channel devices contain an un-depleted N-type channel region that provides a current path for drain current flow at zero gate bias. This channel region must be depleted by a negative gate bias creating a normally-on device structure which is not suitable for power electronics applications.

The maximum blocking voltage capability of the shielded 4H-SiC planar-gate power MOSFET structure is determined by the drift region doping concentration and thickness as already discussed in chapter 3. However, to fully utilize the high breakdown electric field strength available in SiC, it is important to screen the gate oxide from the high field within the semiconductor. In the shielded 4H-SiC planar-gate power MOSFET structure, this is achieved by the formation of a potential barrier at location A by the depletion of the JFET region at a drain bias voltage well below the blocking voltage rating of the device.

11.2.3 Inversion Channel Structure Simulations

The results of two-dimensional numerical simulations of the planar-gate 4H-SiC shielded inversion-mode planar-gate MOSFET structure are provided here to give insight into its operation. A drift region doping concentration of 1×10^{16} cm^{-3} and thickness of 10 μm was chosen corresponding to a device with a blocking voltage rating of 1200 volts. The baseline device had a gate oxide thickness of 400 Å and a P^+ shielding region depth of 1 μm. The P-base region had a thickness of 0.2 μm with a doping concentration of 9×10^{16} cm^{-3}. The JFET width (space between the P^+ shielding regions) for the baseline device was

1.5 μm. The channel length was 1.0 μm. The cell pitch for the structure, corresponding to the cross-section shown in Fig. 11.4(a), was 3.25 μm.

The blocking capability of the planar-gate 4H-SiC shielded inversion-mode power MOSFET was investigated by maintaining zero gate bias while increasing the drain voltage. It was found that the drain current remains below 1×10^{-13} amperes up to a drain bias of 1200 volts. Consequently, the shielding of the P-base region is very effective for preventing the reach-through breakdown problem allowing the device to operate up to the full capability of the drift region.

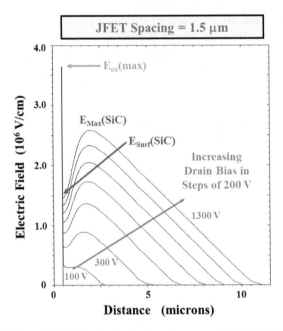

Fig. 11.5 Electric field distribution in the planar-gate 4H-SiC shielded inversion-mode power MOSFET structure for JFET width of 1.5 μm.

In the planar-gate 4H-SiC shielded inversion-mode MOSFET structure, the largest electric field at the gate oxide interface occurs at the center of the JFET region. Vertical profiles of the electric field, obtained at increasing drain bias voltages, at this location in the cross-section are shown in Fig. 11.5 for the case of a JFET width of 1.5 μm. From this figure, it is apparent that there is considerable shielding of the gate oxide by the JFET region due to the formation of a potential barrier when this region becomes depleted at lower drain voltages. The maximum electric field $E_{Max}(SiC)$ inside the semiconductor occurs at a depth of about 2 μm rather than at the surface due to the presence of the P⁺ shielding region. The electric field in the oxide $E_{ox}(max)$ reaches a magnitude of 3.5 x 10⁶ V/cm at a drain bias of 1300 volts as indicated by the green arrow. This value is sufficiently low to allow reliable operation of the shielded 4H-SiC planar-gate power MOSFET structure up to 275 °C as discussed in a subsequent section.

A potential barrier is formed in the P-base region at zero gate bias to prevent the follow of electrons from the N⁺ source region to the JFET region. This potential distribution along the channel is provided in Fig. 11.6 for the inversion-mode structure at various drain bias voltages. It can be seen that a large potential barrier of 2.8 eV in magnitude is created due to the presence of the P-base region. The potential barrier extends over a width of about 0.5 μm in the P-base region. Its height does not change with drain bias up to 1300 V providing the desired suppression of current via the P-base region during the blocking-mode.

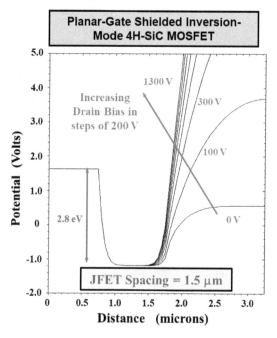

Fig. 11.6 Channel potential barrier in the planar-gate 4H-SiC shielded inversion-mode power MOSFET structure.

11.2.4 Accumulation Channel Structure Simulations

Two-dimensional numerical simulations of the planar-gate 4H-SiC shielded accumulation-mode power MOSFET structure can provide valuable insight into its operation in the blocking mode. A drift region doping concentration of 1×10^{16} cm^{-3} and thickness of 10 μm was chosen corresponding to a device with a blocking voltage rating of 1200 volts. The baseline device had a gate oxide thickness of 400 Å and a P$^+$ shielding region depth of 1 μm. The N-base region had a thickness of 0.2 μm with a doping concentration of 8.5×10^{15} cm^{-3}. The JFET width (space between the P$^+$ shielding regions) for the baseline device was 1.5 μm. The channel length was 1.0 μm. The cell pitch for the structure, corresponding to the cross-section shown in Fig. 11.4(b), was 3.25 μm.

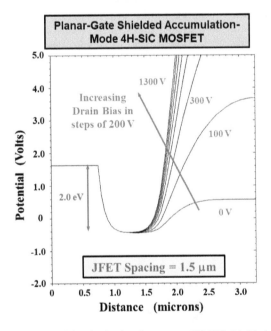

Fig. 11.7 Channel potential barrier in the planar-gate 4H-SiC shielded accumulation-mode power MOSFET structure.

The blocking capability of the planar-gate 4H-SiC shielded accumulation-mode power MOSFET was investigated by maintaining zero gate bias while increasing the drain voltage. It was found that the drain current remains below 1×10^{-13} amperes up to a drain bias of 1300 volts. This demonstrates that the depletion of the N-base region by the built-in potential of P^+/N junction creates a potential barrier for electron transport through the base region. In addition, the shielding of the N-base region by the underlying P^+ region is very effective for preventing the reach-through breakdown problem allowing the device to operate up to the full capability of the drift region.

It is instructive to examine the potential distribution along the channel in order to understand the ability to suppress current flow in the accumulation-mode structure with an N-base region. The variation of the potential along the channel is shown in Fig. 11.7 for the planar-gate 4H-SiC shielded accumulation-mode power MOSFET described above for various drain bias voltages when the gate bias voltage is held at zero volts. It can be seen that there is a potential barrier in the channel with a magnitude of 2 eV at zero drain bias, which is smaller than observed for the inversion-mode case. This is still a large potential barrier for electron transport from the N^+ source to the JFET region. This barrier for the transport of electrons from the source to the drain is upheld even when the drain bias is increased to 1300 volts. The fundamental operating principle for creating a normally-off device with a depleted N-base region formed using the built-in potential of the P^+/N is demonstrated by this plot.

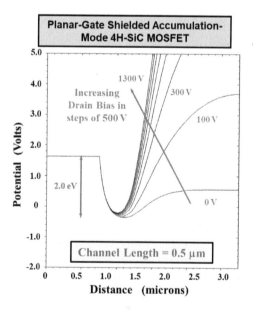

Fig. 11.8 Channel potential barrier in the planar-gate 4H-SiC shielded accumulation-mode power MOSFET structure.

The normally-off feature can be preserved in the planar-gate 4H-SiC shielded accumulation-mode power MOSFET structure even when the channel length is reduced to 0.5 µm. This can be demonstrated using the results of numerical simulations. The potential distribution along the channel for the accumulation channel structure with 0.5 µm channel length is shown in Fig. 11.8 for various drain bias voltages. It can be seen that, although the width of the barrier along the channel (x-direction in Fig. 11.8) is smaller than for the structure with the 1 µm channel length, the magnitude of the potential barrier for the transport of electrons from the source to the drain is still maintained at 2.0 eV. This is sufficient for obtained excellent blocking capability in the planar-gate 4H-SiC shielded accumulation-mode power MOSFET.

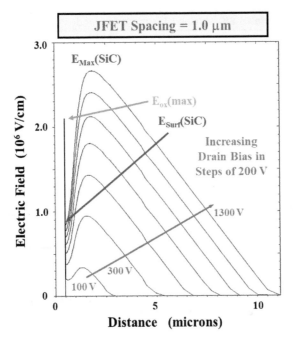

Fig. 11.9 Electric field distribution in the planar-gate 4H-SiC shielded accumulation-mode power MOSFET structure for JFET width of 1.0 µm.

The largest electric field at the gate oxide interface occurs at the center of the JFET region in the planar-gate 4H-SiC shielded accumulation-mode MOSFET structure. The behavior of this electric field with increasing drain bias was found to be identical to the profiles shown in Fig. 11.5 for the inversion-mode structure with the same JFET width of 1.5 µm. A further reduction of the electric field in the gate oxide can be achieved by reducing the width of the JFET region for both the inversion and accumulation mode structures. In order to illustrate this, the electric field distribution is shown in Fig. 11.9 for the case of a planar-gate 4H-SiC shielded accumulation-mode MOSFET structure with JFET width of 1 µm. It can be seen that the maximum electric field in the SiC at the gate oxide interface ($E_{Surf}(SiC)$) is reduced to 8.5 x 10^5 V/cm resulting in a maximum electric field in the gate oxide ($E_{ox}(max)$) of only 2.1 x 10^6 V/cm at a drain bias of 1300 volts. This value is sufficiently low for reliable operation of the structure even at 300 °C especially due to the planar gate structure, where there are no localized electric field enhancements under the gate electrode.

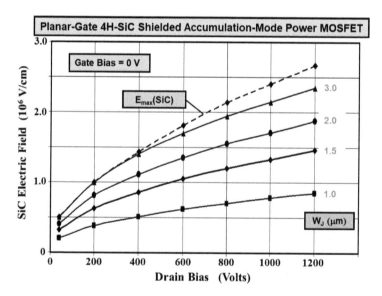

Fig. 11.10 Electric field suppression in the planar-gate 4H-SiC shielded accumulation-mode MOSFET structure.

The magnitude of the electric field developed in the vicinity of the gate oxide interface in the planar-gate 4H-SiC shielded accumulation-mode and inversion-mode MOSFET structures is dependent upon the width of the JFET region. The electric field at the gate oxide interface becomes smaller as the JFET width is reduced as shown in Fig. 11.10. It is reduced from close to the maximum electric field in the drift region ($E_{Max}(SiC)$) for a JFET width of 3.0 µm to 1.5 x 10^6 V/cm for a JFET width of 1.5 µm. For the structure with a drift region doping concentration of 1 x 10^{16} cm^{-3}, the optimum JFET width lies between 1 and 1.5 microns. The JFET width cannot be arbitrarily reduced because the resistance of the JFET region becomes very large when the width approaches the zero-bias depletion width of the P$^+$/N junction. The zero-bias depletion width is approximately 0.6 μm for a drift region doping concentration of 1 x 10^{16} cm^{-3}. Consequently, using a JFET width of 1.5 μm provides adequate space in the JFET region for current flow as shown subsequently in the chapter. The JFET width can be reduced to 0.7 mm by increasing the doping in the JFET region to 3 x 10^{16} cm^{-3}.

11.3 Threshold Voltage

The threshold voltage of the power MOSFET is an important design parameter from an application stand-point. A minimum threshold voltage must be maintained at above 1 volt for most system applications to provide immunity against inadvertent turn-on due to voltage spikes arising from noise. At the same time, a high threshold voltage is not desirable because the voltage available for creating the charge in the channel inversion layer is determined by ($V_G - V_T$) where V_G is the applied gate bias voltage and V_T is the threshold voltage. Most power electronic systems designed for high voltage operation (the most suitable application area for silicon carbide devices) provide a gate drive voltage of 15 volts. Based upon this criterion, the threshold voltage should be kept below 5 volts in order to obtain a low channel resistance contribution.

11.3.1 Inversion-Mode Channel

Manufacturers of SiC power MOSFETs define the threshold voltage as the gate bias at which a certain drain current is observed and do not scale this the die current rating. For an analytic model based on device physics, the threshold voltage is defined as the gate bias required for the on-set of *strong inversion* in the channel. This voltage can be determined using[10]:

$$V_{TH} = \frac{\sqrt{4\varepsilon_S kT N_A \ln(N_A / n_i)}}{C_{ox}} + \frac{2kT}{q} \ln\left(\frac{N_A}{n_i}\right) \qquad [11.3]$$

where N_A is the doping concentration of the P-base region, k is Boltzmann's constant, and T is the absolute temperature. The presence of positive fixed oxide charge shifts the threshold voltage in the negative direction by:

$$\Delta V_{TH} = \frac{Q_F}{C_{ox}}$$ [11.4]

A further shift of the threshold voltage in the negative direction by 1 volt can be achieved by using heavily doped N-type polysilicon as the gate electrode as routinely done for silicon power MOSFETs.

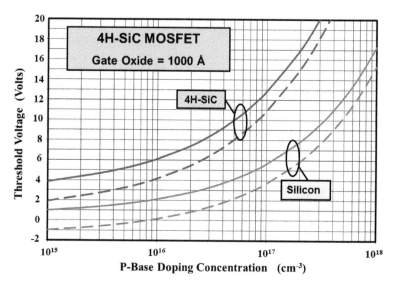

Fig. 11.11 Inversion-mode threshold voltages of 4H-SiC MOSFETs compared with Si MOSFETs for 1000 Å gate oxide.

(Dashed lines: With N$^+$ polysilicon gate and an oxide fixed charge of 2 x 10^{11} cm^{-2})

The analytically calculated threshold voltage for 4H-SiC planar power MOSFETs is shown in Fig. 11.11 for the case of a gate oxide thickness of 1000 Å. The results obtained for a Si power MOSFET with the same gate oxide thickness is also provided in this figure for comparison. In both cases, the impact of using an N$^+$ polysilicon gate electrode and taking account of a fixed oxide charge of 2 x 10^{11} cm^{-2} is shown by the dashed lines. This case is applicable to practical devices. In the case of Si devices, a threshold voltage of about 4 V is obtained for a P-base doping concentration of 1 x 10^{17} cm^{-3}. At this doping concentration, the depletion width in the P-base region for Si devices is less than 0.5 μm, as shown earlier in Fig. 11.3, even when the electric field in the semiconductor approaches the critical electric field for breakdown. This allows the design of silicon power MOSFETs with channel lengths of below 0.5 μm without encountering reach-through breakdown limitations. In contrast, a P-base doping concentration of about 3×10^{17} cm^{-3} is required in 4H-SiC (see Fig. 11.3) to keep the depletion width in the P-base region below 1 μm when the electric field in the semiconductor approaches the critical electric field for breakdown. At this doping concentration, the threshold voltage for the 4H-SiC MOSFET approaches 20 V. The much larger threshold voltage for 4H-SiC devices is related to its larger band gap as well as the higher P-base doping concentration required to suppress reach-through breakdown. This indicates a fundamental problem for achieving reasonable levels of threshold voltage in 4H-SiC power MOSFETs if the conventional Si structure is utilized.

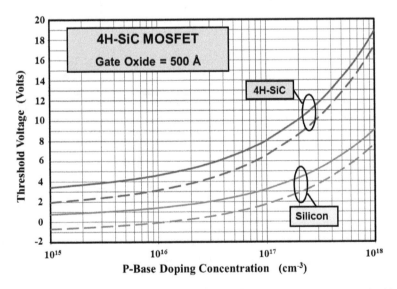

Fig. 11.12 Inversion-mode threshold voltages of 4H-SiC MOSFETs compared with Si MOSFETs for 500 Å gate oxide.

(Dashed lines: With N$^+$ polysilicon gate and an oxide fixed charge of 2×10^{11} cm^{-2})

The threshold voltage for a MOSFET can be reduced by decreasing the gate oxide thickness. The threshold voltage for the Si power MOSFET decreases to about 3 V as shown in Fig. 11.12 when the gate oxide thickness is reduced to 500 Å. This is common practice for the design of low voltage Si power MOSFETs that are often driven with logic-level (5 volt) gate signals. In the case of the 4H-SiC MOSFET with P-base doping concentration of 3×10^{17} cm^{-3}, the threshold voltage is reduced to 8 volts but this is still too large from an applications standpoint.

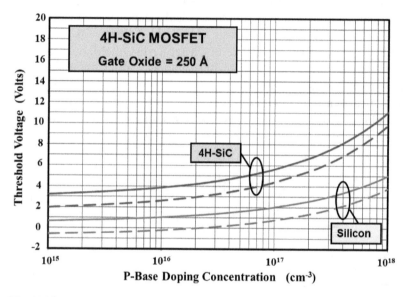

Fig. 11.13 Inversion-mode threshold voltages of 4H-SiC MOSFETs compared with Si MOSFETs for 250 Å gate oxide.

(Dashed lines: With N$^+$ polysilicon gate and an oxide fixed charge of 2×10^{11} cm^{-2})

A further reduction of the threshold voltage can be obtained by reducing the gate oxide thickness to 250 Å as shown in Fig. 11.13. For this gate oxide thickness, the threshold voltage for the Si MOSFET drops below 1 volt indicating the need to increase the P-base doping concentration to 2×10^{17} cm^{-3}. For the case of 4H-SiC MOSFETs, a threshold voltage now becomes about 6 volts for a P-base doping concentration to 3×10^{17} cm^{-3} which is still too high.

The above analysis indicates the P-base doping concentration for the 4H-SiC power MOSFETs must be reduced to the $1\text{-}2 \times 10^{16}$ cm^{-3} range to obtain threshold voltages of about 3 V. This would lead to reach-through breakdown voltage reduction for devices with P-base (and hence channel length) of 0.5 µm. This problem can be resolved by using the 4H-SiC planar-gate power MOSFET structure with a P^+ shielding region discussed the previous section.

The threshold voltage of power MOSFETs decreases with increasing temperature. This variation is shown in Fig. 11.14 for the case of 4H-SiC and Si MOSFETs using a gate oxide thickness of 500 Å. It can be seen that there is a small reduction in the threshold voltage with temperature for both materials. The shift for the case of 4H-SiC case is less than for the Si case.

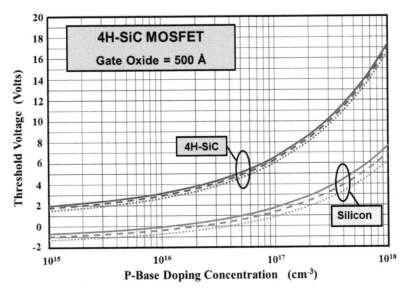

Fig. 11.14 Inversion-mode threshold voltages of 4H-SiC MOSFETs compared with Si MOSFETs for 3 temperatures.

(Solid line: 300 °K; Dashed line: 400 °K; Dotted line: 500 °K)

11.3.2 Accumulation-Mode Channel

For the inversion-mode MOSFET, the threshold voltage can be modeled by defining it as the gate bias at which on-set of *strong inversion* begins to occur in the channel. This voltage can be determined using. [11.3]. 4H-SiC inversion-channel power MOSFETs have a high threshold voltage, as shown in the previous section, due to much larger band bending required for this wider bandgap semiconductor when compared with silicon. The band bending required to create a channel in the accumulation-mode MOSFET is much smaller than required for the inversion mode device. This provides the opportunity to reduce the threshold voltage for 4H-SiC MOSFET while obtaining the desired normally-off device behavior.

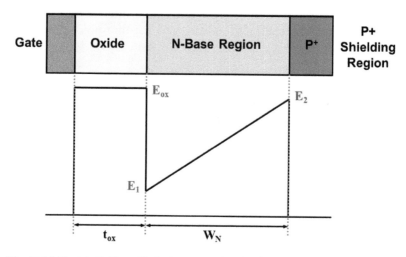

Fig. 11.15 Electric field profile in the gate region for the accumulation-mode 4H-SiC MOSFET structure.

A model for the threshold voltage of accumulation-mode MOSFETs has been developed[11] using the electric field profile shown in Fig. 11.15 when the gate is biased at the threshold voltage. The N-base region is located on top of the P^+ shielding region, which is heavily doped. The doping concentration N_D and width W_N of the N-base region are chosen so that it is completely depleted at zero gate bias by the built-in potential of the P-N junction. This produces the desired enhancement-mode or normally-off behavior of the accumulation-channel device. A positive gate bias opposes the built-in potential leading to the formation of an accumulation layer of electrons in the N-base region at the interface with the gate oxide. The formation of the accumulation layer begins when the gate bias is sufficient to reduce electric field E_1 to zero. This criterion can be used to derive an equation for the threshold voltage for the accumulation-mode case.

The electric fields in the semiconductor and oxide in Fig. 11.15 are given by:

$$E_1 = \frac{V_{bi}}{W_N} - \frac{qN_DW_N}{2\varepsilon_S} \qquad [11.5]$$

$$E_2 = \frac{V_{bi}}{W_N} + \frac{qN_DW_N}{2\varepsilon_S} \qquad [11.6]$$

$$E_{ox} = \frac{\varepsilon_S}{\varepsilon_{ox}} E_1 \qquad [11.7]$$

Note that this model is based upon neglecting any voltage supported within the P⁺ region under the assumption that it is very heavily doped. Using these equation, the threshold voltage is found to be given by:

$$V_{TH} = \phi_{MS} + \left(\frac{\varepsilon_S V_{bi}}{\varepsilon_{ox} W_N} - \frac{qN_DW_N}{2\varepsilon_{ox}} \right) t_{ox} \qquad [11.8]$$

The first term in this equation accounts for the work function difference between the gate material and the lightly doped N-base region. The second term represents the effect of the built-in potential of the P⁺/N junction that depletes the N-base region.

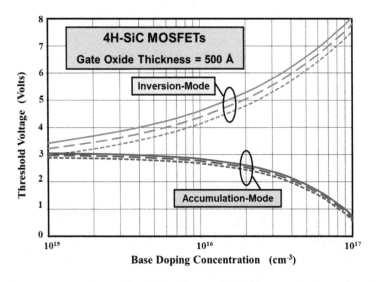

Fig. 11.16 Comparison of threshold voltages of 4H-SiC accumulation-mode and inversion-mode MOSFETs.

(Solid line: 300°K; Dashed line: 400°K; Dotted line: 500°K)

The analytically calculated threshold voltages for 4H-SiC accumulation-mode MOSFETs are provided in Fig. 11.16 for the case of a gate oxide thickness of 500 Å and N-base thickness of 0.2 μm as a function of the N-base doping concentration with the inclusion of a metal-semiconductor work-function difference of 1 volt. For comparison purposes, the threshold voltage for the inversion-mode 4H-SiC MOSFET is also given in this figure for the same gate oxide thickness. A strikingly obvious difference between the structures is a decrease in the threshold voltage for the accumulation-mode structure with increasing doping concentration in the N-base region. This occurs due to the declining influence of the P^+/N junction at the gate oxide interface when the doping concentration of the N-base region is increased. It can also be noted that the temperature dependence of the threshold voltage is smaller for the accumulation-mode structure. Of course, the most important benefit of the accumulation-mode is that lower threshold voltages can be achieved than in the inversion-mode structures. At an N-base doping concentration of 1×10^{16} cm^{-3}, the threshold voltage for the accumulation-mode structure is 2.8 V. This will be reduced to just below 2 V in the presence of typical fixed oxide charge in the 4H-SiC/oxide system. This model for the threshold voltage for the accumulation-channel MOSFET structure has been verified by numerical simulations[12]. The larger channel mobility and lower threshold voltage for the accumulation-channel 4H-SiC MOSFETs has also been experimentally confirmed[13].

All of the discussion presented on threshold voltage in this section is applicable to both the planar-gate and trench-gate 4H-SiC power MOSFET structures. The trench-gate structures are discussed in the next chapter.

11.4 Gate Oxide Reliability

In any MOSFET structure, the injection of electrons into the gate oxide can occur when the electrons gain sufficient energy in the semiconductor to surmount the potential barrier between the semiconductor and the oxide. The injection of these 'hot' electrons in the gate oxide can lead to shift in threshold voltage. This instability is highly undesirable for products operating over long time spans in applications.

The energy band offsets between the semiconductor and silicon dioxide are shown in Fig. 11.17 for Si and 4H-SiC for comparison. Due to the larger band gap of 4H-SiC, the band offset between the conduction band edges for the semiconductor and silicon dioxide is significantly smaller than for the case of Si. It is reduced from 3.15 eV to 2.70 eV. This makes it easier for electrons to surmount the barrier and transition from 4H-SiC to SiO₂ leading to threshold voltage instability.

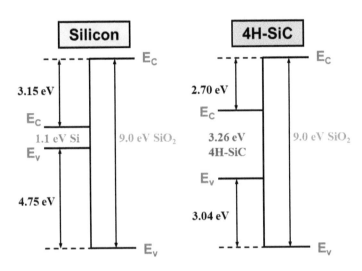

Fig. 11.17 Band offsets between silicon dioxide and semiconductors Si and 4H-SiC.

The band diagram for the 4H-SiC/SiO₂ interface is shown in Fig. 11.18 when a positive bias is applied to the gate. This bias condition is typical for the on-state mode of operation in power MOSFETs. The gate was assumed to be formed using polysilicon in this illustration. It can be seen that a narrow barrier is formed at the semiconductor-oxide interface which can be penetrated by the tunneling of electrons from the conduction band into the oxide. This produces a Fowler-Nordheim tunneling current that injects electrons into the oxide. This current has been observed in measurements reported on both 6H-SiC[14] and 4H-SiC[15] MOS-capacitors. The trapping of these electrons within the gate oxide can cause shifts in the threshold voltage of the MOSFET leading to reliability problems[16]. The reliability of the gate oxide has been determined by time dependent dielectric breakdown studies[17,18]. It was found that a 100-year mean-time-to-failure (MTTF) was achievable at 175 °C if the electric field in the gate oxide was kept below 6 MV/cm.

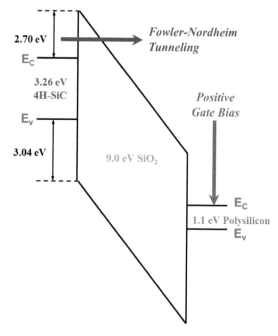

Fig. 11.18 Energy band diagram for the polysilicon/oxide/4H-SiC structure.

The maximum blocking voltage capability of the power MOSFET structure is determined by the drift region doping concentration and thickness as already discussed in chapter 3. However, in the SiC power MOSFET structure, a very high electric field also develops in the gate oxide in the JFET region under forward blocking conditions as shown in a previous section. For an MOS structure, the electric field developed in the oxide (E_{Oxide}) is related to the electric field in the underlying semiconductor by Gauss's Law:

$$E_{Oxide} = \left(\frac{\varepsilon_{Semi}}{\varepsilon_{Oxide}} \right) . E_{Semi} \qquad [11.9]$$

where ε_{Semi} and ε_{Oxide} are the dielectric constants of the semiconductor and the oxide and E_{Semi} is the electric field in the semiconductor. In the case of both Si (with $\varepsilon_r = 11.7$) and 4H-SiC (with $\varepsilon_r = 9.7$), the electric field in the silicon dioxide (with $\varepsilon_r = 3.85$) is about 3 times larger than in the semiconductor. Since the maximum electric field in the Si drift region remains below 3×10^5 V/cm, the electric field in the oxide does not exceed its reliability limit of about 3×10^6 V/cm. However, for 4H-

SiC, the electric field in the oxide reaches a value of 9×10^6 V/cm when the field in the semiconductor reaches its breakdown strength of about 3×10^6 V/cm. This value not only exceeds the reliability limit but can cause rupture of the oxide leading to catastrophic breakdown. It is therefore important to monitor the electric field in the gate oxide when designing and modeling the SiC MOSFET structures.

The failure rate for the gate oxide has been measured as a function of the electric field strength during the blocking mode[19,20]. The 63 % failure time (t_{63}) of 100 years was obtained at 175 °C at an oxide field of 6.5 MV/cm. The 63 % failure time (t_{63}) of 100 years can be achieved at 275 °C and 300 °C by reducing the oxide electric field to 4 M/cm and 1.5 MV/cm, respectively. From this data, it can be concluded that the width of the JFET region in the 4H-SiC planar-gate power MOSFET design must be optimized to not only reduce the specific on-resistance as performed for silicon devices but must be designed to adequately reduce the electric field in the oxide. Obtaining an electric field in the SiC less than 1 MV/cm below the gate oxide in the blocking mode is adequate for reliable operation. This can be accomplished by using the shielded planar-gate power MOSFET structure discussed in a previous section.

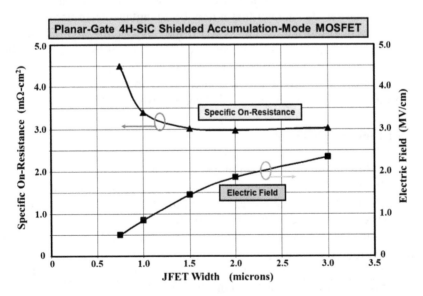

Fig. 11.19 Optimization of JFET width in the planar 4H-SiC shielded accumulation-mode MOSFET.

The optimization of the JFET width requires simultaneously taking into consideration the specific on-resistance and the electric field developed at the gate oxide interface in the blocking mode. The largest electric field at the boundary between the SiO_2 and 4H-SiC occurs at the middle of the JFET region. The changes in these parameters obtained using numerical simulations are illustrated in Fig. 11.19 for the case of an accumulation-channel planar-gate 4H-SiC power MOSFET. It can be seen that the electric field in the SiC below the gate oxide at the middle of the JFET region can be reduced to less than 1 MV/cm when the JFET width is reduced to 1 μm with a degradation of the specific on-resistance by about 10 %. The same results are obtained for the inversion-channel case. This demonstrates that a reliable accumulation-channel (or inversion channel) shielded 4H-SiC planar power MOSFET structure can be created by proper choice of the JFET width. This optimization has been discussed in the literature[21].

11.5 On-State Resistance

The on-resistance of the 4H-SiC power MOSFET is often the primary parameter used for its selection in a power electronic application. It will be shown later in the chapter that it may be advantageous to use the high-frequency figures-of-merit (HF-FOM) if the devices are targeted for use in circuits operating at high frequencies. The focus of this section is the optimization of the cell structure to achieve the lowest possible specific on-resistance. The commonly used linear-cell topology is discussed first followed by other cell geometries that can improve the HF-FOM.

11.5.1 Linear Cell Topology

Current flow between the drain and source can be induced in the power MOSFET structure by creating an inversion layer channel on the surface of the P-base region. The current path is illustrated in Fig. 11.20 by the green shaded area. The current flows through the inversion layer channel formed due to the applied gate bias into the JFET region via the accumulation layer formed above it under the gate oxide. It then spreads into the N-drift region at a 45 degree angle and becomes uniform through the rest of the structure. The total on-resistance for the planar-gate power MOSFET structure is determined by the resistances of all the components shown in Fig. 11.20 in the current path:

$$R_{on,sp} = R_{CH} + R_A + R_{JFET} + R_D + R_{subs} \qquad [11.10]$$

where R_{CH} is the channel resistance, R_A is the accumulation region resistance, R_{JFET} is the resistance of the JFET region, R_D is the resistance of the drift region after taking into account current spreading from the JFET region, and R_{subs} is the resistance of the N^+ substrate. In addition, the contact resistance to the N^+ source region must be included if the specific contact resistance is significant. This can happen if the contact is annealed at lower temperatures. The above resistances can be analytically modeled by using the current flow pattern indicated by the shaded regions in Fig. 11.20. In this figure, the depletion region boundaries have also been shown using red dashed lines.

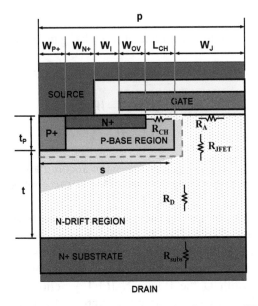

Fig. 11.20 Current flow path and resistances in the planar-gate 4H-SiC power MOSFET structure.

The specific contact resistance to the N^+ source region is given by:

$$R_{CS} = \rho_C \frac{W_{N+}}{p} \qquad [11.11]$$

where ρ_C is the specific contact resistance, W_{N+} is the width of contact to the N^+ source region shown in Fig. 11.20, and p is the cell pitch.

The specific channel resistance is given by:

$$R_{CH} = \frac{(L_{CH} \cdot p)}{\mu_{inv} C_{ox} (V_G - V_T)} \qquad [11.12]$$

where L_{CH} is the channel length as defined in Fig. 11.20, μ_{inv} is the mobility for electrons in the inversion layer channel, C_{ox} is the specific capacitance of the gate oxide, V_G is the applied gate bias, and V_T is the threshold voltage. The specific capacitance can be obtained using:

$$C_{ox} = \frac{\varepsilon_{ox}}{t_{ox}} \qquad [11.13]$$

where ε_{ox} is the dielectric constant for the gate oxide and t_{ox} is its thickness.

The specific resistance of the accumulation region is given by:

$$R_A = \frac{K(W_J - W_P) p}{\mu_a C_{ox} (V_G - V_{TA})} \qquad [11.14]$$

where μ_a is the mobility for electrons in the accumulation layer, C_{ox} is the specific capacitance of the gate oxide, V_G is the applied gate bias, and V_{TA} is the threshold voltage for forming an accumulation layer over the JFET region (close to zero). The factor K is used to account for two-dimensional current spreading from the channel into the JFET region with a typical value of 0.6 for silicon devices. The same value can also be applied for 4H-SiC power MOSFETs. In this equation, W_P is the zero-bias depletion width at the P-base/N-JFET junction. The JFET region doping concentration ($N_{D,JFET}$) is often increased above the drift region doping concentration for power MOSFETs with larger breakdown voltages. It can be determined using:

$$W_P = \sqrt{\frac{2\varepsilon_S V_{biP}}{q N_{D,JFET}}} \qquad [11.15]$$

where the built-in potential V_{biP} for the P-N junction is typically 3.3 V for 4H-SiC (can be calculated using Eq. [2.8]).

The specific JFET region resistance is given by:

$$R_{JFET} = \rho_D.t_P \left(\frac{p}{W_J - W_P} \right)$$
[11.16]

where t_p is the depth of the P-base region.

The drift region spreading resistance can be obtained by using:

$$R_D = \rho_D.p.\ln \left(\frac{p}{W_J - W_P} \right) + \rho_D.(t - s - W_P)$$
[11.17]

where t is the thickness of the drift region below the P-base region and s is the width of the P-base region.

The contribution to the resistance from the N^+ substrate is given by:

$$R_{subs} = \rho_{subs}.t_{subs}$$
[11.18]

where ρ_{subs} and t_{subs} are the resistivity and thickness of the substrate, respectively. A typical value for the N^+ substrate resistivity for 4H-SiC is 0.020 Ω-cm and its thickness if typically 300 μm leading to a contribution of 7 x 10^{-4} Ω-cm^2.

The design of a 1.2 kV 4H-SiC planar-gate power MOSFET is performed here as an example of device analysis and optimization using the above analytical models for the specific on-resistances. These devices are typical fabricated using a drift layer with thickness of 10 μm and doping concentration of 8 x 10^{15} cm^{-3}. The actual breakdown voltage for these devices is typically 1650 V. The hybrid-JTE edge termination design has a breakdown voltage larger then this because it is preferable for the avalanche current to be spread across the active area. The P-base region (including the P^+ shielding region that was previous discussed) has a depth of 0.8 μm. The typical size of the various regions shown in the cross-section of Fig. 11.20 based on modern fabrication tolerances are: $W_{P+} = 0.5$ μm; $W_{N+} = 0.5$ μm; $W_I = 0.5$ μm; $W_{OV} = 0.5$ μm; and $L_{CH} = 0.5$ μm. The current spreading factor (K in Eq. [11.14]) was 0.6 as also used for Si power MOSFETs[2]. A gate oxide thickness of 500 Å was used because most 4H-SiC power MOSFETs are manufactured with this thickness. A gate bias of 20 V was used with a threshold voltage of 2 V. The specific contact resistance (ρ_C) value of 0.01 mΩ-cm^2 was used for this case. This value can be obtained by annealing a Ni contact to 4H-SiC at 1000 °C. A typical value for the N^+ substrate resistivity for 4H-SiC is

0.020 Ω-cm and its thickness is typically 300 μm leading to a substrate contribution of 7×10^{-4} Ω-cm^2.

Using these parameters, the width of the JFET region (W_J) can be optimized to achieve the smallest specific on-resistance[20] as shown in Fig. 11.21. This example is called Case A in this section. It can be seen that the JFET and drift resistance components increase rapidly when the JFET width becomes smaller than 0.5 μm. The other components increase monotonically with increasing JFET width because of an increase in the cell pitch. The minimum specific on-resistance occurs at an optimum JFET width of close to 0.7 μm with a value of 3.15 mΩ-cm^2. It is worth pointing out that the N$^+$ substrate contribution is 21 % of the total specific on-resistance. This has been reduced by device manu-facturers by thinning the N$^+$ substrates on the back-side of the wafers after fabrication of the device structure on the top surface.

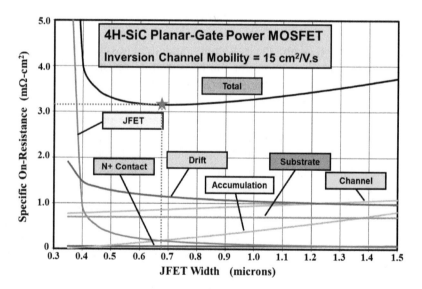

Fig. 11.21 Case A: Optimization of the on-resistance of an inversion-mode 1.2 kV rated 4H-SiC Planar-Gate MOSFET with channel length of 0.5 μm.

One of the design options to reduce the specific on-resistance is to place the P$^+$ contact region orthogonal to the cross-section at regular intervals[21]. Removal of the P$^+$ contact region from the cell cross-section reduces its cell pitch leading to lower specific on-resistance. This is illustrated in Fig. 11.22 as Case B. The specific on-resistance is reduced by 12 % to 2.82 mΩ-cm^2 with the same optimum JFET width.

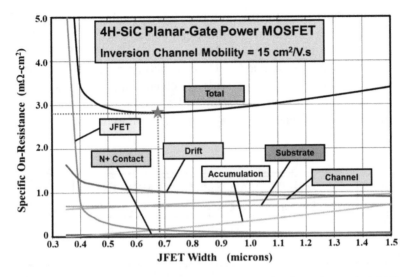

Fig. 11.22 Case B: Optimization of the on-resistance of an inversion-mode 1.2 kV rated 4H-SiC Planar-Gate MOSFET with channel length of 0.5 μm.

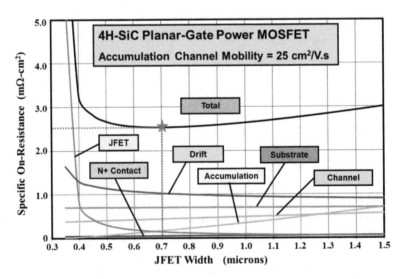

Fig. 11.23 Case C: Optimization of the on-resistance of an accumulation-mode 1.2 kV rated 4H-SiC Planar-Gate MOSFET with channel length of 0.5 μm.

The above results are based upon using an inversion-channel 4H-SiC planar-gate power MOSFET structure with channel mobility of 15 cm²/V-s. Most groups working on 4H-SiC power MOSFETs have

reported similar values for the inversion layer mobility in 4H-SiC structures[22]. However, the channel mobility can be increased to 25 cm²/V-s by
using the accumulation-channel device structure in Fig. 11.4[13,23]. The
specific on-resistance obtained in Case C with an accumulation channel
structure is shown in Fig. 11.23. Only the channel mobility was increased
while keeping the structure the same as Case B. It can be observed that
the specific on-resistance decreased to 2.53 mΩ-cm², a reduction of
11 %.

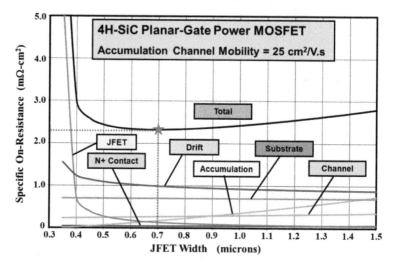

Fig. 11.24 Case D: Optimization of the on-resistance of an accumulation-mode
1.2 kV rated 4H-SiC Planar-Gate MOSFET with channel length of 0.3 μm.

A further reduction in the specific on-resistance can be achieved
by reduction of the channel length. Making the channel length too small
can lead to punch-through of the P-base region leading to poor blocking
characteristics. Numerical simulation have demonstrated that the channel
length can be reduced to 0.3 μm without encountering this problem[24].
The specific on-resistance obtained in Case D with an accumulation
channel structure with channel length of 0.3 μm is shown in Fig. 11.24.
Only the channel length was reduced while keeping the structure the
same as Case C. It can be observed that the specific on-resistance
decreased to 2.32 mΩ-cm², an improvement of 9 %. This behavior has
been experimentally confirmed for devices with 600 V blocking rating[24].

It is worth emphasizing that achieving low specific on-resistance
for the 4H-SiC power MOSFETs required obtaining a low specific

contact resistance for the N^+ source region. In some instances, it is not possible to anneal the contact at a high temperature (1000 °C). One example is when a low leakage current Schottky contact must be simultaneously achieved using same Ni metal layer as in the case of JBSFETs that are discussed in the next chapter. The specific on-resistance obtained in Case E with a high specific N^+ source contact resistance of 0.8 mΩ-cm^2 is shown in Fig. 11.25. Only the contact resistance was altered while keeping the structure the same as Case C. It can be observed that the minimum specific on-resistance increased substantially to 6.66 mΩ-cm^2, a degradation by 263 %.

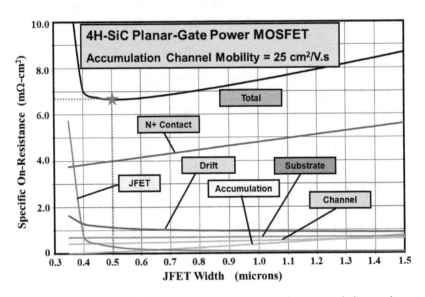

Fig. 11.25 Case E: Optimization of the on-resistance of an accumulation-mode 1.2 kV rated 4H-SiC Planar-Gate MOSFET with high N^+ source contact resistance.

11.5.2 Various Gate Electrode Topologies

In addition to the linear cell topology described in the previous section, Si planar-gate power MOSFETs have been developed using the hexagonal, square, and atomic-lattice polysilicon gate topologies[25]. Equations for the specific on-resistance for these cases have been derived in this reference. A novel octagonal cell topology was proposed and experimentally demonstrated for 4H-SiC planar-gate power MOSFETs more recently[26,27]. It was created to improve the high frequency figures of merit for SiC power MOSFETs.

The square cell topology for the polysilicon gate is illustrated in Fig. 11.26. In this case, a square shaped opening is etched in the polysilicon gate electrode with a square cell array. In the case of 4H-SiC planar-gate power MOSFETs, the positions of the boundaries for the N^+ source region and the base and P^+ shielding region boundaries are defined by the mask used to etch a thick oxide that serves as the ion-implantation mask. The channel is created by the separation of these boundaries. The P^+ plug to contact the P^+ shielding region is located in the middle of the polysilicon window. The contact window defines the area for making contact to the N^+ source region and the P^+ plug. The line A-B corresponds to the cross-section shown in Fig. 11.4. The JFET region extends beyond the edges of the base and P^+ shielding region boundary.

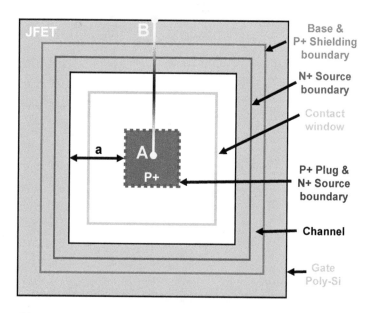

Fig. 11.26 Square Cell Topology for the 4H-SiC Planar-Gate MOSFET.

The main components of the specific on-resistance are: N^+ source contact $R_{CS,sp}$; channel $R_{CH,sp}$; accumulation layer $R_{A,sp}$; JFET region $R_{JFET,sp}$, and drift region $R_{D,sp}$. The analytical solutions for the specific on-resistance components derived for the square cell 4H-SiC inversion-channel planar-gate power MOSFET using a square shaped geometry are:

$$R_{CH,SP} = \frac{L_{CH}W_{Cell}^2}{4\left(W_{PW} + 2x_{JN+}\right)\mu_{ni}C_{OX}\left(V_G - V_{TH}\right)} \qquad [11.19]$$

$$R_{A,SP} = K_A \frac{\left(W_G - 2x_{JP}\right)W_{Cell}^2}{8\left(W_{PW} + 2x_{JP}\right)\mu_{nA}C_{OX}\left(V_G - V_{TH}\right)} \qquad [11.20]$$

$$R_{JFET,SP} = \frac{\rho_{JFET}x_{JP}W_{Cell}}{2\left(W_G - 2x_P - 2W_0\right)} \qquad [11.21]$$

$$R_{D,SP} = \frac{\rho_D W_{Cell}}{4}\ln\left[\frac{a + 2t}{a}\right] \qquad [11.22]$$

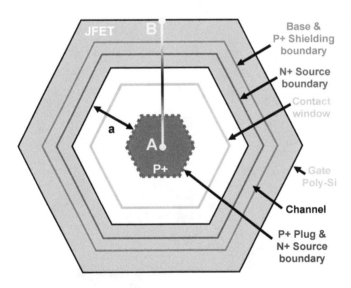

Fig. 11.27 Hexagonal Cell Topology for the 4H-SiC Planar-Gate MOSFET.

The Hexagonal cell topology has been commercialized for Si planar-gate power MOSFETs under the HEXFET moniker. This cell topology can be applied to 4H-SiC power MOSFETs as well. Analytical solutions for the specific on-resistance components derived for the Hexagonal cell 4H-SiC accumulation-channel planar-gate power MOSFET based up on a circular geometry are:

$$R_{CS,sp} = \rho_C \frac{\left(W_{AA'}\right)^2}{2r_C W_{N+}} \qquad [11.23]$$

$$R_{CH,sp} = \frac{L_{CH}(W_{AA'})^2}{2r_{CH}\mu_{NA}C_{OX}(V_G-V_{TH})}$$ [11.24]

$$R_{A,sp} = \frac{(W_{AA'})^2}{2\mu_{NA}C_{OX}(V_G-V_{TH})}\ln\left[\frac{r_{CH}+K_AW_{JFET}}{r_{CH}}\right]$$ [11.25]

$$R_{JFET,sp} = \frac{\rho_{JFET}x_{JP+}(W_{AA'})^2}{\left[(W_{AA'})^2-(r_{P+})^2\right]}$$ [11.26]

$$R_{D,sp} = \frac{\rho_D W_{AA'}}{2}\ln\left[\left(\frac{W_{AA'}}{W_{JFET}-W_{D,JFET}}\right)\right.$$
$$\left.\left(\frac{2W_{AA'}-W_{JFET}-W_{D,JFET}}{W_{AA'}}\right)\right]+\rho_D\left(t_{EPI}-x_{JP+}-r_{P+}\right)$$ [11.27]

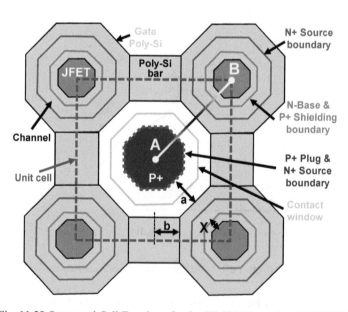

Fig. 11.28 Octagonal Cell Topology for the 4H-SiC Planar-Gate MOSFET.

The Octagonal cell topology was proposed for 4H-SiC power MOSFETs to improve the high-frequency figures-of-merit. Analytical solutions for the specific on-resistances derived for the Octagonal cell 4H-SiC accumulation-channel planar-gate power MOSFET based up on a circular geometry are:

$$R_{CS,sp} = \rho_C \frac{(W_{AA'})^2}{\pi r_c W_{N+}} \qquad [11.28]$$

$$R_{CH,sp} = \frac{(W_{AA'})^2}{\pi \mu_{NA} C_{OX}(V_G - V_{TH})} \ln\left[\frac{L_{CH} + W_{JFET}}{W_{JFET}}\right] \qquad [11.29]$$

$$R_{A,sp} = \frac{(W_{AA'})^2}{\pi \mu_{NA} C_{OX}(V_G - V_{TH})} \ln\left[\frac{W_{JFET} - W_{D,JFET}}{K_A W_{JFET}}\right] \qquad [11.30]$$

$$R_{JFET,sp} = \frac{2\rho_{JFET} x_{JP+}(W_{AA'})^2}{\left[\pi(W_{JFET} - W_{D,JFET})^2\right]} \qquad [11.31]$$

$$R_{D,sp} = \frac{2\rho_D W_{AA'}(W_{AA'} - W_{JFET})}{\pi W_{JFET}} + \rho_D(t_{EPI} - x_{JP+} - r_{P+}) \qquad [11.32]$$

In addition, the contribution from the N+ substrate must be added to all the cell topologies:

$$R_{SUB,SP} = \rho_{SUB} t_{SUB} \qquad [11.33]$$

The parameters used in these equations are defined in the Table I below. The radii in the table are defined along the line marked A-B in Fig. 11.27 and Fig. 11.28 for the hexagonal and octagonal cases. The width of the polysilicon window W_{PW} is the sum of W_{P+}, W_{N+}, and W_I; x_{JP} is the extension of the P^+ shielding region beyond the edge of the polysilicon gate edge; ρ_{JFET} is the resistivity of the JFET region; ρ_{SUB} and t_{SUB} are the resistivity and thickness of the N^+ substrate; $W_{AA'}$ is the width of the line A-B in the figures. V_G is the gate bias voltage and V_{TH} is the threshold voltage.

A comparison of the specific on-resistance components for the linear, square, hexagonal, and octagonal cell topologies obtained by using the above models for the case of 1.2 kV 4H-SiC planar-gate accumulation-channel power MOSFETs is provided in Table II. A gate oxide thickness of 500 Å was used with gate drive voltage of 20 V and threshold voltage of 2 V. A JFET width of 0.7 μm was used for all the cell topologies with a distance A-B of 2.8 μm. An accumulation-channel mobility of 25 cm²/V-s was used based on measured data on devices in the literature.

Table I: Definition of Device Parameters

Parameter	Definition
ρ_C	Specific contact resistance to the N+ source region
r_C	Contact radius
L_{CH}	Channel Length
r_{CH}	Channel radius
C_{OX}	Gate oxide specific capacitance
K_A	Current spreading factor
W_{JFET}	Half-cell JFET width
ρ_{JFET}	JFET region resistivity
X_{JP+}	Depth of P+ shielding region
r_{P+}	Radius of P+ shielding region
ρ_D	Resistivity of drift region
W_{DJFET}	Depletion width in JFET region
μ_{NA}	Accumulation channel mobility
μ_{ni}	Inversion channel mobility
t_{EPI}	Epitaxial layer thickness
W_{P+}	Width of P+ contact region
W_{N+}	Width of N+ contact region
W_I	Width of contact to poly-gate
W_{OV}	Width of overlap between gate and N+ source
W_{PW}	Width of Polysilicon Window

Table II: Specific On-Resistance in $m\Omega\text{-}cm^2$

Cell Type	Linear	Square	Hexagonal	Octagonal
$R_{CS,SP}$	0.056	0.105	0.078	0.067
$R_{CH,SP}$	0.457	0.320	0.284	0.439
$R_{A,SP}$	0.178	0.108	0.199	0.126
$R_{JFET,SP}$	0.149	0.083	0.094	0.016
$R_{D,SP}$	0.97	0.746	0.815	1.465
$R_{SUB,SP}$	0.70	0.70	0.70	0.70
$R_{TOTAL,SP}$	**2.510**	**2.062**	**2.171**	**2.813**

It be observed from Table II that the lowest total specific on-resistance $R_{TOTAL,SP}$ is obtained with the square cell topology. It is better than the commonly used linear cell case by 22 %. The hexagonal cell topology has the next best performance. The highest $R_{TOTAL,SP}$ is observed for the Octagonal cell topology. However, it has a very low gate-drain capacitance and charge as shown later in the chapter, which yield superior high frequency figures-of-merit. The above trends observed using the analytical models have been reported for fabricated devices[28].

11.5.3 Implant Straggle

In the previous section 11.5.1, it was shown that the width of the JFET region must be optimized to achieve the lowest specific on-resistance for 4H-SiC planar-gate power MOSFETs. In this structure, the P$^+$ shielding region is formed by ion-implantation of aluminum to the desired depth. The Al ions have been found to scatter under the SiO$_2$ mask creating a sideways extension of the P-N junction. This is referred to as the *ion-implant straggle*. The Al ion implantation energy used for the typical P$^+$ shielding region depth of 0.8 μm produces a lateral straggle of 0.33 μm. The impact of this straggle on the cell structure is illustrated in Fig. 11.29. The width of the JFET region is shortened from 0.70 to 0.37 μm. This increases the JFET and drift region resistance components. Equally importantly, the channel length of the MOSFET is increased by the straggle from 0.3 μm to 0.63 μm in the example. This occurs because the P-base region is formed above the P$^+$ shielding region with a self-aligned process for these region. This increases the channel resistance component and reduces the transconductance as well.

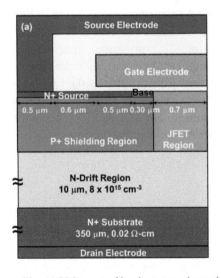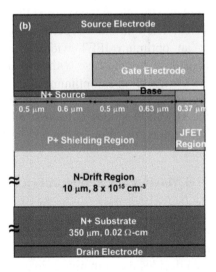

Fig. 11.29 Impact of implant straggle on the 4H-SiC Planar-Gate MOSFET structure.

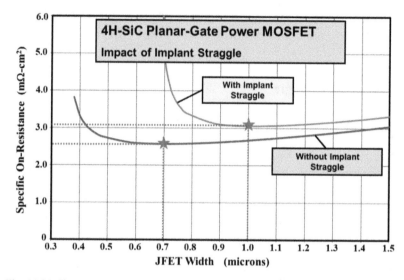

Fig. 11.30 Change in specific on-resistance of the 4H-SiC Planar-Gate MOSFET due
to ion implant straggle of the P^+ shielding region.

The impact of the ion implant straggle of the P^+ shielding region
on the specific on-resistance is demonstrated in Fig. 11.30 for the 1.2 kV
4H-SiC planar-gate power MOSFET case D with channel length of
0.3 μm. The red line in the figure for the specific on-resistance without
implant straggle is the same as the total specific on-resistance line in Fig.
11.24. The minimum specific on-resistance has a value of 2.58 mΩ-cm²
at an optimum JFET width of 0.7 μm. The minimum specific on-
resistance for the case with implant straggle taken into consideration is
3.07 mΩ-cm² at an optimum JFET width of 1.0 μm. The implant straggle
increases the best achievable specific on-resistance by 19 %. It also alters
the HF-FOM values a discussed in a subsequent section. This behavior
has been reported in the context of experimental results[29].

11.6 Maximum Current Density

Most of the emphasis during the development and commercialization of
4H-SiC planar-gate power MOSFETs has been on the specific on-
resistance because it determines the active area of the devices. The active
area decides the chip dimensions which in turn determines the number of
devices that are manufactured on a single wafer. The device production

cost is reduced when more devices are manufactured on each wafer. The active area for the 4H-SiC power MOSFET is decided by the maximum allowable current density.

The maximum current density (J_{DM}) allowable for the power MOSFET as limited by continuous on-state operation is given by:

$$J_{DM} = \sqrt{\frac{\left(T_{JM} - T_A\right)}{R_{ON,SP} \cdot R_\theta}}$$ [11.34]

where T_{JM} is the maximum junction temperature, T_A is the ambient temperature, and R_θ is the steady-state thermal resistance. The typical maximum junction temperature for Si power MOSFETs is 150 °C but 4H-SiC devices are projected to operate up to 175 °C. From this equation, it can be concluded that the current handling capability for the 4H-SiC power MOSFET can be increased by reducing its specific on-resistance. For a particular current rating I_{DR}, the die active area can be obtained by dividing J_{DM} with I_{DR}. The operating current density for 4H-SiC power MOSFETs with different blocking voltages are discussed later in the book.

However, the cost of 4H-SiC power MOSFET is considerably ($\sim 3x$) larger than for Si IGBTs with the same ratings due to the high cost of the wafers. The justification for replacing Si IGBTs with 4H-SiC power MOSFETs requires reduction in the cost of the overall power electronic system. This is achievable if the frequency of operation of the power circuit is increased substantially. The larger operating frequency enables reduction in the size, weight, and cost of passive energy storage elements (inductors and capacitors) and filters used for noise abatement. At these higher operating frequencies, the switching losses in the 4H-SiC power MOSFETs becomes larger than the conduction losses incurred from the on-resistance. Device structures that can reduce the switching losses are therefore desired.

11.7 High-Frequency Figures-of-Merit

The turn-off switching waveforms for the 4H-SiC power MOSFET are shown in Fig. 11.31 for the case of an inductive load[30]. The turn-off occurs in two stages after an initial delay period where the gate voltage reduces exponentially to the plateau voltage (V_{GP}). In the first stage t_a to t_b, the drain voltage rises from the on-state voltage drop $V_{ON}(V_{GS})$ to the

DC supply voltage V_{DS}. During the second stage t_b to t_c the drain current drops from the on-state value I_L flowing through the load to zero. The switching losses occur during the time interval from t_a to t_c when both the drain current and voltage have a large magnitude simultaneously. The largest time interval is observed during the drain voltage transient from t_a to t_b, producing most of the total turn-off switching loss. During this period of time, the gate voltage remains constant at a plateau value V_{GP}. This is referred to as the *plateau phase*. The duration of the plateau is determined by the charging of the gate-drain capacitance (C_{GD})[30].

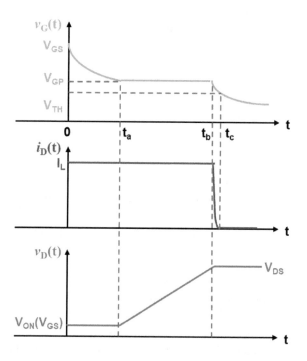

Fig. 11.31 Turn-off switching waveforms for the 4H-SiC Planar-Gate MOSFET for an inductive load.

The specific gate-drain capacitance for the planar-gate power MOSFET structure is given by[31]:

$$C_{GD,SP} = \frac{(W_G - 2x_{PL})}{W_{Cell}} \left(\frac{C_{OX} C_{S,M}}{C_{OX} + C_{S,M}} \right) \quad \text{[11.35]}$$

where C_{OX} is the specific oxide capacitance, $C_{S,M}$ is the specific semi-conductor capacitance under the gate oxide. The dimension $(W_G - 2x_{PL})$ in the equation is the same as the JFET width (W_{JFET}). The specific capacitance for the semiconductor is obtained using:

$$C_{S,M} = \frac{\varepsilon_S}{W_{D,MOS}}$$ [11.36]

with the depletion width under the MOS-gate region given by:

$$W_{D,MOS} = \frac{\varepsilon_S}{C_{OX}}\left\{\sqrt{1 + \frac{2V_D C_{OX}^2}{q\varepsilon_S N_D}} - 1\right\}$$ [11.37]

From these equations, it can be concluded that $C_{GD,SP}$ will decrease rapidly with increasing drain bias. Its value therefore changes during the drain voltage transient in Fig. 11.31.

A better measure of the duration of the drain voltage transient can be obtained by using the gate-drain charge (Q_{GD})[32].

$$Q_{GD} = J_G(t_3 - t_2) = \frac{2K_G q\varepsilon_S N_D}{C_{OX}}\left[\sqrt{1 + \frac{2V_{DS} C_{OX}^2}{q\varepsilon_S N_D}} - \sqrt{1 + \frac{2V_{ON} C_{OX}^2}{q\varepsilon_S N_D}}\right]$$

[11.38]

where V_{ON} is the on-state voltage drop and V_{DS} is the drain supply voltage. The parameter K_G for the planar-gate MOSFET is given by:

$$K_G(VD - MOSFET) = \left(\frac{W_G - 2x_{PL}}{W_{Cell}}\right)$$ [11.39]

Since the conduction power loss is determined by R_{on} and the switching loss by either C_{GD} or Q_{GD}, two suitable high-frequency figures-of-merit can be defined as HF-FOM[$R_{on}*C_{GD}$] and HF-FOM[$R_{on}*Q_{GD}$]. These figures-of-merit provide an assessment of the overall performance of a power MOSFET device technology. They can be used across different materials platforms (such Si, 4H-SiC and GaN) as long as the devices have the same voltage rating. They allow comparison of different device cell structures and cell architectural modifications.

Another important issue during operation of power MOSFETs in high frequency circuit power circuits is the rapid transition of the drain voltage while the device is in the off-state with zero gate bias. The high [dV$_D$/dt] at the drain can induce an increase in the gate voltage which is determined by the ratio [(C$_{GS}$ + C$_{GD}$)/C$_{GD}$][33]. The power MOSFET can be turned on by the [dV$_D$/dt] if the induced voltage at the gate exceeds the threshold voltage. The immunity from [dV$_D$/dt] induced turn-on can be assessed using another FOM[C$_{GS}$/C$_{GD}$].

The relative performance of four cell topologies discussed previously in section 11.5.2 has been experimentally evaluated for 1.2 kV rated 4H-SiC power MOSFETs with accumulation and inversion mode channels[28]. A summary of the measured data for the accumulation channel devices is given in Table III. The specific on-resistance follows the trends discussed in section 11.5.2 with lowest values for the Square and Hexagonal cell cases. However, the C$_{GD,SP}$ and Q$_{GD,SP}$ are much larger for the Square and Hexagonal cell topology when compared with the linear cell case. This makes their HF-FOM[R$_{ON}$*C$_{GD}$] and HF-FOM[R$_{ON}$*C$_{GD}$] much worse (larger) than the linear cell case. In contrast, C$_{GD,SP}$ and Q$_{GD,SP}$ are much smaller for the Octagonal cell topology when compared with the linear cell case. This makes the HF-FOM[R$_{ON}$*C$_{GD}$] and HF-FOM[R$_{ON}$*C$_{GD}$] for the Octagonal cell topology much better (smaller) than the linear cell case. This experimental data confirms the performance expected from the 4 types of cell designs.

Table III: Experimental Results

Structure	Linear	Square	Hexagonal	Octagonal
Breakdown Voltage (V)	1628	1338	1436	1605
Threshold Voltage (V)	1.96	2.16	2.14	2.12
R$_{ON,SP}$ (mΩ-cm^2)	5.61	5.53	5.50	8.47
C$_{GD,SP}$ (pF/cm^2)	106	392	386	48
Q$_{GD,SP}$ (nC/cm^2)	311	667	644	144
FOM[R$_{ON}$*C$_{GD}$]	595	2168	2123	407
FOM[R$_{ON}$*Q$_{GD}$]	1745	3689	3542	1220
FOM[C$_{GS}$/C$_{GD}$]	266	61	59	765

11.8 Enhanced HF-FOM Device Structures

4H-SiC planar-gate power MOSFET structures that allow reduction of the gate-drain capacitance (C$_{GD}$) and charge (Q$_{GD}$) have been investigated. Most often, this is achieved with additional process steps and at the expense of larger specific on-resistance. Many papers have been published on "proposed" SiC planar-gate power MOSFET structures with performance analyzed with numerical simulations alone. The simulations are performed with idealized structures that cannot be fabricated for experimental confirmation. Consequently, such structures are not included in the book.

11.8.1 Central Implanted Structure

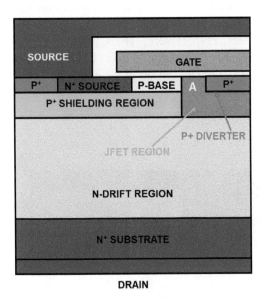

Fig. 11.32 4H-SiC Planar-Gate MOSFET structure with central implanted region, also referred to as a P+ diverter.

A 4H-SiC planar-gate power MOSFET structure containing a P^+ region in the center of the JFET region as shown in Fig. 11.32 was reported[34] in 2015. The structure was called the CI-MOSFET because the authors call this P^+ region a Central Implant region. The CI region is connected to the source electrode at a location orthogonal to the cross-section (not shown in the figure). The upper structure for this device is exactly the same as that reported[35] in 1994 for improving the latch-up current and reducing the gate-collector (Miller) capacitance for silicon IGBTs. It was experimentally demonstrated that the Miller capacitance could be reduced by a factor of 1.6-times in silicon IGBTs by incorporation of the P^+ diverter because it screens the collector from the gate electrode.

The same effect occurs in the 4H-SiC CI-MOSFET structure thereby reducing the gate-drain capacitance C_{GD} and the gate-drain charge Q_{GD}. However, a narrow width JFET region is formed in region A which can greatly increase the on-state resistance. By optimization of the CI structure, the gate-drain capacitance (C_{GD}) was reduced by a factor of 3 times and the gate-drain charge (Q_{GD}) was reduced by a factor of 2 times. In addition, the electric field in the gate oxide was reduced by 2 MV/cm. However, the addition of the CI region increased the specific on-resistance by 1.7 times from 3 to 5 mΩ-cm^2 as expected due to an enhanced JFET effect at point A in the cross-section. Consequently, the HF-FOM[R_{on}*C_{GD}] and HF-FOM[R_{on}*Q_{GD}] were improved by factors of 1.76 and 1.17 times, respectively. The CI-MOSFET can be fabricated without additional process steps if the CI region is formed simultaneously with the P$^+$ contact region in the cell.

11.8.2 Split-Gate Structure

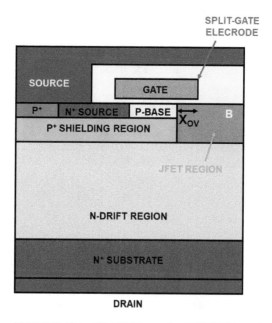

Fig. 11.33 Split-Gate 4H-SiC Planar-Gate MOSFET structure.

The gate-drain capacitance (C_{GD}) and charge (Q_{GD}) are created by the overlap of the gate electrode and the JFET region because the JFET region is connected to the drift region. These parameters can be reduced by forming a split-gate (SG) 4H-SiC planar-gate MOSFET structure shown in Fig. 11.33. The gate electrode is split to open a gap in the middle of the JFET region. The gate overlaps the JFET region with a design dimension X_{OV}. A smaller value for X_{OV} will reduce the overlap of the gate with the JFET region and make the gate-drain capacitance (C_{GD}) and charge (Q_{GD}) smaller.

A silicon power MOSFET with reduced reverse transfer capacitance (C_{GD}) was demonstrated in 1989[36]. A split-gate (SG) 4H-SiC planar gate power MOSFET structure with rating of 1.2 kV was therefore analyzed using numerical simulations and experimental data obtained on fabricated devices[37]. The drift region has a doping concentration of 8 x 10^{15} cm^{-3} and thickness of 10 μm. A gate oxide thickness of 550 Å was used to match experimentally fabricated devices. A JFET region width of 0.9 μm was used with doping enhanced to 3 x 10^{16} cm^{-3}. The variation of the gate-drain capacitance (C_{GD}) and charge (Q_{GD}) with changes in X_{OV} are shown in Fig. 11.34. A very large monotonic reduction in these parameters occurs when X_{OV} is reduced from 0.9 μm to 0.1 μm, which is main virtue of this structure.

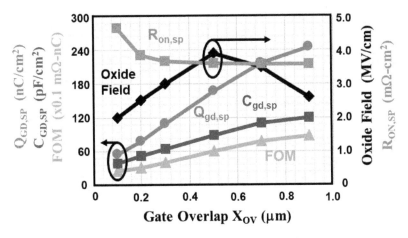

Fig. 11.34 Variation of device parameters with gate overlap X_{OV} in the Split-Gate 4H-SiC Planar-Gate MOSFET structure.

The changes in the specific on-resistance $R_{ON,SP}$ with reduction of X_{OV} is also tracked in Fig. 11.34. The resistance begins to increase when X_{OV} is made less than 0.3 μm. This is due to absence of the accumulation layer in the SG-MOSFET structure in portion B above the JFET region.

The electrons leaving the channel have to spread over a greater distance when the gate electrode does not extend across the entire JFET region which increases the resistance.

The sharp edge of the gate electrode created with the split-gate structure produces enhanced electric field in the gate oxide E_{GOX} in the blocking mode[37]. This electric field enhancement is mitigated by the presence of the source electrode over the gap in the gate electrode. It is important to ensure that the gate oxide electric field remains below 3 MV/cm for reliable operation. The variation of electric field E_{GOX} with the dimension X_{OV} is therefore tracked in Fig. 11.34. It has a maximum value when X_{OV} is 0.5 μm. Electric field E_{GOX} is reduced at smaller X_{OV} due to better shielding from the P^+ shielding region. Electric field E_{GOX} is reduced at larger X_{OV} due to the smaller gap between the gate electrodes. An Electric field E_{GOX} of less than 3 MV/cm is obtained when X_{OV} is less than 0.3 μm.

The improvement in the HF-FOM[$R_{on}*Q_{GD}$] with changes in X_{OV} are also shown in Fig. 11.34. A substantial reduction is observed with decreasing X_{OV} making the SG-MOSFET structure attractive for high frequency applications.

Table IV: 4H-SiC power SG-MOSFET Experimental Results

Structure	Conventional	Split-Gate
Breakdown Voltage (V)	1634	1626
Threshold Voltage (V)	2.00	2.08
$R_{ON,SP}$ (mΩ-cm^2)	6.35	6.30
$C_{GD,SP}$ (pF/cm^2)	110	82
$Q_{GD,SP}$ (nC/cm^2)	351	149
HF-FOM[$R_{ON}*C_{GD}$]	766	589
HF-FOM[$R_{ON}*Q_{GD}$]	2230	938
FOM[C_{GS}/C_{GD}]	367	492

The 4H-SiC power SG-MOSFET structure was fabricated simultaneously with the conventional structure with no additional process steps. The measured values for various device parameters of 1.2 kV 4H-SiC power SG-MOSFET devices fabricated in a 6 inch SiC wafer foundry are given in Table IV[37]. A summary of the data is provided in Table IV. The measured values of the breakdown voltage, threshold voltage and $R_{ON,SP}$ for the SG-MOSFET were the same as for the conventional structure. The $C_{GD,SP}$ measured at a drain bias of 1000 V for the SG-MOSFET was 1.34 times smaller than the conventional structure.

The $Q_{GD,SP}$ measured for the SG-MOSFET was 2.36 times smaller than the conventional structure. Consequently, the figures-of-merit HF-FOM[$R_{on}*C_{GD}$] and HF-FOM[$R_{on}*C_{GD}$] for the SG-MOSFET structure were 1.3 and 2.4 times superior to the conventional MOSFET. The FOM[C_{GS}/C_{GD}] is also improved by a factor of 1.3 times. It is remarkable that such a large improvement in performance can be obtained with no change in device fabrication steps.

11.8.3 Buffered-Gate Structure

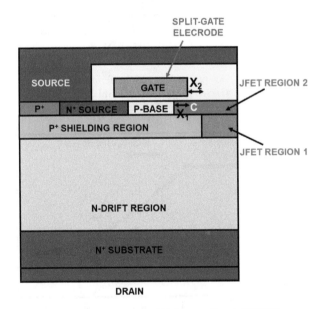

Fig. 11.35 Buffered-Gate 4H-SiC Planar-Gate MOSFET structure.

The buffered-gate (BG) 4H-SiC planar-gate power MOSFET structure was conceived to reduce the gate-drain capacitance (C_{GD}) and charge (Q_{GD}) even lower than possible with the SG-MOSFET structure[38]. In this structure, illustrated in Fig. 11.35, the P$^+$ shielding region extends beyond the edge of the split gate electrode by a buffering distance X_2. The built-in potential of the junction between the P$^+$ shielding region and the JFET region 1 is sufficient to completely deplete the region marked C in the figure. This will produce a very high on-resistance. This issue can be solved by including a second JFET region 2 with higher doping concentration near the top surface. Making this regions adds a process step during device fabrication.

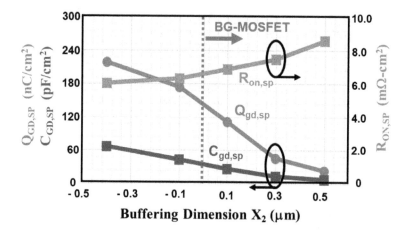

Fig. 11.36 Variation of device parameters with buffering dimension X₂ in the
Buffered-Gate 4H-SiC Planar-Gate MOSFET structure.

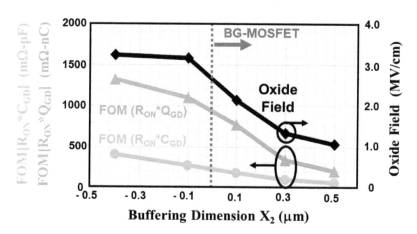

Fig. 11.37 Variation of device parameters with buffering dimension X₂ in the
Buffered-Gate 4H-SiC Planar-Gate MOSFET structure.

The buffered-gate (BG) 1.2 kV rated 4H-SiC planar gate power MOSFET structure was analyzed using numerical simulations[39]. The drift region has a doping concentration of 8×10^{15} cm^{-3} and thickness of 10 μm. A gate oxide thickness of 550 Å was used to match experimentally fabricated devices. A JFET region-1 width of 0.7 μm was used with doping enhanced to 3×10^{16} cm^{-3}.

The variation of the gate-drain capacitance (C_{GD}) and charge (Q_{GD}) with changes in buffering dimension X_2 are shown in Fig. 11.36. A very large reduction in these parameters occurs when X_2 is increased from 0 μm to 0.5 μm, which is main advantage of this structure. The plots include negative values for X_2, which changes the structure to the SG-MOSFET case. The $R_{on,sp}$ is observed to increase when dimension X_2 is enlarged. This is due to the extra resistance contributed by the second JFET region-2.

The sharp edge of the gate electrode in the split-gate structure produces an enhanced electric field in the gate oxide E_{GOX} in the blocking mode. This problem is eliminated with the buffered gate structure because the P^+ shielding region extends beyond the sharp edge of the gate electrode. The variation of electric field E_{GOX} with the dimension X_2 is shown in Fig. 11.37. Very low electric fields E_{GOX} are observed for the BG-MOSFET structure ensuring reliable operation.

Improvement in the HF-FOM[$R_{on}*C_{GD}$] and HF-FOM[$R_{on}*Q_{GD}$] are shown in Fig. 11.37 with changes in X_2. A substantial reduction of these metrics is observed with the SG-MOSFET structure making it attractive for high frequency applications.

Table V: 4H-SiC power BG-MOSFET Experimental Results

Structure	Conventional	Buffered-Gate
Breakdown Voltage (V)	1689	1617
Threshold Voltage (V)	1.84	2.04
$R_{ON,SP}$ (mΩ-cm^2)	4.78	7.39
$C_{GD,SP}$ (pF/cm^2)	121	23
$Q_{GD,SP}$ (nC/cm^2)	347	60
HF-FOM[$R_{ON}*C_{GD}$]	698	194
HF-FOM[$R_{ON}*Q_{GD}$]	2006	503
FOM[C_{GS}/C_{GD}]	333	1756

The BG-MOSFET structure was fabricated simultaneously with the conventional structure with the additional JFET region 2 ion implantation step. The measured values for various device parameters of 1.2 kV 4H-SiC planar-gate BG-MOSFET devices fabricated in a 6 inch SiC wafer foundry are given in Table V[39]. A summary of the data is provided in Table V. The measured values of the breakdown voltage and threshold voltage for the BG-MOSFET were close to the conventional structure. The $R_{ON,SP}$ for the BG-MOSFET was 1.5 times larger than the conventional structure. The $C_{GD,SP}$ measured at a drain bias of 1000 V for the BG-MOSFET was 5.3 times smaller than the conventional structure. The $Q_{GD,SP}$ measured for the BG-MOSFET was 5.8 times smaller than the conventional structure. Consequently, the figures-of-merit HF-FOM[$R_{on}*C_{GD}$] and HF-FOM[$R_{on}*C_{GD}$] for the SG-MOSFET structure were 3.6 and 4.0 times superior. The FOM[C_{GS}/C_{GD}] is also improved by a factor of 5.3 times.

11.8.4 Octagonal Cell Structure

The octagonal cell topology for 4H-SiC planar-gate power MOSFETs was discussed in section 11.5.2 and shown in Fig. 11.28. The specific on-resistance for this cell topology was shown to be larger than for the commonly used linear cell case. However, this cell topology has much smaller JFET density which reduces the gate-drain capacitance (C_{GD}) and charge (Q_{GD}).

Table VI: 4H-SiC power OCTFET Experimental Results

Structure	Conventional	Octagonal
Breakdown Voltage (V)	1628	1605
Threshold Voltage (V)	1.96	2.02
$R_{ON,SP}$ (mΩ-cm^2)	5.61	12.82
$C_{GD,SP}$ (pF/cm^2)	106	28
$Q_{GD,SP}$ (nC/cm^2)	347	113
HF-FOM[$R_{ON}*C_{GD}$]	595	359
HF-FOM[$R_{ON}*Q_{GD}$]	1745	1449

Experimental results on the performance of 1.2 kV 4H-SiC planar-gate power MOSFETs, named OCTFETs, with the octagonal cell topology have been obtained and reported[27]. These devices were fabricated using the same process steps as the conventional linear cell topology. A summary of the data is provided in Table VI. The measured values of the breakdown voltage and threshold voltage for the Octagonal cell case were close to the conventional structure. The $R_{ON,SP}$ for the Octagonal cell case was 2.3 times larger than the conventional structure due to its smaller channel density. However, as expected the $C_{GD,SP}$ measured at a drain bias of 1000 V for the Octagonal cell case was 3.8 times smaller than the conventional structure, and the $Q_{GD,SP}$ measured for the BG-MOSFET was 3.1 times smaller than the conventional structure. Consequently, the figures-of-merit HF-FOM[$R_{on}*C_{GD}$] and HF-FOM[$R_{on}*C_{GD}$] for the Octagonal cell case were 1.7 and 1.2 times superior.

The Octagonal cell topology can be combined with the SG-MOSFET structure to derive even lower values for gate-drain capacitance (C_{GD}) and charge (Q_{GD}). This was experimentally verified for 1.2 kV 4H-SiC planar-gate power MOSFETs[40]. A summary of the data is provided in Table VII. The measured values of the breakdown voltage and threshold voltage for the SG-OCTFET case were close to the OCTFET case. The $R_{ON,SP}$ for the SG-OCTFET case was very close to the Octagonal cell case. The $C_{GD,SP}$ measured at a drain bias of 1000 V for the SG-OCTFET case was 2.3 times smaller than the OCTFET case. The $Q_{GD,SP}$ measured for the SG-OCTFET case was 3.4 times smaller than the OCTFET case. Consequently, the figures-of-merit HF-FOM[$R_{on}*C_{GD}$] and HF-FOM[$R_{on}*C_{GD}$] for the SG-OCTFET case were 2.3 and 2.6 times superior to the OCTFET case. This makes the SG-OCTFET cell topology an attractive option for devices employed in high frequency power circuits.

Table VII: 4H-SiC power SG-OCTFET Experimental Results

Structure	Octagonal	SG-Octagonal
Breakdown Voltage (V)	1607	1625
Threshold Voltage (V)	2.12	2.02
$R_{ON,SP}$ (mΩ-cm^2)	8.38	8.51
$C_{GD,SP}$ (pF/cm^2)	62	27
$Q_{GD,SP}$ (nC/cm^2)	233	68
HF-FOM[$R_{ON}*C_{GD}$]	520	230
HF-FOM[$R_{ON}*Q_{GD}$]	1953	749

11.9 Thinner Gate Oxide Devices

There has been a trend towards reducing the gate oxide thickness for Si power MOSFETs to improve their performance over their history. Until recently, the 4H-SiC power MOSFET developments have mostly been performed using 500 Å gate oxide thickness. This value is used for most 4H-SiC planar-gate power MOSFET commercial products. Reduction of the gate oxide thickness has not been pursued due to reliability concerns.

It is possible to reduce the gate oxide thickness for 4H-SiC planar-gate power MOSFETs if care is taken to ensure that the electric field in the gate oxide is sufficiently low during on-state and blocking mode operation. Stable operation of 4H-SiC power MOSFETs is projected for 1000 years if an electric field below 6 MV/cm is maintained even at 175 °C during on-state operation[41]. Operation of the

4H-SiC power MOSFET with 500 Å is typically specified at a gate bias (V_{GS}) of 20 V. This produces an oxide electric field of 4.0 MV/cm which meets the reliability criterion. Operation of a 4H-SiC power MOSFET with thinner 270 Å gate oxide at the same 20 V gate bias will produce an electric field of 7.4 MV/cm which violates the reliability criterion. However, the reliability criterion can be met by operating the 270 Å gate oxide device at a gate bias of 15 V because the electric field drops to 5.6 MV/cm. The same conclusions can be made by using the reliability results reported in 2010[42]. The lifetime for the case of an electric field of 5.6 MV/cm at 175 °C is estimated to be over 1000 years when using the models in this article. The lifetime exceeds 10,000 years for an electric field of 4 MV/cm. Although the projected lifetime for the 270 Å gate oxide with 15 V gate drive is much smaller, it is still sufficient from an applications perspective.

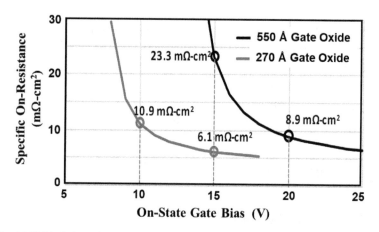

Fig. 11.38 Variation of specific on-resistance with gate bias for 4H-SiC Planar-Gate MOSFET structures with 550 and 270 Å gate oxide thickness.

The benefits of reducing the gate oxide thickness for 1.2 kV 4H-SiC planar-gate inversion-channel power MOSFETs with the linear cell topology has been experimentally quantified[43]. The drift region had a doping concentration of 8×10^{15} cm^{-3} and thickness of 10 μm. A JFET region width of 0.7 μm was used with doping enhanced to 3×10^{16} cm^{-3}. Devices fabricated with gate oxide thickness of 270 Å were compared with devices fabricated with the conventional 550 Å thickness. The peak inversion channel mobility was found to be close to 15 cm^2/V-s for both gate oxide thickness cases.

The specific on-resistance for the devices with 270 and 550 Å gate oxide thickness are compared in Fig. 11.38. The thinner oxide device has a specific on-resistance of 6.1 mΩ-cm^2 at a gate bias of 15 V compared with 8.9 mΩ-cm^2 at a gate bias of 20 V for the 550 Å gate oxide case, an improvement of 1.46 times. The 550 Å gate oxide device has a high specific on-resistance of 23.3 mΩ-cm^2 at a gate bias of 15 V. The 270 Å gate oxide device has a specific on-resistance of 10.9 mΩ-cm^2 at a gate bias of 10 V, making this gate bias an option.

Table VIII: Thin Gate Oxide 4H-SiC power MOSFET Experimental Results

Structure	550 Å Case	270 Å Case
Breakdown Voltage (V)	1711	1715
Threshold Voltage (V)	3.78	2.15
$R_{ON,SP}$ (mΩ-cm^2)	8.88	6.10
$C_{GD,SP}$ (pF/cm^2)	102	111
$Q_{GD,SP}$ (nC/cm^2)	311	322
HF-FOM[$R_{ON}*C_{GD}$]	906	677
HF-FOM[$R_{ON}*Q_{GD}$]	2762	1964
FOM[C_{GS}/C_{GD}]	287	395

A comparison of the experimentally measured device parameters for the two oxide thicknesses is provided in Table VIII. The breakdown voltages are identical despite the thinner oxide. The threshold voltage is reduced for the smaller gate oxide thickness as expected from Eq. [11.3] for the threshold voltage because the oxide capacitance C_{OX} is doubled. The specific gate-drain capacitance at V_D = 1000 V ($C_{GD,SP}$) and specific gate-drain charge ($Q_{GD,SP}$) are only slightly larger because the semiconductor capacitance is dominant at high drain voltages. Consequently, the figures-of-merit HF-FOM[$R_{on}*C_{GD}$] and HF-FOM[$R_{on}*C_{GD}$] for the 270 Å gate oxide case are 1.3 and 1.4 times superior to the 550 Å case. The FOM[C_{GS}/C_{GD}] is also improved by a factor of 1.4 times due to an increase in the input capacitance. These experimental results quantify the benefits of reducing the gate oxide thickness for 4H-SiC planar-gate power MOSFETs.

The reduction of the gate oxide thickness for 4H-SiC planar-gate power MOSFETs has been shown to improve the switching and short-circuit performance as well[44]. The maximum electric field in the gate oxide under in the blocking mode was also examined in this paper by numerical simulations. It was shown that the maximum electric field at a drain bias of 1200 V is 2.2 MV/cm for the 270 Å gate oxide thickness versus 1.9 MV/cm for the 550 Å case. Consequently, the thinner gate oxide does not degrade the reliability in the blocking mode. The transconductance of a power MOSFET is inversely proportional to the gate oxide thickness in the current saturation regime[45]. The measured transconductance of the device with 270 Å gate oxide thickness of 6.33 S was 1.8 times the value of 3.54 S measured for the device with 550 Å gate oxide thickness.

Switching loss measurements were performed on devices with active area of 0.045 cm² at a drain current of 10 A using the double-pulse method with an inductive load and 800 V DC supply voltage. A summary of the measured turn-on, turn-off, and total energy loss per cycle is given in Table IX. Values for the 270 Å gate oxide thickness case with gate bias of 15 V closely match those for the 550 Å case with gate bias of 20 V. The losses are 1.4 times larger when the device with 270 Å gate oxide thickness is operated with a gate drive of 10 V.

Table IX: Thin Gate Oxide 4H-SiC power MOSFET
Experimental Results

Structure	550 Å Case	270 Å Case	270 Å Case
Gate Bias (V)	20	15	10
Transconductance (S)	3.54	6.33	6.33
E_{ON} (µJ)	307	311	444
E_{OFF} (µJ)	70	68	72
E_{TOTAL} (µJ)	377	379	516
$I_{P,SC}$ (A)	140	190	105
t_{SC} (µs)	3.7	2.7	5.0
E_{SC} (mJ)	302	305	309

Short-circuit withstand capability of power transistors is an important selection criterion in motor drive applications[46]. Si IGBTs are designed and optimized by manufacturers to have short-circuit withstand time (t_{SC}) of at least 10 µs when operating at the full gate drive voltage and a DC supply voltage of two-thirds of the device voltage rating. The 4H-SiC power MOSFETs must exhibit similar capability for acceptance in industrial and transportation (e.g., electric vehicle) motor drives. The measured t_{SC} for commercially available 1.2 kV 4H-SiC planar-gate power MOSFETs is typically 3.5 µs[47]. This is too small for safe protection of the devices with IGBT gate drive circuits using DESAT protection. The t_{SC} measured for the 1.2 kV rated fabricated devices with

270 and 550 Å gate oxide thickness using a DC supply voltage of 800 V are given in Table IX. The t_{SC} measured for the 550 Å gate oxide thickness device was 3.5 μs, which is similar to the commercial products. A t_{SC} of 5.0 μs was measured for the 270 Å gate oxide thickness device for a gate drive voltage of 10 V. The t_{SC} reduced to 2.7 μs for the 270 Å gate oxide thickness device for a gate drive voltage of 15 V. The peak short circuit currents ($I_{P,SC}$) observed during the tests are given in Table IX. The t_{SC} values are inversely proportional to the $I_{P,SC}$ as expected from the adiabatic heating model for the short-circuit event[45]. The short-circuit energy E_{SC} for each case is given in Table IX. The same value is observed in all cases.

11.10 600 V Rated Devices

Most of the interest in the commercialization of 4H-SiC planar-gate power MOSFETs was initially focused on 1200 V rated devices for the replacement of Si IGBT in motor drive applications for industrial and transportation applications. There is need for 600 V rated devices as well that can compete with Si power MOSFETs, particularly the super-junction structures.

11.10.1 Gate Electrode Topology

Table X: 600 V 4H-SiC power MOSFET Cell Topology
Experimental Results

Structure	Linear	Square	Hexagonal	Octagonal
Breakdown Voltage (V)	693	537	585	707
Threshold Voltage (V)	3.84	3.52	3.52	3.76
$R_{ON,SP}$ (mΩ-cm^2)	9.94	7.93	7.46	12.3
$C_{GD,SP}$ (pF/cm^2)	324	799	825	71
$Q_{GD,SP}$ (nC/cm^2)	300	589	622	124
FOM[$R_{ON}*C_{GD}$]	3221	6336	6155	873
FOM[$R_{ON}*Q_{GD}$]	2982	4671	4640	1525
FOM[C_{GS}/C_{GD}]	69	32	30	480

The measured performance of 600 V rated 4H-SiC planar-gate power MOSFETs with different cell topologies fabricated in a 6 inch foundry was reported in 2019[48]. The devices were fabricated with a drift region doping concentration of 2.4 x 10^{16} cm^{-3} and thickness of 6 μm. A gate oxide thickness of 550 Å was grown to form inversion-channel structures. A summary of the measured data is given in Table X. The breakdown voltage of the square and hexagonal cell cases was found to be below the 600 V rating. This is due to the sharp corners in the cell geometries which produce enhanced electric fields in the blocking mode. The specific on-resistances follow the same trends discussed previously in section 11.5.2. These devices were fabricated with a low N$^+$ source contact anneal temperature of 900 °C and inversion mode channels which makes their specific on-resistance large. The relative performance of the devices is still insightful. The gate-drain capacitance (measured at 400 V) and the gate-drain charge also follow the trends described for the 1.2 kV devices in section 11.7. The best HF-FOM is obtained using the Octagonal cell topology.

The performance of these 600 V rated 4H-SiC planar-gate power MOSFET devices was compared with the 7th generation Si super-junction product CoolMOS IPL60R365P7. The HF-FOM[$R_{ON}*C_{GD}$] and HF-FOM[$R_{ON}*Q_{GD}$] for this device are 775 and 1240. The HF-FOM for the commonly used linear cell topology is much worse than the Si super-junction product. Using the Octagonal cell topology brings down the HF-FOM values close to those for the super-junction device. The performance of the 600 V 4H-SiC power MOSFETs will be superior to that for the COOLMOS product if the contacts are annealed at 1000 °C.

11.10.2 Reduced Gate Oxide Thickness

Table XI: Thin Gate Oxide 600 V 4H-SiC power MOSFET
Experimental Results

Structure	550 Å Case	270 Å Case
Gate Voltage (V)	20	15
Breakdown Voltage (V)	703	846
Threshold Voltage (V)	3.56	1.90
$R_{ON,SP}$ (mΩ-cm^2)	6.27	3.78
$C_{GD,SP}$ (pF/cm^2)	239	234
$Q_{GD,SP}$ (nC/cm^2)	233	247
HF-FOM[$R_{ON}*C_{GD}$]	1499	885
HF-FOM[$R_{ON}*Q_{GD}$]	1461	934
FOM[C_{GS}/C_{GD}]	120	185

The benefits of reducing gate oxide thickness for the 1200 V rated 4H-SiC planar-gate power MOSFET was described in section 11.9. This approach is even more impactful for 600 V rated devices where the channel resistance plays a larger role.

Experimental results on 600 V rated 4H-SiC planar-gate inversion-channel power MOSFETs with 550 and 270 Å gate oxide thickness were compared in 2019[49]. A summary of the measured data is given in Table XI. A gate bias of 15 V was used for the 270 Å gate oxide case compared with 20 V for the 550 Å gate oxide case. The specific on-resistance for the 270 Å gate oxide case was 1.7 times smaller than the 550 Å gate oxide case. The $C_{GD,SP}$ and $Q_{GD,SP}$ for the two cases were similar in magnitude. Consequently, the HF-FOM for the 270 Å gate oxide case were much superior. The HF-FOM[$R_{ON}*Q_{GD}$] could be made superior the 7th generation super-junction product by using the 270 Å gate oxide thickness for 600 V rated 4H-SiC planar-gate inversion-channel power MOSFETs. The performance of the thinner gate oxide 600 V 4H-SiC power MOSFETs will be even better if the contacts are annealed at 1000 °C

Table XII: Thin Gate Oxide 600 V 4H-SiC power MOSFET
Experimental Results

Gate Oxide	550 Å	550 Å	270 Å	270 Å
Gate Voltage (V)	20	15	15	10
Breakdown Voltage (V)	700	700	850	850
Threshold Voltage (V)	3.56	3.56	1.90	1.90
$R_{ON,SP}$ (mΩ-cm^2)	6.27	16.4	3.78	7.1
$C_{GD,SP}$ (pF/cm^2)	239	239	234	234
$Q_{GD,SP}$ (nC/cm^2)	233	233	247	247
FOM[$R_{ON}*C_{GD}$]	1499	3920	885	1661
FOM[$R_{ON}*Q_{GD}$]	1461	3821	934	1754
FOM[C_{GS}/C_{GD}]	120	120	185	185
E_{ON} (μJ)	213	-	208	312
E_{OFF} (μJ)	34	-	39	40
E_{TOTAL} (μJ)	247	-	247	252
$I_{D,SAT}$ (A)	149	74	209	101
t_{SC} (μs)	5.7	10	4.4	8.4
E_{SC} (mJ)	243	289	249	268

A detailed experimental comparison of the switching and short circuit performance of the 270 and 550 Å gate oxide thickness 600 V rated 4H-SiC planar-gate inversion-channel power MOSFETs has been published in 2020[50]. These devices had a channel length of 0.5 μm and an active area of 0.045 cm². A summary of the measured data is given in Table XII. Operating the 270 Å gate oxide device with gate bias of 15 V enables obtaining a low specific on-resistance of 3.78 mΩ-cm² compared with 6.27 mΩ-cm² for the 550 Å gate oxide device with gate bias of 20 V. Consequently, the best HF-FOM is obtained under these conditions. The inductive load switching loss measured showed the same values for the 270 Å gate oxide case as the 550 Å case. The high voltage drain current saturation values for the devices were measured using the short-circuit set up with 1 μs pulses, as given in Table XII. The short-circuit withstand times were inversely proportional to these drain current saturation values as expected.

In general, a trade-off must be performed between increasing short-circuit withstand time and an increase in the specific on-resistance for 4H-SiC power MOSFETs. This trade-off curve is shown in Fig. 11.39 for the devices with the 270 Å and 550 Å gate oxide thicknesses. It can be observed that the trade-off curve is better with the thinner gate oxide. This behavior was first projected in 2019[44]. It is another proven benefit of using a thinner gate oxide for 4H-SiC planar-gate power MOSFETs.

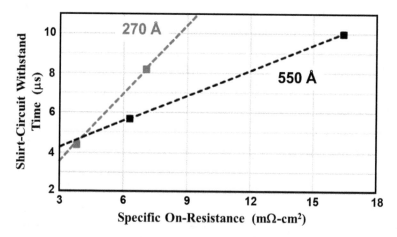

Fig. 11.39 Trade-off curves between short-circuit withstand time and specific on-resistance for the 550 and 270 Å gate oxide thickness cases. Data is for inversion channel 600 V 4H-SiC planar-gate power MOSFETs.

A detailed comparison of the thin gate oxide 600 V rated 4H-SiC planar-gate inversion-channel power MOSFETs with a Si super-junction device was reported in 2021[51]. The 4H-SiC devices included a structure with short channel length of 0.3 μm (4H-SiC-2); and a device with the split-gate design (4H-SiC-3). A summary of the experimental data is given in Table XIII. A gate drive voltage of 10 V was used for compatibility with the drive circuits for Si super-junction products. The Si CoolMOS product was chosen with similar on-resistance as the baseline 4H-SiC power MOSFET (4H-SiC-1). The Si CoolMOS product has very small values for the gate-drain capacitance (C_{GD}) at a drain bias of 400 V; and small gate charge (Q_{GD}). Comparable values are observed for the 4H-SiC MOSFET (4H-SiC-3) by employing the split-gate structure. However, the Si CoolMOS device has a much larger C_{GD} at a small drain bias of 1 V, which adversely impacts its turn-off switching loss.

Table XIII: Thin Gate Oxide 600 V 4H-SiC power MOSFET Experimental Results

Structure	4H-SiC-1	4H-SiC-2	4H-SiC-3	Si
Gate Structure	Standard	Standard	Split-Gate	-
Channel Length (μm)	0.5	0.3	0.5	-
Gate Oxide (Å)	270	270	270	-
Gate Voltage (V)	10	10	10	10
Breakdown Voltage (V)	850	850	850	710
Threshold Voltage (V)	1.9	1.8	2.0	3.5
R_{ON} (mΩ)	160	115	160	180
C_{GD} (pF) @ 400 V	11	11	6.8	4
C_{GD} (pF) @ 1 V	90	80	60	900
Q_{GD} (nC)	14	14	9	9
Reverse recovery Charge (nC)	235	235	235	6500
E_{ON} (μJ)	210	124	180	2650
E_{OFF} (μJ)	25	24	12	55
E_{TOTAL} (μJ)	235	148	192	2705
t_{SC} (μs)	8.4	5.0	8.4	19

The inductive load switching losses were measured using the double-pulse method with a drain current of 10 A and a DC bus of 400 V. The turn-off switching loss for the Si CoolMOS device was 2.2 times larger than the baseline 4H-SiC MOSFET (4H-SiC-1). The reverse recovery performance of the internal body diode of the Si CoolMOS product was very poor as documented in other papers. Its reverse recovery charge was found to be 28 times larger than for all the 4H-SiC MOSFETs. These values make the turn-off and total switching energy losses for the 4H-SiC MOSFETs (4H-SiC-1 and 4H-SiC-3) with 0.5 μm channel length 13 times better than the Si CoolMOS product. Even superior performance is observed for the 4H-SiC MOSFET (4H-SiC-2) with channel length reduced to 0.3 μm. The turn-off and total switching energy losses become 18 times better than the Si CoolMOS product.

The Si CoolMOS product has excellent short-circuit withstand capability as seen from the measured value of 19 μs for a DC supply voltage of 400 V and 10 V gate drive in the table. The baseline 4H-SiC MOSFET (4H-SiC-1) with channel length of 0.5 μm has an acceptable short-circuit withstand time of 8.4 μs. It is reduced to 5.0 μs for 4H-SiC MOSFET (4H-SiC-2) with channel length reduced to 0.3 μm.

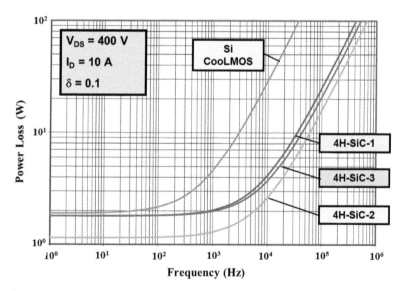

Fig. 11.40 Comparison of power losses for the three 4H-SiC planar-gate MOSFETs with the Si CoolMOS product.

The change in power losses for the devices in Table XIII with increasing operating frequency are quantified in Fig. 11.40 for the case of a duty cycle of 0.1. It can be seen that the 4H-SiC power MOSFETs can be operated at 30 kHz with a power loss of 10 W. In contrast, the same power loss is observed for the Si CoolMOS device at 3 kHz. These results demonstrate that the operating frequency for power circuits can be increased by about 10-times if the Si CoolMOS device is replaced by the 4H-SiC power MOSFETs. The benefits of this are a reduction in the size, weight, and cost of passive components.

11.11 1700 V Rated Devices

4H-SiC power MOSFETs with 1700 V rating are needed for the replacement of Si IGBT in higher power industrial motor drive and solar inverter applications. The results of a systematic investigation of designs suitable for this voltage ratings are discussed in this section.

11.11.1 Gate Electrode Topology

The measured performance of 1700 V rated 4H-SiC planar-gate power MOSFETs with different cell topologies fabricated in a 6 inch foundry was reported in 2019[52]. The breakdown voltage of these devices was 2300 V. The devices were fabricated with a drift region doping concentration of 6 x 10^{15} cm^{-3} and thickness of 17 μm. A gate oxide thickness of 550 Å was grown to form accumulation-channel structures with channel length of 0.5 μm. The devices had the cross-section shown in Fig. 11.4 with the P$^+$ contact in the cell. The JFET width was 1.1 μm for the linear, square, and hexagonal cell topologies. A larger JFET width of 1.5 μm was need for the octagonal cell case to reduce the JFET resistance component.

A summary of the measured data on 1700 V rated devices is given in Table XIV. The breakdown voltage of the square and hexagonal cell cases was found to be smaller than for the linear and octagonal cell cases. This is due to the sharp corners in these cell geometries which produce enhanced electric fields in the blocking mode. The specific on-resistances follow the same trends discussed previously in section 11.5.2 for the 1200 V rated devices with the lowest value for the hexagonal cell case. The gate-drain capacitance measured at 1000 V and the gate-drain charge also follow the trends described for the 1.2 kV devices in section 11.6. The best HF-FOM is obtained using the Octagonal cell topology due to its low C_{GD} and Q_{GD} values. This is the most beneficial cell topology for high frequency applications.

Table XIV: 1.7 kV 4H-SiC Planar-Gate MOSFETs
Experimental Results

Structure	Linear	Square	Hexagonal	Octagonal
Cell Pitch (μm)	4.2	4.2	4.2	5.0
Breakdown Voltage (V)	2390	2050	2200	2380
Threshold Voltage (V)	2.4	2.2	2.2	2.3
$R_{ON,SP}$ (mΩ-cm^2)	8.0	6.7	6.5	10.5
$C_{GD,SP}$ (pF/cm^2)	87	244	271	45
$Q_{GD,SP}$ (nC/cm^2)	340	542	538	222
FOM[R_{ON}*C_{GD}]	696	1635	1762	463
FOM[R_{ON}*Q_{GD}]	2720	3631	3497	2331
FOM[C_{GS}/C_{GD}]	254	100	87	726

11.11.2 Split-Gate Structure

The split-gate structure was shown to greatly reduce the gate-drain capacitance and charge for 1200 V rated devices in section 11.8.2. A similar impact can be expected for the 1700 V rated devices. This has been experimentally confirmed with quantification of the performance enhancement[53]. The electric field in the gate oxide may become larger in these devices compared with the 1200 V case due to the larger blocking voltage. However, numerical simulations performed to examine the electric field in the gate oxide at a drain bias of 2000 V showed values below the allowable maximum of 4 MV/cm that is required for reliable operation.

Table XV: 1.7 kV 4H-SiC SG-MOSFETs
Experimental Results

Structure	Conventional	Split-Gate
Breakdown Voltage (V)	2390	2380
Threshold Voltage (V)	2.1	2.1
$R_{ON,SP}$ (mΩ-cm^2)	8.43	8.12
$C_{GD,SP}$ (pF/cm^2)	63	18
$Q_{GD,SP}$ (nC/cm^2)	356	202
HF-FOM[R_{ON}*C_{GD}]	531	146
HF-FOM[R_{ON}*Q_{GD}]	2485	1438
FOM[C_{GS}/C_{GD}]	451	1667

A summary of the measured data for the fabricated split-gate and conventional 1.7 kV 4H-SiC power MOSFETs is given in Table XV. The split-gate design has the same breakdown and threshold voltage as the conventional design. Its specific on-resistance is very close to that for the conventional design. Its gate-drain capacitance was 3.5 times smaller at a drain bias of 1000 V. A 1.8 times reduction of the gate-drain charge was observed. This resulted in much better high frequency figures-of-merit making the split-gate design an important approach to build 1700 V rated devices for higher frequency applications.

11.11.3 Reduced Gate Oxide Thickness

The benefits of reducing gate oxide thickness for the 1700 V rated 4H-SiC planar-gate power MOSFET is not as obvious as for devices with lower blocking voltage ratings. The channel contributes a smaller amount to the total specific on-resistance in higher blocking voltage devices due to the rapid increase in drift region resistance. However, a thinner gate oxide has still been found to be beneficial to their performance.

Table XVI: Thin Gate Oxide 1.7 kV 4H-SiC Planar-Gate Power MOSFET Experimental Results

Structure	550 Å Case	270 Å Case
Channel Type	Accumulation	Inversion
Breakdown Voltage (V)	2380	2390
Threshold Voltage (V)	2.1	1.90
$R_{ON,SP}$ (mΩ-cm^2)	8.7	6.7
$C_{GD,SP}$ (pF/cm^2)	70	70
$Q_{GD,SP}$ (nC/cm^2)	356	362
HF-FOM[$R_{ON}*C_{GD}$]	609	469
HF-FOM[$R_{ON}*Q_{GD}$]	3097	2425
FOM[C_{GS}/C_{GD}]	400	614

Experimental results on 1700 V rated 4H-SiC planar-gate inversion-channel power MOSFETs with 270 Å gate oxide thickness were compared to 550 Å gate oxide devices with accumulation-mode channels in 2022[54]. Although a higher channel mobility is obtained for the accumulation mode channel, it cannot be used with the 270 Å gate oxide due to making the threshold voltage too low. A summary of the measured data is given in Table XVI. A gate bias of 15 V was used for both cases. The specific on-resistance for the 270 Å gate oxide case was 1.3 times smaller than the 550 Å gate oxide case. The $C_{GD,SP}$ and $Q_{GD,SP}$

for the two cases were similar in magnitude. Consequently, the HF-FOM for the 270 Å gate oxide case were much superior. As in the case of 600 V rated devices, the short-circuit performance of the 1700 V rated devices should also improve with a thinner gate oxide.

11.12 3300 V Rated Devices

Increasing the blocking voltage rating of 4H-SiC power MOSFETs to 3300 V is desirable for the replacement of Si IGBTs in higher power motor drives for electric rail transportation applications. This blocking voltage can be achieved by using a drift region with doping concentration of 3×10^{15} cm^{-3} and thickness of 30 μm. For reference, the ideal specific on-resistance for 3300 V 4H-SiC drift region is 4 mΩ-cm^2.

Early devices reported in 2009 had a specific on-resistance ($R_{on,sp}$) of 27 mΩ-cm^2 at a gate bias of 20 V[55]. Devices reported in 2015 with an active area of 0.83 cm^2 had an improved $R_{on,sp}$ of 21 mΩ-cm^2 at a gate bias of 20 V[56]. The measured switching losses E_{ON} and E_{OFF} of the devices was 36 and 85 mJ per cycle, which is one-third of 3300 V Si-IGBTs.

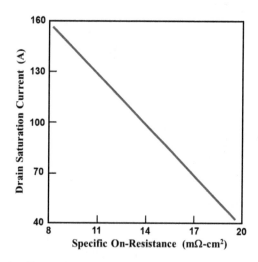

Fig. 11.41 Trade-off curve between drain saturation current of 3300 V rated 4H-SiC planar-gate MOSFETs and the specific on-resistance.

A study of cell designs was performed for 3300 V rated 4H-SiC planar-gate power MOSFETs to examine the trade-off between specific on-resistance and short-circuit withstand capability[57]. In addition to conventional linear cell topology, designs with reduced channel and JFET density were explored by alterations to the cells orthogonal to the cross-section. It was found that the specific on-resistance increases for structures that produce smaller drain saturation current as shown in Fig. 11.41 as expected due to a reduction of channel density. The short-circuit time for the conventional cell design was 7.5 μs for a DC supply voltage of 1500 V and 20 V gate drive. This corresponds to a peak drain current of 144 A and specific on-resistance of 11 mΩ-cm^2. A desirable short-circuit withstand time of 10 μs occurs for a peak drain current of 108 A. The specific on-resistance for this case is increased to 14 mΩ-cm^2.

3300 V rated 4H-SiC planar-gate power MOSFETs with active area of 0.4 cm^2 were reported in 2019[58]. The devices had a specific on-resistance ($R_{ON,SP}$) of 18 mΩ-cm^2 at a gate bias of 20 V. The short-circuit withstand time (t_{SC}) for the device at a DC supply of 1800 V was 4.5 μs for the gate drive voltage of 20 V. The t_{SC} was increased to 8 μs by decreasing the gate drive voltage to 15 V. However, the $R_{ON,SP}$ was found to increase by 65 %. The t_{SC} values will reduce by 1.2 times if the DC supply voltage is increased to two-thirds of the blocking voltage rating.

The short-circuit withstand capability of 3300 V rated planar-gate power MOSFETs with short and long channels (values not revealed) was reported in 2020 with DC supply voltage of 2200 V[59]. The long channel devices had a t_{SC} of 7 μs compared with 5 μs for the short channel devices. This increase in t_{SC} is obtained with an increase in on-resistance by 30 %.

Table XVII: 3.3 kV 4H-SiC Planar-Gate Power MOSFET Experimental Results

Structure	Accumulation	Inversion
Breakdown Voltage (V)	>3000	>3000
Threshold Voltage (V)	2.7	4.9
$R_{ON,SP}$ (mΩ-cm^2)	13.8	19.8
$C_{GD,SP}$ (pF/cm^2)	80	67
HF-FOM[R_{ON}*C_{GD}]	1104	1327
FOM[C_{GS}/C_{GD}]	242	333

Experimental results obtained on 4H-SiC planar-gate power MOSFETs with 3300 V rating were reported in 2020 with accumulation and inversion channel designs[60]. A summary of the device characteristics is given in Table XVII. An improvement in $R_{ON,SP}$ by 43 % was achieved with the accumulation-channel design. This indicates that the channel resistance component is still significant in 3300 V rated devices.

11.13 6500 V Rated Devices

An even higher blocking voltage of 6.5 kV is needed for SiC power MOSFETs for use in high power 'medium voltage' industrial motor drives and for high speed bullet trains. The development of these devices required maturing of the technology for the growth of 60 μm thick epitaxial layers with lower doping concentration of 1×10^{15} cm^{-3}. This has been achieved since 2015. For reference, the ideal specific on-resistance for 6500 V 4H-SiC drift region is 25 mΩ-cm^2.

The development of a 6.5 kV 4H-SiC planar-gate power MOSFET was reported in 2017 by using the above drift layer speci-fications[61]. The JFET width was optimized to 4 μm for obtaining a maximum electric field of 1.1 MV/cm in the SiC below the gate oxide. The fabricated devices had a channel length of 1.5 μm and gate oxide thickness of 550 Å. The edge termination utilized 55 floating-field rings of 3 μm in width spanning 450 μm at the periphery of the 0.01 cm^2 active area. A specific on-resistance of 83 mΩ-cm^2 was measured at a gate bias of 20 V. The measured breakdown voltage was 8 kV.

The 6.5 kV 4H-SiC planar-gate power MOSFET was further optimized to achieve a lower specific on-resistance of 59 mΩ-cm^2 as reported in 2021[62]. A JFET region of 3.2 μm width and doping con-centration of 1×10^{16} cm^{-3} was chosen to keep the gate oxide electric field at 3 MV/cm in the blocking state. Current flow via the channel was identified during third quadrant operation with zero gate bias. A relatively high voltage drop of 9-10 V was observed for this body diode.

The optimization and fabrication of 6.5 kV 4H-SiC planar-gate power MOSFETs was reported in 2022 leading to a specific on-resistance of 47 mΩ-cm^2 for a device with channel length of 1 μm[63]. The drift layer specifications were the same as given above. An optimum JFET width of 1.5 μm in the cross-section shown in Fig. 11.4 was defined by numerical simulations for a JFET region doping concentration of 3×10^{16} cm^{-3}. This is larger than the typical 0.7 μm width used for 1.2 kV devices due to the stronger influence of implant straggle (discussed in section 11.5.3) at the lower drift region doping levels according to the authors. Several edge terminations structures were explored including the hybrid JTE and floating field rings (FFR). The highest breakdown voltage of 7.9 kV was obtained for the FFR case. Devices with channel length of 2 μm were also fabricated to improve the short-circuit withstand time. It was increased from 6.2 μs for the device with channel length of 1 μm and JFET width of 3 μm to 13 μs for the device with channel length of 2 μm and JFET width of 3 μm. This increase occurred at the expense of an increase in the specific on-resistance to 55 mΩ-cm^2 (17 %). This trade-off is much better than observed for 1.2 kV devices because the channel resistance is a much smaller component in these higher blocking voltage structures.

11.14 10 kV Rated Devices

Ultra-high voltage SiC power devices are desirable for utility scale applications such solid-state-transformers used in microgrids[64]. Although the specific on-resistance goes up rapidly with blocking voltage for all power MOSFETs, its value for 4H-SiC is still in the reasonable range to make switches for these applications. The alternative of utilizing a 4H-SiC IGBT is not competitive in terms on the on-state voltage drop and switching losses at the 10 kV voltage rating[65]. For reference, the ideal specific on-resistance for 10 kV 4H-SiC drift region is 20 mΩ-cm^2.

A 10 kV 4H-SiC planar-gate power MOSFET was reported in 2004[66]. The devices were fabricated using 85 μm thick epitaxial layers with doping concentration of 8 x 10^{14} cm^{-3}. They had a large cell pitch of 11.5 μm with channel length of 1.5 μm and gate oxide thickness of 600 Å. The devices had low threshold voltage of 1 V requiring negative gate bias to operate them in the blocking mode. The measured specific on-resistance was 123 mΩ-cm^2 at a gate bias of 18 V.

10 kV 4H-SiC planar-gate power MOSFETs were reported in 2006[67] fabricated using 100 μm thick epitaxial layers with doping concentration of 6 x 10^{14} cm^{-3}. They had a reduced cell pitch of 7 μm with gate oxide thickness of 500 Å. The JFET region doping was increased to 5 x 10^{15} cm^{-3}. The channel length was not disclosed. A 65 floating field ring edge termination with extension of 550 μm was used. The devices had a threshold voltage of 3.5 V. The measured specific on-resistance was 111 mΩ-cm^2 at a gate bias of 15 V.

The characteristics of a 10 kV 4H-SiC planar-gate power MOSFET was described in 2015[68]. These devices with chip size of 0.30 cm^2 had a measured specific on-resistance was 122 mΩ-cm^2 at a gate bias of 18 V. The measured turn-on and turn-off switching losses were 6.2 and 1.3 mJ at a drain current of 6 A and voltage of 6 kV.

A 4H-SiC planar-gate power MOSFET with breakdown voltage of 13 kV was reported in 2017[69]. It was fabricated using 150 μm thick epitaxial layers with doping concentration of 6.7 x 10^{14} cm^{-3}. The JFET region had a peak doping concentration 2 x 10^{17} cm^{-3} and surface concentration of 2 x 10^{16} cm^{-3}. A gate oxide thickness of 500 Å was used with channel length of 1 μm. A JFET width of 2 μm was adopted to achieve a specific on-resistance was 167 mΩ-cm^2 at a gate bias of 20 V. The electric field in the gate oxide was found to be 3 MV/cm with the JFET width in the blocking mode.

Many publications on the short-circuit (SC) withstand capability of 10 kV 4H-SiC planar-gate power MOSFET have been published. The SC tests were performed at DC supply voltage of 6 kV with gate bias of 18 V[70] for previously described devices[67] with specific on-resistance of 263 mΩ-cm^2. A SC failure time of 8.6 μs was observed. The peak SC current (260 A) was 26 times larger than the rated current. However, the device metallization was observed to degrade after a 5.9 μs SC pulse[71].

Single shot unclamped inductive switching (UIS) avalanche capability of 10 kV 4H-SiC planar-gate power MOSFET have been experimentally evaluated[72]. A model for the temperature rise of the chip was derived based on adiabatic heating. The devices had an avalanche energy of 1.4 J at a critical junction temperature of 533 °C.

11.15 Experimental Results: Channel Mobility

The need to obtain a high quality interface between silicon carbide and the gate dielectric was identified as a challenging endeavor from the inception of interest in the development of unipolar transistors from this semiconductor material[73]. Initially, it was impossible to fabricate silicon carbide power MOSFETs with specific on-resistances below those reported for silicon devices until the interface was sufficiently improved to obtain adequate inversion layer mobility. Further, early work on planar MOSFETs did not sufficiently take into consideration the fundamental issues that have been discussed in the previous sections of this chapter dealing with the reach-through problem and the high electric field in the oxide. These issues are discussed here in the historical context of developing silicon carbide planar power MOSFET structures.

11.15.1 Inversion Layer Mobility

Early investigations of the interface between P-type silicon carbide and thermally grown oxide indicated a high density of interface states and positive charge in the oxide. Significant improvement in the interface quality was achieved for 6H-SiC by anneal the thermally grown oxide in a NO ambient[74] leading to a peak inversion layer mobility of 70 cm²/Vs. However, the inversion layer mobility for 4H-SiC was reported[75,76] to be less than 1 cm²/V-s.

In 1998, a break-through was achieved at PSRC[77] with the use of deposited oxides on 4H-SiC leading to a reported[78] record high inversion layer mobility of 165 cm²/Vs. A detailed study[79] of the process steps responsible for producing the improved interface resulting in the high channel mobility was also undertaken at PSRC. This work produced the first observation of phonon scattering limited inversion layer mobility (which decreased with increasing temperature), and demonstrated that a wet oxide anneal of the deposited oxide was the critical step for producing the high inversion layer mobility. The process proposed and demonstrated at PSRC was subsequently reproduced by the sponsors[80] as well by other research groups[81]. These results indicate that it is possible to achieve sufficiently high inversion layer mobility in 4H-SiC power MOSFETs to obtain low specific on-resistance in high voltage structures.

The low inversion layer mobility observed in 4H-SiC MOSFETs fabricated using thermally grown gate oxides has been traced to the trapping of the carriers at interface states. Hall-effect measurements performed on lateral MOSFETs have demonstrated that the effective Hall mobility for carriers in the inversion layer is high when the trapping effect is taken into consideration[82]. Due to the trapping effect, the measured effective mobility in 4H-SiC MOSFETs was reported[83] to be less than 10 cm²/V-s when thermal oxidation is used to form the gate oxide. In these devices, the effective mobility was found to increase with temperature which is a signature of trap dominated current conduction in the channel. By using NO ambient anneals of the thermally grown gate oxide, an improvement in the effective channel mobility to 30-35 cm²/V-s was reported[84] in 2001.

Considerable effort was undertaken to understand the interface between SiO₂ and 4H-SiC and correlate this with the inversion layer mobility[85]. The best method for improvement of effective mobility in 4H-SiC for MOSFETs fabricated using thermally grown oxides has been reported to be by post-oxidation annealing in nitric oxide (NO) and nitrous oxide (N_2O). It has been reported that the channel mobility is inversely proportional to the interface state density. A significant reduction in the interface state density has been accomplished by performing annealing at 1175 °C in a nitric oxide (NO) ambient for 2 hours[24,86,87,88]. An effective channel mobility for electrons of 30-35 cm^2/V-s was achieved using this process at the operating gate bias. More recent work[89,90] indicates that charge trapping has been sufficiently suppressed by the nitric oxide annealing leading to effective channel mobility of about 60 cm^2/V-s.

It would be preferable to fabricate 4H-SiC power MOSFETs using ion-implanted P-base regions as in the case of silicon devices. Due to the low diffusion rate for dopants in the 4H-SiC, it is necessary to stagger the edge for the implantation of the P-base and N$^+$ source regions for the 4H-SiC devices[5,6] to create the DiMOSFET structure. The damage in the ion implanted regions must be removed by annealing followed by surface preparation to reduce interface states. The inversion layer mobility in n-channel lateral MOSFETs fabricated on aluminum implanted layers in 4H-SiC has been reported[91]. The ion-implant dose and energy was selected to achieve a surface doping concentration of 1 x 10^{17} cm^{-3} followed by annealing for 10 minutes at 1600 °C. The gate oxide was grown at 1200 °C and then placed in an alumina environment. Peak inversion layer mobility of 100 cm^2/V-s was observed with a high threshold voltage of about 10 volts.

Formation of silicon dioxide on 4H-SiC at a higher temperatures of 1500 °C has been shown to enhance growth rates[92]. The interface state density for this process has been found to be smaller than for oxides typically grown at 1200 °C. This produced an improved field effect mobility of 40 cm^2/V-s for electrons in the inversion layer.

A high peak inversion layer mobility for electrons of 132.6 cm^2/V-s has been obtained by using a gate dielectric stack consisting of 1 nm thick layer of La_2O_3 by Molecular-Beam-Epitaxy followed by a 20 nm layer of SiO_2 by Atomic-Layer-Deposition[93]. The samples were annealed at 900 °C in nitrous oxide by using RTA. The inversion layer mobility reduced sharply with increasing gate bias to a value of 90 cm^2/V-s at a gate voltage of 6 volts. This approach utilizes high-k dielectrics to passivate the SiC surface.

It is worth pointing out that the inversion-channel mobility of interest to achieve a low specific on-resistance in 4H-SiC planar-gate power MOSFETs is the value at the on-state gate bias, which is typically 20 V for a gate oxide thickness of 500 Å. Many papers report high peak inversion-layer mobility observed at a gate bias close to the threshold voltage with much smaller mobility at the gate bias voltage. This is not valuable for improving the on-resistance of 4H-SiC planar-gate power MOSFET. 4H-SiC power MOSFETs fabricated in a foundry using thermally grown gate oxide with NO anneal have been reported[94] to have inversion-channel mobility of 15 cm^2/V-s at the on-state gate bias of 20 V. This is the state-of-the-art for practical devices.

11.15.2 Accumulation Layer Mobility

It has been established that the accumulation layer mobility is significantly greater than the inversion layer mobility in silicon MOSFET structures[95]. This is due to the smaller band bending at the semiconductor surface which reduces surface scattering. The same effect should be applicable to silicon carbide. The first planar silicon carbide accumulation-channel vertical power MOSFET structure, named the planar ACCUFET, was developed at PSRC using 6H-SiC as the semi-conductor material[96,97]. The effective accumulation layer mobility extracted[98] from these structures was 120 cm^2/Vs for a structure fabricated using thermally grown gate oxide, which was considerably larger than the best inversion layer mobility (70 cm^2/Vs) reported[8] at that time. Subsequently, 6H and 4H-SiC accumulation-channel planar power MOSFETs were compared using thermally grown gate oxide[99]. The effective mobility for the 4H-SiC structures was found to be much smaller than for the 6H-SiC devices. The control of the threshold voltage for accumulation-mode 4H-SiC lateral MOSFETs was demonstrated by using counter-doping of the P-shielding layer with nitrogen ion implants[100]. A peak channel field-effect mobility of 35 cm^2/V-s was obtained using this approach.

More recently[101], the accumulation layer mobility has been measured in 4H-SiC MOSFETs using the Hall bar structure to differ-entiate between the effective mobility, which is limited by charge trapping, and the intrinsic mobility for free carriers in the channel. Note that the gate oxide process used for the fabrication of these MOSFETs was similar to that developed at PSRC[76] for 6H-SiC MOSFETs. The use of deposited oxides on 4H-SiC produced a reported[102] record high inversion layer mobility of 165 cm^2/V-s. It was found that the accu-mulation mobility decreased from 350 cm^2/V-s in the weak accumulation regime of operation to 200 cm^2/V-s in the strong accumulation regime of operation.

The use of thermal oxidation has become standard practice for manufacturing 4H-SiC planar-gate power MOSFETs. In 1999, an effective accumulation-layer mobility of 20-30 cm^2/V-s was reported[99] by using nitrogen ion implantation to form the N-base region. Lateral 4H-SiC MOSFETs were reported in 2001 with thermally grown oxide using nitrogen ion implants to create the accumulation-mode device[103]. The nitrogen concentration was kept fixed at 1×10^{17} cm^{-3} and the thickness of the N-type region was varied from 0.15 to 0.20 to 0.25 μm. The threshold voltage was found to reduce with increasing thickness of the N-type layer as predicted by the analytical model in section 11.3.2. A threshold voltage of 0.3 volts was observed for a thickness of 0.2 μm which is in good agreement with the value calculated using the analytical model (see Fig. 11.16). For this case, a peak channel mobility of 140 cm^2/V-s was observed. In 2001, a significantly larger accumulation-layer effective mobility of 200 cm^2/V-s was reported[104] by using a stacked gate oxide process. The stacked gate oxide consisted of a thermally grown layer with thickness of 0.02 μm followed by a NSG-CVD deposited layer with a thickness of 0.03 μm. These results have established the ability to obtain relatively high accumulation-layer mobility in 4H-SiC indicating the possibility for fabrication of high performance vertical power MOSFETs.

As in the case of inversion-channel MOSFET, it is worth pointing out that the accumulation-channel mobility of interest to achieve a low specific on-resistance in 4H-SiC planar-gate power MOSFETs is the value at the on-state gate bias, which is typically 20 V for a gate oxide thickness of 500 Å. Many papers report high peak accumulation-layer mobility observed at a gate bias close to the threshold voltage with much smaller mobility at the gate bias voltage. This is not valuable for improving the on-resistance of 4H-SiC planar-gate power MOSFET. 4H-SiC power MOSFETs fabricated in a foundry using thermally grown gate oxide with NO anneal have been reported[93] to have accumulation-channel mobility of 20 cm^2/V-s at the on-state gate bias of 20 V. This is the state-of-the-art for practical devices.

11.16 Experimental Results: Legacy Devices

The need to obtain a high quality interface between silicon carbide and the gate dielectric was identified as a challenging endeavor from the inception of interest in the development of unipolar transistors from this semiconductor material[73]. Initially, it was impossible to fabricate silicon carbide power MOSFETs with specific on-resistances below those reported for silicon devices until the interface was sufficiently improved to obtain adequate inversion layer mobility. Even in recent years, poor inversion layer mobility values (~ 15 cm^2/V-s) have been reported due to trapping of charge at the oxide-semiconductor interface. To overcome this technological barrier and to obtain a lower threshold voltage, the accumulation-mode structure was proposed[7]. This structure was also designed to shield the gate oxide from high electric fields in the semiconductor drift region. Experimental results on the shielded inversion-channel and accumulation-channel planar power MOSFET structures are discussed in this section.

11.16.1 Inversion-Channel Devices

In recognition of the low diffusion coefficients for dopants in silicon carbide, it was proposed[5] that the P-base and N$^+$ source ion implantations for the planar silicon carbide power MOSFET be staggered by using photoresist masks rather than be defined by the gate edge as conventionally done for silicon devices. The idea to incorporate a sub-surface P-type layer to shield the channel was also proposed at PSRC and subsequently patented[7]. This idea was first successfully demonstrated[105] for 6H-SiC devices in 1997 under the DI-MOSFET moniker. The authors fabricated the devices using multiple energy boron implants to form a P-base region with a box profile at a depth of 1 micron. The energy and dose for the implants was chosen to produce a retrograde doping profile on one of the wafers. This creates a low doped P-base region with an under-lying highly doped P$^+$ region that shields it from the high electric fields developed in the drift region. Devices were designed with channel length of 2 and 5 μm, and the JFET region width (W_J in Fig. 11.20) was varied from 2.5 to 15 μm. The channel inversion layer mobility was found to be about 20 cm^2/Vs for these 6H-SiC MOSFETs fabricated using a thermally grown oxide. The best specific on-resistance of 130 mΩ-cm^2 was obtained for the smallest JFET width and channel length. The breakdown voltage of the device was found to be 760 volts as limited by reach-through as well as gate oxide rupture leading to catastrophic failure indicating that the design did not provide adequate shielding.

   The concept of shielding the P-base region was also reported[106] using a triple ion-implantation process to fabricate 6H-SiC vertical power MOSFETs. The ion-implant steps were designed to produce a low P-base surface concentration of 7 x 10^{16} cm^{-3} with the doping increasing to 1 x 10^{18} cm^{-3} at a depth of 0.4 μm. This profile enabled achieving a threshold voltage of 3 volts with a thermally grown gate oxide thickness of 360 Å. A breakdown voltage of 1800 volts was obtained for this device by using a drift region doping concentration of 6.5 x 10^{15} cm^{-3} and thickness of 15 μm. A specific on-resistance of 82 mΩ-cm^2 was observed at a gate bias of 10 volts, which is an order of magnitude better than values that can be obtained with silicon technology. Good dynamic switching performance with ruggedness was confirmed[107] for these MOSFETs.

A DI-MOSFET structure was reported[108] from 4H-SiC in 2001 using 25 μm thick epitaxial layers with doping concentration of 3 x 10^{15} cm^{-3}. In spite of using the previously discussed deposited oxide process[109], an inversion layer mobility of only 14 cm^2/Vs was observed. Due to the low channel mobility, the devices exhibited a relatively large specific on-resistance of 55 mΩ-cm^2 even when a high gate bias of 25 volts was applied. The device was able to support nearly 2000 volts at zero gate bias. The authors associated the blocking voltage to be limited by open-base bipolar breakdown, namely, the reach-through problem discussed earlier in this chapter. This work was extended[110] to achieve a breakdown voltage of 2400 volts with a specific on-resistance of 42 mΩ-cm^2 in large area (0.1 cm^2) device structures. Higher voltage devices were discussed in previous sections.

In 2004, a novel staggered implant process was proposed to reduce the channel length and applied towards the fabrication of high voltage planar 4H-SiC MOSFETs[111,112]. In this process, oxidation of a sacrificial polysilicon layer is used to form a sidewall spacer that serves as a mask to stagger the P-base and N$^+$ source implants to achieve a channel length of less than 0.5 μm. The retrograde ion implant profile discussed earlier was also utilized for these devices to reduce the P-base doping concentration and suppress the reach-through problem. In addition a nitrogen counter-doping ion implant step was used. This may have resulted in accumulation-channel devices although the authors did not indicate this in the paper. Planar 4H-SiC inversion-mode MOSFETs were successfully fabricated with breakdown voltage of 2 kV with a specific on-resistance of 27 mΩ-cm^2 at a gate bias of 20 volts.

The optimization of a 1-kV DIMOSFET structure was reported in 2007[113] including a current spreading layer (CSL) as shown in Fig. 11.42. The current spreading layer was formed by epitaxial growth of a more highly doped n-type layer on top of the n-type drift layer. Optimization of the structure indicated that the lowest specific-on-resistance can be achieved by using a CSL doping concentration of 1 x 10^{17} cm^{-3}. The same doping concentration was found to be suitable for the JFET region. However, it is worth pointing out that the numerical simulations of the structure show a catastrophic drop in breakdown voltage if the JFET width is increased beyond 1 μm or when the CSL doping concentration exceeds 2 x 10^{17} cm^{-3}. This makes the processing of the structure challenging. Nevertheless, the authors were able to obtain functional devices with a specific on-resistance of 6.95 mΩ-cm^2. This value is much larger than the ideal value due to the large channel resistance contribution despite using a self-aligned process to reduce the channel length to 0.3 μm.

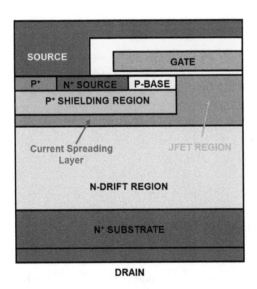

Fig. 11.42 Planar 4H-SiC power MOSFET with current spreading layer.

With increasing maturity of the 4H-SiC technology to provide 3 inch diameter wafers, large area (0.45 cm x 0.45 cm chips with 0.15 cm^2 active area) planar power MOSFETs could be fabricated in 2010 with blocking voltage of 1200 volts[114]. These devices could carry 40 amperes in the on-state with a specific on-resistance of 7.1 mΩ-cm^2. This value is close to the analytically computed specific on-resistance for an inversion layer mobility of 15 cm^2/V-s indicating that the performance is limited by the channel resistance.

4H-SiC planar power MOSFETs with a blocking voltage of 1500 volts were reported[115] in 2011 with a specific on-resistance of 3.7 mΩ-cm^2. This value is close to the analytically computed specific on-resistance for an inversion layer mobility of 15 cm^2/V-s indicating that the performance is limited by the channel resistance. The devices were fabricated using a self-aligned process to achieve a channel length of 0.5 μm. The authors point out that the sub-threshold slope for the devices is large resulting in a low threshold voltage which must be increased to achieve normally-off operation. Improved high-current devices with blocking voltage of 1600 volts were reported[116] by the authors in 2013 with a specific on-resistance of 7 mΩ-cm^2. These devices had a chip area of 0.56 cm^2 and active area of 0.40 cm^2 allowing a drain current of 150 A. The devices were demonstrated to have much smaller switching losses at elevated temperature when compared with silicon IGBTs making them good candidates for high frequency, high power applications.

Further progress towards the development of commercially viable 4H-SiC planar power MOSFETs was reported[117] in 2014 with the fabrication of devices blocking 1700 volts with specific on-resistance of 5.5 mΩ-cm^2. This value is close to the analytically computed specific on-resistance for an inversion layer mobility of 15 cm^2/V-s indicating that the performance is still limited by the channel resistance. The devices exhibited a threshold voltage shift of -0.25 volts under a gate bias stress of -15 volts at 225 °C for 20 minutes. The authors claim that this is evidence of stable operation for their devices at 225 °C.

11.16.2 Accumulation-Channel Devices

The first planar shielded accumulation-mode MOSFET structure was fabricated[95] at PSRC in 1997 using 6H-SiC. This device, named the planar ACCUFET, was conceived to circumvent the problems observed with obtaining high inversion layer mobility as well as to screen the channel and gate oxide from high electric fields developed in the drift region. The devices were fabricated using a drift region with doping concentration of 1 x 10^{16} cm^{-3} and thickness of 10 μm, corresponding to a breakdown voltage of 1500 volts. The sub-surface P$^+$ region used to shield the channel and gate oxide was formed by a single boron ion implant with energy of 380 keV and dose of 1 x 10^{14} cm^{-2}. This produced an N-base region with thickness of about 0.3 μm. The gate oxide with thickness of 125 Å was formed using thermal oxidation followed by a re-oxidation anneal.

The un-terminated devices had a breakdown voltage of 350 V. For the structure with cell pitch of 21 μm (channel length of 2.5 μm and JFET width of 4 μm), a specific on-resistance of 18 mΩ-cm^2 was measured at a gate bias of only 5 volts. This was possible because of the low threshold voltage (~ 1 volt) and high transconductance of the structure achieved with the small gate oxide thickness. The measured specific on-resistance was within 2.5 times the specific on-resistance of the drift region (8 mΩ-cm^2) despite the rather large cell pitch. In spite of the very thin gate oxide, no evidence of gate rupture was observed in the blocking state due to the shielding by the P$^+$ region. The measured specific on-resistance for these MOSFETs is about 30 times smaller than that for silicon MOSFETs with blocking voltage capability of 1500 volts.

A detailed analysis[118] of the operation and design of the 6H-SiC ACCUFET was published in 1999. In this paper, it was pointed out that a trade-off between reducing the electric field at the gate oxide and minimizing the specific on-resistance must be performed by optimizing the width of the JFET region. It was also found that the specific on-resistance for the ACCUFET increases with increasing temperature. This had not been previously observed in silicon carbide power MOSFETs because the channel conductance improved rapidly with temperature due to trap limited effective inversion-layer mobility. In contrast, the extracted accumulation-layer mobility was found to remain independent of temperature resulting in a positive temperature coefficient for the specific on-resistance due to increase in resistance of the bulk components.

The ACCUFET structure was successfully fabricated using 4H-SiC in 2000 with high blocking voltage capability[119]. These devices were labeled SIAFETs even though the operating principle for the devices was acknowledged by the authors to be identical to that of ACCUFET structures. The authors achieved a blocking voltage capability of 4580 V with normally-off operation at zero gate bias by using a drift region with a doping concentration of 5 x 10^{14} cm^{-3} and thickness of 75 μm. These devices exhibited a specific on-resistance of 1200 mΩ-cm^2 in spite of using a gate bias of 40 volts because of a low accumulation-layer mobility of 0.5 cm^2/V-s. The specific on-resistance was found to reduce by a factor of 6 times by the application of a positive bias to the sub-surface P$^+$ region. Unfortunately, this entails a more complex package and gate drive circuit for the devices that departs from mainstream silicon technology. The performance of this structure, renamed SEMOSFET, was extended[120] to a 5 kV blocking voltage capability with a specific on-resistance of 88 mΩ-cm^2 in the presence of a positive bias of 2 volts applied to the buried P$^+$ region with 20 volts applied to the MOS-gate electrode. Since the bias applied to the buried P$^+$ region was less than the junction potential, these is no minority carrier injection from the P$^+$ region. Consequently, these devices exhibit very fast switching speeds with turn-on and turn-off times of less than 50 ns while operating at on-state voltage drops slightly less than that for a 4.5 kV IGBT.

4H-SiC ACCUFETs were demonstrated with a blocking voltage of 400 volts and a high specific on-resistance of 90 mΩ-cm^2 in 2000[121] because the accumulation mobility observed for these devices was low ($\sim$ 8 cm^2/V-s). The channel mobility was found to increase with temperature indicating that the channel charge was dominated by traps. A 4H-SiC ACCUFET device was reported[122] in 2002 with breakdown voltage of 600 volts and specific on-resistance of 13 mΩ-cm^2. The authors estimated an accumulation channel mobility of 450 cm^2/V-s validating this approach.

High current 4H-SiC ACCUFETs were demonstrated[123,124] in 2003 with blocking voltages up to 900 V and drain current of 20 A. These devices were fabricated by the grown of an N-type epitaxial layer on top of an ion implanted P$^+$ region to form the N-base region. Devices were found to have a specific on-resistance of 22 mΩ-cm^2 with a breakdown voltage of 550 volts. The authors observed an accumulation channel mobility of 18 cm^2/V-s by using a thermally grown gate oxide followed by N$_2$O anneal.

A double-epitaxial layer process was reported[125,126] in 2004 for the fabrication of an ACCUFET structure called the DEMOSFET by the authors. A highly doped P-type epitaxial layer was first grown to form the P$^+$ shielding regions. This layer was etched to open the JFET regions followed by a second low doped P-type epitaxial layer. Nitrogen ion implantation was used to form the N-base region with a concentration of 1.2 x 10^{17} cm^{-3} and thickness of 0.2 μm. The devices had a threshold voltage of 3 volts and a specific on-resistance of 8.5 mΩ-cm^2. For devices with blocking voltage of 600 volts, the authors reported a high accumulation channel mobility of 105 cm^2/V-s by using a thermally grown gate oxide followed by pyrogenic re-oxidation at 950 °C.

A 4H-SiC ACCUFET structure was reported[127] in 2006 with an epitaxially grown N-type layer to form the N-base region. The doping and thickness of the N-base region were not provided but the threshold voltage of the device was close to zero. A specific on-resistance of 5 $m\Omega$-cm^2 was observed for a gate bias of 20 volts. This is about 10-times larger than the ideal specific on-resistance. No channel mobility data was provided.

In 2008, the blocking voltage for the 4H-SiC ACCUFETs was increased to 10-kV by using a 100 μm thick epitaxial layer with doping concentration of 5 x 10^{14} cm^{-3}. These devices also utilized a 0.1 μm thick epitaxially grown N-base region[128,129]. A three-zone, 750 μm wide, JTE edge termination was employed to achieve the breakdown voltage of 10-kV. A specific on-resistance of 170 $m\Omega$-cm^2 was observed for a gate bias of 10 volts. This value is within 3-times the ideal case because the channel contribution is becoming a smaller fraction of the total resistance at the high breakdown voltage. The channel mobility was reported to have a value of 15 cm^2/V-s at a gate bias of 15 volts.

The 4H-SiC ACCUFET structure with the epitaxially grown N-base region was used to create 40 A devices with blocking voltage of 1000 V[130]. The devices had a specific on-resistance of 3.5 $m\Omega$-cm^2 and a threshold voltage of 2.3 volts. The specific on-resistance is limited by the channel resistance according to the analytical model. The devices were shown to be suitable for induction cook-top applications at an operating frequency of 30 kHz. The switching loss was reduced from 19 watts for the silicon IGBT to 5 watts with the SiC device.

Based up on the results reported in the literature, it can be concluded that the ACCUFET concept has become popular for creating high voltage 4H-SiC power MOSFETs with low specific on-resistance and low threshold voltages. It has been conclusively demonstrated that channel mobility can be increased by an order of magnitude by using the accumulation-mode rather than the inversion-mode. This is particularly important for planar-gate 4H-SiC power MOSFETs with blocking voltages below 3000 volts.

11.17 Experimental Results: Recent Devices

Recent progress with planar-gate 4H-SiC power MOSFETs has been described in previous sections. In particular, significant progress has been made in increasing the blocking voltage capability, as well as investigating 600 V devices for replacement of Si super-junction MOSFETs. Additional innovations in device structures are covered in this section.

A planar-gate 4H-SiC power MOSFET with a deeper P^+ shielding region was fabricated using implant channeling[131]. The channeling of the aluminum ions was achieved by tilting the wafers at an angle of 4 degrees with an implant energy of 350 keV to get an increase in junction depth from 0.7 μm to 1.8 μm. This was also used for the Phosphorus ions with an implant energy of 960 keV to make a deep CSL layer. The conventional and deep P^+ shielding region structures had a specific on-resistance of 4.13 and 4.25 mΩ-cm^2. No change in blocking voltage was confirmed. However, the short-circuit withstand time was improved from 2 to 8 μs. This is due to the reduction of the drain saturation current produced by the stronger JFET effect on the output characteristics.

The deep P^+ shielding region produced using channeling was found to enable fabrication of devices with channel length of 0.3 μm[132]. Devices fabricated by the authors with channel length of 0.3 μm with the conventional P^+ shielding region depth of 0.7 μm were found to exhibit high leakage current leading to low blocking voltage of only 250 V. The breakdown voltage increased to 1600 V with the deep P^+ shielding region. The short-circuit withstand time for these devices was 5 μs. It is worth pointing out that planar-gate 4H-SiC power MOSFETs fabricated in a foundry with a non-self-aligned process with channel lengths of 0.3 μm have been reported with low leakage current and good parametric distribution[24].

A bridged hexagonal cell topology for the planar-gate 4H-SiC power MOSFET was reported in 2021[133]. The P-well bridges were placed at the sharp corners of the hexagonal windows to prevent the high electric field that reduced the breakdown voltage as discussed in section 11.9.1. This design increased the specific on-resistance by 21 % while the breakdown voltage was close to the conventional hexagonal cell topology. The measured short-circuit withstand time of 1.3 μs for these devices was remarkably small.

11.18 Summary

It has been established in this chapter that the incorporation of a sub-surface P^+ region into the planar-gate 4H-SiC power MOSFET structure enables shielding the P-base region from reach-through limited break-down and preventing high electric fields from developing across the gate oxide during the blocking mode. Since relatively low inversion layer mobility has been reported for 4H-SiC MOSFETs, an accumulation-mode structure was proposed with an N-base region that is completely depleted by the built-in potential of the underlying P^+/N junction. This structure takes advantage of the much larger accumulation mobility observed in semiconductors.

The operating principle of the planar shielded MOSFET structures has been reviewed in the chapter providing guidelines for the design of the structures. It has been demonstrated that the JFET width is a critical parameter that controls the electric field at the gate oxide interface as well as the specific on-resistance. Its optimization is important for obtaining high performance devices. In the case of the accumulation-mode structure, the appropriate combination of the doping concentration and thickness of the N-base region must be chosen to ensure that it is completely depleted by the built-in potential of the underlying P^+/N junction. With adequate shielding of the base region, it is found that short channel (0.3-0.5 μm) devices will support high blocking voltages limited only by the properties of the drift region. These devices have excellent safe-operating-area and fast switching speed. This technology has potential for use in systems operating at up to at least 10,000 volts.

Due to the low switching losses for silicon carbide power MOSFETs, they are good competitors to silicon IGBTs in circuits operating at higher frequencies. One example is a 1 MVA solid-state power substation (SSPS) designed using 10-kV SiC modules[134] soft-switching at 20 kHz. Twenty-four MOSFETs and twelve Schottky diodes were used per module to achieve a current handling capability of 120 A per switch. Low voltage silicon Schottky diodes were placed in series with the SiC power MOSFETs to prevent conduction of the body diode. The SSPS converted 13.8-kV to 300-V with 97 % efficiency resulting in 75 % reduction in weight and 50 % reduction in size over the conventional 60-Hz transformer.

4H-SiC power MOSFETs have also been used to create a solid-state transformer (SST) to convert the 3.6-kV distribution grid voltage to 400-V DC and 240/120-V AC voltage[135]. By using 13 kV SiC power MOSFETs on the primary side, the topology of the SST is simplified to a single H-bridge AC/DC rectifier, an isolated dual half-bridge (DHB) DC/DC converter, and a DC/AC inverter. The DC link operates at 6 kV inside the SST. The DHB is operated at 15 kHz to reduce the size and weight of the high-frequency transformer. The switching losses in the SiC power MOSFETs are reduced by soft-switching. 1.2 kV SiC power MOSFETs are used on the secondary side to produce the 400-V DC and

220/120V AC outputs. The rectifier stage and the DHB were found to have an efficiency of over 98 % while the peak efficiency for the inverter stage was 97 %.

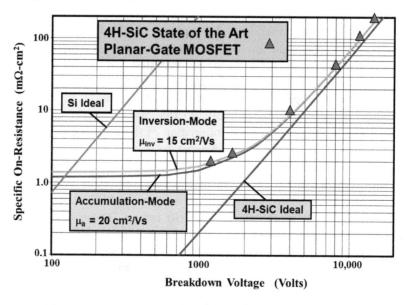

Fig. 11.43 State-of-the-art for planar-gate 4H-SiC power MOSFETs.

An assessment of the state-of-the-art for 4H-SiC planar power MOSFETs from a commercial stand point was reported[136] in 2014. The specific on-resistance for devices with various breakdown voltages from this paper are shown in Fig. 11.43 by the red triangular symbols. It is worth pointing out that the device blocking voltage rating is about 75 % of the breakdown voltage used in the plot. The specific on-resistance obtained using the analytical model with accumulation and inversion mobilities of 20 and 15 cm^2/V-s are shown by the purple and green lines. A channel length of 0.5 μm, JFET width of 0.7 μm with enhanced doping of 3 x 10^{16} cm^{-3}, and cell pitch of 2.8 μm was used in the model. The gate oxide thickness of 500 Å was used with gate drive voltage of 20 V and threshold voltage of 2.5 V. At high breakdown voltages (above 5 kV), the specific on-resistance becomes close to the ideal value plus the contribution of 0.04 mΩ-cm^2 from the substrate. The specific on-resistance follows the analytically computed values for the accumulation-channel and inversion-channel devices. It can be concluded that the channel resistance is limiting the lowest specific on-resistance achievable for devices with breakdown voltages below 4000 V. These devices can benefit from improvements in channel mobility.

In conclusion, silicon carbide power MOSFET have reached a sufficient degree of maturity to find many applications. They can replace silicon IGBTs in applications where the switching losses are dominant to achieve significant reduction of size and weight of the power electronics and also improve efficiency. This will be an important factor for deployment of electric vehicles in the future.

References

[1] D. A. Grant and J. Gowar, "Power MOSFETs: Theory and Applications", John Wiley and Sons, 1989.

[2] B. J. Baliga, "Fundamentals of Power Semiconductor Devices", Second Edition, Chapter 1, pp. 8-10, Springer-Science, New York, 2019.

[3] L. Lorenz, G. Deboy, A. Knapp, and M. Marz, "COOLMOS – A New Milestone in High Voltage Power MOS", IEEE International Symposium on Power Semiconductor Devices and ICs, Abstract 1.1, pp. 3-10, 1999.

[4] B. J. Baliga, "Power Semiconductor Devices for Variable Frequency Drives", Proceedings of the IEEE, Vol. 82, pp. 1112-1122, 1994.

[5] B. J. Baliga and M. Bhatnagar, "Method of Fabricating Silicon Carbide Field Effect Transistor", U. S. Patent 5,322,802, Issued June 21, 1994.

[6] J. N. Shenoy, J. A. Cooper, and M. R. Melloch, "High Voltage Double-Implanted Power MOSFETs in 6H-SiC", IEEE Electron Device Letters, Vol. 18, pp. 93-95, 1997.

[7] B. J. Baliga, "Silicon Carbide Semiconductor Devices having Buried Silicon Carbide Conduction Barrier Layers Therein", U. S. Patent 5,543,637, Issued August 6, 1996.

[8] B. J. Baliga and D. A. Girdhar, "Paradigm Shift in Planar Power MOSFET Technology", Power Electronics Technology Magazine, pp. 24-32, November 2003.

[9] S. T. Sheppard, M. R. Melloch, and J. A. Cooper, "Characteristics of Inversion-Channel and Buried-Channel MOS Devices in 6H-SiC", IEEE Transactions on Electron Devices, Vol. 41, pp. 1257-1264, 1994.

[10] B. J. Baliga, "Fundamentals of Power Semiconductor Devices", Second Edition, Chapter 6.5, pp. 305-325, Springer-Science, New York, 2019.

[11] N. Thapar and B. J. Baliga, "Analytical Model for the Threshold Voltage of Accumulation Channel MOS-Gated Devices", Solid State Electronics, Vol. 42, pp. 1975-1979, 1998.

[12] B. J. Baliga, "Silicon Carbide Power Devices", World Scientific Publishers, Singapore, 2005.

[13] W. Sung, K. Han, and B. J. Baliga, "A Comparative Study of Channel Designs for SiC MOSFETs: Accumulation Mode Channel versus Inversion Mode Channel", IEEE International Symposium on Power Semiconductor Devices and ICs, Abstract SiC-P9, pp. 375-378, 2017.

[14] D. Alok, P. McLarty, and B. J. Baliga, "Electrical Properties of Thermal Oxide Grown on N-type 6H-Silicon Carbide", Applied Physics Letters, Vol. 64, pp. 2845-2846, 1994.

[15] J. B. Casady, et al, "4H-SiC Power Devices: Comparative Overview of UMOS, DMOS, and GTO Device Structures", Material Society Research Symposium Proceedings, Vol. 483, pp. 27-38, 1998.

[16] A. K. Agarwal, et al, "Temperature Dependence of Fowler-Nordheim Current in 6H and 4H-SiC MOS Capacitors", IEEE Electron Device Letters, Vol. 18, pp. 592-594, 1997.

[17] S. Krishnaswami, et al, "Gate Oxide Reliability of 4H-SiC MOS Devices", IEEE International Reliability Physics Symposium, pp. 592-593, 2005.

[18] M. K. Das, et al, "SiC MOSFET Reliability Update", Mater. Sci. Forum, Vols. 717-720, pp. 1073-1076, 2012.

[19] L. Yu, et al, "Oxide Reliability for SiC MOS devices", IEEE International Integrated Reliability Workshop Report, pp. 141-144, 2008.

[20] M. K. Das, et al, "SiC MOSFET Reliability Update", Material Science Forum, Vol. 717-720, pp. 1073-1076, 2012.

[21] W. Sung, K. Han, and B. J. Baliga, "Optimization of JFET Region of 1.2 kV SiC MOSFETs for improved High Frequency Figure of Merit", IEEE Workshop on Wide Bandgap Power Devices and Applications", pp. 238-241, 2017.

[22] S-H Ryu, et al, "Design and Process Issues for Silicon Carbide Power DiMOSFETs", Material Research Society Symposium Proceeding, Vol. 640, pp. H4.5.1-H4.5.6, 2001.

[23] W. Sung, K. Han, and B. J. Baliga, "A Comparative Study of Channel Designs for SiC MOSFETs: Accumulation Mode Channel Versus Inversion Mode Channel", IEEE International Symposium on Power Semiconductor Devices and ICs, Abstract SiC-P9, pp. 375-378, 2017.

[24] A. Agarwal and B. J. Baliga, "Impact of Channel Length on Characteristics of 600V 4H-SiC Inversion-channel Planar MOSFETs", European Solid-State Device Research Conf., pp. 78-81, 2019.

[25] B. J. Baliga, "Fundamentals of Power Semiconductor Devices", Second Edition, Chapter 6.5, pp. 355-363, Springer-Science, New York, 2019.

[26] B. J. Baliga, "Power MOSFET and JBSFET cell topologies with superior high frequency figure of merit", U.S. Patent 62,624,989, Issued February 1, 2018.

[27] K. Han and B. J. Baliga, "The 1.2-kV 4H-SiC OCTFET: A New Cell Topology with improved High-Frequency Figures-of-Merit", IEEE Electron Device Letters, Vol. 40, pp. 299-302, 2019.

[28] K. Han and B. J. Baliga, "Comparison of Four Cell Topologies for 1.2-kV Accumulation- and Inversion-Channel 4H-SiC MOSFETs: Analysis and Experimental Results", IEEE Transactions on Electron Devices, Vol. 66, pp. 2321-2326, 2019.

[29] A. Agarwal and B. J. Baliga, "Implant Straggle Impact on 1.2 kV SiC Power MOSFET Static and Dynamic Parameters", IEEE Journal of the Electron Devices Society, Vol. 10, pp. 245-255, 2022.

[30] B. J. Baliga, "Fundamentals of Power Semiconductor Devices", Second Edition, Chapter 6, pp. 446-449, Springer-Science, New York, 2019.

[31] B. J. Baliga, "Fundamentals of Power Semiconductor Devices", Second Edition, Chapter 6, pp. 396-397, Springer-Science, New York, 2019.

[32] B. J. Baliga, "Fundamentals of Power Semiconductor Devices", Second Edition, Chapter 6, pp. 414-422, Springer-Science, New York, 2019.

[33] B. J. Baliga, "Fundamentals of Power Semiconductor Devices", Second Edition, Chapter 6, pp. 449-451, Springer-Science, New York, 2019.

[34] Q. Zhang, et al, "Latest Results on 1200 V 4H-SiC CIMOSFETs with $R_{sp,on}$ of 3.9 mΩ-cm2 at 150 °C", IEEE International Symposium on Power Semiconductor Devices and ICs, pp. 89-92, 2015.

[35] N. Thapar and B. J. Baliga, "A New IGBT Structure with a wider Safe Operating Area (SOA)", IEEE International Symposium on Power Semiconductor Devices and ICs, Paper 4.3, pp. 177-182, 1994.

[36] T. Sakai and N. Murakami, "A new VDMOSFET structure with reduced reverse transfer capacitance", IEEE Trans. Electron Devices, vol. 36, pp. 1381-1386, 1989.

[37] K. Han, W. Sung and B. J. Baliga, "Split-Gate 1.2-kV 4H-SiC MOSFET: Analysis and Experimental Validation", IEEE Electron Device Letters, Vol. 38, pp. 1437-1440, 2017.

[38] B. J. Baliga, "Power MOSFETs with Superior High Frequency Figure-of-Merit", U. S. Patent 10,355,132, Issued July 16, 2019.

[39] K. Han, W. Sung and B. J. Baliga, "A Novel 1.2 kV 4H-SiC Buffered-Gate (BG) MOSFET: Analysis and Experimental Results", IEEE Electron Device Letters, Vol. 39, pp. 248-251, 2018.

[40] K. Han, W. Sung and B. J. Baliga, "Analysis and Experimental Quantification of 1.2-kV 4H-SiC Split-Gate Octagonal MOSFET", IEEE Electron Device Letters, Vol. 40, pp. 1163-1166, 2019.

[41] M. K. Das, et al, "SiC MOSFET Reliability Update", Material Science Forum, Vols. 717-720, pp. 1073-1076, 2012.

[42] L. C. Yu, et al, "Reliability issues of SiC MOSFETs: A technology for high temperature environments", IEEE Trans. Device Material Reliability, Vol. 10, pp. 418-426, 2010.

[43] A. Agarwal and B. J. Baliga, "Impact of Gate Oxide Thickness on Electrical Characteristics of 1200 V 4H-SiC Planar-Gate Power MOSFETs", IEEE Device Research Conf., pp. 237-238, 2019.

[44] A. Agarwal, et al, "Impact of Gate Oxide Thickness on Switching and Short Circuit Performance of 1200 V 4H-SiC Inversion-channel MOSFETs", IEEE Workshop on Wide Bandgap Power Devices and Applications", pp. 59-62, 2019.

[45] B. J. Baliga, "Fundamentals of Power Semiconductor Devices", Second Edition, Chapter 6, pp. 330-331, Springer-Science, New York, 2019.

[46] B. J. Baliga, "Fundamentals of Power Semiconductor Devices", Second Edition, Chapter 6, pp. 978-983, Springer-Science, New York, 2019.

[47] A. Kanale and B. J. Baliga, "A New User-Configurable Method to Improve Short-Circuit Ruggedness of 1.2-kV SiC Power MOSFETs", IEEE Trans. Power Electronics, Vol. 36, pp. 2059-2067, 2021.

[48] A. Agarwal, K. Han and B. J. Baliga, "Impact of Cell Topology on Characteristics of 600V 4H-SiC Planar MOSFETs", IEEE Electron Device Letters, Vol. 40, pp. 773-776, 2019.

[49] A. Agarwal, K. Han and B. J. Baliga, "600 V 4H-SiC MOSFETs Fabricated in Commercial Foundry With Reduced Gate Oxide Thickness of 27 nm to Achieve IGBT-Compatible Gate Drive of 15 V", IEEE Electron Device Letters, Vol. 40, pp. 1792-1795, 2019.

[50] A. Agarwal, et al, "Switching and Short-Circuit Performance of 27 nm Gate Oxide, 650 V SiC Planar-Gate MOSFETs with 10 to 15 V Gate Drive Voltage", IEEE International Symposium on Power Semiconductor Devices and ICs, pp. 250-253, 2020.

[51] A. Agarwal, A. Kanale and B. J. Baliga, "Advanced 650 V SiC Power MOSFETs with 10 V Gate Drive Compatible with Si Superjunction Devices", IEEE Tran. Power Electronics, Vol. 36, pp. 3335-3345, 2021.

[52] A. Agarwal, K. Han and B. J. Baliga, "Comparison of 2.3-kV 4H-SiC Accumulation-Channel Planar Power MOSFETs Fabricated With Linear, Square, Hexagonal, and Octagonal Cell Topologies", IEEE Tran. Electron Devices, Vol. 67, pp. 6773-6778, 2020.

[53] A. Agarwal, K. Han and B. J. Baliga, "2.3 kV 4H-SiC Accumulation-Channel Split-Gate Planar Power MOSFETs with reduced Gate Charge", Journal of the Electron Device Society, Vol. 8, pp. 499-502, 2020.

[54] A. Agarwal, K. Han and B. J. Baliga, "Performance Enhancement of 2.3 kV 4H-SiC Planar-Gate MOSFETs using reduced Gate Oxide Thickness", IEEE Tran. Electron Devices, Vol. 68, pp. 5029-5033, 2022.

[55] L. Chen, et al, "3300 V, 30 A 4H-SiC Power DMOSFETs", Int. Semiconductor Device Research Symposium, pp. P1-P2, 2009.

[56] M. Imaizumi and N. Miura, "Characteristics of 600, 1200, and 3300 V Planar SiC-MOSFETs for Energy Conversion Applications", IEEE Tran. Electron Devices, Vol. 62, pp. 390-395, 2015.

[57] X. Huang, et al, "Design and Fabrication of 3.3 kV SiC MOSFETs for Industrial Applications", IEEE International Symposium on Power Semiconductor Devices and ICs, pp. 255-258, 2017.

[58] V. Mulpuri, et al, "Characterization and Robustness Evaluation of 3.3 kV/40 mΩ SiC DMOSFETs", IEEE Workshop on Wide Bandgap Power Devices and Applications, pp. 130-136, 2019.

[59] D. Xing, et al, "3.3-kV SiC MOSFET Performance and Short-Circuit Capability", IEEE Workshop on Wide Bandgap Power Devices and Applications, pp. P1-P6, 2020.

[60] A. Agarwal, et al, "3.3 kV 4H-SiC Planar-Gate MOSFETs Manufactured using Gen-5 PRESiCE^{TM} Technology in a 4-inch Wafer Commercial Foundry", IEEE SouthEastCON, pp. P1-P6, 2021.

[61] S. Li, et al, "Simulation, Fabrication and Characterization of 6500V 4H-SiC power DMOSFETs", Int. Forum on Wide Bandgap Semiconductors, pp. 144-147, 2017.

[62] T. Lixin, et al, "Development and Analysis of 6500V SiC Power MOSFET", Int. Forum on Wide Bandgap Semiconductors, pp. 6-9, 2021.

[63] N. Yun, et al, "Critical Design Considerations for Static and Dynamic Performances on 6.5 kV 4H-SiC MOSFETs Fabricated in a 6-inch SiC Foundry", IEEE Workshop on Wide Bandgap Power Devices and Applications, pp. 361-365, 2021.

[64] A. Huang and B. J. Baliga, "FREEDM System: Role of Power Electronics and Power Semiconductors in Developing an Energy Internet", IEEE Int. Symp. On Power Semiconductor Devices and ICs, Plenary Session Paper, pp. 9-12, 2009.

[65] E. V. Brunt, et al, "Development of Medium Voltage SiC Power Technology for Next Generation Power Electronics", IEEE Int. Workshop on Integrated Power Packaging, pp. 72-74, 2015.

[66] S-H Ryu, et al, "10-kV, 123-mΩ–cm^2 4H-SiC Power DMOSFETs", IEEE Electron Device Letters, Vol. 25, pp. 556-558, 2004.

[67] S-H Ryu, et al, "10-kV, 5 A 4H-SiC Power DMOSFETs", IEEE Int. Symp. On Power Semiconductor Devices and ICs, Plenary Session Paper, pp. P1-P4, 2006.

[68] E. P. Eni, et al, "Characterization of 10 kV 10 A SiC MOSFET", Int. Aegean Conf. on Electrical Machines and Power Electronics, pp. 675-680, 2015.

[69] H. Kitai, et al, "Low On-Resistance and Fast Switching of 13 kV SiC MOSFETs with Optimized Junction Field Effect Transistor Region", IEEE Int. Symp. On Power Semiconductor Devices and ICs, pp. 343-346, 2017.

[70] E. P. Eni, et al, "Short-Circuit Characterization of 10 kV 10A 4H-SiC MOSFET", IEEE Applied Power Electronics Conf., pp. 974-978, 2016.

[71] E. P. Eni, et al, "Short-Circuit Degradation of 10-kV 10-A SiC MOSFET", IEEE Tran. Power Electronics, Vol. 32, pp. 9342-9354, 2017.

[72] A. Kumar, et al, "Single Shot Avalanche Energy Characterization of 10kV, 10A 4H-SiC MOSFETs", IEEE Applied Power Electronics Conf., pp. 2737-2742, 2018.

[73] B. J. Baliga, "Impact of SiC on Power Devices", Proceedings of the 4th International Conference on Amorphous and Crystalline Silicon Carbide, pp. 305-313, 1991.

[74] L. Lipkin and J. W. Palmour, "Improved Oxidation Procedures for Reduced SiO$_2$/SiC Defects", J. Electronic Materials, Vol. 25, pp. 909-915, 1996.

[75] R. Schorner, et al, "Significantly improved performance of MOSFETs on Silicon Carbide using the 15R-SiC Polytype", IEEE Electron Device Letters, Vol. 20, pp. 241-244, 1999.

[76] A. V. Suvorov, et al, "4H-SiC Self-Aligned Implant-Diffused Structure for Power DMOSFETs", Materials Research Forum, Vol. 338-342, pp. 1275-1278, 2000.

[77] S. Sridevan and B. J. Baliga, "Lateral N-channel Inversion Mode 4H-SiC MOSFETs", PSRC Technical Report TR-97-019, 1997.

[78] S. Sridevan and B. J. Baliga, "Lateral N-channel Inversion Mode 4H-SiC MOSFETs", IEEE Electron Device Letters, Vol. 19, pp. 228-230, 1998.

[79] S. Sridevan and B. J. Baliga, "Phonon Scattering Limited Mobility in SiC Inversion Layers", PSRC Technical Report TR-98-03, 1998.

[80] D. Alok, E. Arnold, and R. Egloff, "Process Dependence of Inversion Layer Mobility in 4H-SiC Devices", Silicon Carbide and Related Materials – 1999, Material Science Forum, Vol. 338-342, pp. 1077-1080, 2000.

[81] K. Chatty, et al, "Hall Measurements of Inversion and Accumulation-Mode 4H-SiC MOSFETs", Material Science Forum, Vol. 389-393, pp. 1041-1044, 2002.

[82] N. S. Saks, S. S. Mani, and K. Agarwal, Applied Physics Letters, Vol. 76, pp. 2250-2251, 2000.

[83] S. Harada, et al, "Temperature Dependence of the Channel Mobility and Threshold Voltage in 4H and 6H-SiC MOSFETs", Material Society Research Symposium Proceedings, Vol. 640, pp. H5.37.1-H5.37.6, 2001.

[84] G. Y. Chung, et al, "Improved Inversion Channel Mobility for 4H-SiC MOSFETs following High Temperature Anneals in Nitric Oxide", IEEE Electron Device Letters, Vol. 22, pp. 176-178, 2001.

[85] R. H. Ryu, et al, "Critical Issues for MOS Based Power Devices in 4H-SiC" Material Science Forum, Vol. 615-617, pp. 743-748, 2009.

[86] J. R. Williams, et al, "Passivation of the 4H-SiC/SiO2 Interface with Nitric Oxide", Material Science Forum, Vol. 389-393, pp. 967-972, 2002.

[87] S. Dhar, et al, "Effect of Nitric Oxide Annealing on the Interface Trap Density near the Conduction Band Edge of 4H-SiC at the oxide/(1120) 4H-SiC Interface", Applied Physics Letters, Vl. 84, pp. 1498-1500, 2004.

[88] C-Y Lu, et al, "Effect of Process Variations and Ambient Temperature on Electron Mobility at the SiO2/4H-SiC Interface", IEEE Transactions on Electron Devices, Vol. 50, pp. 1582-1588, 2003.

[89] S. Dhar, et al, "Inversion Layer Carrier Concentration and Mobility in 4H-SiC MOSFETs", Journal of Applied Physics, Vol. 108, pp. 054509, 2010.

[90] S. Dhar, et al, "Temperature Dependence of Inversion Layer Carrier Concentration and Hall Mobility in 4H-SiC MOSFETs", Material Science Forum, Vol. 717-720, pp. 713-716, 2012.

[91] G. Gudjonsson, et al, "High Field-Effect Mobility in n-Channel Si Face 4H-SiC MOSFETs with Gate Oxide Grown on Aluminum Ion-Implanted Material", IEEE Electron Device Letters, Vol. 26, pp. 96-98, 2005.

[92] S. M. Thomas, et al, "Enhanced Field Effect Mobility on 4H-SiC by Oxidation at 1500 °C", Journal of the Electron Device Society, Vol. 2, pp. 114-117, 2014.

[93] X. Yang, B. Lee, and V. Misra, "High Mobility 4H-SiC Lateral MOSFETs using Lanthanum Silicate and Atomic Layer Deposited SiO2", IEEE Electron Device Letters, Vol. 36, pp. 312-314, 2015.

[94] K. Han and B. J. Baliga, "Operation of 1.2-kV 4H-SiC Accumulation and Inversion Channel Split-Gate (SG) MOSFETs at Elevated Temperatures", IEEE Transactions on Electron Devices, Vol. 65, pp. 3333-3338, 2018.

[95] S. C. Sun and J. D. Plummer, "Electron Mobility in Inversion and Accumulation Layers on Thermally Oxidized Silicon Surfaces", IEEE Transactions on Electron Devices, Vol. 27, pp. 1497-1508, 1980.

[96] P. M. Shenoy and B. J. Baliga, "The Planar 6H-SiC ACCUFET", IEEE Electron Device Letters, Vol. 18, pp. 589-591, 1997.

[97] P. M. Shenoy and B. J. Baliga, "Analysis and Optimization of the Planar 6H-SiC ACCUFET", Solid State Electronics, Vol. 43, pp. 213-220, 1999.

[98] P. M. Shenoy and B. J. Baliga, "High Voltage Planar 6H-SiC ACCUFET", Material Science Forum, Vol. 264-268, pp. 993-996, 1998.

[99] R. K. Chilukuri, P. M. Shenoy, and B. J. Baliga, "Comparison of 6H-SiC and 4H-SiC High Voltage Planar ACCUFETs", IEEE International Symposium on Power Semiconductor Devices and ICs, Abstract 6.1, pp. 115-118, 1998.

[100] K. Ueno and T. Oikawa, "Counter-Doped MOSFETs of 4H-SiC", IEEE Electron Device Letters, Vol. 20, pp. 624-626, 1999.

[101] K. Chatty, et al, "Accumulation-Layer Electron Mobility in n-Channel 4H-SiC MOSFETs", IEEE Electron Device Letters, Vol. 22, pp. 212-214, 2001.

[102] S. Sridevan and B. J. Baliga, "Lateral N-channel Inversion Mode 4H-SiC MOSFETs", IEEE Electron Device Letters, Vol. 19, pp. 228-230, 1998.

[103] S. Harada, et al, "High Channel Mobility in Normally-Off 4H-SiC Buried Channel MOSFETs", IEEE Electron Device Letters, Vol. 22, pp. 272-274, 2001.

[104] S. Kaneko, et al, "4H-SiC ACCUFET with a Two-Layer Stacked Gate Oxide", Silicon Carbide and Related Materials – 2001, Material Science Forum, Vol. 389-393, pp. 1073-1076, 2002.

[105] J. N. Shenoy, J. A. Cooper, and M. R. Melloch, "High Voltage Double-Implanted Power MOSFETs in 6H-SiC", IEEE Electron Device Letters, Vol. 18, pp. 93-95, 1997.

[106] D. Peters, et al, "An 1800V Triple Implanted Vertical 6H-SiC MOSFET", IEEE Transactions on Electron Devices, Vol. 46, pp. 542-545, 1999.

[107] R. Schorner, et al, "Rugged Power MOSFETs in 6H-SiC with Blocking Voltage Capability upto 1800V", Silicon Carbide and Related Materials – 1999, Material Science Forum, Vol. 338-342, pp. 1295-1298, 2000.

[108] S-H Ryu, et al, "Design and Process Issues for Silicon Carbide Power DiMOSFETs", Material Science Forum, Vol. 640, pp. H4.5.1-H4.5.6, 2001.

[109] S. Sridevan and B. J. Baliga, "Inversion Layer Mobility in SiC MOSFETs", Material Science Forum, Vol. 264-268, pp. 997-1000, 1998.

[110] S-H. Ryu, et al, "Large-Area (3.3 mm x 3.3 mm) Power MOSFETs in 4H-SiC", Silicon Carbide and Related Materials – 2001, Material Science Forum, Vol. 389-393, pp. 1195-1198, 2002.

[111] M. Matin, A. Saha, and J. A. Cooper, "Self-Aligned Short-Channel Vertical Power DMOSFETs in 4H-SiC", Material Science Forum, Vol. 457-460, pp. 1393-1396, 2004.

[112] M. Matin, A. Saha, and J. A. Cooper, "A Self-Aligned Process for High-Voltage Short-Channel Vertical DMOSFETs in 4H-SiC", IEEE Transactions on Electron Devices, Vol. 51, pp. 1721-1725, 2004.

[113] A. Saha and J. A. Cooper, "A 1-kV 4H-SiC Power DMOSFET Optimized Low On-Resistance", IEEE Transactions on Electron Devices, Vol. 55, pp. 2786-2791, 2007.

[114] L. Stevanovic, et al, "Realizing the Full Potential of Silicon Carbide Power Devices", IEEE Workshop on Controls and Modelling of Power Electronics, pp. 1-6, 2010.

[115] S-H Ryu, et al, "3.7 mW-cm2, 1500 V 4H-SiC DMOSFETs for Advanced High Power, High Frequency Applications", IEEE International Symposium on Power Semiconductor Devices and ICs, pp. 227-230, 2011.

[116] L. Cheng, et al, "High Performance, Large-Area, 1600 v? 150 A, 4H-SiC DMOSFET for Robust High-Power and High-Temperature

Applications", IEEE International Symposium on Power Semiconductor Devices and ICs, Paper 2-2, pp. 47-50, 2013.

[117] K. Matocha, et al, "1700V, 5.5mOhm-cm^2 4H-SiC DMOSFET with Stable 225°C Operation", Material Science Forum, Vol. 778-780, pp. 903-906, 2014.

[118] P. M. Shenoy and B. J. Baliga, "Analysis and Optimization of the Planar 6H-SiC ACCUFET", Solid State Electronics, Vol. 43, pp. 213-220, 1999.

[119] Y. Sugawara, et al, "4.5 kV Novel High Voltage High Performance SiC-FET (SIAFET)", IEEE International Symposium on Power Semiconductor Devices and ICs, pp. 105-108, 2000.

[120] Y. Sugawara, et al, "5.0 kV 4H-SiC SEMOSFET with Low RonS of 88 mOcm2", Material Science Forum, Vol. 389-393, pp. 1199-1202, 2002.

[121] R. Singh, S-H Ryu, and J. W. Palmour, "High Temperature, High Current, 4H-SiC Accu-DMOSFET", Material Science Forum, Vol. 338-342, pp. 1271-1274, 2000.

[122] F. Nallet, et al, "Very Low R_{ON} measured on 4H-SiC Accu-MOSFET High Power Device", IEEE International Symposium on Power Semiconductor Devices and ICs, pp. 209-212, 2002.

[123] R. Singh, et al, "High Channel Density, 20A 4H-SiC ACCUFET with R_{onsp} = 15 mΩ-cm^2", Electronics Letters, Vol. 39, p. 152-153, 2003.

[124] R. Singh, et al, "Development of High Current 4H-SiC ACCUFET", IEEE Transactions on Electron Devices, Vol. 50, pp. 471-477, 2003.

[125] S. Harada, et al, "8.4 mW-cm2 600-V Double-Epitaxial MOSFETs in 4H-SiC", IEEE Electron Device Letters, Vol. 25, pp. 292-294, 2004.

[126] S. Harada, et al, "An Ultra-Low Ron in 4H-SiC Vertical MOSFET: Buried Channel Double-Epitaxial MOSFET", IEEE International Symposium on Power Semiconductor Devices and ICs, pp. 313-316, 2004.

[127] N. Miura, et al, "Successful Development of 1.2 kV 4H-SiC MOSFETs with Very Low On-Resistance of 5 mΩ-cm2", IEEE International Symposium on Power Semiconductor Devices and ICs, pp. 1-4, 2006.

[128] R. S. Howell, et al, "A 10-kV Large-Area 4H-SiC Power DMOSFET with Stable Subthreshold behavior independent of Temperature", IEEE Transactions on Electron Devices, Vol. 55, pp. 1807-1815, 2008.

[129] R. S. Howell, et al, "Comparison of Design and Yield for Large Area 10-kV 4H-SiC DMOSFETs", IEEE Transactions on Electron Devices, Vol. 55, pp. 1816-1823, 2008.

[130] M. Kitabatake, et al, "4H-SiC DIMOSFET Power Device for Home Appliances", IEEE International Power Electronics Conference, pp. 3249-3253, 2010.

[131] D. Kim, et al, "Improved Short-Circuit Ruggedness for 1.2 kV 4H-SiC MOSFET using a Deep P-Well implemented by Channeling Implantation", IEEE Electron Device Letters, Vol. 42, pp. 1822-1825, 2021.

[132] D. Kim, et al, "Implementation of a short channel (0.3 μm) for 4HSiC MOSFETs with deep P-well using 'channeling' implantation", IEEE International Symposium on Power Semiconductor Devices and ICs, pp. 217-220, 2022.

[133] D. Kim, et al, "A Static, Switching, Short-circuit Characteristics of 1.2 kV 4H-SiC MOSFETs: Comparison between Linear and (Bridged) Hexagonal Topology", IEEE International Symposium on Power Semiconductor Devices and ICs, pp. 9-13, 2021.

[134] M. K. Das, et al, "10 kV, 120 A SiC Half H-Bridge Power MOSFET Modules Suitable for High Frequency, Medium Voltage Applications", IEEE Energy Conversion Congress and Exposition, pp. 2689-2692, 2011.

[135] F. Wang, et al, "A 3.6kV High Performance Solid State Transformer Based on 13kV SiC MOSFET", IEEE Energy Conversion Congress and Exposition, pp. 4553-4560, 2014.

[136] J. Palmour, et al, "Silicon Carbide Power MOSFETs: Breakthrough Performance from 900 V up to 15 kV", IEEE International Symposium on Power Semiconductor Devices and ICs, pp. 79-82, 2014.

Chapter 12

Trench-Gate Power MOSFETs

Silicon trench-gate power MOSFETs were developed in the 1990s by borrowing the trench technology originally developed for DRAMs. Before the introduction of the trench-gate structure, it was found that the ability to reduce the specific on-resistance for Si power MOSFETs was constrained by the poor channel density and the JFET region resistance[1]. The improvements to the DMOSFET structure were saturating despite the use of more advanced lithographic design rules enabling a steady reduction of the specific on-resistance in the 1970s and early 1980s[2]. The trench-gate or UMOSFET structure enabled significant increase in the channel density and elimination of the JFET resistance contribution resulting in a major enhancement in low voltage (<50 volt) Si power MOSFET performance. The first trench-gate devices[3,4] were fabricated in the mid-1980s and shown to have significantly lower specific on-resistance than the DMOSFET structure. However, problems with controlling the quality of the trench surface and oxide reliability problems needed to be solved before the introduction of commercial devices. Eventually, this technology overtook the planar DMOSFET technology in the 1990s and has now taken a dominant position in the industry for serving portable appliances, such as laptops, PDAs, etc.

In the Si power DMOSFET structure, the channel and JFET resistances were found to become the dominant components when the breakdown voltage was reduced below 50 V because of the low resistance of the drift region. Similarly, due to the much lower specific on-resistance for the drift region in 4H-SiC power MOSFETs, the channel and JFET contributions become dominant for breakdown voltages below 5000 V, especially if the channel mobility is poor. This motivated the development of the trench-gate 4H-SiC power MOSFETs in the 1990s. At that time, the P-base region for the trench-gate device could be fabricated using epitaxial growth which was at a more advanced state than the ability to use ion implantation to create P-type layers in

SiC. This allowed the fabrication of these structures before the planar structures. However, their performance was limited by issues unique to SiC created by simply replicating the Si device structure[5].

This chapter reviews the basic principles of operation of the trench-gate SiC power MOSFET structure. The specific on-resistance for this structure is shown to be significantly lower than that for the DMOSFET structure. However, the gate oxide in the UMOSFET structure is exposed to the very high electric field developed in the SiC drift region during the blocking-mode. This is a major limitation to adopting the basic UMOSFET structure from Si to 4H-SiC. Two fundamental approaches to solving this problem are discussed in the chapter: (a) the use of high-k dielectrics as the gate insulator and (b) the shielding of the gate oxide from the high electric field in the SiC drift region.

Structures designed to reduce the electric field at the gate oxide by using a shielding region are essential to realization of practical 4H-SiC power MOSFET structures[6]. In this chapter, analytical models of the basic and shielded trench-gate silicon carbide MOSFET structure are provided followed by the description of experimental results on relevant structures to define the state of the development effort on these devices.

12.1 Basic Device Structure

The basic structure of the trench-gate power MOSFET is shown in Fig. 12.1. The structure can be fabricated by either the epitaxial growth of the P-base region over the drift region or by introducing the P-type dopants using ion-implantation. The first 4H-SiC UMOSFET structure was fabricated by the epitaxial growth of the P-base region due to problems with activation of P-type ion implanted dopants in silicon carbide[5]. However, this requires either removal of the P-type layer on the edges of the structure to form a mesa edge termination[5] or multiple trench-isolated guard rings[7]. The trench-gate structure can be fabricated by using reactive-ion etching of the SiC layers to form the U-shaped trenches. The gate oxide was then created by thermal oxidation followed by refilling the trench with polysilicon as done for Si UMOSFET structures.

Note that the P-base region is short-circuited to the N^+ source region by the source metal. This is routinely done in Si devices using a common Aluminum ohmic contact metal for both the N^+ and P-type regions. In the case of 4H-SiC, it has been shown that Nickel annealed at 1000 °C makes a good ohmic contact to N^+ and P^+ regions.

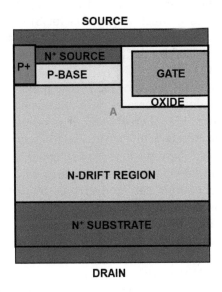

Fig. 12.1 Basic 4H-SiC trench-gate power MOSFET structure.

12.1.1 Blocking Characteristics

When the 4H-SiC trench-gate power MOSFET structure is operating in the forward blocking mode, the voltage is supported by a depletion region formed on both sides of the P-base/N-drift junction. The maximum blocking voltage can be determined by the electric field at this junction becoming equal to the critical electric field for breakdown if the parasitic $N^+/P/N$ bipolar transistor is completely suppressed. This suppression is accomplished by short-circuiting the N^+ source and P-base regions using the source metal as shown on the upper left hand side of the cross-section. A highly doped P^+ region that is shown in Fig. 12.1 is used to reduce the contact resistance to the P-base region. However, a large leakage current can occur when the depletion region in the P-base region reaches-through to the N^+ source region. The doping concentration and thickness of the P-base region must be designed to prevent the reach-through phenomenon from limiting the breakdown voltage. The physics governing the reach-through process is identical to that already described in chapter 11 for the 4H-SiC planar-gate power

MOSFET structure. Consequently, the design rules provided earlier with the aid of Fig. 11.3 can be applied to the trench-gate structure as well. This implies that the minimum channel length required for the 4H-SiC trench-gate MOSFETs is much larger than for Si devices resulting in a substantial increase in the on-resistance. The degradation of the on-resistance is compounded by the lower channel inversion layer mobility observed for 4H-SiC.

The minimum thickness of the P-base region required to prevent reach-through breakdown decreases with increasing doping concentration as shown in Fig. 11.3. For 4H-SiC, it is necessary to increase the P-base doping concentration to above 2×10^{17} cm^{-3} to prevent reach-through with a 1 μm P-base thickness. This higher doping concentration makes the threshold voltage prohibitively large as already discussed in chapter 11. This conundrum can be overcome by using shielding of the P-base region as discussed in this chapter.

The maximum blocking voltage capability of the 4H-SiC trench-gate MOSFET structure is determined by the drift region doping concentration and thickness as already discussed in chapter 3. However, in the 4H-SiC trench-gate MOSFET structure, the gate extends down into the drift region exposing the gate oxide to the high electric field developed in the drift region in 4H-SiC under forward blocking conditions. For 4H-SiC, the electric field in the oxide reaches a value of 9×10^6 V/cm when the field in the semiconductor reaches its breakdown strength of about 3×10^6 V/cm. This value not only exceeds the reliability limit but can cause rupture of the oxide leading to catastrophic breakdown because the problem is exacerbated by electric field enhancement at the corners of the trenches at location A in the figure. Novel structures[6] that shield the gate oxide from high electric field have been proposed and demonstrated to resolve this problem. These structures are discussed in a subsequent section.

12.1.2 On-Resistance

Current flow between the drain and source of the 4H-SiC trench-gate power MOSFET can be induced by creating an inversion layer channel on the surface of the P-base region adjacent to the vertical sidewall of the trench. The current path is illustrated in Fig. 12.2 by the green shaded area. The current flows from the source region into the drift region through the inversion layer channel formed on the vertical side-walls of the trench due to the applied gate bias. It then spreads into the N-drift region from the bottom of the trench at a 45 degree angle and becomes uniform through the rest of the structure.

The total on-resistance for the 4H-SiC trench-gate power MOSFET structure is determined by the resistance of these components in the current path:

$$R_{on,sp} = R_{CH} + R_D + R_{subs} \qquad [12.1]$$

where R_{CH} is the channel resistance, R_D is the resistance of the drift region after taking into account current spreading from the channel, and R_{subs} is the resistance of the N$^+$ substrate. These resistances can be analytically modeled by using the current flow pattern indicated by the shaded regions in Fig. 12.2. Note the absence of the JFET resistance component of the planar-gate structure. This allows reduction of the total $R_{on,sp}$ because the cell pitch can be reduced.

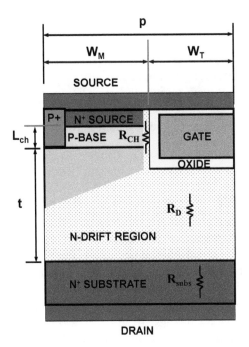

Fig. 12.2 Current flow path in the trench-gate 4H-SiC power MOSFET.

The specific channel resistance is given by:

$$R_{CH} = \frac{L_{CH} \cdot p}{\mu_{inv} C_{ox} (V_G - V_T)}$$ [12.2]

where L_{CH} is the channel length determined by the depth of the P-base and the N^+ source regions as shown in Fig. 12.2, p is the cell pitch, μ_{inv} is the mobility for electrons in the inversion layer channel, C_{ox} is the specific capacitance of the gate oxide, V_G is the applied gate bias, and V_T is the threshold voltage. The specific capacitance can be obtained using:

$$C_{ox} = \frac{\varepsilon_{ox}}{t_{ox}}$$ [12.3]

where ε_{ox} is the dielectric constant for the gate oxide and t_{ox} is its thickness.

The drift region spreading resistance can be obtained by using:

$$R_D = \rho_D \cdot p \cdot \ln\left(\frac{p}{W_T}\right) + \rho_D \cdot (t - W_M)$$ [12.4]

where ρ_D is the resistivity of the drift region, t is the thickness of the drift region below the P-base region and W_T, W_M are the half-widths of the trench and mesa regions, respectively, as shown in the figure.

The contribution to the resistance from the N^+ substrate is given by:

$$R_{subs} = \rho_{subs} \cdot t_{subs}$$ [12.5]

where ρ_{subs} and t_{subs} are the resistivity and thickness of the substrate, respectively. A typical value for this contribution is 4×10^{-4} Ω-cm^2 based up on a substrate thickness of 200 microns and resistivity of 0.02 Ω-cm.

The specific on-resistances of 1200-V rated 4H-SiC trench MOSFETs can be modeled using the above analytical expressions. These devices are fabricated with drift region doping concentration of 8×10^{15} cm^{-3} and thickness of 10 μm. The device breakdown voltage is typically 1600 V. A gate oxide thickness of 500 Å was used in this example. The mesa width (W_M) and trench width (W_T) for the structure shown in Fig. 12.2 were kept at 0.5 μm resulting in a pitch (p) of 1.0 μm. This aggressive design is chosen to evaluate the potential capability of the trench-gate structure. The gate bias voltage (V_G) was assumed to be 20 volts with a threshold voltage (V_T) of 2.5 volts.

The various components of the on-resistance are shown in Fig. 12.3 with impact of increasing the channel length for the case of a channel mobility of 100 cm^2/V-s, a relatively high value. As expected, only the channel resistance increases with increasing channel length. The other components are unaffected by the increase in channel length because the cell pitch remains unaltered. It can be seen that the drift region resistance is dominant in this case with high channel mobility. A total specific on-resistance of 1.12 mΩ-cm^2 is obtained for a channel length of 1.0 μm, which is within two times the ideal specific on-resistance of the drift region.

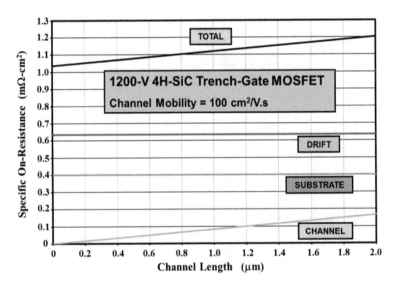

Fig. 12.3 On-resistance components for 4H-SiC trench-gate MOSFETs for channel mobility of 100 cm^2/V-s.

The above calculations are based upon using a channel mobility of 100 cm^2/Vs. Most groups working on 4H-SiC power MOSFETs have reported much lower magnitudes for the channel mobility[8]. Consequently, the impact of reducing the channel mobility for the 4H-SiC trench-gate MOSFET structure is shown in Fig. 12.4 and 12.5 for the case of mobility values of 20 and 5 cm^2/V-s. With a practical channel mobility of 20 cm^2/V-s, the specific on-resistance increasing to a value of 1.45 mΩ-cm^2 for a channel length of 1.0 μm. When the channel mobility is reduced to 5 cm^2/Vs, the channel resistance exceeds that of the drift region, as shown in Fig. 12.5, with an increase in the specific on-resistance to a value of 2.70 mΩ-cm² for a channel length of 1.0 μm. This value is 4 times the ideal drift region resistance for a breakdown voltage of 1600 V.

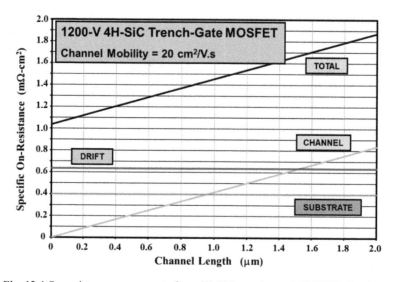

Fig. 12.4 On-resistance components for a 4H-SiC trench-gate MOSFETs for channel mobility of 20 cm²/V-s.

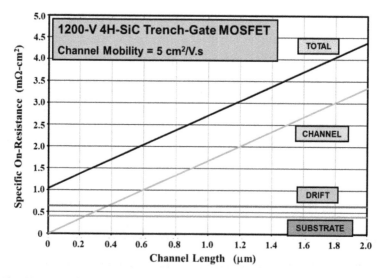

Fig. 12.5 On-resistance components for 4H-SiC trench-gate MOSFETs for channel mobility of 5 cm²/V-s.

These results indicate that the channel resistance can become dominant even in the 4H-SiC trench-gate MOSFET structure despite the high channel density if the channel mobility is low. The relative contribution from the channel resistance in the trench-gate MOSFET structure depends upon the drift region resistance which is a function of the breakdown voltage of the device. This can be demonstrated by considering a 4H-SiC trench-gate MOSFET design with a cell pitch of 1.0 μm, channel length of 1.0 μm and gate oxide thickness of 500 Å, while the properties of the underlying drift region are adjusted to obtain the desired breakdown voltage. The gate bias voltage (V_G) was assumed to be 20 volts with a threshold voltage (V_T) of 2.5 volts. The specific on-resistance for this trench-gate 4H-SiC MOSFET structure is plotted in Fig. 12.6 as a function of the breakdown voltage using a channel mobility of 20 cm^2/V-s.

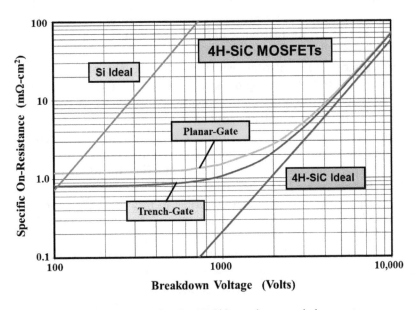

Fig. 12.6 Specific on-resistance for 4H-SiC trench-gate and planar-gate power MOSFETs for channel mobility of 20 cm^2/V-s.

In performing this modeling, it is important to recognize that the thickness of the drift region (parameter 't' in Fig. 12.2) can become smaller than the mesa width (W_M) at lower breakdown voltages. Under these conditions, the current does not distribute at a 45 degree angle into the drift region from the bottom of the trench. Instead, the current flows from a cross-sectional width of (W_T) to a cross-section of ($p = W_M + W_P$). The drift region resistance for these cases can be modeled using:

$$R_D = \rho_D . p . \ln\left(\frac{p}{W_T}\right) \qquad\qquad \text{[12.6]}$$

From Fig. 12.6, it can be concluded that the specific on-resistance of 4H-SiC trench-gate MOSFETs approaches the ideal specific on-resistance (plus 0.4 mΩ-cm^2 contribution from the N$^+$ substrate) when the breakdown voltage exceeds 5000 V even with a channel mobility of 20 cm^2/V-s. However, the channel resistance limits the performance of the trench-gate 4H-SiC MOSFET structure when the breakdown voltage falls below 2000 V. For the case of a breakdown voltage of 1000 V, the anticipated improvement in specific on-resistance over silicon power MOSFETs is then about 100 times (as opposed to the 1000x improvement in the specific on-resistance of the drift region alone).

For a better perspective, the performance of the planar 4H-SiC MOSFET structure is also shown in the figure. The planar MOSFET analysis was based upon using the same channel length, gate oxide thickness, and channel mobility as the trench-gate structure. A cell-pitch of 2.8 μm was used for the planar structure as in chapter 11. It can be seen that the trench-gate structure offers a reduction of the specific-on-resistance by about 40 %. Both the planar and trench-gate structures can benefit from improvement of the channel mobility for lower breakdown voltage devices.

The on-resistance model presented in this section was originally described[9] to highlight the importance of improving the channel inversion layer mobility for silicon carbide trench-gate MOSFETs. This model assumes that all the applied drain bias is supported within the N-drift region. For devices with lower breakdown voltages, the doping concentration in the N-drift layer becomes comparable to that for the P-base region. Consequently, a substantial fraction of the applied drain bias is supported within the P-base region as well. A model for the specific on-resistance that takes this into consideration indicates further reduction of the specific on-resistance[10]. However, the specific on-resistance of the trench-gate structure is still limited by the channel inversion layer mobility for devices designed to support 1000 V.

12.1.3 Threshold Voltage

The threshold voltage of the 4H-SiC trench-gate power MOSFET structure is determined by the doping concentration of the P-base region along the sidewalls of the trench region. A minimum threshold voltage must be maintained at above 2 V for most system applications to provide immunity against inadvertent turn-on due to voltage spikes arising from noise. At the same time, a high threshold voltage is not desirable because the voltage available for creating the charge in the channel inversion layer is determined by $(V_G - V_T)$ where V_G is the applied gate bias voltage and V_T is the threshold voltage. Most power electronic systems designed for high voltage operation (the most suitable application area for SiC power devices) provide a gate drive voltage of up to 20 V. Based upon this criterion, the threshold voltage should be kept below 5 volts in order to obtain a low channel resistance contribution.

The threshold voltage for the trench-gate inversion-mode MOSFET structure can be modeled using the same physics described in chapter 11 for the planar gate inversion-mode MOSFET structure. The threshold voltage for 4H-SiC devices can be obtained using the graphs provided in that chapter. Based upon that analysis, it is preferable to use a gate oxide thickness of 500 Å and a P-base doping concentration of 1 x 10^{17} cm^{-3} to obtain a threshold voltage of about 5 volts. However, this P-base doping concentration leads to a reach-through induced breakdown problem as discussed in chapter 11. This problem can be overcome using shielding of the P-base region as discussed in the next section.

12.2 Trench-Gate 4h-SiC Power MOSFET with Base P$^+$ Shielding Region

A structural enhancement that can circumvent the P-base reach-through problem is shown in Fig. 12.7. This idea was originally described in a book published in 2005[11]. A P$^+$ region is incorporated into the trench-gate MOSFET structure under the source region to suppress the extension of the depletion region in this portion of the cell structure. A relatively thin, lightly doped P-base region is retained adjacent to the trench sidewalls. The doping concentration of this P-base region is chosen to obtain the desired threshold voltage.

It has been confirmed by numerical simulations that the presence of the P$^+$ region suppresses reach-through within the adjacent lightly doped P-base region allowing the structure to support high drain voltages up to the breakdown voltage capability of the drift region.

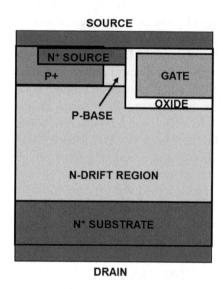

Fig. 12.7 Trench-gate 4H-SiC power MOSFET structure with base P⁺ shielding region.

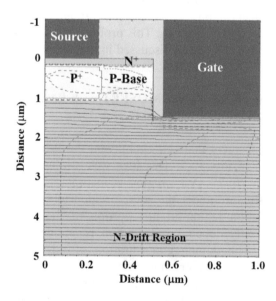

Fig. 12.8 Potential distribution in blocking mode for the trench-gate 4H-SiC power MOSFET structure with base P⁺ shielding region.

   The potential distributions obtained by numerical simulations in the blocking mode for this structure are shown in Fig. 12.8. The potential contours show no penetration of the electric field into the P-base region. This demonstrates suppression of the reach-through breakdown problem with the base P^+ shielding region. However, a high electric field occurs in the gate oxide at the bottom of the trench as shown in Fig. 12.9. The electric field in the gate oxide (E_{OX}) reaches 9 MV/cm at a drain bias of 1000 V, which is close to the rupture strength for the silicon dioxide. The electric field in the 4H-SiC below the gate oxide is less than 2 MV/cm at this drain bias. This is well below the critical electric field for breakdown in 4H-SiC preventing full utilization of its capability.

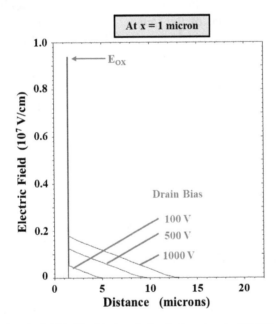

Fig. 12.9 Electric field in blocking mode for the trench-gate 4H-SiC power MOSFET structure with base P^+ shielding region.

12.3 Trench-Gate Power MOSFET Structure with Dual P^+ Shielding Regions

In the previous section, it was demonstrated that the performance of the trench-gate 4H-SiC power MOSFET structure is severely compromised by the development of a high electric field in the gate oxide during the blocking mode of operation. This problem occurs because the trench penetrates below the P-base region exposing the gate oxide at the bottom of the trench to the high electric field in the 4H-SiC drift region. The electric field in the gate oxide reaches its rupture strength well before the electric field in the semiconductor approaches its breakdown field strength. Consequently, in order to operate at any given blocking voltage, the drift region doping concentration has to be reduced and its thickness increased until the specific on-resistance becomes 25 times larger than that for the ideal drift region. This problem inhibited the performance of the first trench-gate 4H-SiC power MOSFETs.

In order to suppress the development of high electric fields in the gate oxide, a dual-shielded trench-gate power MOSFET structure was proposed and patented in 1995[6] with a second P[+] shielding region incorporated at the bottom of the trench. The basic principles of operation of this dual-shielded trench-gate 4H-SiC power MOSFET structure are discussed in this section. The impact of the JFET region, formed by the incorporation of the second P[+] shielding region, on the specific on-resistance for this structure is analyzed here. It is demonstrated that the JFET resistance can be reduced by enhancement of the doping concentration of the JFET layer between the P[+] shielding regions while retaining a small cell pitch to obtain a high channel density as first disclosed in the patent[6].

12.3.1 Device Structure

The basic structure of the dual-shielded trench-gate 4H-SiC power MOSFET is shown in Fig. 12.10. The second shielding region consists of a heavily doped P-type (P[+]) region located at the bottom of the trench. This P[+] shielding region is connected to the source electrode at a location orthogonal to the device cross-section.

The dual-shielded 4H-SiC trench-gate power MOSFET structure can be fabricated by using the same process used for the conventional trench-gate device structure with the addition of an ion implantation step to form the P[+] shielding region. The ion implant used to form the second P[+] shielding region must be performed after etching the trenches. It is worth pointing out that this implantation step should not dope the sidewalls of the trenches. This can be accomplished by doing the ion implant orthogonal to the wafer surface. Alternately, a conformal oxide can be deposited on the trench sidewalls and removed from the trench bottom using anisotropic reactive ion etching to selectively expose the trench bottom to the P-type dopant during the ion implantation. Another option to reduce the introduction of P-type doping on the trench sidewalls is by using a relatively low P-type doping concentration for the shielding region. The shielding is effective as long as the gate oxide is buffered from the high electric field in the N-drift region.

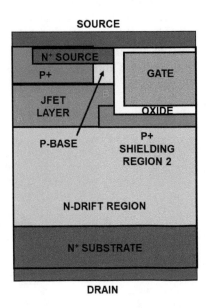

Fig. 12.10 Trench-gate 4H-SiC power MOSFET structure with Dual P$^+$ shielding regions.

Although the second P$^+$ shielding region can be confined to just the bottom of the trench, it is preferable that it overlaps the trench corner as illustrated in Fig. 12.10. The overlap can be a natural outcome of the straggle in the ion implant or the removal of some of the masking oxide on the trench sidewall if its profile is slightly tapered.

12.3.2 Blocking Characteristics

The dual-shielded trench-gate 4H-SiC power MOSFET operates in the forward blocking mode when the gate electrode is shorted to the source by the external gate drive circuit. At low drain bias voltages, the voltage is supported by a depletion region formed on both sides of the P-base/N-drift junction. Consequently, the drain potential appears across the MOSFET located at the top of the structure. This produces a positive potential at location 'A' in Fig. 12.10, which reverse biases the junction

between the second P⁺ shielding region and the N-drift region because
the second P⁺ shielding region is held at zero volts. The depletion region
that extends from the P⁺/N junction pinches off the JFET region producing a potential barrier at location 'A'. The potential barrier shields the
P-base region from any additional bias applied to the drain electrode.
Consequently, a high electric field can develop in the N-drift region
below the P⁺ shielding region while the electric field at the P-base region
remains low. This has the beneficial effects of mitigating the reach-
through of the depletion region within the P-base region and in keeping
the electric field in the gate oxide low at location 'B' where it is exposed
to the N-drift region.

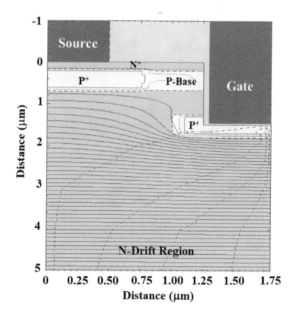

Fig. 12.11 Potential distribution in blocking mode for the trench-gate 4H-SiC power
MOSFET structure with dual P⁺ shielding regions.

The effectiveness of the second P⁺ shielding region can be
demonstrated by examining the potential distribution in the blocking
mode obtained by numerical simulations as shown in Fig. 12.11. The
second P⁺ shielding region completely isolates the trench bottom oxide
from the drain bias. It also reduces the potential below the P-base region.
This allows reducing its thickness and hence the channel length to
improve the specific on-resistance.

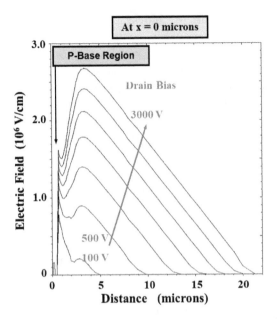

Fig. 12.12 Electric field in blocking mode at x = 0 μm for the trench-gate 4H-SiC power MOSFET structure with dual P⁺ shielding regions.

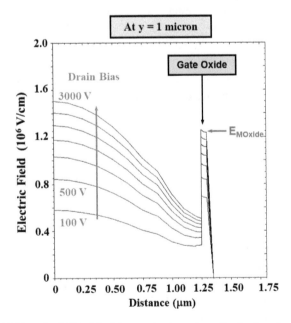

Fig. 12.13 Electric field in blocking mode at y = 1 μm for the trench-gate 4H-SiC power MOSFET structure with dual P⁺ shielding regions.

The electric field in the blocking mode for the dual-shielded trench-gate 4H-SiC power MOSFET structure is shown in Fig. 12.12 along the left side of the structure (x = 0 μm). The peak in the electric field occurs at a depth of about 3 μm in the 4H-SiC. It has a high value of 2.7 MV/cm which is close to the critical electric field for breakdown showing effective utilization of the material. The electric field is suppressed at the P-base region due to the potential barrier produced at location A in Fig. 12.10 by the second P$^+$ shielding region.

The electric field in the blocking mode for the dual-shielded trench-gate 4H-SiC power MOSFET structure is shown in Fig. 12.13 along the horizontal direction at y = 1.0 μm just below the P-base region. The electric field below the P-base region rises to only 1.55 MV/cm. This suppresses electric field penetration into the P-base region allowing reducing its thickness (and hence the channel length) to 0.5 μm. The electric field is also suppressed in the gate oxide at location B in Fig. 12.10 by the second P$^+$ shielding region. The electric field in the oxide rises to only 1.3 MV/cm. This ensures reliable operation of this structure.

It is worth pointing out that the P$^+$ shielding region must be adequately short-circuited to the source terminal in order for the shielding to be fully effective. The location of the P$^+$ region at the bottom of the trench implies that contact to it must be provided at selected locations orthogonal to the cross-section of the device shown in Fig. 12.10. Since the sheet resistance of the ion implanted P$^+$ region can be quite high, it is important to provide the contact to the P$^+$ region frequently in the orthogonal direction during chip design. This must be accomplished without significant loss of channel density if low specific on-resistance is to be realized.

12.3.3 Forward Conduction

In the dual-shielded trench-gate 4H-SiC power MOSFET structure, current flow between the drain and source can be induced by creating an inversion layer channel on the surface of the P-base region along the trench sidewalls. The current flows from the source region into the drift region through the inversion layer channel formed on the vertical side-walls of the trench due to the applied gate bias. It must then flow from point 'B' in the cross-section shown in Fig. 12.10 through a first JFET region. It then flows through a second JFET region at location 'A' shown in the cross-section. The current then spreads into the N-drift region at a 45 degree angle and becomes uniform through the rest of the structure.

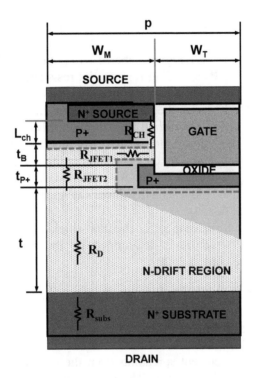

Fig. 12.14 Current flow path in the dual shielded trench-gate 4H-SiC power
MOSFET structure.

The on-state current flow path in the dual-shielded trench-gate
4H-SiC power MOSFET structure is illustrated in Fig. 12.14 by the
green shaded area together with the zero-bias depletion boundaries of the
junctions indicated by the red dashed lines. It can be seen that the
addition of the second P^+ shielding region has introduced *two* JFET
regions into the basic trench-gate MOSFET structure. The first one,
labeled R_{JFET1} in the figure, is formed between the P-base region and the
second P^+ shielding region with the current constricted by their zero-bias
depletion boundaries. The spacing between these regions (labeled t_B in
the figure) must be chosen to prevent it from becoming completely
depleted in the on-state. For a typical N-drift region doping concentration
of 8×10^{15} cm^{-3} used for 1200 V rated devices with breakdown voltage of
1650 V, the zero-base depletion width is about 0.6 μm. In this case, the
spacing (t_B) would have to be about 1.5 μm to ensure the existence of an
un-depleted path for the transport of electrons. This large spacing can be
reduced if the doping concentration in the JFET region is selectively

increased[6] when compared with the N-drift region as indicated in Fig. 12.10.

The second JFET region, labeled R_{JFET2} in Fig. 12.14, is formed between the second P$^+$ shielding regions. Its resistance is determined by the thickness of the P$^+$ shielding region (labeled t_{P+} in the figure), which can be assumed to be twice the junction depth of the P$^+$ shielding region. Since the cross-section for current flow through this region is constricted by the zero-bias depletion width of the P$^+$/N junction, it is again advantageous to increase the doping concentration in the JFET region[6] to avoid having to enlarge the mesa width. A smaller mesa width allows maintaining a smaller cell pitch which reduces the specific on-resistance due to a larger channel density.

The total on-resistance for the dual-shielded trench-gate 4H-SiC power MOSFET structure is determined by the resistance of all the components in the current path:

$$R_{on,sp} = R_{CH} + R_{JFET1} + R_{JFET2} + R_D + R_{subs} \qquad [12.7]$$

where R_{CH} is the channel resistance, R_{JFET1} and R_{JFET2} are the resistances of the two JFET regions, R_D is the resistance of the drift region after taking into account current spreading from the channel, and R_{subs} is the resistance of the N$^+$ substrate. These resistances can be analytically modeled by using the current flow pattern indicated by the green shaded regions in Fig. 12.14.

The specific channel resistance is given by:

$$R_{CH} = \frac{(L_{CH} \cdot p)}{\mu_{inv} C_{ox} (V_G - V_T)} \qquad [12.8]$$

where L_{CH} is the channel length determined by the width of the P-base region as shown in Fig. 12.14, μ_{inv} is the mobility for electrons in the inversion layer channel, C_{ox} is the specific capacitance of the gate oxide, V_G is the applied gate bias, and V_T is the threshold voltage. The specific capacitance can be obtained using:

$$C_{ox} = \frac{\varepsilon_{ox}}{t_{ox}} \qquad [12.9]$$

where ε_{ox} is the dielectric constant for the gate oxide and t_{ox} is its thickness.

The specific resistance of the first JFET region can be calculated using:

$$R_{JFET1} = \rho_{JFET} \cdot p \cdot \left(\frac{x_{P+} + W_P}{t_B - 2W_P} \right)$$ [12.10]

where ρ_{JFET} is the resistivity of the JFET region, x_{P+} is the junction depth of the P^+ shielding region, and W_P is the zero-bias depletion width *in the JFET region*. The resistivity and zero-bias depletion width used in this equation must be computed using the enhanced doping concentration of the JFET region. The specific resistance of the second JFET region can be calculated using:

$$R_{JFET2} = \rho_{JFET} \cdot p \cdot \left(\frac{t_{P+} + 2W_P}{W_M - x_{P+} - W_P} \right)$$ [12.11]

The drift region spreading resistance can be obtained by using:

$$R_D = \rho_D \cdot p \cdot \ln \left(\frac{p}{W_M - x_{P+} - W_P} \right) + \rho_D \cdot (t - W_T - x_{P+} - W_P)$$ [12.12]

where t is the thickness of the drift region below the P^+ shielding region and W_T, W_M are the widths of the trench and mesa regions, respectively, as shown in the figure.

The contribution to the resistance from the N^+ substrate is given by:

$$R_{subs} = \rho_{subs} \cdot t_{subs}$$ [12.13]

where ρ_{subs} and t_{subs} are the resistivity and thickness of the substrate, respectively. A typical value for this contribution is 4×10^{-4} Ω-cm^2.

The specific on-resistances of 1200-V rated 4H-SiC dual-shielded trench MOSFETs were modeled using the above analytical expressions. An ideal breakdown voltage of 1670 volts is obtained for a 4H-SiC drift region with doping concentration of 8×10^{15} cm^{-3} and thickness of 10 μm. A gate oxide thickness of 500 Å was used. The mesa width (W_M) and trench width (W_T) for the structure shown in Fig. 12.14 were kept at 1.0 μm and 0.25 μm resulting in a pitch (p) of 1.25 μm. The wider mesa region for the dual-shielded trench-gate structure is required to allow for the depletion region from the second shielding region. This enlarges the cell pitch. The gate bias voltage (V_G) was assumed to be

20 V with a threshold voltage (V_T) of 2.5 V. The junction depth of the P$^+$ shielding region was assumed to be 0.2 μm and the space between it and the P-base region (t_B) was chosen as 0.8 μm. The JFET region doping concentration was enhanced to 5 x 10^{16} cm^{-3} to reduce its resistance contribution.

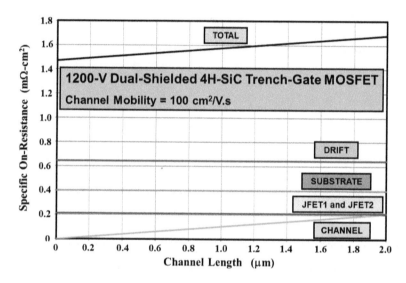

Fig. 12.15 On-resistance components for a 1.2 kV rated 4H-SiC dual shielded trench-gate MOSFET structure with 100 cm²/V-s channel mobility.

The calculated values for the various components of the on-resistance for the 4H-SiC dual-shielded trench MOSFETs are plotted in Fig. 12.15 when a channel mobility of 100 cm²/Vs is used. As in the case of the trench-gate MOSFET structure, the channel resistance increases with increasing channel length. The other components are unaffected by the increase in channel length because the cell pitch remains unaltered. The JFET1 and JFET2 components have the same magnitude for the assumptions used for the structure. The sum of these two components adds 0.42 mΩ-cm² to the total specific on-resistance. It can be seen that the drift region resistance is dominant here while the channel resistance is small because of the high channel mobility. Due to the shielding of the P-base region by the second P$^+$ region, the channel length for the dual-shielded trench-gate 4H-SiC power MOSFET structure can be reduced to 0.5 μm compared with 1.0 μm for the unshielded trench-gate MOSFET structure. A total specific on-resistance of 1.52 mΩ-cm² is obtained for the dual-shielded structure, which is within two times the ideal specific on-resistance of the drift region.

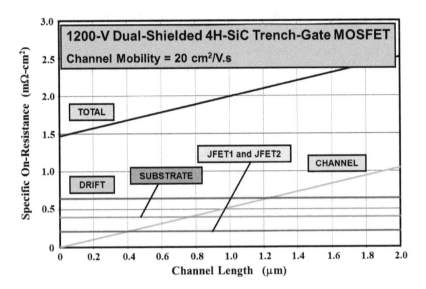

Fig. 12.16 On-resistance components for a 1.2 kV rated 4H-SiC dual shielded trench-gate MOSFET structure with 20 cm²/V-s channel mobility.

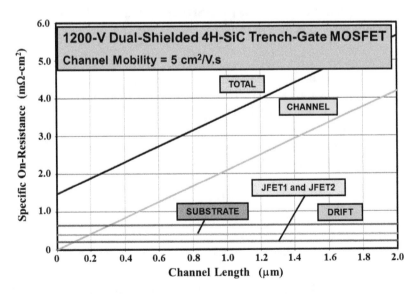

Fig. 12.17 On-resistance components for a 1.2 kV rated 4H-SiC dual shielded trench-gate MOSFET structure with 5 cm²/V-s channel mobility.

The impact of reducing the channel mobility for the dual-shielded trench-gate 4H-SiC power MOSFET structure is depicted in Fig. 12.16 and 12.17 for the case of mobility values of 20 and 5 cm²/V-s. With a practical channel mobility of 20 cm²/Vs, the channel contribution remains smaller than the contribution from the drift region for a channel length of 0.5 μm. This results in the specific on-resistance increasing to a value of 1.73 mΩ-cm². When the channel mobility is reduced to 5 cm²/Vs, the channel resistance becomes dominant as shown in Fig. 12.17, with an increase in the specific on-resistance to a value of 2.52 mΩ-cm² for a channel length of 0.5 μm.

For the case of a channel mobility of 20 cm²/V-s, the specific on-resistance of the dual-shielded trench-gate 4H-SiC MOSFET structure with a channel length of 0.5 μm is found to be larger than for the conventional trench-gate structure with a channel length of 1.0 μm due to additional resistances of the two JFET regions. However, the second P^+ shielding region is required to resolve the problem of high electric field in the gate oxide observed for the conventional trench-gate structure. The behavior of the dual-shielded structure with respect to other blocking voltages is similar to that provided for the conventional-trench gate structure in the previous section.

12.4 Trench-Gate Power MOSFET Structure with High Permittivity Gate Insulator

As already discussed in a previous section of this chapter, a high electric field is developed in the gate oxide at the bottom of the trench in the 4H-SiC trench-gate MOSFET structure. The electric field in the gate oxide can exceed its rupture strength at relatively low drain bias voltages limiting the blocking voltage capability of the trench-gate structure. The electric field in the oxide (E_{OX}) is related to the electric field in the underlying semiconductor (E_S) by Gauss's Law:

$$E_{OX} = \left(\frac{\varepsilon_S}{\varepsilon_{OX}} \right) . E_S \qquad [12.14]$$

where ε_{OX} is the dielectric constant of the gate oxide and ε_S is the dielectric constant of the semiconductor. The relative dielectric constant (permittivity) for 4H-SiC is 9.7 while that for silicon dioxide is 3.85.

Using these values, the electric field in the gate oxide is a factor of 2.5 times that in the semiconductor.

   In recognition of this problem, it was proposed[12] that silicon dioxide be replaced by a gate insulator with high permittivity – preferably at least 10 times that of free space. With the increased dielectric constant for the gate insulator, the electric field developed in the gate dielectric would become closer to that developed in the semi-conductor[13]. This implies that the maximum electric field in the gate dielectric can be reduced to 3×10^6 V/cm, which should be satisfactory for reliable operation. This approach can take advantage of the large effort being undertaken to develop high dielectric constant insulators for mainstream silicon DRAM chips.

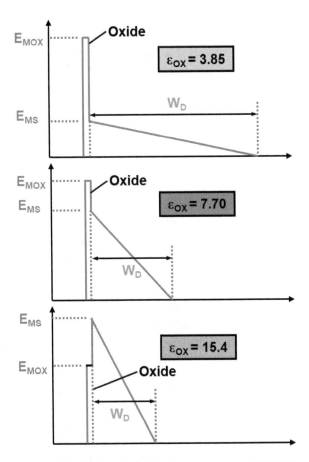

Fig. 12.18 Electric field distribution in the trench-gate power MOSFET structure.

A simple one-dimensional analysis of the metal-oxide-semiconductor structure provides interesting insight into the benefits of using high permittivity gate insulators in silicon carbide MOSFETs. Since the highest electric field occurs at the flat bottom of the trench region in the trench-gate MOSFET structure, a one dimensional analysis is a reasonable approximation for analytical purposes.

The electric field profile in the MOS gate stack is illustrated in Fig. 12.18 for three cases of dielectric constants when it is supporting the same voltage (e.g. 1650 V for 1200 V rated devices). In the first two cases with permittivity of 3.85 (corresponding to silicon dioxide) and 7.7 (corresponding to silicon nitride), it is assumed that the field distribution is constrained by reaching a maximum electric field of 3×10^6 V/cm in the gate dielectric. This value was chosen based upon the maximum electric field in oxides for reliable operation. Under this constraint, the maximum electric field in the silicon carbide becomes much lower than its breakdown field strength (1.2×10^6 V/cm for the permittivity of 3.85 and 2.4×10^6 V/cm for the permittivity of 7.7). However, when the permittivity is increased to 15.4, the electric field distribution becomes constrained by the maximum allowable electric field in the silicon carbide (e.g. 2.5×10^6 V/cm for 4H-SiC at a doping concentration of 1×10^{16} cm^{-3}). Under this limitation, the electric field in the oxide is reduced to about 2×10^6 V/cm for the permittivity of 15.4.

12.4.1 Specific On-Resistance

The changes in the electric field distribution have a strong impact on the doping concentration and thickness of the drift region required to support the drain bias (e.g. 1650 V for 1200 V rated devices) as illustrated in Fig. 12.18. For the lower dielectric constants, a much thicker drift region with lower doping concentration (reflected in the smaller slope of the electric field profile in the semiconductor) is required because of the reduced maximum electric field, when compared with the properties of the ideal drift region. For the high dielectric constant case, the electric field in the semiconductor becomes identical to that for the ideal one-dimensional parallel plane abrupt junction. Thus, the specific on-resistance is equal to that for the ideal drift region only for the case of the high permittivity gate dielectric and much larger for the other cases.

In the above discussion, it was pointed out that the gate MOS stack operates in one of two regimes of operation – namely with the electric field constrained by a maximum allowable value in the gate insulator or by the electric field constrained by the maximum allowable value in the semiconductor. The results of the analytically calculated electric fields in the gate insulator and the semiconductor under these constraints are shown in Fig. 12.19. It can be seen that the transition occurs at a permittivity given by:

$$\varepsilon_{OX} = \left(\frac{E_{MS}(4H-SiC)}{E_{MOX}} \right) \cdot \varepsilon_S \qquad [12.15]$$

where E_{MS}(4H-SiC) is the critical electric field for breakdown in 4H-SiC and E_{MOX} is the maximum electric field in the dielectric for reliable operation. For the values for these parameters described above, the transition occurs at a permittivity of 10.7. This is the minimum permittivity needed to reduce the specific on-resistance of the drift region to that for the ideal drift region.

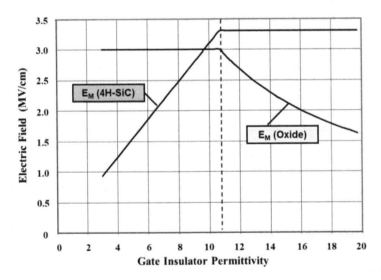

Fig. 12.19 Electric field distribution in the trench-gate 4H-SiC power MOSFET structure for gate insulators with different permittivity.

The permittivity of the gate insulator has a strong influence on the doping concentration and thickness of the drift region. This is shown in Fig. 12.20. The doping concentration of the drift region (N_D) increases and its thickness (W_D)decreases as the permittivity is increased up to a value of 10. This results in a drastic reduction of the specific on-resistance of the drift region. As examples, points are shown for selected insulators on the graph. In the case of the commonly used silicon dioxide gate insulator, the specific resistance of the drift region is degraded by a factor of 25 times. If silicon nitride is used as the gate insulator, the drift region resistance becomes only 3 times larger than the ideal case. With the use of a much higher dielectric constant of 15 with titanium dioxide as the insulator, the ideal drift region resistance can be obtained together with reduced electric field in the insulator. Other high-k dielectrics that could be potential candidates based on their applications in silicon CMOS technology include aluminum oxide and hafnium oxide[14].

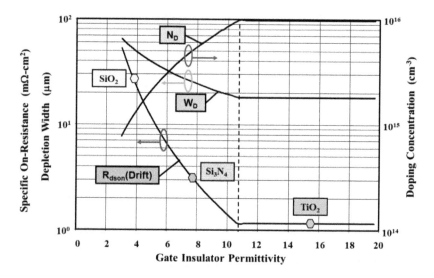

Fig. 12.20 Impact of gate insulator permittivity for the trench-gate 4H-SiC power MOSFET structure.

12.4.2 Threshold Voltage

A larger dielectric constant for the gate insulator is also beneficial for achieving a lower threshold voltage with any given insulator thickness. This is demonstrated in Fig. 12.21 for the case of a gate oxide thickness of 500 Å. The calculations of the threshold voltage were performed using the same assumptions regarding a work-function difference of 1 V and the presence of a fixed oxide charge of 2×10^{11} cm^{-2} used in chapter 11. At a P-base doping concentration of 3×10^{17} cm^{-3}, the threshold voltage is reduced from 10 V for the silicon dioxide case (permittivity of 3.85) to 6 V for the silicon nitride case (permittivity of 7.7), and even further to about 3 V for a permittivity of 15.4. This is favorable for increasing the charge induced in the channel for a typical gate bias of 15 volts resulting in reducing the specific on-resistance.

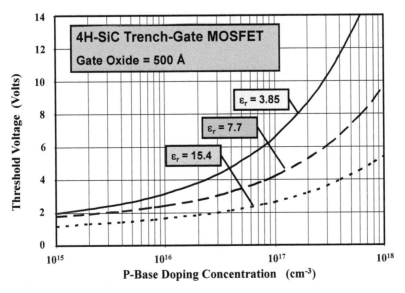

Fig. 12.21 Impact of gate insulator permittivity on the threshold voltage of the trench-gate 4H-SiC power MOSFET structure.

12.4.3 Reliability

The analysis described above highlights the benefits of using gate insulators with high permittivity. However, it must be pointed out that the breakdown strength of insulators has been empirically found to reduce with increasing permittivity. Consequently, care must be taken to ensure that the gate insulator with high permittivity will operate in a reliable manner even when the electric field in it has been reduced as described above. In addition, the band offset between the gate insulator and silicon carbide should be examined to make sure that the Fowler-Nordheim tunneling described in chapter 11 does not create instabilities.

The high temperature reliability of various gate dielectrics has been investigated[15]. The study considered silicon nitride (7.5), aluminum nitride (8,4), aluminum oxy-nitride (12.4), titanium oxide (30-40), and tantalum oxide (25) due to their larger permittivity's when compared to silicon dioxide (3.85) as given in brackets. Experimental investigations were performed with the silicon nitride grown by low pressure chemical vapor deposition, the aluminum nitride layers grown by metal-organic chemical vapor deposition, and aluminum oxy-nitride (ALO:N) by thermal oxidation of AlN. The maximum breakdown electric field strength was found to be 10 MV/cm for SiO_2, 5.8 MV/cm for Si_3N_4, 1 MV/cm for AlN, and 4.8 MV/cm for AlO:N. The most favorable gate dielectric was found to be silicon nitride. In addition, an oxide-nitride-oxide sandwich was reported to have good breakdown strength. The inversion layer mobility for this sandwich was reported to be as high as 40 cm^2/V-s. The high temperature reliability of this dielectric sandwich was found to be 100-times superior to that for deposited silicon dioxide.

12.5 Trench-Gate Power MOSFET Structure with Thick Trench Bottom Oxide

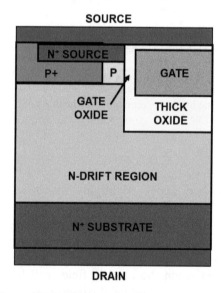

Fig. 12.22 Trench-gate 4H-SiC power MOSFET structure with thick oxide at the trench bottom.

The electric field in the oxide at the bottom of the trench in the 4H-SiC power MOSFET can be reduced by increasing the oxide thickness[16]. The trench-gate 4H-SiC power MOSFET with a thick trench bottom oxide is shown in Fig. 12.22. An analytical model for the electric field in the trench bottom oxide has been reported and validated using numerical simulations[17].

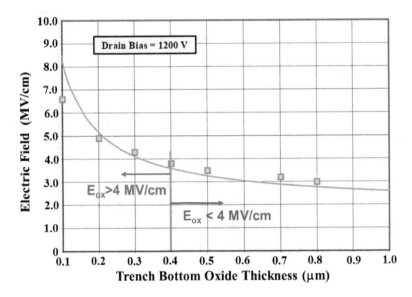

Fig. 12.23 Electric field in the trench bottom oxide in the 4H-SiC power MOSFET structure at a drain bias of 1200 V.

The electric field in the trench bottom oxide calculated using the analytical model is shown in Fig. 12.23 by the blue line for the case of the 1200 V rated 4H-SiC power MOSFET structure. According to the models, this electric field becomes less than 4 MV/cm when the oxide thickness is larger than 4000 Å, which satisfies reliability criteria. The squares in the figure obtained by numerical simulations validate the analytical model. A trench-gate 4H-SiC power MOSFET with cell pitch of 1.3 μm was found to have a specific on-resistance of 1.89 mΩ-cm². This indicates very good performance is possible by using this structure.

The fabrication of a 4H-SiC power MOSFET structure with thick oxide at the bottom of the trench was reported in 2013[16]. It was fabricated by refilling the gate trench region with SiO_2 and then etching it down to obtained a thickness that was not disclosed. A breakdown voltage of 1400 V was observed by using a drift region with doping concentration of 5.9×10^{15} cm^{-3} and thickness of 13 μm. A relatively large specific on-resistance of 4.4 mΩ-cm² was measured for devices with cell pitch of 4.5 μm and gate oxide thickness of 750 Å with gate drive of 20 V. A $Q_{gd,sp}$ of 540 nC/cm² was obtained by numerical simulations, resulting in a HF-FOM[$R_{on}*Q_{gd}$] of 2376 mΩ-nC. The edge termination for the devices were floating field rings created by etching trenches through the epitaxially grown P-base layer. This concept was first proposed[18] and patented in 1993. A specific on-resistance of 4.6 mΩ-cm^2 was observed at a gate bias of 20-V for devices with gate oxide thickness of 750 Å.

12.6 Trench-Gate Power MOSFET Structure with Deep P$^+$ Shielding Region

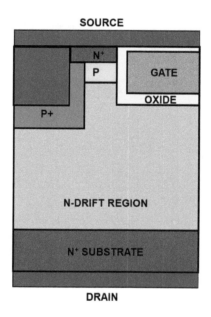

Fig. 12.24 Trench-gate 4H-SiC power MOSFET structure with second trench containing P$^+$ region.

An alternate approach, shown in Fig. 12.24, to reduce the electric field in the gate oxide is by incorporation of a second trench with a P$^+$ region[19]. The P$^+$ regions in the second trench behave like a JFET producing a potential barrier under the gate trench region. This reduces the electric field in the gate oxide. The results of numerical simulations[17] of this structure demonstrated a reduction of the gate oxide electric field but the blocking voltage was reduced by reach-through breakdown at 756 V for a drift region capable of supporting 1650 V. The fabricated devices[18] were reported to have a specific on-resistance of 2.99 mΩ-cm^2 for a device with breakdown voltage of 1720 V.

Another approach to reduce the electric field in the gate oxide is based on the structure shown in Fig. 12.25. Here, deep P^+ regions are formed using high energy ion-implantation of Aluminum and Boron ions[20]. The addition of these regions enlarges the cell pitch of the structure. The deep P^+ region on the right side overlaps the gate trench reducing the channel density is half compared to the previous trench-gate structures. The fabricated devices were reported to have a specific on-resistance of 3.3 mΩ-cm^2 for a device with breakdown voltage of 1600 V. Although the specific on-resistance is large, a very low electric field in achieved in the gate oxide using this structure to ensure reliable operation. The reduced channel density increases the short-circuit withstand time.

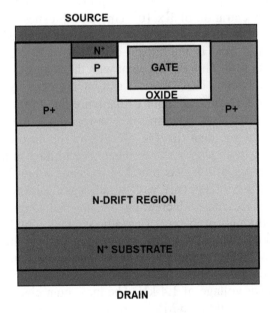

Fig. 12.25 Trench-gate 4H-SiC power MOSFET structure with a deep P^+ region.

12.7 Experimental Results: Legacy Devices

The lack of significant diffusion of dopants in silicon carbide motivated the investigation of trench-gate structures before planar-gate structures. The need to obtain a high quality interface between silicon carbide and the gate dielectric was identified as a challenging endeavor from the inception of interest in the development of unipolar transistors from this semiconductor material[21]. In addition, the problem of high electric fields developed across the gate oxide, especially at the trench corners, was identified as a limitation to achieving high electric fields within the semiconductor[10]. These issues were indeed found to be a major limitation on the performance of the first trench-gate 4H-SiC power MOSFET structures.

The first reported[5] trench-gate power MOSFETs fabricated using 4H-SiC were limited to a blocking voltage of 260 V due to rupture of the gate oxide. The specific on-resistance of 18 mΩ-cm^2, measured at a gate bias of 22 V, was inferior to that of Si power MOSFETs because of a large cell pitch and low channel mobility ($\sim$ 10 cm^2/V-s).

Subsequently, a trench-gate 4H-SiC power MOSFET structure with breakdown voltage of 1100 V was reported[22] by using a drift region with doping concentration of 1 x 10^{15} cm^{-3} and thickness of 12 μm. The low doping concentration in the drift region was required to keep the maximum electric field in the silicon carbide to only 1 x 10^6 V/cm to prevent oxide rupture. This is consistent with the analysis in the previous sections of this chapter. These devices exhibited a very high specific on-resistance (over 1 Ω-cm^2) at room temperature due to the poor channel mobility ($\sim$ 1.5 cm^2/V-s). The specific on-resistance reduced to about 180 mΩ-cm^2 (using data in Fig. 3 in the publication) at higher temperatures due to an increase in the channel mobility. In these devices, a threshold voltage of 5 V was obtained by using a low P-base doping concentration of 6.5 x 10^{16} cm^{-3} with a gate oxide thickness of 1000 Å. However, this necessitated increasing the channel length to 4 μm to prevent reach-through problems. The large channel length, in conjunction with the poor channel mobility, was responsible for the poor (worse than Si power MOSFETs) specific on-resistance of the devices.

A trench-gate 4H-SiC power MOSFET was reported[23] in 1998 with a breakdown voltage of 1.4 kV. The maximum electric field in the gate oxide was reduced to 2.5 MV/cm by reducing the maximum electric field in the silicon carbide to only 1.3 MV/cm. This required reducing the doping concentration of the drift region to 1 x 10^{15} cm^{-3} and increasing its thickness to 25 μm. This approach, consistent with Fig. 12.20, produces a huge increase in the specific on-resistance to 30 mΩ-cm^2 from an ideal value of less than 1 mΩ-cm^2. Moreover, the threshold voltage for the devices was reported to be 24-28 V resulting in a measured specific on-resistance of 311 mΩ-cm^2 in spite of a gate bias of 40 V.

In chapter 11, an accumulation-mode 4H-SiC planar-gate power MOSFET structure was described as an approach to reduce the specific on-resistance due to an increase in the channel mobility. An accumulation-mode structure that combines a trench-gate structure with a depleted N-base region located adjacent to a P-N junction has been proposed[24] and experimentally demonstrated. This structure, shown in Fig. 12.26, contains an N-base region that is epitaxially grown on the trench sidewall surface. The authors observed an accumulation layer mobility of 108 cm^2/V-s for this structure resulting in a specific on-resistance of 11 $m\Omega$-cm^2 at a gate bias of 10 V. The breakdown voltage of 500 V for this structure was limited by the development of high electric field in the gate oxide.

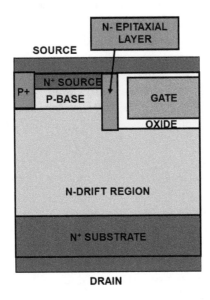

Fig. 12.26 Epitaxial-channel accumulation-mode trench-gate 4H-SiC power MOSFET structure.

Experimental results for inversion-mode trench-gate 4H-SiC power MOSFETs with a P^+ shielding region incorporated at the bottom of the trench were first reported[25] in 2002. These devices had all the features previously described in 1995[6]. The structures were fabricated using 50 μm thick N-type drift regions with doping concentration of 8.5 x 10^{14} cm^{-3}. An N-type layer with doping concentration of 2 x 10^{17} cm^{-3} was grown on the drift region to provide the enhanced doping in the JFET region. The P-base region was formed by growth of a 1 μm thick

P-type layer with doping concentration of 2 x 10^{17} cm^{-3} followed by the N$^+$ source region with doping concentration of 1 x 10^{19} cm^{-3}. The P$^+$ shielding regions were formed (after etching the trenches) with a junction depth of 0.8 µm by using aluminum ion implantation with a dose of 4 x 10^{13} cm^{-2}. The authors used two sacrificial thermal oxidation steps to remove any surface residue remaining from the implant anneal step. This may have also removed any P-type doping on the trench sidewalls. A relatively thick gate oxide of 2750 Å was prepared by the thermal oxidation of a deposited layer of polysilicon into the trench to avoid the different thicknesses of thermally grown oxide on the trench sidewall and bottom surfaces due to crystal orientation. The thick gate oxide resulted in a high threshold voltage of 40 V. The devices exhibited a breakdown voltage of 3000 V by the use of a JTE edge termination. A specific on-resistance of 120 mΩ-cm^2 was observed at a gate bias of 100 V. The relatively high specific on-resistance is due to the poor channel density in the cell design, the large gate oxide thickness, and the low inversion layer channel mobility (2 cm^2/V-s) observed by the authors. However, these results demonstrated the ability to support high voltage in the drift region without encountering gate oxide rupture in a trench-gate device. The authors subsequently reported[26] the fabrication of devices using 115 µm thick N-type drift regions with 7.5 x 10^{14} cm^{-3} doping concentration. These devices exhibited a specific on-resistance of 228 mΩ-cm^2 at a gate bias of 40 V. The epitaxial layer was stated to be capable of supporting 14 kV although the actual measured breakdown voltage was only 5 kV.

The accumulation-mode trench-gate MOSFET structure with an epitaxially grown N-base region on the trench sidewalls (see Fig. 12.26) was supplemented with shielding provided by a P-type region implanted at the bottom of the trenches to prevent gate oxide rupture[27]. These devices were fabricated using 10 µm thick N-type drift regions with doping concentration of 2.5 x 10^{15} cm^{-3} to obtain a breakdown voltage of 1400 V. The rest of the process was similar to that described in the previous paragraph. A gate oxide thickness of 1300 Å was formed by thermal oxidation of a polysilicon layer deposited in the trenches. A specific on-resistance of 16 mΩ-cm^2 was observed at a gate bias of 40 V. This improved specific on-resistance was correlated with an accumulation layer mobility of 9-30 cm^2/V-s by the authors.

Accumulation-mode shielded trench-gate MOSFETs fabricated from 4H-SiC were also reported[24] with breakdown voltage of 3360 V. These devices had a specific on-resistance of 199 mΩ-cm^2 at a gate bias of 100 V, which was worse than that for the inversion-mode structures.

In addition, the leakage current for the accumulation-mode structure was reported to be about 100 times worse than for the inversion-mode structure.

Improvement in performance of the shielded trench-gate 4H-SiC power MOSFET, shown in Fig. 12.10, was achieved by using two JFET layers[28]. The goal was to reduce the JFET resistance (R_{JFET1}) by enhancing the doping concentration between the P-base region and the P^+ shielding regions by using JFET layer 1 and to reduce the JFET resistance (R_{JFET2}) between the P^+ shielding regions by using JFET layer 2. The authors used a JFET layer 1 doping concentration of 0.5-1 x 10^{17} cm^{-3} with a thickness of 0.5 μm and a JFET layer 2 doping concentration of 1-2 x 10^{16} cm^{-3} with a thickness of 3 μm. A blocking voltage of 1600 V was observed for the case of a drift layer with doping concentration of 3-5 x 10^{16} cm^{-3} with a thickness of 25 μm. These JFET layers must be removed from the periphery of the active area to allow application of the JTE edge termination. A specific on-resistance of 50 mΩ-cm^2 was observed for devices when a gate bias of 60 V was applied. The high gate bias was required due to the large gate oxide thickness of 1600 Å. An important conclusion made in this work was that the inversion layer mobility is 20-times larger when the trench is oriented orthogonal to the wafer flat because of conduction along the (112-0) plane as opposed to the (1100) plane when the trenches are oriented parallel to the flat.

It is necessary to connect the shielding P^+ region to the source contact to achieve the desired shielding of the gate oxide. These devices had a square cell layout with the cross-section shown in Fig. 12.10. The contact to the shielding P^+ region must be performed at selected locations. Various layout designs for this connection have been explored[29]. It was found that at least one ground for every 9 cells was required to get good SC-SOA.

The trench-gate 4H-SiC power MOSFET structure shown in Fig. 12.27 has been developed using V-groove etching by thermochemical etching in a chlorine ambient[30]. The process exposes the (0-33-8) surface of 4H-SiC which the authors report have superior MOS interface properties. The device fabrication consists of first growing the n-type drift layer with doping concentration of 4.5 x 10^{15} cm^{-3} with a thickness of 12 μm. The buried P^+ regions were then formed by ion implantation of Aluminum followed by growth of a second n-type epitaxial layer with doping concentration of 7 x 10^{15} cm^{-3} with a thickness of 3 μm. The P-base and N^+ source regions were created by Al and P ion implantation to obtain a channel length of 0.6 μm on the trench sidewalls. The P^+ regions protect the gate oxide from high electric fields generated in the drift region. Devices with the buried P$^+$ regions displayed a breakdown voltage of 1700 V compared with only 575 V without them due to rupture of the gate oxide. A specific on-resistance of 3.6 mΩ-cm^2 was observed at a gate bias of 18 V with the P$^+$ buried grid versus 3.1 mΩ-cm^2 without the P$^+$ buried grid. The channel inversion layer mobility along the trench sidewalls was reported[31] to be 80 cm^2/V-s. A hexagonal layout design for these devices was optimized[32] by varying the area occupied by the P$^+$ buried regions. It was found that the designs where the P$^+$ regions occupy 30 % of the active area produce the best compromise between low specific on-resistance and high breakdown voltage. The gate oxide reliability of these structures was reported to be satisfactory due to shielding of the gate oxide by the buried P$^+$ regions[33].

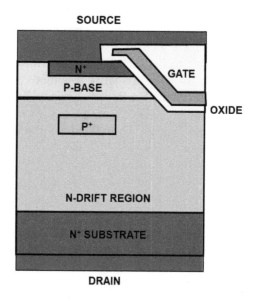

Fig. 12.27 V-groove trench-gate 4H-SiC power MOSFET structure with P$^+$ shielding region.

12.8 Experimental Results: Recent Devices

There have been a large number of papers published recently on 'proposed' trench-gate 4H-SiC power MOSFET structures with performance analysis done using numerical simulations. The authors do not adequately take fabrication issues and design rules into account when doing the analysis making the results of questionable value. These papers are therefore not included in this book.

The dual P^+ region shielded 4H-SiC trench-gate power MOSFET structure was discussed in section 12.3. It is important that the P^+ shielding region located under the gate oxide in the trenches be connected to the source electrode and not left at a floating potential. This has been confirmed by numerical simulations that show degradation of the oxide shielding and switching performance[34]. In addition, an on-resistance variation during switching at high drain bias voltages, called dynamic on-resistance, has been reported due to charge storage.

The performance of fabricated 4H-SiC trench-gate power MOSFETs with a P^+ shielding region under the gate trenches was reported in 2020[35]. A breakdown voltage of 1100 V was achieved by using a 1 μm deep P^+ shielding region. A low specific on-resistance of 1.2 mΩ-cm^2 was observed at a gate bias of 20 V.

A 4H-SiC trench-gate power MOSFET with high-permittivity gate dielectric was discussed in section 12.4. This structure was experimentally demonstrated to achieve good performance[36]. The permittivity of the high-k dielectric can be estimated to be 8.2 based on the published capacitance-voltage data. This is close to the value for silicon nitride that was discussed in section 12.4. The specific on-resistance was reduced by 35 % compared with silicon dioxide as the gate dielectric. The good stability of the threshold voltage for these devices was reported in 2020[37]. The reliability of this high-k dielectric was confirmed in 2021[38]. Devices with blocking voltage of 3.3 kV were demonstrated with the high-k dielectric in 2021[39]. The devices had a specific on-resistance of 16 mΩ-cm^2 at a gate bias of 15 V, which is only 3-times the ideal value for the drift region. Good switching behavior with wide RBSOA was confirmed. A short-circuit withstand time of 3 μs was observed with a drain bias of 1.8 kV and gate bias of 15 V with 150 °C ambient temperature. In 2021, the authors revealed that the high-k gate dielectric was SiN and provided stability data on threshold voltage[40].

12.9 Summary

The trench-gate 4H-SiC vertical power MOSFET structure was the first approach explored by the silicon carbide community because the P-base region could be epitaxially grown rather than formed by ion implantation, which was a less mature technology. Although devices with breakdown voltages of up to 1100 volts were fabricated, their performance was severely limited by the on-set of rupture of the gate oxide and the poor channel mobility. In order to overcome these problems, it was necessary to shield the gate oxide from the high electric field developed in the drift region or use high-k gate dielectrics.

The dual P^+ region shielded trench-gate power MOSFET structure was proposed for silicon carbide in order to protect the P-base region and the gate oxide from the high electric field generated in the drift region during the blocking mode. The shielding can be provided by the addition of a P^+ region located at the bottom of the trenches. This P-type shielding region must be grounded by connection to the source electrode. Its presence creates two JFET regions in the trench gate structure, which can increase the on-resistance unless the doping concentration in the vicinity of the trenches is enhanced. With the enhanced doping concentration, it has been found that the full blocking voltage capability of the drift region in 4H-SiC can be utilized with low electric field at the P-base region and the gate oxide. This provides a very attractive power MOSFET structure that can be made from 4H-SiC with specific on-resistance approaching the ideal specific on-resistance of the drift region if a channel mobility of 20 cm^2/V-s is achieved.

Table I: Comparison of 4H-SiC Trench-Gate MOSFET Structures

Structure	Cell Pitch (μm)	$R_{on,sp}$ ($m\Omega$-cm^2)	Breakdown Voltage (V)	$C_{gd,sp}$ (pF/cm^2)	HF-FOM ($m\Omega$-pF)
Basic	1.3	1.80	1645	734	1321
Thick Trench Bottom Oxide	1.3	1.89	1610	417	788
Dual P^+ Shield	1.3	2.68	1672	289	775
Rohm Deep P^+	3.0	2.44	756	366	893
Infineon Deep P^+	2.8	3.77	1538	10	37

Two other commercialized approaches for making trench-gate 4H-SiC power MOSFETs are with addition of P^+ regions which are deeper than the gate trench region. The first one of these fabricated by Rohm was shown in 12.24, while the one commercialized by Infineon was shown in Fig. 12.25. A systematic comparison of the trench-gate 4H-SiC power MOSFETs using the same drift region parameters was published in 2018[17]. A summary of the data obtained by numerical simulations is provided in Table I. The basic trench-gate structure has the lower $R_{on,sp}$ but the electric field in the gate oxide is very high. The structure with the thick trench bottom oxide has a $R_{on,sp}$ only 5 % larger. The Rohm structure has the next best $R_{on,sp}$ but showed reach-through limited low breakdown voltage. The structure with dual P^+ shielding region has the next best $R_{on,sp}$ and a good HF-FOM. The Infineon structure has a relatively large $R_{on,sp}$ but its HF-FOM is very good.

References

[1] B. J. Baliga, "Fundamentals of Power Semiconductor Devices", Chapter 6, pp. 283-471, Second Edition, Springer-Science, 2019.

[2] B. J. Baliga, "Evolution of MOS-Bipolar Power Semiconductor Technology", Proceeding of the IEEE, Vol. 74, pp. 409-418, 1988.

[3] D. Ueda, H. Takagi, and G. Kano, "A New Vertical Power MOSFET Structure with Extremely Reduced On-Resistance", IEEE Transactions on Electron Devices, Vol. 32, pp. 2-6, 1985.

[4] H-R. Chang, et al, "Ultra-Low Specific On-Resistance UMOSFET", IEEE International Electron Devices Meeting, Abstract 28.3, pp. 642-645, 1986.

[5] J. W. Palmour, et al, "4H-Silicon Carbide Power Switching Devices", Silicon Carbide and Related Materials – 1995, Institute of Physics Conference Series, Vol. 142, pp. 813-816, 1996.

[6] B. J. Baliga, "Silicon Carbide Switching Device with Rectifying Gate", U. S. Patent 5,396,085, Issued March 7, 1995.

[7] B. J. Baliga, "Silicon Carbide Power MOSFET with Floating Field Ring and Floating Field Plate", U. S. Patent 5,233,215, Issued August 3, 1993.

[8] S-H Ryu, et al, "Design and Process Issues for Silicon Carbide Power DiMOSFETs", Material Research Society Symposium Proceeding, Vol. 640, pp. H4.5.1-H4.5.6, 2001.

[9] B. J. Baliga, "Critical Nature of Oxide/Interface Quality for SiC Power Devices", INFOS'95, Paper 1.1, June 1995. Published in Microelectronics Journal, Vol. 28, pp. 177-184, 1995.

[10] M. Bhatnagar, D. Alok, and B. J. Baliga, "SiC Power UMOSFET: Design, Analysis, and Technological Feasibility", Silicon Carbide and Related Materials – 1993, Institute of Physics Conference Series, Vol. 137, pp. 703-706, 1994.

[11] B. J. Baliga, "Silicon Carbide Power Devices", World Scientific Press, Singapore, 2005.

[12] S. Sridevan, P. K. McLarty, and B. J. Baliga, "Silicon Carbide Switching Devices having Near Ideal Breakdown Voltage Capability and Ultra-Low On-State Resistance", U. S. Patent 5,742,076, Issued April 21, 1998.

[13] S. Sridevan, P. K. McLarty, and B. J. Baliga, "Analysis of Gate Dielectrics for SiC Power UMOSFETs", IEEE International Symposium on Power Semiconductor Devices and ICs, pp. 153-156, 1997.

[14] G. D. Wilk, R. M. Wallace, and J. M. Anthony, "High-k Gate Dielectrics: Current Status and materials Properties Considerations", Journal of Applied Physics, Vol. 89, pp. 5243-5275, 2001.

[15] L. A. Lipkin and J. W. Palmour, "Insulator Investigation on SiC for Improved Reliability", IEEE Transactions on Electron Devices, Vol. 46, pp. 525-532, 1999.

[16] H. Takaya, et al, "A 4H-SiC Trench MOSFET with Thick Bottom Oxide for Improving Characteristics", IEEE International Symposium on Power Semiconductor Devices and ICs, pp. 43-46, 2013.

[17] A. Agarwal, K. Han, and B. J. Baliga., "Analysis of 1.2 kV 4H-SiC Trench-Gate MOSFETs with Thick Trench Bottom Oxide", IEEE Workshop on Wide Band Gap Power Devices and Applications, pp. 125-129, 2018.

[18] B. J. Baliga, "Silicon Carbide Power MOSFET with Floating Field Ring and Floating Field Plate", U.S. Patent 5,233,215, Issued August 3, 1993.

[19] T. Nakamura, et al, "Novel developments towards increased SiC power device and module efficiency", IEEE Energytech, pp. 1-6, 2012.

[20] D. Peters, et al, "The new CoolSiC trench MOSFET technology for low gate oxide stress and high performance", Power Conversion and Intelligent Motion Europe, pp. 1-7, 2017.

[21] B. J. Baliga, "Impact of SiC on Power Devices", Proceedings of the 4th International Conference on Amorphous and Crystalline Silicon Carbide", pp. 305-313, 1991.

[22] A. K. Agarwal, et al, "1.1 kV 4H-SiC Power UMOSFETs", IEEE Electron Device Letters, Vol. 18, pp. 586-588, 1997.

[23] Y. Sugawara and K. Asano, "1.4kV 4H-SiC UMOSFET with Low Specific On-Resistance", IEEE International Symposium on Power Semiconductor Devices and ICs, pp. 119-122, 1998.

[24] K. Hara, "Vital Issues for SiC Power Devices", Silicon Carbide and Related Materials – 1997, Materials Science Forum, Vols. 264-268, pp. 901-906, 1998.

[25] Y. Li, J. A. Cooper, and M. A. Capano, "High Voltage (3kV) UMOSFETs in 4H-SiC", IEEE Tran. on Electron Devices, Vol. 49, pp. 972-975, 2002.

[26] Y. Sui, T. Tsuji, and J. A. Cooper, "On-State Characteristics of SiC Power UMOSFETs on 115 micron Drift Layers", IEEE Electron Device Letters, Vol. 26, pp. 255-257, 2005.

[27] J. Tan, J. A. Cooper, and M. R. Melloch, "High Voltage Accumulation-Layer UMOSFETs in 4H-SiC", IEEE Electron Device Letters, Vol. 19, pp. 487-489, 1998.

[28] Q. Zhang, et al, "1600V 4H-SiC UMOSFETs with Dual Buffer Layers", IEEE International Symposium on Power Semiconductor Devices and ICs, pp. 159-162, 2005.

[29] R. Tanaka, et al, "Impact of Grounding the Bottom Oxide Protection Layer on the Short-Circuit Ruggedness of 4H-SiC Trench MOSFETs", IEEE International Symposium on Power Semiconductor Devices and ICs, pp. 75-78, 2014.

[30] K. Wada, et al, "Fast Switching 4H-SiC V-groove Trench MOSFETs with Buried P+ Structure", IEEE International Symposium on Power Semiconductor Devices and ICs, pp. 225-228, 2014.

[31] Y. Mikamura, et al, "Novel Designed SiC Devices for High Power and High Efficiency Systems", IEEE Transactions on Electron Devices, Vol. 62, pp. 382-389, 2015.

[32] K. Uchida, et al, "The Optimized Design and Characterization of 1200 V/2.0 mΩ-cm^2 4H-SiC V-groove Trench MOSFETs", IEEE International Symposium on Power Semiconductor Devices and ICs, pp. 85-88, 2015.

[33] T. Hiyoshi, et al, "Gate Oxide Reliability of 4H-SiC V-groove Trench MOSFET under Various Stress Conditions", IEEE International Symposium on Power Semiconductor Devices and ICs, pp. 39-42, 2016.

[34] J. Wei, et al, "Dynamic Degradation in SiC Trench MOSFET with a Floating p-Shield Revealed with Numerical Simulations", IEEE Tran. Electron Devices, Vol. 64, pp. 2592-2598, 2017.

[35] H. Takaya, et al, "4H-SiC Trench MOSFET with low on-resistance at high temperature", IEEE International Symposium on Power Semiconductor Devices and ICs, pp. 118-121, 2020.

[36] S. Wirths, et al, "Vertical 1.2kV SiC Power MOSFETs with High-k/Metal Gate Stack", IEEE International Symposium on Power Semiconductor Devices and ICs, pp. 103-106, 2019.

[37] S. Wirths, et al, "Vertical Power SiC MOSFETs with High-k Gate Dielectrics and Superior Threshold Voltage Stability", IEEE International Symposium on Power Semiconductor Devices and ICs, pp. 226-229, 2020.

[38] S. Wirths, et al, "Study of 1.2kV High-k SiC Power MOSFETS under Harsh Repetitive Switching Conditions", IEEE International Symposium on Power Semiconductor Devices and ICs, pp. 107-110, 2021.

[39] G. Romano, et al, "Rugged Dynamic Behaviour of 3.3kV SiC Power MOSFETs with High–k Gate Dielectric", IEEE International Symposium on Power Semiconductor Devices and ICs, pp. 263-266, 2021.

[40] S. Wirths, et al, "Gate Stress Study on SiN-Based SiC Power MOSFETs", IEEE International Symposium on Power Semiconductor Devices and ICs, pp. 245-248, 2022.

Chapter 13

Power JBSFETs

It is attractive to utilize the body diode in the 4H-SiC power MOSFET structure as the anti-parallel diode in power circuits to avoid adding an external diode as required for silicon IGBTs. The body diode behaves as a P-i-N rectifier with high-level injection in the on-state. However, it has been reported[1] that the on-state voltage drop of the body diode increases after it was turned-on for even a short duration of 1 hour in case of the 100 μm thick drift layers required for 10-kV devices. The reason for the degradation of the diode characteristics has been found to be the generation of stacking faults at basal-plane-dislocations (BPDs) in the epitaxial layer. The recombination of the injected electrons and holes provides the energy for this process. This phenomenon was discussed in detail in chapter 7 on P-i-N rectifiers.

It was found that the generation of stacking faults degrades the on-resistance of the 4H-SiC power MOSFET as well. No change in the threshold voltage was observed. It was speculated that the increase in on-resistance is either due to bulk mobility degradation due to additional scattering at the stacking faults or due to reduced concentration of electrons in the drift layer by compensation of dopants at the stacking faults.

This problem is not as significant in the case of devices with lower breakdown voltages (600 to 1200 V) due to the thin drift layers. This has been demonstrated[2] by performing tests on 1200-V 4H-SiC power MOSFETs. The body diode on-state voltage drop increased by 0.8 % and the on-resistance of the MOSFET increased by 5.4 % after the conduction of the body diode for 1000 hours. In addition, high temperature gate bias (HTGB) stress at a gate bias of -15 V and 150 °C led to a threshold voltage shift of -90 mV in 1000 hours and a high temperature gate bias (HTGB) stress at a gate bias of +20 V and 175 °C led to a threshold voltage shift of 280 mV in 1000 hours. These results indicate that the gate oxide has been sufficiently shielded from the high electric field in the silicon carbide. The effect is still a concern during long term operation of the 4H-SiC power MOSFETs in applications.

However, the reverse recovery of the body diode produces an increase in the turn-on switching losses for the 4H-SiC power MOSFETs at elevated temperatures[3]. A sharp increase in reverse recovery charge and peak reverse recovery current were also reported for SiC power MOSFETs when the temperature increased beyond 350 °K (77 °C)[4]. Similar observations have been reported in other publications[5,6]. This problem can be mitigated by connecting a SiC JBS diode in anti-parallel with the SiC power MOSFET[5]. This adds another packaged component and significant cost to the power electronics[6].

An elegant solution to the poor performance of the body diode in SiC power MOSFETs is the integration of the JBS diode into the cell structure. This not only eliminates a separate packaged component but also reduces the net SiC chip area due to utilization of a common edge termination for both components. This device structure is called the JBSFET for 'Junction-Barrier Schottky diode integrated Field Effect Transistor'. This chapter reviews the basic concept of the JBSFET and its merits. The practical implementation of the structure with the planar-gate and trench-gate MOSFETs is then reviewed.

13.1 Planar-Gate Power JBSFET Structure

Planar-gate 4H-SiC JBSFETs have been created using two approaches. In the first approach, the JBS diode is created in a separate portion of the active area from the MOSFET cells. In the second approach, the JBS diode is integrated into the MOSFET cells.

13.1.1 Separate JBS Diode Area

In this approach, with chip design illustrated in Fig. 13.1[7], the JBS diode is created in a separate portion (area shown in red) of the active area from the MOSFET cells (area shown in purple). The JBS diode is placed in the middle of the chip so that the gate pad can access all the MOSFET cells. The JBS diodes have the cross-section previously shown in chapter 6 and the planar-gate MOSFETs have the cross-section previously shown in chapter 11. Both of these devices share a common edge termination shown in blue. In low current 4H-SiC devices with smaller active areas, the edge termination and scribe lane can occupy a large fraction of the total chip area. The integration of the JBS diode with the MOSFET can then reduce the total SiC area substantially because the two structures share a common edge termination.

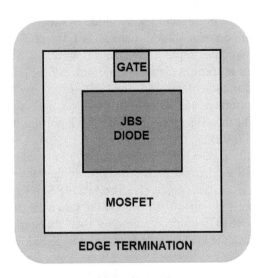

Fig. 13.1 The 4H-SiC planar-gate JBSFET structure with separate areas for the MOSFET cells and the JBS diode.

A 1.2 kV rated 4H-SiC JBSFET was reported in 2016 with 45 % of the active area allocated to the MOSFET cells[7]. A single Nickel metal layer was used to simultaneously form the ohmic contact to the N^+ source and P^+ base contact regions as well as the Schottky barrier for the JBS diode. A high specific on-resistance was observed for the MOSFET portion after rapid-thermal-annealing (RTA) of the Ni contact at 850 °C for 2 min, while the Schottky contact leakage current became large when the RTA of the Ni contact was done at 950 °C for 2 min. It was discovered that performing the RTA of the Ni contact at 900 °C for 2 min produced good Schottky and ohmic contacts simultaneously. The specific contact resistance to the N^+ source region was 1.7 x 10^{-4} Ω-cm^2 under these process conditions, which is much larger than the 0.045 mΩ-cm^2 value when the contact is annealed at 1000 °C. This increases the specific on-resistance of the MOSFET cells.

The JBSFET had a specific on-resistance of 12.5 mΩ-cm^2 after including the JBS diode area, compared with 7.25 mΩ-cm^2 for a MOSFET with the same active area as the JBSFET (with both MOSFET and JBS diode). The blocking characteristics of the JBSFET and

MOSFET fabricated alongside were identical in the first quadrant. In the third quadrant, the JBSFET had an on-state voltage drop of 1.9 V at a current density of 100 A/cm^2 compared to 4.7 V for the body diode of the MOSFET. This demonstrated the ability of the JBSFET structure to suppress current flow through the body diode of the MOSFET.

A comparison of a 1.2 kV rated JBSFET with 5 A current rating was performed with the separate MOSFET and JBS diode case[8]. The maximum allowable current densities of pure MOSFET and pure JBS diode, were determined to be 236 and 190 A/cm^2, respectively, when assuming a maximum power density of 300 W/cm^2. Using these values, the active areas for the JBS diode and MOSFET portion were determined to be 0.0263 and 0.0212 cm^2, respectively, for the 5 A rating. The total chip area, including the edge termination and scribe lane, for the MOSFET, the JBS diode, and the JBSFET were then found to be 0.0322, 0.0385, and 0.0635 cm^2, respectively. The total JBSFET chip area is then 11 % smaller than the sum of the MOSFET and JBS diode chip areas. This makes the JBSFET chip cost smaller than the sum of the separate devices and reduces the cost of an additional package as well.

13.1.2 JBS Diode Integrated into MOSFET Cells

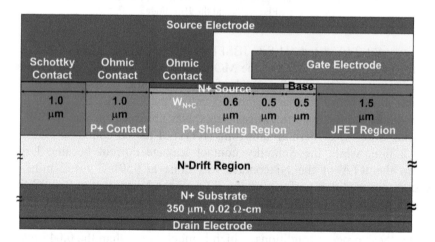

Fig. 13.2 The 4H-SiC planar-gate JBSFET structure with JBS diode integrated within MOSFET cell.

The second 4H-SiC JBSFET approach is the place the JBS diode inside the MOSFET cells[9] as shown in Fig. 13.2. The JBS diode is placed in the middle of the polysilicon gate window allowing the use of the P$^+$ contact region for shielding the Schottky contact. The typical dimensions for each of the regions is provided in the figure. A 1 μm width for the Schottky contact in the JBS diode produces sufficiently low voltage drop in the third quadrant to bypass the MOSFET body diode while producing sufficiently low leakage current. An accumulation channel device is illustrated in Fig. 13.2 because of larger channel mobility. The ohmic contact to the N^+ source region, shown as W_{N+C} in Fig. 13.2, is typically 0.5 μm in size. The addition of the JBS diode enlarges the cell pitch from 4.1 μm for the MOSFET to 5.6 μm for the JBSFET. This increase in cell pitch by a factor of 1.37-times proportionally increases the on-resistance of the channel, accumulation, and JFET regions.

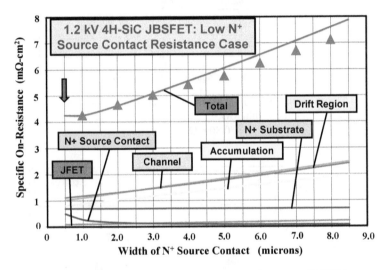

Fig. 13.3 The on-resistance of a 1.2 kV rated 4H-SiC planar-gate JBSFET structure with JBS diode integrated within MOSFET cell: Low N^+ source contact resistance of 0.045 mΩ-cm².

The specific on-resistance for the linear cell 4H-SiC JBSFET can be modelled using the same equations as developed for the power MOSFET in chapter 11 and textbook[10]. The components for the specific on-resistance together with the total value are shown in Fig. 13.3 for the case of an N^+ source contact resistance of 0.045 mΩ-cm². This can be achieved by annealing the Ni ohmic contact at 1000 °C for 2 min. The blue triangles show values obtained by numerical simulations. The lowest specific on-resistance of 4.2 mΩ-cm² occurs for the smallest N^+ source contact width of 0.5-1.0 μm. This result is not achievable

because of degradation of the Ni Schottky contact at this high annealing
temperature.

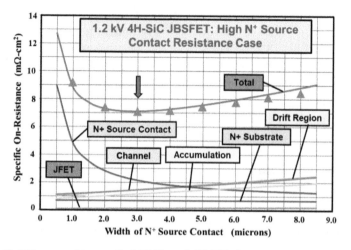

Fig. 13.4 The on-resistance of a 1.2 kV rated 4H-SiC planar-gate JBSFET structure
with JBS diode integrated within MOSFET cell: High N$^+$ source contact resistance of
0.80 mΩ-cm^2.

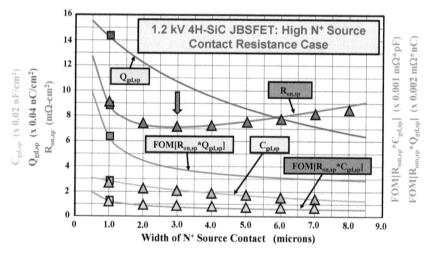

Fig. 13.5 1.2 kV rated 4H-SiC planar-gate JBSFET structure with JBS diode
integrated within MOSFET cell: $R_{on,sp}$, C_{gdsp}, $Q_{gd,sp}$, and HF-FOM.

The contact resistance to the N$^+$ source region increases to 0.80
mΩ-cm^2 when the Ni contact is annealed at 900 °C to simultaneously

achieve good Schottky contacts[9]. The components for the specific on-resistance together with the total value obtained by using this value are shown in Fig. 13.4. The blue triangles show values obtained by numerical simulations. The lowest specific on-resistance decreases to 7.1 $m\Omega$-cm^2 at an optimum N^+ source contact width of 3.0 μm[11].

The switching losses of the JBSFET are governed by the same gate-drain capacitance (C_{gd}) and charge (Q_{gd}) as the MOSFETs discussed in chapter 11. These device parameters can be analytically modelled as described in the textbook[12]. The values for C_{gd} and Q_{gd} reduce monotonically when the contact size to the N^+ source region is enlarged as shown in Fig. 13.5. This produces an significant improvement (reduction) of the high-frequency figures-of-merit [$R_{on}*C_{gd}$] and [$R_{on}*Q_{gd}$] as shown in Fig. 13.5. A remarkable 65 % improvement is projected by this analysis[11].

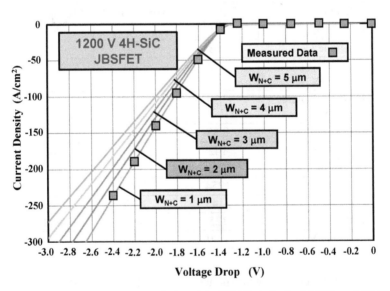

Fig. 13.6 Third quadrant characteristics of the JBS diode in the 1.2 kV rated 4H-SiC planar-gate JBSFET structure.

The density of the JBS diode in the JBSFET structure is determined by the ratio of the width of the Schottky contact to the cell pitch. The cell pitch is 6.1 μm for the case of an N^+ source contact width of 1 μm (see Fig. 13.2). The JBS diode density is 0.164 in this case. The measured third quadrant i-v characteristics for this case is shown in Fig. 13.6 by the blue squares. The i-v characteristics of the JBS diode in the

JBSFET can be modelled by using the equations in chapter 6 after account for current spreading from the Schottky contact across the entire JBSFET cell pitch. The results of the analytical modelling are shown in Fig. 13.6 for various values of the N^+ source contact width[11]. The on-state voltage drop at 100 A/cm^2 for the JBS diode in the JBSFET increases from 1.8 to 1.9 V when the N^+ source contact width is increased from 1 µm in the fabricated devices to the optimum value of 3 µm to minimize the specific on-resistance. This voltage drop is still sufficiently low to suppress any current flow via the body diode.

13.1.3 Planar-Gate 1.2 kV Devices: Cell Topologies

Table I: Experimental Results on 1.2 kV 4H-SiC JBSFETs:
Impact of Cell Topology

Structure	Linear	Hexagonal	Octagonal
Cell Pitch (µm)	6.1	6.6	5.9
JBS Diode Density	0.164	0.052	0.054
Breakdown Voltage (V)	1556	1351	1625
Threshold Voltage (V)	2.34	2.28	2.26
$R_{ON,SP}$ (mΩ-cm^2)	8.83	6.90	11.0
$C_{GD,SP}$ (pF/cm^2)	142	314	47
$Q_{GD,SP}$ (nC/cm^2)	356	578	147
FOM[$R_{ON}*C_{GD}$]	1254	2167	517
FOM[$R_{ON}*Q_{GD}$]	3143	3988	1617
FOM[C_{GS}/C_{GD}]	125	63	638
JBS Diode V_{ON} (V)	1.90	2.35	2.40

The measured electrical performance of three cell topologies for the 1.2 kV rated 4H-SiC planar-gate JBSFETs were reported in 2019[13]. The drift region had a doping concentration of 8 x 10^{15} cm^{-3} and thickness of 10 µm. A gate oxide thickness of 550 Å was thermally grown to form inversion-channel structures. The cell pitch for each cell design is given in the table together with the JBS diode density. The JBS diode density was about 3-times larger for the linear cell case compared to the hexagonal and octagonal cell designs.

The breakdown voltage for the hexagonal cell design is 85 % of the other cases due to electric field enhancement at the sharp cell corners within the cell. The smallest specific on-resistance is obtained with the hexagonal layout but it has large values for the gate-drain capacitance ($C_{GD,SP}$) and charge ($Q_{GD,SP}$). The best high-frequency figures-of-merit (HF-FOM) are obtained with the Octagonal cell topology as also noted for the power MOSFETs in chapter 11. The on-state voltage drop at 100 A/cm^2 in the third quadrant is 1.26-times large for the hexagonal and octagonal cell designs compared to the conventional linear cell case due to the lower JBS diode density for these cases. However, the on-state voltage drop of 2.4 V for these cases is still sufficiently low to suppress current flow via the body diode.

13.1.4 Planar-Gate 650 V Devices: Cell Topologies

The characteristics of 650 V rated 4H-SiC JBSFETs fabricated in a foundry with a drift region doping concentration of 2.4 x 10^{16} cm^{-3} and thickness of 6 μm were reported in 2021 for the case of three cell topologies[14]. A gate oxide thickness of 550 Å was grown to form inversion-channel structures.

Table II: Experimental Results on 650 V 4H-SiC JBSFETs:
Impact of Cell Topology

Structure	Linear	Hexagonal	Octagonal
Breakdown Voltage (V)	681	561	710
Threshold Voltage (V)	4.0	3.9	4.0
$R_{ON,SP}$ (mΩ-cm^2)	10.7	8.60	10.9
$C_{GD,SP}$ (pF/cm^2)	340	670	110
$Q_{GD,SP}$ (nC/cm^2)	333	667	171
FOM[$R_{ON}*C_{GD}$]	3366	5360	1133
FOM[$R_{ON}*Q_{GD}$]	3297	5336	1761
FOM[C_{GS}/C_{GD}]	51.8	30.0	279
JBS Diode V_{ON} (V)	1.90	2.35	2.40

A summary of the measured data for the three cell topologies is given in Table II. The breakdown voltage of the hexagonal cell design was found to be below the 650 V rating due to the sharp corners in the cell which produce enhanced electric fields in the blocking mode. The specific on-resistances follow the same trends discussed previously in section 11.10 for the 650 V 4H-SiC power MOSFETs. The 650 V rated

4H-SiC planar-gate JBSFETs were fabricated with a low N^+ source contact anneal temperature of 900 °C and inversion mode channels which makes their specific on-resistance large. The gate-drain capacitance (measured at 400 V) and the gate-drain charge also follow the trends described for the 600 V 4H-SiC planar-gate MOSFETs in section 11.10. The HF-FOMs obtained using the Octagonal cell topology are much better than the linear and hexagonal cells cases. The on-state voltage drop at 200 A/cm^2 in the third quadrant is 1.26-times larger for the hexagonal and octagonal cell designs compared to the conventional linear cell case due to the lower JBS diode density for these cases (see Table II). However, the on-state voltage drop of 2.4 V for these cases is still sufficiently low to suppress current flow via the body diode.

13.1.5 Planar-Gate 1.7 kV Devices: Cell Topologies

The measured characteristics of 1.7 kV rated 4H-SiC planar-gate JBSFETs with breakdown voltage of 2350 V were reported in 2021 for the case of three cell topologies[15]. The devices were fabricated in a foundry with a drift region doping concentration of 6.0 x 10^{15} cm^{-3} and thickness of 17 μm. A gate oxide thickness of 550 Å was grown to form accumulation-channel structures.

Table III: Experimental Results on 2300 V 4H-SiC JBSFETs:
Impact of Cell Topology

Structure	Linear	Hexagonal	Octagonal
Breakdown Voltage (V)	2324	2079	2377
Threshold Voltage (V)	2.5	2.5	2.5
$R_{ON,SP}$ (mΩ-cm^2)	9.5	8.60	11.3
$Q_{GD,SP}$ (nC/cm^2)	422	644	182
FOM[$R_{ON}*Q_{GD}$]	4136	5216	2239
JBS Diode V_{ON} (V)	2.0	2.6	2.7
FOM[$V_{ON}*Q_{GD}$]	894	1674	491

A summary of the measured data for the three cell topologies is given in Table III. The breakdown voltage of the hexagonal cell design was found to be below 2300 V due to the sharp corners in the cell which produce enhanced electric fields in the blocking mode. The specific on-resistances follow the same trends discussed previously in section 11.11

for the 1.7 kV 4H-SiC power MOSFETs. The 1.7 kV rated 4H-SiC planar-gate JBSFETs were fabricated with a low N^+ source contact anneal temperature of 900 °C making the specific contact resistance large (0.8 mΩ-cm^2). Analytical modelling of the specific on-resistance showed that the N^+ source contact resistance contributes 40-50 % of the total value even for the higher voltage rating. The gate-drain charge also follows the trends described for the 1.7 kV 4H-SiC planar-gate MOSFETs in section 11.11. The HF-FOMs obtained using the Octagonal cell topology are much better than the linear and hexagonal cells cases.

The on-state voltage drop at 100 A/cm^2 in the third quadrant is 1.3-times larger for the hexagonal and octagonal cell designs compared to the conventional linear cell case due to the lower JBS diode density for these cases (see Table I). However, the on-state voltage drop of 2.4 V for these cases is still sufficiently low to suppress current flow via the body diode. A new FOM[$V_{ON}*Q_{GD}$] was defined in this paper to allow comparison of 4H-SiC JBSFETs to highlight the third-quadrant voltage drop. The best (lowest) value is observed for the Octagonal cell design,

13.1.6 Thin Gate Oxide

The benefits of reducing the gate oxide thickness for planar-gate 4H-SiC power MOSFETs was documented in chapter 11. These benefits have been quantified for 650 V planar-gate 4H-SiC power JBSFETs as well[16]. A gate oxide thickness of 270 Å was used instead of 550 Å used for devices in the previous sections of this chapter.

The performance of 650 V inversion-channel devices with three cell topologies was measured on devices fabricated using 6 μm thick, n-type epitaxial layers with doping concentration of 2.4 x 10^{16} cm^{-3}. The breakdown voltages for the Linear and Octagonal cells were above 800 V with a lower value (715 V) observed for the Hexagonal cell case as previously noted for the devices with gate oxide thickness of 550 Å. The specific on-resistance of the Hexagonal cell design was the lowest with a value 21 % smaller than the Linear cell design case. The specific on-resistance of the Octagonal cell design was close to the Linear cell design case.

The gate-drain charge for the Hexagonal cell design was twice that for the Linear cell case, while that for the Octagonal cell design was about half that of the Linear design case. Consequently, the best FOM[$R_{ON}*Q_{GD}$] was obtained with the Octagonal cell topology.

The on-state voltage drop at 200 A/cm^2 of the integrated JBS diode in the third quadrant is given in Table IV for the three cell designs. The values are all satisfactory for suppressing current flow from the body diode. The JBSFET FOM[$V_{ON}*Q_{GD}$] is found to be the best for the Octagonal cell case.

Table IV: Experimental Results on 650 V 270 Å Gate Oxide
4H-SiC JBSFETs

Structure	Linear	Hexagonal	Octagonal
Breakdown Voltage (V)	820	715	850
Threshold Voltage (V)	2.10	2.00	2.05
$R_{ON,SP}$ (mΩ-cm^2)	6.4	5.3	6.9
$Q_{GD,SP}$ (nC/cm^2)	333	667	178
FOM[$R_{ON}*Q_{GD}$]	2131	3535	1228
JBS Diode V_{ON} (V)	2.1	2.5	2.5
FOM[$V_{ON}*Q_{GD}$]	699	1667	445

13.2 Trench Gate Power JBSFET Structure

The JBS diode can also be integrated into the trench-gate 4H-SiC power MOSFET structure to create JBSFETs. A structure that has been experimentally demonstrated is shown in Fig. 13.7 where the JBS diode is formed on the sidewall of the trench using Titanium as the Schottky barrier metal. The P-base region and P$^+$ shielding region serve as the junctions that shield the Schottky contact to reduce the electric field. The P$^+$ shielding region is used under the Schottky contact and the gate oxide to protect both regions. As in the case of the trench-gate power MOSFETs with P$^+$ shielding region under the gate oxide discussed in section 12.3, a JFET is formed between these regions at point A. This is beneficial for shielding the Schottky contact and P-base regions from the high electric fields generated in the drift region in the structure shown in Fig. 13.7.

Analysis of the trench-gate 4H-SiC JBSFET structure shown in Fig. 13.7, called the SWITCH-MOS, was reported in 2017 for 1.2 kV rated devices[17]. It was shown that the extension (X in Fig. 13.7) of the P$^+$ shielding region determines the maximum electric field at the Schottky contact and the gate oxide on the sidewall. The maximum electric field could be reduced to 1.5 MV/cm at a drain bias of 1200 V with X values of 0.1 – 0.2 μm. The leakage current was reduced with these values for X with breakdown voltage of 1500 V achieved.

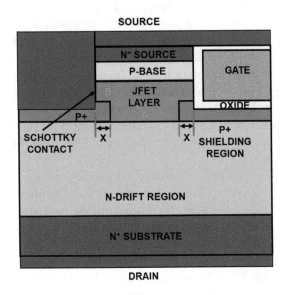

Fig. 13.7 The 4H-SiC trench-gate JBSFET structure with JBS diode formed on the trench sidewall (called SWITCH-MOS).

Devices fabricated with 800 Å thick gate oxide had a specific on-resistance of 3.1 mΩ-cm^2 at a gate bias of 20 V and cell pitch of 5 μm. The third quadrant *i-v* characteristics had a knee at about 1 V demonstrating conduction via the Schottky contact. The on-state voltage drop was about 2 V at 100 A/cm^2. Body diode conduction was observed when the current density was raised to 200 A/cm^2. The bipolar degradation effect was shown to be suppressed in the SWITCHMOS structure in contrast with the MOSFET structure.

The switching performance of the SWITCH-MOS structure was reported in 2019[18]. The third quadrant on-state voltage drop of a 3 x 3 mm^2 SWITCHMOS device was found to be 3.3 V at 175 °C compared with 4.3 V for the body diode. The reverse recovery current and charge for the SWITCHMOS was shown to be much smaller than for the trench-gate MOSFET without the JBS diode. This resulted in a reduction of the turn-on switching loss by 29 % compared with the conventional trench-gate structure without the JBS diode.

The short-circuit (SC) withstand capability of the SWITCH-MOS device was reported in 2020[19]. The test were conducted using a drain bias of 800 V and gate bias of 15 V although the on-state resistance was measured at a gate bias of 20 V. The SC withstand time of 6 μs for the SWITCH-MOS was found compared with 10 μs for the trench-gate MOSFET with P[+] shielding region. This was attributed to enhanced leakage current flow via the Schottky contact at the high SC induced temperature. In addition, damage to the Schottky contact was observed after SC tests of 5 μs in duration[20]. An increase in leakage current by 3-orders of magnitude was observed. This behavior was not observed for the trench-gate MOSFET with P[+] shielding region. In contrast, the reverse-bias-safe-operating-area (RBSOA) of the SWITCH-MOS device was reported to be identical to the trench-gate MOSFET with P[+] shielding region[21].

The SC withstand capability of the SiC power MOSFET has been shown to be related to a rise in the junction temperature to above 1000 °C during the SC stress. Increasing the SC withstand time by the attachment of a copper block to the source metal was attempted[22]. The transfer of heat into the copper block increase the thermal mass that is heated during the SC stress. Although this was found to increase the SC withstand time by 15 % for a drain bias of 100 V, it had no impact for the practical drain bias of 800 V because the regions outside the location of the copper block reach a high temperature.

13.3 Experimental Results: Recent Devices

Many papers have been published on 'proposed' device structures with numerical simulations of the resulting characteristics. These results are not included in the book because the proposed structure are 'idealized' cases that cannot be fabricated to produce the results projected by the numerical simulations. The characteristics of fabricated 4H-SiC JBSFETs that have not been covered in the previous sections are discussed here.

The optimization of the 1.2 kV rated planar-gate JBSFET structure shown in Fig. 13.2 was reported in 2021 with breakdown voltage of 1600 V. The impact of reducing the cell pitch by 18 % with unstated adjustments to the JFET width and other cell dimensions was analyzed[23]. The specific on-resistance was reduced by 39 % with the smaller cell pitch. The third quadrant on-state voltage drop of 2.4 V at

300 A/cm^2 was close to the same for both devices. The switching loss was reduced by 16 % for the device with smaller cell pitch due to an increase in the transconductance. The short-circuit withstand time was measured at a drain bias of 600 V. It improved from 1 μs to 1.25 μs with decrease in the cell pitch even though the peak SC current was larger by 10 %. The authors associate the improved SC withstand time with a reduction of the JFET width although this should have reduced the peak SC current. The observed SC withstand time are very low compared with a desired value of 10 μs that is exhibited by Si IGBTs.

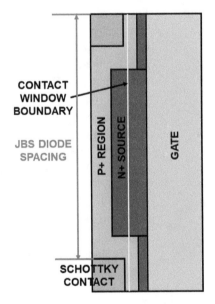

Fig. 13.8 The 4H-SiC planar-gate JBSFET structure layout with JBS diode distributed along cell stripes.

The density of the JBS diode in the JBSFET can be adjusted by limiting its location along the linear cell strips as illustrated in Fig. 13.8. The impact of the JBS diode spacing on the performance of 1.2 kV 4H-SiC planar-gate JBSFETs has been experimentally examined[24]. The cell pitch for the JBSFETs was 8.4 μm compared to 5.4 μm for the MOSFET cells. This increased the specific on-resistance of the JBSFETs to 5 mΩ-cm^2 compared with 3.67 mΩ-cm^2 for the MOSFET. The third quadrant on-state voltage drop at 100 A/cm^2 for the JBSFET for Nickel JBS diodes with spacing of 16, 8, and 4 μm was 2.34, 2.11, and 1.85 V, respectively.

Planar-gate 4H-SiC JBSFETs with other voltage ratings have also been reported. Accumulation-channel JBSFETs with 600 V rating were reported[25] in 2020 with the JBS diode layout shown in Fig. 13.8. The specific on-resistance of the JBSFETs was 5.58 compared with 4.54 $m\Omega$-cm^2 for the MOSFET. These values are larger than those reported for the 1.2 kV devices[24] despite using an accumulation-mode channel. The third quadrant on-state voltage drop at 100 A/cm^2 for the JBSFET for Nickel JBS diodes was 2.1 V compared with 3.2 V for the MOSFET.

Experimental results on planar-gate 4H-SiC JBSFETs with voltage rating of 3300 V were reported in 2020 with different areas for the integrated JBS diode[26]. The third quadrant on-state voltage drop at 100 A/cm^2 for the devices increased from 2.2 V to 3.2 V to 4.4 V with JBS diode area reduction from 25 % to 14 % to 10 %. The specific on-resistance of the 3.3 kV 4H-SiC planar-gate JBSFETs increased from 12.23 to 12.59 to 13.53 $m\Omega$-cm^2 when the JBS diode area was increased from 10 to 14 to 25 %. A larger specific on-resistance by 11 % is traded-off with the benefits of having the integrated JBS diode to suppress conduction via the body diode. A short circuit withstand time of 2 μs was obtained at a drain bias of 1500 V and gate bias of 20 V. This will reduce to 1.35 μs at a typical drain bias of 2200 V for this voltage rating.

Experimental results on 6500 V rated planar-gate 4H-SiC JBSFETs were reported in 2021 with 25 % area used for the integrated JBS diode[27]. The devices had a breakdown voltage of 8000 V. The specific on-resistance of the JBSFET was 39 $m\Omega$-cm^2, an increase of only 5 % over the MOSFET device and 15 % larger than that of the drift layer. The JBS diode functioned up to 80 A/cm^2 in the third quadrant and showed a transition into the MPS-mode beyond this point at 25 °C. This transition point reduced to 20 A/cm^2 at 175 °C. A short circuit withstand time of 5 μs was observed at a drain bias of 3600 V and gate bias of 20 V compared to 6 μs for the MOSET.

Fabrication of a 6500 V planar-gate 4H-SiC JBSFET was reported[28] in 2022 using a process to make the JBS diode Schottky contact with Titanium and Ohmic contacts to the N^+ source and P^+ plug regions using Nickel. The cell width was given as 13.6 μm for the JBSFET, compared to 9.6 μm for the MOSFET, with a JFET and Schottky width of 2.5 μm. The specific on-resistance of the JBSFET was 45 $m\Omega$-cm^2 compared to 40.6 $m\Omega$-cm^2 for the MOSFET, increase of 11 %. The third quadrant on-state voltage drop at 50 A/cm^2 for the JBSFET increased from 4.0 V to 7.0 V from 25 to 200 °C. The MPS-mode was evident at higher temperatures.

Improvement in the performance of the 1.2 kV planar-gate 4H-SiC JBSFET was accomplished by using a layout similar to that shown in Fig. 13.8 and employing 1.8 μm deep P$^+$ regions[29]. Channeling of the Aluminum ion implantation was accomplished using a tilt angle of 4 degrees with 350 keV energy to make the 1.8 μm deep P-well. The CSL under the P-well was made by Phosphorus channeling implant. The deep P$^+$ region suppressed the leakage current during the blocking mode by more than 3 orders of magnitude. A short circuit withstand time of 4 μs was observed at a drain bias of 800 V and gate bias of 20 V.

13.4 Summary

The integration of a JBS diode with the MOSFET cells to create the 4H-SiC JBSFET structure has been discussed in this chapter for both the planar-gate and trench-gate cases. Current flow via the body diode of the MOSFET in the third quadrant is suppressed by the JBS diode due to its smaller voltage drop. A low leakage current for the JBS diode can be achieved by proper design of the Schottky contact width. The JBSFET structures allows significant savings in SiC chip area because of a common edge termination for the JBS diode and the MOSFET. In addition, an additional package is eliminated reducing space in power electronic boards.

The Schottky contact to the drift region and ohmic contact to the N$^+$ source region can be simultaneously achieved by annealing a Nickel contact at 900 °C. The relatively large N$^+$ contact resistance can be compensated by enlarging the N$^+$ source contact width from 0.5 to 3 μm. This approach produces reduced specific on-resistance and improvements in the high-frequency figures-of-merit.

The JBSFET can be designed with many cell topologies, including the Linear, Hexagonal, and Octagonal cases. Among these, the hexagonal cell produces the lowest specific on-resistance and largest high frequency figures-of-merit. In contrast, the octagonal cell produces the best high-frequency figures-of-merit but has larger specific on-resistance. This has been demonstrated for devices with voltage ratings of 600, 1200, and 1700 V.

The JBSFET concept has also been applied to make devices with voltage ratings of 3300 and 6500 V. At these larger voltages, the MPS-mode of operation is observed especially at elevated temperatures. This is acceptable for reducing reverse recovery induced power losses.

References

[1] A. Agarwal, et al, "A New Degradation Mechanism in High-Voltage SiC Power MOSFETs", IEEE Electron Device Letters, Vol. 28, pp. 587-589, 2007.

[2] B. Hull, et al, "Reliability and Stability of SiC Power MOSFETs and Next Generation SiC MOSFETs", IEEE Workshop on Wide Bandgap Power Devices and Applications, pp. 139-142, 2014.

[3] B. Hull, et al, "Switching Performance Comparison of 1200 V and 1700 V SiC Optimized Half Bridge Power Modules with SiC Anti-parallel Schottky Diodes versus MOSFET Intrinsic Body Diodes", IEEE Applied Power Electronics Conf., pp. 2297-2304, 2017.

[4] J. Qi, et al, "Dynamic Characterization of 1.2 kV SiC Power MOSFET Body Diode at Cryogenic and High Temperatures", IEEE Workshop on Wide Bandgap Power Devices and Applications, pp. 179-183, 2018.

[5] M. R. Ahmed, R. Todd, and A. J. Forsyth, "Switching Performance of a SiC MOSFET Body Diode and SiC Schottky Diodes at Different Temperatures", IEEE Energy Conversion Congress and Exhibition, pp. 5487-5494, 2017.

[6] D. Martin, et al, "Switching Performance Comparison of 1200 V and 1700 V SiC Optimized Half Bridge Power Modules with SiC Anti-parallel Schottky Diodes versus MOSFET Intrinsic Body Diodes", IEEE Applied Power Electronics Conf., pp. 2297-2304, 2017.

[7] W. Sung and B. J. Baliga, "Monolithically Integrated 4H-SiC MOSFET and JBS Diode (JBSFET) Using a Single Ohmic/Schottky Process Scheme", IEEE Electron Device Letters, Vol. 37, pp. 1605-1608, 2016.

[8] W. Sung and B. J. Baliga, "On Developing One-Chip Integration of 1.2 kV SiC MOSFET and JBS Diode (JBSFET)", IEEE Tran. Industrial Electronics, Vol. 64, pp. 8206-8212, 2017.

[9] K. Han, A. Agarwal, and B. J. Baliga, "Comparison of New Octagonal Cell Topology for 1.2 kV 4H-SiC JBSFETs with Linear and Hexagonal Topologies: Analysis and Experimental Results", IEEE Workshop on Wide Bandgap Power Devices and Applications, pp. 159-162, 2019.

[10] B. J. Baliga, "Gallium Nitride and Silicon Carbide Power Devices", World Scientific Press, Singapore, 2017.

[11] A. Agarwal and B. J. Baliga, "Optimization of linear cell 4H-SiC power JBSFETs: Impact of N^+ source contact resistance", Power Electronic Devices and Components, Vol. 2, pp. P1-P11, Elsevier, 2022.

[12] B. J. Baliga, "Fundamentals of Power Semiconductor Devices", Second Edition, Springer-Science, 2019.

[13] K. Han, A. Agarwal, and B. J. Baliga, "Comparison of New Octagonal Cell Topology for 1.2 kV 4H-SiC JBSFETs with Linear and Hexagonal Topologies: Analysis and Experimental Results", IEEE Int. Symp. Power Semiconductor Devices and ICs, pp. 159-162, 2019.

[14] A. Agarwal, K. Han, and B. J. Baliga, "650-V 4H-SiC Planar Inversion-Channel Power JBSFETs with 55-nm Gate Oxide: Relative Performance of Three Cell Types", IEEE Transactions on Electron Devices, Vol. 68, pp. 2395-2400, 2021.

[15] A. Agarwal, K. Han, and B. J. Baliga, "2.3 kV 4H-SiC Planar-Gate Accumulation Channel Power JBSFETs: Analysis of Experimental Data", IEEE Journal of the Electron Devices Society, Vol. 9, pp. 324-333, 2021.

[16] A. Agarwal, K. Han, and B. J. Baliga, "Assessment of Linear, Hexagonal, and Octagonal Cell Topologies for 650 V 4H-SiC Inversion-Channel Planar-Gate Power JBSFETs Fabricated With 27 nm Gate Oxide Thickness", IEEE Journal of the Electron Devices Society, Vol. 9, pp. 79-88, 2021.

[17] Y. Kobayashi, et al, "Body PiN diode inactivation with low on-resistance achieved by a 1.2 kV-class 4H-SiC SWITCH-MOS", IEEE Int. Electron Devices Meeting, pp. 9.1.1-9.1.4, 2017.

[18] R. Aiba, et al, "Experimental Demonstration on Superior Switching Characteristics of 1.2 kV SiC SWITCH-MOS", IEEE Int. Symp. Power Semiconductor Devices and ICs, pp. 23-26, 2019.

[19] M. Okawa, et al, "First Demonstration of Short-Circuit Capability for a 1.2 kV SiC SWITCH-MOS ", IEEE Journal of the Electron Devices Society, Vol. 7, pp. 613-620, 2019.

[20] M. Okawa, et al, "Analysis of 1.2 kV SiC SWITCH-MOS after Short-circuit Stress", IEEE Int. Symp. Power Semiconductor Devices and ICs, pp. 74-77, 2020.

[21] S. Todaka, et al, "Experimental and Numerical Demonstration of Superior RBSOAs in 1.2 kV SiC Trench and SBD-integrated Trench MOSFETs", IEEE Int. Symp. Power Semiconductor Devices and ICs, pp. 219-222, 2021.

[22] K. Yao, et al, "Enhanced Short-circuit Capability for 1.2 kV SiC SBD-integrated Trench MOSFETs Using Cu Blocks Sintered on the Source Pad", IEEE Int. Symp. Power Semiconductor Devices and ICs, pp. 297-300, 2022.

[23] H. Kono, et al, "Improving the specific on-resistance and short-circuit ruggedness tradeoff of 1.2-kV-class SBD embedded SiC MOSFETs through cell pitch reduction and internal resistance optimization", IEEE Int. Symp. Power Semiconductor Devices and ICs, pp. 227-230, 2021.

[24] S. A. Mancini, et al, "Increased 3rd Quadrant Current Handling Capability of 1.2kV 4H-SiC JBS Diode-Integrated MOSFETs (JBSFETs) with Minimal Impact on the Forward Conduction and Blocking Performances", IEEE Workshop on Wide Bandgap Power Devices and Applications, pp. 101-106, 2021.

[25] N. Yun, et al, "Area-Efficient, 600V 4H-SiC JBS Diode-Integrated MOSFETs (JBSFETs) for Power Converter Applications", IEEE Journal of Emerging and Selected Topics in Power Electronics, pp. 16-23, 2020.

[26] S. Sundaresan, et al, "3300 V SiC MOSFETs with integrated Schottky Rectifiers", IEEE Int. Symp. Power Semiconductor Devices and ICs, pp. 206-209, 2020.

[27] S. Sundaresan, et al, "Performance and Robustness of 6500 V SiC DMOSFETs with Integrated MPS diodes", IEEE Int. Symp. Power Semiconductor Devices and ICs, pp. 235-238, 2021.

[28] H. Chen, et al, "High temperature performance of 6500V 4H-SiC MOSFET with embedded Schottky barrier diode", IEEE Electron Devices Technology Manufacturing Conf., pp. 198-200, 2022.

[29] D. Kim, et al, "An Optimal Design for 1.2kV 4H-SiC JBSFET (Junction Barrier Schottky Diode Integrated MOSFET) with Deep P-Well", IEEE Electron Device Letters, Vol. 43, pp. 785-788, 2022.

Chapter 14

Super-Junction MOSFETs

The super-junction (SJ) concept is based on charge coupling between adjacent P-type and N-type drift regions as described in chapter 4. It was shown by analytical modelling that the drift region specific on-resistance for a device with breakdown voltage of 8 kV (rated blocking voltage of 6.5 kV) can be reduced from 40 mΩ-cm^2 for the conventional 1D device structure to 1.5 mΩ-cm^2 for SJ case with N and P-type regions of 5 μm in size. This large 26-fold reduction in specific on-resistance has been pursued by development of technology for the fabrication of the 2D charge-coupled drift region. A target specific on-resistance of 20 mΩ-cm^2 for a SJ MOSFET with breakdown voltage of 8 kV was projected in 2018[1]. This value is far (10-times) larger than the projected drift region specific on-resistance.

As stated in previous chapter, many papers have been published on novel 'proposed' device structures that have been analyzed by numerical simulations. These structures are not discussed here because they lack practical demonstration taking into account technological limitations.

14.1 Trench-Gate Device with Multiple Epitaxial Layer Growth

The first experimental results on SJ 4H-SiC power MOSFET device were reported in 2018[2] with a V-groove gate structure as illustrated in Fig. 14.1. The drift region was formed using six epitaxial growth steps of 0.7 μm in size with ion implantation of aluminum with doping concentration of 1 x 10^{17} cm^{-3} to form the P-pillars with width of 1 – 1.45 μm. The current spreading layer had a doping concentration of over 1 x 10^{17} cm^{-3}. The cell had a pitch of 5 μm. A short channel length of 0.17 μm was used with P-base doping of 1 x 10^{18} cm^{-3}. The gate oxide thickness was 500 Å.

The device had a breakdown voltage of 1170 V with a low specific on-resistance of 0.63 mΩ-cm². However, this value is larger than the 0.3 mΩ-cm² for the drift region in the 1D case. It is also much larger than the projected specific on-resistance for the 2D or SJ drift region of 0.13 mΩ-cm² for a cell pitch of 5 μm (see Fig. 4.13). This shows room for further reduction of the SJ SiC power MOSFETs specific on-resistance. The gate-drain capacitance for the fabricated SJ was reported to be 2-time larger than for the conventional structure. This does not favor good performance at high frequencies.

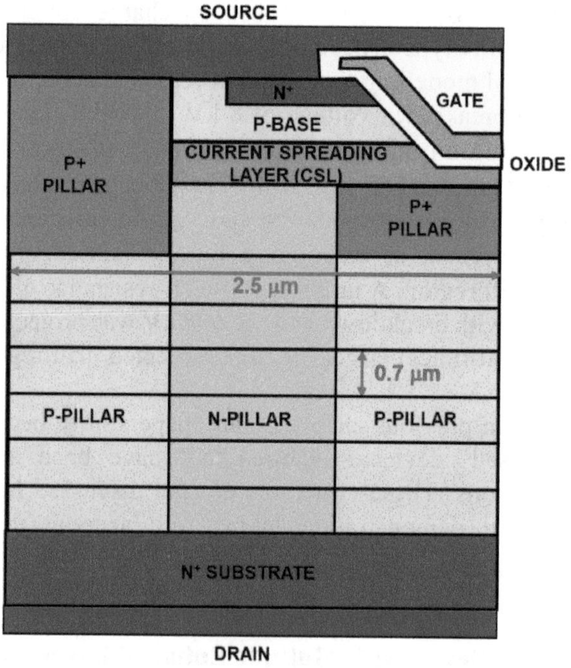

Fig. 14.1 The Super-Junction 4H-SiC V-groove trench-gate MOSFET structure.

One of the challenges of fabricating SJ devices is the formation of an edge termination that can support a high voltage in spite of a larger doping concentration in the drift region than dictated by the 1D breakdown voltage. The edge termination that was used to achieve a high breakdown voltage for the SJ 4H-SiC MOSFET shown in Fig. 14.1 is illustrated in Fig. 14.2. To make this edge termination, the periphery of the active area is etched to remove the more highly doped P-base and N⁺ source regions. A second n-type epitaxial layer then grown to refill the etched region.

P-type ion implants are performed into this second epitaxial layer to create a double JTE zone. It was shown in the paper that an etch depth of about 1 μm is required to achieve a breakdown voltage of 1200 V.

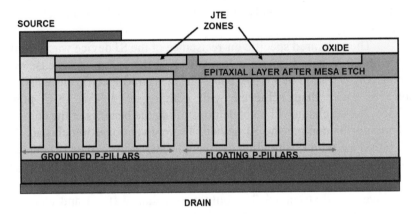

Fig. 14.2 Edge Termination for the Super-Junction 4H-SiC V-groove trench-gate MOSFET.

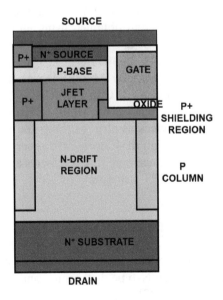

Fig. 14.3 The Super-Junction 4H-SiC shielded trench-gate MOSFET structure.

Fabrication of a 1.2 kV rated trench-gate 4H-SiC SJ MOSFET was reported[3] in 2019 with measured breakdown voltage of 1500 V. This was achieved by growth of a 4.4 μm n-type drift region a 4-degree off-axis 4H-SiC N^+ substrate. The SJ structure was created using 7 epitaxial growth cycles of 0.65 μm in thickness. The p-column was created by eight cycles of aluminum ion implantation carried out after each epitaxial growth step. The fabricated SJ device had a chip size of 0.3 cm x 0.3 cm and active area of 0.055 cm^2.

The measured specific on-resistance of the SJ device was 3.2 mΩ-cm^2 with 20 V gate bias for a 'narrow' N-drift region width case with doping concentration of 5 x 10^{16} cm^{-3}. The measured specific on-resistance value is larger than achieved with planar-gate 4H-SiC SiC power MOSFETs (see chapter 11), not demonstrating the benefits of the complex technology for making the SJ device. The conventional trench-gate 4H-SiC MOSFET with P^+ shielding regions (discussed in chapter 12) made by the authors exhibited a higher specific on-resistance of 3.6 mΩ-cm^2. The on-resistance increased by only 16 % at 175 °C compared with 80 % for the conventional structure. The output capacitance (C_{oss}) and charge of the SJ device was increased by a factor of 3-times compared with the conventional device due to the presence of the P-columns.

The on-state voltage drop of the body diode for the SJ MOSFET was 3.4 V at 100 A/cm^2 compared with 3.6 V for the conventional device. The peak reverse recovery current obtained using an on-state current of 7 A increased from 7 to 10 A at 25 and 175 °C. The reverse recovery charge (Q_{rr}) increased from 288 at 25 °C to 305 nC at 175 °C. In comparison, the Q_{rr} for the conventional trench-gate MOSFET was much smaller and found to increase from 148 nC at 25 °C to 171 nC at 175 °C. These results confirm that the SJ 4H-SiC trench-gate MOSFET has a larger Q_{rr} than conventional trench-gate devices as also observed for Si SJ devices. The SJ devices also exhibited a high dI/dt during the reverse recovery. These results indicate poor performance at high frequencies and that it would be preferable to make a SJ JBSFET structure.

14.2 Trench-Gate Device with Deep Trench Etching and Refilling

The alternative to making the SJ devices with multiple epitaxial layers is by etching deep trenches in an N-type drift region and then refilling them with P-type SiC. A 6.5 kV MOSFET was reported[4] in 2019 with a partial SJ structure as illustrated in Fig. 14.4. A higher breakdown voltage can be achieved with this approach with trenches of smaller depths than required to obtain the same breakdown voltage with the full SJ structure. The N-buffer had 41 μm thickness (t_2 in Fig. 14.4) with doping concentration of 2×10^{15} cm^{-3}. This doping level is close to the 1D case discussed in chapter 3. The portion with the SJ structure had 22 μm thickness (t_1 in Fig. 14.4) with doping concentration of 1.5×10^{16} cm^{-3}.

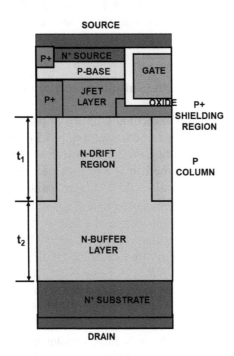

Fig. 14.4 The partial Super-Junction 4H-SiC shielded trench-gate MOSFET structure.

The fabrication of the partial SJ structure requires etching the 22 μm deep trenches first followed by epitaxial refill with p-type 4H-SiC. The refill occurs with growth of the p-type 4H-SiC on top of the mesa regions as well. A 'quasi-selective growth' in the trenches occurs for an HCl/SiH4 ratio of 50 with a 5 μm layer on the mesa regions. This overgrowth is removed by grinding and polishing followed by growth of an n-type layer in which the gate structure can be fabricated. The drift layer ($t_1 + t_2$) was estimated to have a specific resistance of 13 mΩ-cm^2. This is an order of magnitude larger than the projected ideal drift region resistance of 1.5 mΩ-cm^2 for the SJ device with N-drift region width of 5 μm (see Fig. 4.13). The specific on-resistance of the partial SJ 4H-SiC trench-gate MOSFET with 10 μm cell pitch was 17.8 mΩ-cm^2 at a gate bias of 20 V. This is half of the ideal specific on-resistance for the drift region in the 1D case.

Consequently, the fabricated partial SJ devices outperformed the conventional 4H-SiC MOSFET and the ideal 1D limit.

A large leakage current was observed in the partial SJ devices when there were voids in the refilled regions within the trenches. Elimination of the voids with optimized growth conditions reduced the leakage current by 5-orders of magnitude and achieved a breakdown voltage of 7.8 kV.

14.3 Planar-Gate Device with Multiple Epitaxial Layer Growth

The multiple epitaxial growth method with ion implantation of aluminum to form the charge coupling regions (see Fig. 14.1) has been employed to make a 4.5 kV planar-gate SJ 4H-SiC power MOSFET[5]. The p-type implanted regions were formed in a mesh shape. The n-type epitaxial growth with doping concentration of 1×10^{16} cm^{-3} was conducted in 4 steps of 12 μm in thickness to obtain a total thickness of 48 μm. This produces p-type regions (grid) at 3 levels inside the n-drift region which must be grounded by using p-type pillars (p-bus) formed by high energy ion-implantation. The p-bus regions are located below the P-base region of the MOSFET structure.

The measured breakdown voltage was 4.5 kV making this a device with less than 4 kV rating. The measured specific on-resistance was 10 mΩ-cm^2 which is equal to the ideal specific on-resistance for the drift region in the 1D case, and about 2-times smaller than the value for the conventional device case. It is 14-times larger than the theoretically projected specific on-resistance for the SJ 4H-SiC ideal case (see Fig. 4.13). Much more effort is therefore required to make the SJ concept practical for 4H-SiC material. Double-pulse tests (DPT) with inductive load performed using the SJ MOSFETs in both the upper and lower leg of the DPT show a large peak reverse recovery current for the body diode of 4-times the on-state value of 50 A/cm^2.

The measured characteristics of the above SJ MOSFETs were reported[6] in 2020 with various sizes for the p-bus and cell pitch. The lowest specific on-resistance was reported for the devices with a wide p-bus and large cell pitch due to reduction of area occupied by the p-type grid. However, these devices had larger leakage current. Double-pulse tests (DPT) with inductive load performed using the SJ MOSFETs in only the lower leg of the DPT with JBS diode in the upper leg show a large peak reverse recovery current of 4-times the on-state value. In addition, a tail in the drain voltage waveform is observed during device turn-on. This is ascribed by the authors as due to the high resistance of p-type regions in 4H-SiC which slows down the charging of the p-grid.

14.4 Summary

The creation of super-junction 4H-SiC power MOSFETs is motived by the opportunity to greatly reduce the specific resistance of the drift region in higher blocking voltage devices. Two fabrication approaches have been explored. The first method employs growth of multiple n-type epitaxial layers with p-type ion-implants to form the charge-coupling regions. The second method employs etching deep trenches in an n-type drift region followed by epitaxial refill of the trenches. Both approaches are immature at this time with the performance of the MOSFETs barely crossing the 1D ideal specific on-resistance limit.

A good comparison of the multiple epitaxy (ME) and trench filling epitaxy (TFE) approaches to make the SJ 4H-SiC power MOSFETs has been performed[7] by fabrication of both structures with same design for the SJ region and gate MOS cell structure. The devices had 5.2 μm deep p-pillars on a 3.8 μm thick n-buffer layer. The cell pitch was 5 μm. The measured performance of 1.2 kV rated devices showed a good breakdown voltage of 1500 V for the ME case with a lower 1200 V value for the TFE case. The specific on-resistance of both structures was 2.8 $m\Omega$-cm^2, which is similar to planar-gate SiC power MOSFETs without the SJ structure. However, the SJ devices showed an increase in specific on-resistance of only 30 % with temperature increase to 150 °C compared with 200 % for the conventional structure. The authors concluded that the TFE method is simpler and more cost effective than the ME case. However, they observed bipolar degradation effects when the body diode was turned on the third quadrant for the TFE case.

References

[1] Y. Yonezawa, et al, "Progress in High and Ultrahigh Voltage Silicon Carbide Device Technology", IEEE Int. Electron Devices Meeting, pp. 19.1.1-19.3.4, 2018.

[2] T. Masuda, et al, "0.63 $m\Omega$-cm^2 / 1170 V 4H-SiC Super Junction V-Groove Trench MOSFET", IEEE Int. Electron Devices Meeting, pp. 8.1.1-8.1.4, 2018.

[3] Y. Kobayashi, et al, "High-temperature Performance of 1.2 kV-class SiC Super Junction MOSFET", IEEE Int. Symp. Power Semiconductor Devices and ICs, pp. 31-34, 2019.

[4] R. Kosugi, et al, "Breaking the Theoretical Limit of 6.5 kV-Class 4H-SiC Super-Junction (SJ) MOSFETs by Trench-Filling Epitaxial Growth", IEEE Int. Symp. Power Semiconductor Devices and ICs, pp. 39-42, 2019.

[5] R. Ghandhi, et al, "4.5kV SiC Charge-Balanced MOSFETs with Ultra-Low On-Resistance", IEEE Int. Symp. Power Semiconductor Devices and ICs, pp. 126-129, 2020.

[6] J. Knoll, et al, "Characterization of 4.5 kV Charge-Balanced SiC MOSFETs", IEEE Applied Power Electronics Conf., pp. 2217-2223, 2021.

[7] M. Sometani, et al, "Comparative Study of Performance of SiC SJMOSFETs Formed by Multi-epitaxial Growth and Trench-filling Epitaxial Growth", IEEE Int. Symp. Power Semiconductor Devices and ICs, pp. 337-340, 2022.

Chapter 15

Short Circuit Capability and BaSIC Topology

One major issue that can impede the commercialization of SiC power MOSFETs for motor drive applications in automotive and industrial settings is inadequate short-circuit withstand capability. This problem is encountered when the power transistor is in its on-state with full gate bias applied to deliver current and power to the motor winding from a DC link power supply. If the motor winding undergoes a short-circuit due to failure of its insulation, the transistor is directly connected across the DC power supply with full gate bias voltage applied to it. This pushes the SiC power MOSFET into its drain current saturation mode at a current level that is more than 10 times the on-state current level. The device must simultaneously support the large DC link voltage and the large saturated drain current. The device then undergoes adiabatic heating because the time is too small for removal of heat from the chip[1]. The surface temperature of the SiC MOSFET can rise very rapidly until the aluminum metallization melts at about 600 °C. This has been found to lead to failure of the device by penetration of the source metal through the inter-electrode dielectric[2].

15.1 Short Circuit Conditions

The applicable circuit under short-circuit conditions is illustrated in Fig. 15.1. The short circuit across the load is illustrated by the switch. This results in connecting the DC power source directly to the drain of the SiC power MOSFET while its on-state gate bias is still being applied. It would be desirable to detect the short circuit condition and turn-off the SiC MOSFET using feedback to the gate drive control circuit before the device undergoes destructive failure. The typical feedback loop can require about 10 µs to detect and respond to the occurrence of the short circuit conditions. For this reason, commercially available IGBTs for motor drive

457

applications are designed to withstand short circuit conditions for more than 10 μs, making this an expected performance specification for power transistors used in motor drive applications.

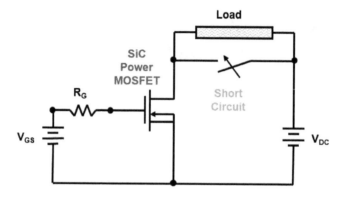

Fig. 15.1 Circuit illustrating short-circuit conditions for a SiC power MOSFET.

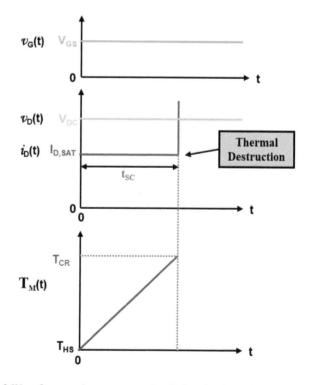

Fig. 15.2 Waveforms and temperature rise during the short-circuited condition.

The waveforms for the SiC power MOSFET gate voltage, drain current and drain voltage are shown in Fig. 15.2 during the short circuit conditions. The gate voltage remains at the on-state value and the drain voltage becomes equal to the DC supply voltage. The current flowing through the SiC power MOSFET becomes limited only by its drain saturation current due to the absence of the load impedance during short-circuit operation. The power being dissipated by the SiC power MOSFET structure per unit area (power density) during the short-circuit condition is therefore given by:

$$p_D = J_{D,SAT} V_{DC} \qquad [15.1]$$

where V_{DC} is the DC supply voltage and $J_{D,SAT}$ is the drain saturation current density determined by the gate bias voltage (V_G). The saturated drain current is determined by the basic power MOSFET cell design parameters:

$$J_{D,SAT} = \frac{\mu_{CH} C_{OX}}{L_{CH} W_{Cell}} (V_G - V_{TH})^2 \qquad [15.2]$$

where μ_{CH} is the channel mobility, C_{OX} is the specific gate oxide capacitance, L_{CH} is the channel length, W_{Cell} is the MOSFET cell width, and V_{TH} is the threshold voltage.

The short circuit duration before device failure is too small to allow removal of heat from the SiC device via the package and heat sink. The junction temperatures increases by adiabatic heating of the SiC volume where the power dissipation is occurring, which is the product of the active area and the drift layer thickness (t_D). The temperature rise is given by:

$$\Delta T(t) = \frac{p_D t}{t_D C_V} = \frac{J_{D,SAT} V_{DC} t}{t_D C_V} \qquad [15.3]$$

where C_V is the volumetric specific heat (2.4 J/cm^3-°K for 4H-SiC). Based on this expression, the temperature increases linearly as a function of time, as illustrated in Fig. 15.2, due to the constant power density during short-circuited operation. In practice, the saturated current does not remain constant during the short circuit as assumed in Fig. 15.2. The temperature rise produces a decrease in the saturation current during the short circuit event due to the reduction of channel mobility as the temperatures rises.

The destruction of the SiC power MOSFET occurs when a critical value (T_{CR}) is reached. One mechanism postulated for the destructive failure of the 4H-SiC power MOSFET is turn-on of the parasitic NPN transistor. In this case, the built-in potential of the source-base junction becomes close to zero at the critical temperature, which turns on the parasitic NPN bipolar transistor even though the N^+ emitter is shorted to the P-base at one edge. The device then undergoes a thermal run-away process leading to destructive failure. For 4H-SiC, the critical temperature is approximately 1100 $°K^2$ for this failure mode.

A second short-circuit failure mechanism that has been postulated is penetration of the source metallization through the junctions at the critical temperature. The Aluminum metallization on the SiC power MOSFET melts at about 600 °C. It can then penetrate through the Ti barrier over N^+ source region and eventually penetrate the source-base junction as well after about 3 μs^2.

The short-circuit withstand time for the SiC power MOSFET can be derived from Eq. [15.3]:

$$t_{SC} = \frac{(T_{CR} - T_{HS}) t_D C_V}{J_{D,SAT} V_{DC}}$$
[15.4]

where T_{HS} is the initial (heat-sink) temperature. From this expression, it can be concluded that the short-circuit withstand time will become smaller if the DC power supply voltage is increased.

The DC supply voltage (V_{DC}) is usually two-thirds of the blocking voltage rating for SiC power MOSFETs in the motor drive applications. It is also apparent that the drain saturated current density ($J_{D,SAT}$) is a critical parameter that determines the short-circuit capability. The gate bias voltage can be reduced to make the drain saturated current smaller but this increases the channel resistance and hence the on-resistance of the SiC power MOSFET. The dependence of the drain saturation current on cell design parameters is discussed in the next section.

15.2 Cell Design Dependence

The planar SiC power MOSFET structure is illustrated in Fig. 11.20 with various design parameters highlighted. Most of the dimensions (W_{P+}, W_{N+}, W_I, W_{OV}) are minimized within photolithographic tolerances to make the cell pitch p as small as possible. This maximizes the channel density to reduce the on-resistance contribution from the channel, one of the dominant components of the total specific on-resistance as shown in chapter 11. The specific channel resistance is given by:

$$R_{CH.sp} = \frac{L_{CH}p}{\mu_{CH}C_{OX}(V_G - V_{TH})} \qquad [15.5]$$

here p is the cell pitch ($W_{Cell}/2$). The channel resistance contribution can be reduced by decreasing the channel length and cell pitch; and by increasing the gate oxide capacitance by reducing the gate oxide thickness. From Eq. [15.2], the drain saturation current can be reduced by increasing the channel length and cell pitch; and by reducing the gate oxide capacitance by increasing the gate oxide thickness. Based up on this, it can be concluded that a trade-off between a decrease in drain saturation current to improve the short circuit withstand time and an increase in specific on-resistance is necessary for the SiC power MOSFET.

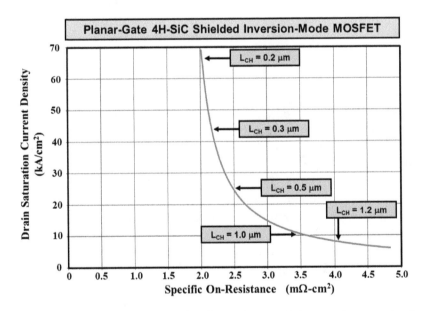

Fig. 15.3 SiC power MOSFET trade-off curve between drain saturation current and specific on-resistance: Channel length as parameter.

An example of the trade-off curve is shown in Fig. 15.3 for the case of a 1.2 kV inversion-channel 4H-SiC planar-gate power MOSFET when the channel length is varied. A channel mobility of 15 cm²/V-s was used in the analytical model with gate oxide thickness of 500 Å. It is worth pointing out that the cell pitch becomes larger with increasing channel length. For a typical channel length of 0.5 μm, the saturated current density is large (25,000 A/cm²), leading to measured short-circuit withstand time of 4.8 μs^3. Based up on Eq. [15.4], the short circuit withstand time can be made larger than 10 μs if the drain saturation current density is reduced to 12,000 A/cm^2. It can be concluded that a channel length of 1 μm will achieve this goal. This will produce an increase in the specific on-resistance from 2.5 to 3.5 mΩ-cm^2, an increase of 40 %.

The impact of adjusting the JFET region width (W_{JFET}) on the short-circuit withstand capability of 3.3 kV SiC planar-gate power MOSFETs has been studied[4]. A square cell topology was used with channel length of 1 μm and gate oxide thickness of 500 Å. The drain saturation current was reduced with increase in W_{JFET} due to smaller channel density resulting from an increase in cell width. The measured improvement in short-circuit withstand time was only 10 % with this approach.

15.3 Source Metallization

There is a rapid rise in the temperature at the upper surface of the SiC power MOSFET chip during the short-circuit event due to adiabatic heating. Some of this heat can be transferred to the source metallization due its proximity to the SiC upper surface. Changing the source metal could mitigate the rise in the temperature at the SiC surface prolonging the short-circuit failure point. The attachment of a 50 μm thick copper foil to the 4 μm thick Aluminum chip metallization by sintering with a 20 μm thick Silver/Nickel layer was performed on a commercial 1.2 kV SiC planar-gate power MOSFET chip[5]. Modelling of the short-circuit event indicated an increase in short-circuit withstand time from 2.2 to 2.8 μs. However, this was not experimentally confirmed. This approach adds to the complexity of device packaging which increases the device cost.

15.4 Gate Bias Dependence

The drain saturation current density can also be reduced by decreasing the gate bias voltage per Eq. [15.2]. A reduction of the gate bias voltage increases the channel resistance per Eq. [15.5], which will increase the total specific on-resistance of the MOSFET. Consequently, a trade-off between the reduction of drain saturation current density and increase in on-resistance becomes necessary. Reducing gate bias is also detrimental to the switching losses.

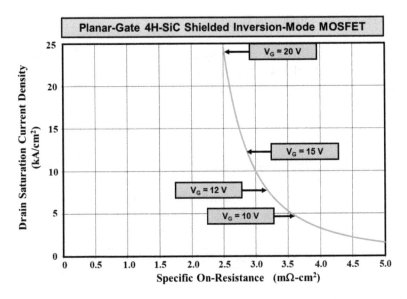

Fig. 15.4 SiC power MOSFET trade-off curve between drain saturation current and specific on-resistance: Gate bias as parameter.

Gate Bias (V)	On-Resistance (mΩ) (% Increase)	Peak Short-Circuit Current (A)	Short-Circuit Withstand Time (μS) (% Increase)
20	346	52	4.8
18	423 (22.3 %)	40	6.8 (41.7 %)
15	575 (66.2 %)	31	9.0 (87.5 %)

Table 15.1 Measured data on a typical commercial SiC power MOSFET.

The trade-off curve, between raising the short-circuit withstand time and an increase in the on-resistance obtained by reducing the gate drive voltage, has been experimentally evaluated with measurements on a typical 1.2 kV SiC planar-gate power MOSFET product (C2M0280120D[6]). A summary of the measured data is given in Table 15.1. The on-resistance was found to increase by 66.2 % when the gate bias is reduced from 20 to 15 V while the short-circuit withstand time increased by 87.5 %[7]. The switching losses increased by about 10 % when the gate bias was reduced from 20 to 15 V. Although this may be a convenient method to achieve a longer short-circuit time, it has a detrimental impact on the power losses and efficiency.

15.5 Gate Oxide Thickness Impact

The short-circuit withstand capability can also be improved by reduction of the gate oxide thickness. This can be understood by writing Eq. [15.5] in terms of the gate oxide thickness ($t_{G,OX}$):

$$R_{CH.sp} = \frac{t_{G,OX} L_{CH} p}{\mu_{CH} \epsilon_{OX} (V_G - V_{TH})} \qquad [15.6]$$

where ϵ_{OX} is the dielectric constant of the gate oxide. Based on this equation, the channel resistance remains the same if the gate oxide thickness is reduced by a factor ζ while also reducing the effective gate drive voltage ($V_G - V_{TH}$) by a factor ζ.

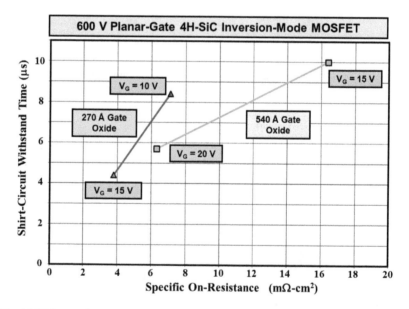

Fig. 15.5 Measured trade-off curves between short-circuit withstand time and specific on-resistance for 600 V 4H-SiC planar-gate power MOSFETs with two gate oxide thicknesses.

The drain saturation current density (Eq. [15.2]) can also be written in terms of the gate oxide thickness:

$$J_{D,SAT} = \frac{\mu_{CH} \epsilon_{OX}}{t_{G,OX} L_{CH} W_{Cell}} (V_G - V_{TH})^2 \qquad [15.2]$$

From this expression, the drain saturation current density will be reduced by a factor ζ if the gate oxide thickness and the effective gate drive voltage $(V_G - V_{TH})$ are both reduced by a factor ζ. Consequently, the specific on-state resistance of the SiC power MOSFET will remain the same, while the drain saturation current density will be reduced by a factor ζ allowing increasing the short circuit withstand time by a factor ζ.

This theoretical prediction was experimentally validated in 2020 after a three-year effort to design and fabricate 600 V SiC planar-gate power MOSFETs with gate oxide thicknesses of 270 and 540 Å[8]. The static and dynamic characteristics of these devices were discussed in chapter 11. The measured trade-off curve between short-circuit withstand time and specific on-resistance obtained by varying the gate bias is shown in Fig. 15.5. It can be observed that the curve for the 270 Å gate oxide case lies on the left side of the curve for the 540 Å gate oxide case; and it has a steeper slope. This demonstrates that the short-circuit withstand time can be increased using the thinner gate oxide with less increase in the specific on-resistance. For the 270 Å gate oxide case, the short-circuit withstand time was increased by a factor 2 times with an 84 % increase in specific on-resistance.

15.6 Embedded Series Resistance

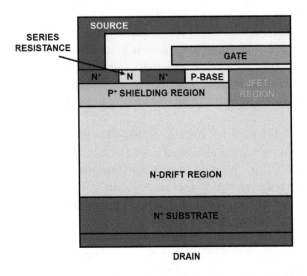

Fig. 15.6 4H-SiC planar-gate power MOSFET structure with embedded series resistance.

The drain saturation current of the SiC power MOSFET can be reduced by adding a resistance in series with the source region. The flow of short-circuit current through the series resistance produces a voltage drop than opposes the applied gate drive voltage to the SiC power MOSFET. The reduction of the gate-to-source voltage pulls down the drain saturation current to increase the short-circuit withstand time. The resistance can be embedded within the SiC planar-gate power MOSFET structure as illustrated in Fig. 15.6. This requires extra masking and ion-implantation steps. In addition, the cell window must be enlarged to accommodate the N-region that produces the series resistance. The specific on-resistance of the SiC power MOSFET is therefore increased with this approach. This idea has been experimentally demonstrated to show a 2-times increase in short-circuit withstand time with 40 % increase in the specific on-resistance[9].

15.7 Deep P-Well Structure

It has been demonstrated that the drain saturation current can be reduced by using a deep P-well (P$^+$ shielding region) structure[10]. This SiC planar-gate power MOSFET structure is similar to that shown in Fig. 11.4 with a P$^+$ region of twice the depth of the conventional structure. The formation of the deeper P$^+$ region was achieved by using much higher energy ion implantation of Al (350 keV) and B (960 keV) with a 4 degree tilt of the wafer to obtain channeling of the dopants. This produces a P$^+$ shielding region depth of 2.2 μm compared with 0.8 μm for the conventional device structure. The enhanced JFET region doping must also extend to the depth of the P$^+$ shielding region. This is accomplished by using phosphorus implantation rather than nitrogen used in the typical SiC power MOSFET process.

The fabricated 1.2 kV SiC planar-gate power MOSFET with the deep P$^+$ shielding region exhibited a short-circuit withstand time of 8 μs compared with 2 μs observed for the conventional structure. The specific on-resistance was reported to increase by only 3 %. This method produces excellent enhancement of the short-circuit withstand time within minimal impact on the on-resistance. However, the process used for the fabrication of the devices significantly departs from that used for conventional SiC planar-gate power MOSFETs due to high implant energies and tilted wafer orientation during the ion implantation.

15.8 The BaSIC Topology

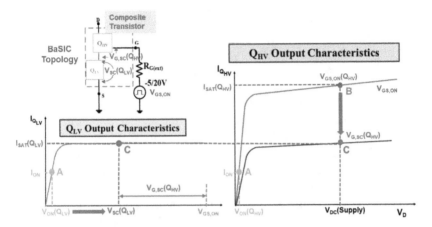

Fig. 15.7 The BaSIC topology for enhancing short-circuit withstand time.

An elegant approach to improve the short circuit withstand time for SiC power MOSFETs was proposed[11] by placing a *non-linear resistance* in series with the source electrode. A schematic diagram of the BaSIC topology is shown in Fig. 15.7 with the output characteristics of the non-linear resistor (called Q_{LV} in the figure) and the output characteristics of the SiC power MOSFET (called Q_{HV} in the figure). The non-linear resistance is chosen with a low resistance value at the on-state current level of the SiC power MOSFET. The non-linear resistance increases in value with increasing current level eventually producing current saturation. The saturation current of the non-linear resistance is chosen to be smaller than the drain current saturation current of the SiC power MOSFET at the on-state gate drive voltage. Note that the non-linear resistor operates within the gate drive loop of the SiC power MOSFET. Consequently, it does not experience any high voltages during operation of the BaSIC topology.

The green dots (A) show the operating points for Q_{LV} and Q_{HV} during the normal on-state conditions with the full gate drive voltage applied. The gate drive voltage is typically 20 V for the case of SiC power MOSFETs. The scales for the voltage axis for the two devices are quite different. It extends to 1000 V for the typical 1.2 kV SiC power MOSFET as Q_{HV}. The scale for Q_{LV} extends to only 25 V. During on-state operation, the voltage drop across both Q_{LV} and Q_{HV} are small due to their low resistances as shown in their characteristics. This ensures that the normal on-state and switching behavior of the SiC power MOSFET is not compromised by the BaSIC topology.

During the short-circuit event, the drain supply voltage (V_{DC}(Supply)) is applied directly across the composite transistor consisting of both devices Q_{LV} and Q_{HV}. In the absence of Q_{LV}, the current in the SiC power MOSFET (Q_{HV}) will increase to $I_{SAT}(Q_{HV})$ at the blue operating point (B) as shown in the figure. This current is typically more than 10 times the on-state value. This results in the observed small short-circuit withstand time for the SiC power MOSFET as discussed earlier. However, in the presence of Q_{LV}, the current will be limited to $I_{SAT}(Q_{LV})$ at the red operating point (C) as shown in the figure. The voltage across Q_{LV} will rise to $V_{SC}(Q_{LV})$ during the short-circuit event. This voltage opposes the gate drive voltage in the gate loop which reduces the gate-to-source voltage of the SiC power MOSFET to $V_{G,SC}(Q_{HV})$ as shown by the red arrow in the figure. The drain saturation current for the SiC power MOSFET will be reduced by the smaller value of $V_{G,SC}(Q_{HV})$ compared with the gate drive voltage $V_{G,ON}$. This is shown on the output characteristics of Q_{HV} on the right hand side as operating point C. An important feature of the BaSIC topology is that the value for $V_{SC}(Q_{LV})$ *automatically adjusts* until the saturation current of the SiC power MOSFET matches the saturation current of $I_{SAT}(Q_{LV})$ of Q_{LV}. The smaller value of the SiC power MOSFET drain saturation current at operating point C will increase the short-circuit withstand time by the ratio of $I_{SAT}(Q_{HV})$ and $I_{SAT}(Q_{LV})$.

The BaSIC topology can be applied to any high voltage switch (Q_{HV}) technology, including Si IGBTs, SiC power MOSFETs, and GaN HEMT devices. The non-linear resistance can be created using a low blocking voltage JFET, MOSFET or MESFET structure made of various semiconductors. It is important to point out that the gate voltage for switching the composite transistor in the BaSIC topology is applied to the SiC power MOSFET (Q_{HV}) in the same manner as for the stand alone device. The BaSIC topology has been experimentally validated for Si IGBTs[12], SiC power MOSFETs[13] and GaN HEMT devices[14]. This section describes the results obtained for commercially available SiC power MOSFETs.

15.8.1 The BaSIC(DMM) Topology

Experimental demonstration of the BaSIC topology was first achieved by using a Si Gate-Source-Shorted (GSS) Depletion-Mode-MOSFET (DMM) as the non-linear resistance[3]. Most of the Si power MOSFET are manufactured as enhancement-mode devices with a positive threshold voltage due to compatibility with power electronics applications. A depletion-mode MOSFET has a negative threshold voltage with normally-on characteristics that is the desired behavior for the non-linear resistor in the BaSIC toplogy. A 100 V, 16 A n-channel Si Depletion-Mode MOSFET (IXTH16N10D2[15]) was found to be most suitable commercially available device. It has an on-resistance of 60 mΩ. This device has a measured breakdown voltage of 150 V, which is far larger than need in this topology because the maximum voltage in the gate loop is less than 30 V. Significantly improved performance is projected for optimized Si GSS DMM devices with lower blocking voltages as discussed later in the chapter.

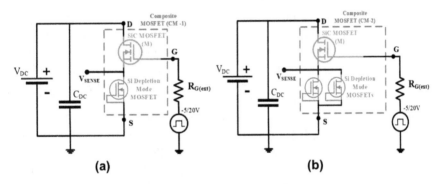

Fig. 15.8 The BaSIC topology implemented using Si Gate-Source-Shorted Depletion-Mode-MOSFETs: (a) single Si DMM; (b) two Si DMMs in parallel.

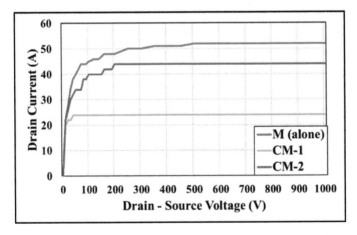

Fig. 15.9 High voltage output characteristics of composite and stand-alone transistors obtained using the SC test setup.

The BaSIC(DMM) topology was implemented as shown in Fig. 15.8 using the Si GSS-DMM to create the composite MOSFET (CM) with a 280 mΩ (typical value) commercial 1.2 kV SiC planar-gate power MOSFET (C2M0280120D[6]). The measured on-resistance of the stand-alone SiC power MOSFET was 346 mΩ, which is within the 30 % larger maximum value in the datasheet. Two cases were evaluated: single GSS DMM (CM-1) and two GSS DMMs in parallel (CM-2) as shown in Fig. 15.8. This allowed adjusting the series resistance of the non-linear resistance and its saturated current level. The measured on-resistance of CM-1 and CM-2 were 405 and 381 mΩ.

The peak current during the short-circuit (SC) event is determined by the saturated drain current of the power device at the DC supply voltage. The output characteristics of commercial devices are not provided at such high voltages to determine the correct drain saturated current. They can be measured by using the SC test-up with short (1.5 μs wide) pulses to prevent destructive failure. The results obtained for the stand-alone MOSFET are shown in Fig. 15.9 (red line) with a saturated drain current of 52 A. In the case of the composite transistor with one GSS DMM device, the saturated drain current is reduced to 24 A. This value corresponds to the saturated current of the Si GSS DMM ($V_G = 0$ curve) in the datasheet, shown in Fig. 15.10 by the purple operating point. The drain voltage at the Si GSS DMM device is only 7-8 V because this value reduces the drain saturation current of the SiC power MOSFET to 24 A. The saturated drain current for the composite MOSFET CM-2 with two

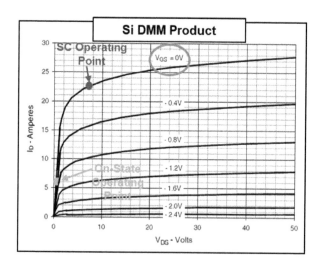

Fig. 15.10 Output characteristics of the Si DMM product.

GSS DMM devices in parallel is 46 A, which is about twice the value for a single device.

The short-circuit waveforms for the three devices are shown in Fig. 15.11. The drain supply voltage is kept at 800 V (black line) with a gate bias of 20 V for all cases. The peak short circuit current values are indicated in the figure. The short circuit withstand time increases from 4.8 μs for the standalone device to 5.3 μs for CM-2 and 7.9 μs for CM-1. A 65 % increase in t_{SC} is achieved with 17 % increase in the on-resistance.

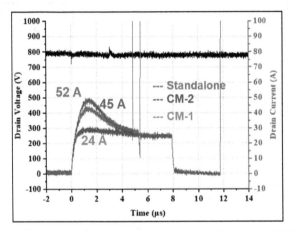

Fig. 15.11 Short-circuit waveforms for the stand alone SiC power MOSFET and the two composite transistors.

The switching losses were also measured for the three cases using the double-pulse method with a supply voltage of 800 V and drain current of 6 A. The total energy loss per cycle was found to increase from 203 mJ for the stand alone SiC MOSFET to 225 mJ for CM-2 and 243 mJ for CM-1. A 65 % increase in t_{SC} is therefore observed with 20 % increase in the total energy loss per cycle. The trade-off between increasing the short circuit time and increase in on-resistance and switching loss can be significantly improved by optimization of the Si GSS DMM device as shown in the next section.

15.8.2 Optimization of Si GSS DMM Device

The Si Gate-Source-Shorted Depletion-Mode-MOSFET used in the previous section was a planar-gate structure with a 100 V rating (measured breakdown voltage of 150 V), which is far larger than required in the BaSIC(DMM) topology. Significant improvement in performance of the

BaSIC(DMM) topology can be achieved by making structural changes to the Si DMM device[16].

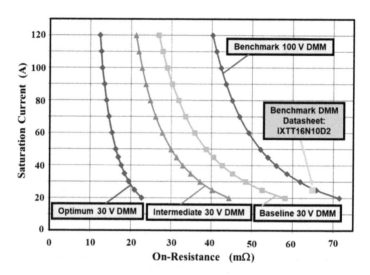

Fig. 15.12 Trade-off curves obtained between saturation current and on-resistance for the D-MOS planar-gate Si GSS-DMM devices with various designs.

Progressively better trade-off curve between drain saturation current and the on-resistance of devices with 0.1 cm^2 active area are shown in Fig. 15.12 for the case of the planar-gate (D-MOS) DMM devices. These curves were obtained by varying the threshold voltage (negative for a DMM device). The purple line shows the case of the benchmark commercial device modelled with a channel length of 1 μm and gate oxide thickness of 500 Å. The baseline Si DMM (green line) has a reduced breakdown voltage of 30 V with same channel length and gate oxide thickness. Achieving a saturation current of 50 A is used here as an example because it allows obtaining a short-circuit time of 10 μs for a particular commercially available SiC power MOSFET as discussed later.

A saturation current of 50 A is obtained for the baseline GSS-DMM D-MOS device with an on-resistance of 39 mΩ compared with 52 mΩ for the 100 V benchmark device. The intermediate Si DMM (blue line) has a breakdown voltage of 30 V with a reduced channel length of 0.3 μm and gate oxide thickness 500 Å. A saturation current of 50 A is obtained for the intermediate GSS-DMM D-MOS device with an on-resistance of 30 mΩ compared with 52 mΩ for the 100 V benchmark device. The optimum Si DMM (red line) has a breakdown voltage of 30 V with a reduced channel length of 0.3 μm and gate oxide thickness 100 Å. A saturation current of 50 A is obtained for the intermediate GSS-DMM D-MOS device with an on-resistance of 16 mΩ compared with 52 mΩ for the 100 V benchmark device. The small gate oxide thickness of 100 Å is acceptable for the Si GSS-DMM device because it operates with gate shorted to the source. There is no gate bias applied that could stress the gate oxide for this device.

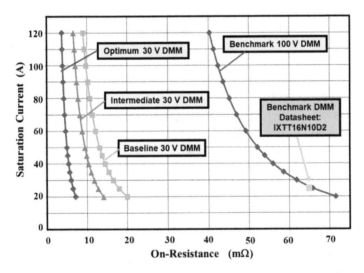

Fig. 15.13 Trade-off curves obtained between saturation current and on-resistance for the U-MOS planar-gate Si GSS-DMM devices with various designs.

A similar analysis can be performed for trench-gate (U-MOS) Si GSS DMM devices. The baseline Si DMM (green line) has a reduced breakdown voltage of 30 V with channel length of 1 μm and gate oxide thickness of 500 Å. A saturation current of 50 A is obtained for the baseline GSS-DMM U-MOS device with an on-resistance of 13 mΩ compared with 52 mΩ for the 100 V benchmark device. The intermediate Si DMM (blue line) has a breakdown voltage of 30 V with a reduced channel length of 0.3 μm and gate oxide thickness 500 Å. A saturation current of 50 A is obtained for the intermediate GSS-DMM U-MOS device with an on-resistance of 10 mΩ compared with 52 mΩ for the 100 V benchmark device. The optimum Si DMM (red line) has a breakdown voltage of 30 V with a reduced channel length of 0.3 μm and gate oxide thickness 100 Å. A saturation current of 50 A is obtained for the intermediate GSS-DMM U-MOS device with an on-resistance of 5 mΩ compared with 52 mΩ for the 100 V benchmark device. The small gate oxide thickness of 100 Å is acceptable for the Si GSS-DMM device because it operates with gate shorted to the source. There is no gate bias applied that could stress the gate oxide for this device. It can be concluded from this analysis that much better trade-off curves can be attained using the U-MOS structure.

The impact of these improved Si GSS DMM devices was evaluated for two commercially available 1.2 kV SiC power MOSFETs with typical on-resistances of 280 mΩ (C2M0280120D) and 160 mΩ (C2M0160120D). The measured trade-off curve between the short-circuit withstand time and drain saturation current for these device obtained by changing the gate bias is shown in Fig. 15.14. The short-circuit withstand time varies inversely with the magnitude of the drain saturation current as expected from Eq. [15.4]. From these curves, it can be concluded that the desirable short-circuit withstand time of 10 μs can be obtained with a drain saturation current of 50 A for the 160 mΩ product and a drain saturation current of 23 A for the 280 mΩ product.

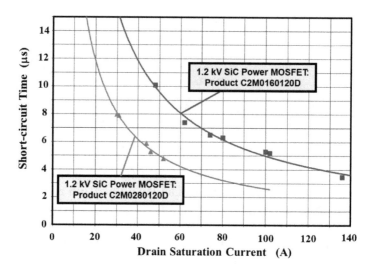

Fig. 15.14 Measured trade-off curves between short-circuit withstand time and drain saturation current for the 1.2 kV SiC power MOSFET C2M0280120D and C2M0160120D products.

The information in Fig. 15.13 and Fig. 15.14 can be combined to generate the trade-off curves for short-circuit withstand time and increase in on-resistance with the U-MOS Si GSS DMM devices as shown in Fig.

15.15 for the 280 mΩ SiC power MOSFET. The 4.8 μs short-circuit withstand time for the stand alone SiC MOSFET is shown on the left hand axis. The measured short circuit withstand time of 7.9 μs with the available Si DMM device is also shown with a 17 % increase in on-resistance. From the graph for the optimum U-MOS DMM device (red line), it can be concluded that it is possible to achieve a 10 μs short-circuit withstand time with only 2 % increase in the on-resistance. This increase in on-resistance falls well below the spread in on-resistance in manufacturer's datasheets.

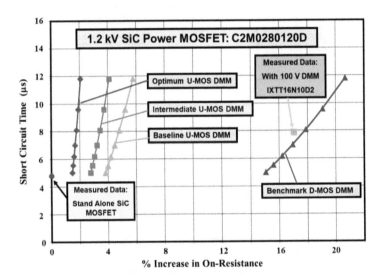

Fig. 15.15 Trade-off curves between short-circuit time and increase in on-resistance for the 1.2 kV SiC power MOSFET C2M0280120D with various cases of the Si GSS-DMM U-MOS devices.

The information in Fig. 15.13 and Fig. 15.14 can also be combined to generate the trade-off curves for short-circuit withstand time and increase in on-resistance with the U-MOS Si GSS DMM devices as shown in Fig. 15.16 for the 160 mΩ SiC power MOSFET. The 3.5 μs short-circuit withstand time for the stand alone SiC MOSFET is shown on the left hand axis. From the graph for the optimum U-MOS DMM device (red line), it is possible to achieve a 10 μs short-circuit withstand time with only 3 % increase in the on-resistance.

These results provide motivation for manufacturing the optimum Si DMM structure by the industry to serve the large future market for SiC power MOSFETs in electric vehicles. These devices can be co-packaged with the SiC power MOSFETs to provide a three terminal switch.

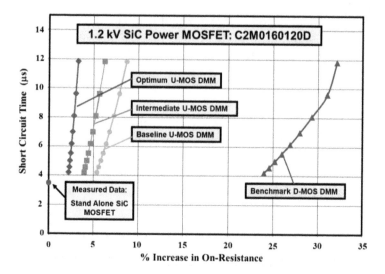

Fig. 15.16 Trade-off curves between short-circuit time and increase in on-resistance for the 1.2 kV SiC power MOSFET C2M0160120D with various cases of the Si GSS U-MOS devices.

15.8.3 The BaSIC(EMM) Topology

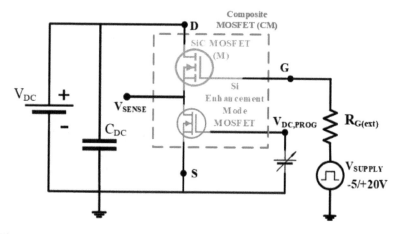

Fig. 15.17 The BaSIC topology implemented using Si Enhancement-Mode-MOSFET with DC gate bias.

As discussed in the previous sections, very few Si depletion-mode-MOSFET devices are commercially available. In contrast, a large number of Si enhancement-mode-MOSFETs (EMMs) are manufactured by the industry with various ratings. These Si EMM devices are also candidates for the non-linear resistor in the BaSIC topology if a DC gate bias is applied to the device to *program* the saturation current as desired for the power electronic application. The BaSIC(EMM) topology is illustrated in Fig. 15.17. It is worth emphasizing that the composite MOSFET formed using the SiC power MOSFET and the Si EMM device is controlled by the gate bias applied to the SiC power MOSFET and not the Si device. The voltage applied to the Si EMM device is held constant at $V_{DC,PROG}$ during power circuit operation. The power electronics engineer can program the value for $V_{DC,PROG}$ to tailor the BaSIC(EMM) topology to achieve the desired short circuit time.

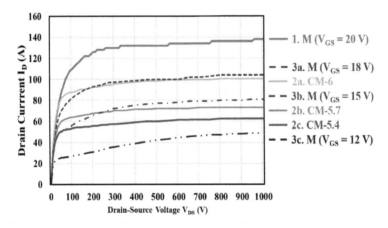

Fig. 15.18 High voltage output characteristics measured for the composite MOSFET in the BaSIC(EMM) topology with three DC gate bias voltages applied to the Si EMM device.

Experimental demonstration of the BaSIC(EMM) topology was first reported with the commercially available 160 mΩ 1.2-kV SiC power MOSFET (Wolfspeed C2M0160120D) and the 40-V Si enhancement mode (EMM) MOSFET (Infineon IPI70N04S4)[17]. The high voltage output characteristics measured for the composite MOSFET is shown in Fig. 15.18 with three values (5.4, 5.7, and 6.0 V) of the DC gate bias applied to the Si EMM device. It can be seen that the drain saturation current can be reduced by changing the DC gate bias applied to the Si DMM device. For comparison, the output characteristics measured with various gate bias voltages applied to the SiC power MOSFET are also shown in the figure. As expected, the drain saturation current becomes smaller when the gate drive voltage is reduced.

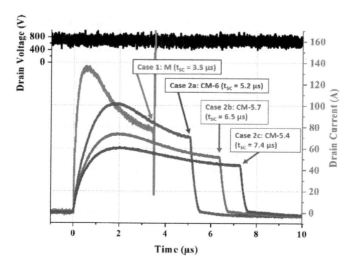

Fig. 15.19 Short-circuit waveforms for the stand alone SiC power MOSFET and the composite MOSFET in the BaSIC(EMM) topology with three DC gate bias voltages applied to the Si EMM device.

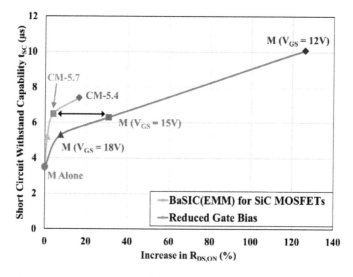

Fig. 15.20 Trade-off curves between short circuit withstand time and increase in on-resistance for the BaSIC(EMM) topology compared to that obtained by reducing the gate bias applied to the SiC power MOSFET.

The measured short-circuit waveforms for the composite transistor in the BaSIC(EMM) topology are shown in Fig. 15.19. The peak short-circuit is reduced with smaller DC gate bias applied to the Si EMM consistent with the output characteristics. This allows increasing the short circuit withstand time from 3.5 μs for the stand alone SiC power MOSFET to 7.4 μs at a DC gate bias of 5.4 V applied to the Si EMM device.

The on-resistances of the Si EMM device and the SiC power MOSFET increase when the gate bias is reduced. The improvement in short circuit withstand time must be traded-off with an increase in on-resistance. The trade-off curves for the two cases can be compared in Fig. 15.20. It can be seen that the short circuit withstand time can be increased from 3.5 μs to 6.5 μs with the BaSIC(EMM) topology with a 4 % increase in on-resistance. The same improvement is obtained when reducing the gate drive voltage applied to the SiC power MOSFET with an increase in on-resistance by 31 %. Consequently, the BaSIC(EMM) topology is a much better option for improving the short circuit withstand time for SiC power MOSFETs.

15.8.4 Selection Methodology for Si EMM Devices

A methodology has been created for selection of the Si EMM device to achieve the best trade-off between short-circuit withstand time enhancement and increase in on-resistance[18]. The Si EMM selection methodology consists of the following steps:

(1) Determine the peak short-circuit current for the SiC power MOSFET ($I_{P,SC}(SiC)$) that allows it to withstand a short-circuit of 10 μs in duration by adjusting its gate drive voltage;

(2) Determine the values for the on-resistance for Si EMM devices at 25 °C from their datasheets at various gate bias voltages. Room temperature on-resistance for the Si EMM device is satisfactory because it undergoes minimal heating during on-state operation due to its small drain voltage;

(3) Determine the values for the drain saturation currents for Si EMM devices at 150 °C (or 175 °C) from their datasheets at various gate bias voltages. The Si EMM device temperature rises during the short-circuit event due to the large current and a higher drain voltage. This raises its temperature to the 150 – 175 °C range;

(4) Prepare a trade-off curve of the drain saturation current at 150 °C (or 175 °C) versus the on-resistance at 25 °C for each Si EMM device using the gate bias as a parametric variable;

(5) Determine the on-resistance for each Si EMM at 25 °C corresponding to the saturation current that matches the $I_{P,SC}(SiC)$ determined in step (1);

(6) Select the Si EMM that produces a drain saturation current at 150 °C (or 175 °C) of $I_{P,SC}(SiC)$ that was determined in step (1) with the smallest on-resistance at 25 °C;

(7) Determine the DC gate bias for the selected Si EMM corresponding to the above operating point.

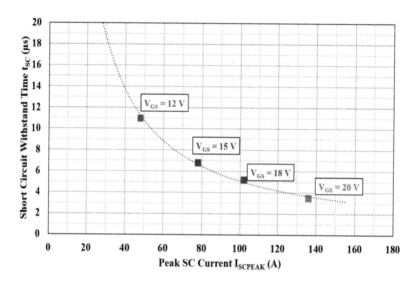

Fig. 15.21 Short-circuit withstand time for the 1.2 kV 160 mΩ SiC power MOSFET product versus the peak short-circuit current.

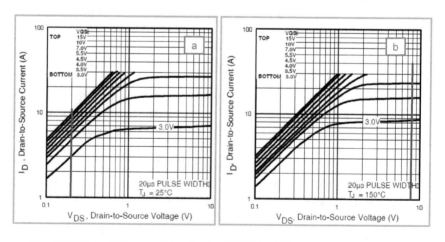

Fig. 15.22 Output Characteristics for the 30 V 23 mΩ Si power MOSFET product IRF7313 with different gate bias voltages: (a) 25 °C; (b) 150 °C

The procedure is illustrated for the case of a SiC power MOSFET product (Wolfspeed C2M0160120D) in this section as an example. Following step (1) of the methodology, its measured short-circuit withstand time is plotted in Fig. 15.21 versus the measured peak short-circuit current as obtained by varying the gate bias. There is an inversely proportional relationship between these values as expected from Eq. [15.4]. It can be concluded that a t_{SC} of 10 µs is achievable for this device if the $I_{P,SC}$ (or I_{SCPEAK}) is reduced to 50 A.

The output characteristics of Si MOSFETs is provided in IRF datasheets. An example is shown in Fig. 15.22 for the IRF7313 product. The on-resistance at 25 °C can be obtained at various gate bias voltages by extracting the drain current at V_{DS} = 0.2 V along the red line in Fig. 15.22(a). The saturated drain current at 150 °C can be extracted at V_{DS} = 8 V for various gate bias voltages along the red line in Fig. 15.22(b). This is the typical drain bias point for the Si EMM under short-circuit conditions. The drain saturation current for the IRF7313 product is observed to decrease by 13 % for a fixed gate bias (e.g. 4.0 V) when the temperature increases from 25 °C to 150 °C. This is a desirable behavior for the Si EMM because it will extend the short-circuit withstand time. This feature is another selection criterion for the Si EMM.

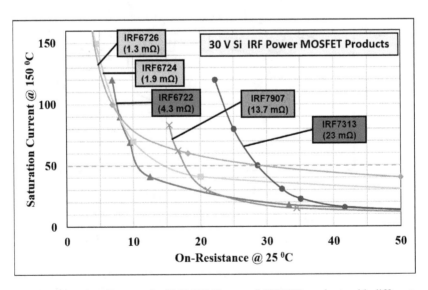

Fig. 15.23 Trade-off curves for 30 V IRF Si power MOSFET products with different on-resistance values using saturation current given at 150 °C in their datasheets.

The extracted data can be combined to produce the trade-off curve for the IRF7313 device as shown in Fig. 15.23 by the purple line. It is found that the on-resistance for this device is 28 mΩ for a drain saturation current of 50 A, indicated by the green dashed line in Fig. 15.23. The on-resistance for the composite MOSFET in the BaSIC(EMM) topology will increase by 17 % over the 168 mΩ value measured for the 1.2 kV SiC power MOSFET product at a gate bias of 20 V. This procedure must be repeated for other available Si EMM products as shown in Fig. 15.23. Among the examined devices, the IRF6722 product had the lowest on-resistance of 10 mΩ which will increase the on-resistance for the composite MOSFET by only 6 % over the standalone 1.2 kV SiC power MOSFET product. It may seem intuitively that Si EMM devices with the lowest on-resistance in the datasheet may be the best choice for the BaSIC(EMM) topology. However, the plots in Fig. 15.23 show that the Si EMM devices with the lowest on-resistance in the datasheet (e.g. IRF6726 product) do not necessarily have the best trade-off curve.

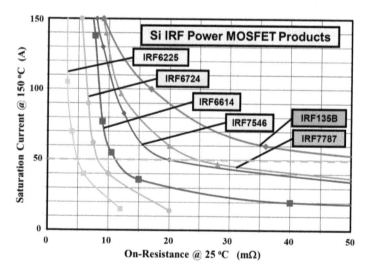

Fig. 15.24 Trade-off curves for IRF Si power MOSFET products with different blocking voltages using saturation current given at either 150 °C or 175 °C.

The trade-off curve between drain saturation current and on-resistance can also be created from information the datasheet of IRF products with various blocking voltage ratings as shown in Fig. 15.24. In this case, there is clear trend with better trade-off curves for devices with lower blocking voltage capability. The best identified device is IRF6225 with a blocking voltage of 20 V which is adequate for the BaSIC(EMM) topology because the device experiences less than 10 V during the short-circuit event. The IRF6225 product has an on-resistance of 5 mΩ which will increase the on-resistance for the composite MOSFET by only 3 % over the standalone 1.2 kV SiC power MOSFET product. This conclusion was validated with short-circuit tests on a composite MOSFET using the IRF6225 device for the Wolfspeed C2M0160120D SiC power MOSFET. The short-circuit waveform in Fig. 15.25 demonstrates a short-circuit withstand time of 11 μs *without failure.*

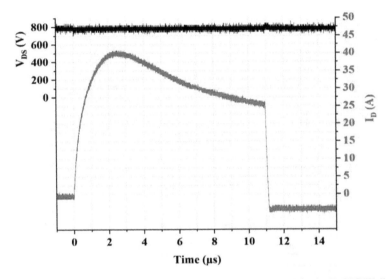

Fig. 15.25 Short-circuit waveforms for the composite MOSFET in the BaSIC(EMM) topology using the IRF6225 product as the Si EMM device.

15.8.5 Current Sensing Capability

The Si DMM and EMM devices operate in their linear-mode during the normal on-state operation of the SiC power MOSFET. The potential at the drain of the Si MOSFET is then proportional to the current flowing in the SiC power MOSFET. The drain terminal of the Si MOSFET can therefore be used as a sense node for the current.

An example of the ability to sense the current flowing through the SiC power MOSFET is shown in Fig. 15.26 by using results from a double-pulse test[19]. When the drain current of the SiC MOSFET ramps up to 6 A, the sense node voltage ramps up to 0.36 V because the Si DMM has a resistance of 60 mΩ. This current sensing capability is an inherent feature of the BaSIC topology eliminating the need for additional current monitoring approaches such as Rogowski coils.

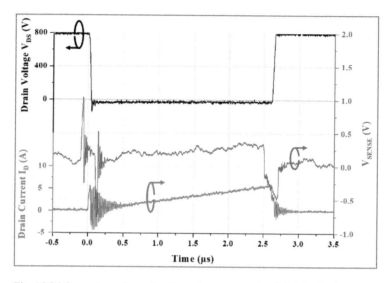

Fig. 15.26 Current sensing using the voltage across the Si DMM device in the BaSIC topology.

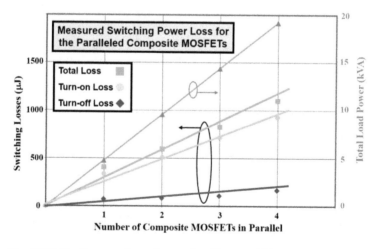

Fig. 15.27 The linear scaling of power handling capability for the Composite MOSFETs in the BaSIC(DMM) topology.

The ability to sense the current flowing in the composite transistor is a useful feature when paralleling the devices[20]. The power handling capability was found to increase linearly with more composite MOSFETs connected in parallel as shown in Fig. 15.27. The switching losses (E_{ON}, E_{OFF}, and E_{TOTAL}) scaled linearly with the output power as well.

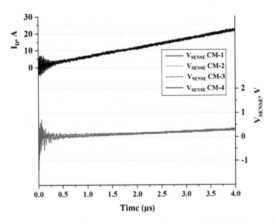

Fig. 15.28 Equal distribution of current among the 4 paralleled Composite MOSFETs in the BaSIC(DMM) topology.

The current distribution among 4 paralleled composite MOSFET could be monitored using the sense node voltage for each composite MOSFET. The current flowing through all 4 devices was found to be identical as shown in Fig. 15.28 by the overlapping sense node voltage waveforms. This confirmed excellent paralleling capability of these composite transistors.

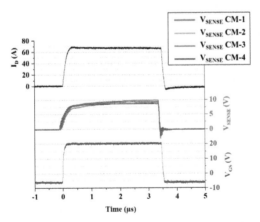

Fig. 15.29 Equal values for the sense node voltage for the 4 paralleled Composite MOSFETs in the BaSIC(DMM) topology during the short-circuit event.

Equal current sharing between the 4 paralleled composite MOSFETs is also important during the short-circuit event. This is evident from the very similar sense node voltage waveforms for the 4 paralleled composite MOSFETs shown in Fig. 15.29 under short-circuit conditions.

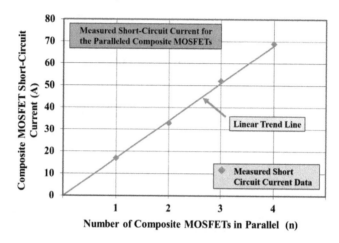

Fig. 15.30 Linear scaling of the short-circuit current for the paralleled Composite MOSFETs in the BaSIC(DMM) topology.

The measured short-circuit current with more composite MOSFETs connected in parallel is shown in Fig. 15.30. The linear increase in the total short-circuit current with number of devices connected in parallel indicates that all the devices are sharing current equally even during the short-circuit event.

15.8.6 DESAT Protection

The short-circuit protection of Si IGBTs is performed using the DESAT circuit, shown in Fig. 15.31, which monitors the collector potential of the device (V_{DCP}). This potential increases above the on-state voltage drop during the short-circuit event due to the larger current level. However, the drain potential undergoes a large change to the DC supply voltage during each switching event. The DESAT circuit must be isolated from this high voltage by using a high voltage diode (SMA STTH112A). A blanking time is also required that extends the time required to detect the short circuit and shut off the gate voltage to protect the Si IGBT. Although the same circuit can be used for SiC power MOSFETs, their smaller (~ 3 μs) short-circuit withstand time is problematic. In addition, the voltage blocking capability of the isolation diode must be increased to match that of the power device. This can become an issue when moving to SiC power MOSFET with more than 5 kV ratings. The reverse recovery time for the blocking diode can become a limiting factor as well.

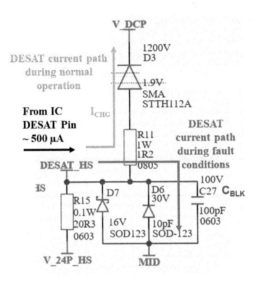

Fig. 15.31 DESAT circuit used for Si IGBT short-circuit protection.

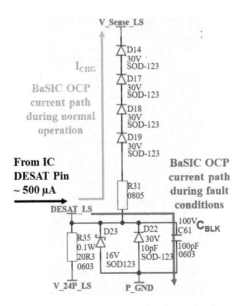

Fig. 15.32 BaSIC OCP circuit used for short-circuit protection.

Over current protection (OCP) can be achieved using the BaSIC topology by using the sense node voltage. This node operates at voltages below 10 volts which eliminates the need for the high voltage isolation diode. The voltage from the sense node ($V_{SENSE-LS}$) can be fed to the conventional DESAT circuit as shown in Fig. 15.32 making it convenient to use this existing technology for Si IGBTs. When the short-circuit occurs, the potential V_{DCP} and $V_{SENSE-LS}$ in the two cases rises to about 6-9 V. This diverts the current I_{CHG} from the green path to the red path. This starts charging the blanking capacitor C_{BLK} until its voltage is sufficient to trigger shutting down the gate drive voltage.

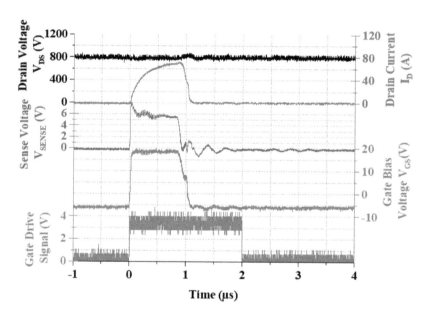

Fig. 15.33 BaSIC OCP circuit waveforms during short-circuit protection.

The waveforms observed during OCP with the BaSIC topology are shown in Fig. 15.33 with a Si EMM device and a SiC power MOSFET. There is an instantaneous rise in the sense node voltage to 6 V, which starts charging the blanking capacitor immediately. The gate drive is shut-off in just 0.85 μs protecting the SiC power MOSFET. This limits the maximum current in the SiC power MOSFET during the short-circuit which is beneficial to keeping its temperature below the melting point of aluminum. This is important to achieving repetitive short-circuit withstand capability of SiC power MOSFETs.

15.9 Summary

The short-circuit withstand capability of SiC power MOSFETs is a critical parameter for many applications, particularly motor drives for electric vehicles. Standalone SiC power MOSFET products are optimized to achieve minimum on-resistance which results in short-circuit withstand capability well below the 10 μs value typically delivered by Si IGBT products. The short-circuit withstand time for SiC power MOSFETs can be increased by alterations to the cell structure. This produces significant (30 - 40 %) increase in the specific on-resistance.

The BaSIC topology has been demonstrated to enhance the short-circuit withstand time by employing a non-linear resistor in series with the SiC power MOSFET source electrode. The most convenient and least expensive implementation of this topology is by using either a Gate-Source-Shorted Depletion-Mode-MOSFET or an Enhancement-Mode-MOSFET with DC gate bias. It has been shown that the short-circuit time can be increased to 10 μs by using the Si GSS-DMM device optimized for this application with only 3 % increase in the on-resistance. A methodology for selection of the Si EMM device has also been developed that allows achieving a short-circuit withstand time of over 10 μs with only 3 % increase in the on-resistance. This approach can be used by power electronics designers to optimize their circuit operation by programming the DC bias applied to the gate of the Si EMM device.

The Si GSS-DMM can be co-packaged with the SiC power MOSFET to create a three-terminal composite transistor. An additional sense terminal at the drain of the Si GSS-DMM device allows monitoring current flowing in the SiC power MOSFET and detecting the short-circuit event. This approach can be used to monitor the current in each individual SiC power MOSFET chip within a module as well.

References

[1] B. J. Baliga, "Fundamentals of Power Semiconductor Devices", Second Edition, Springer-Science, 2019.

[2] K. Han, A. Kanale, B. J. Baliga, B. Ballard, A. Morgan, and D. C. Hopkins, "New Short Circuit Failure Mechanism for 1.2kV 4H-SiC MOSFETs and JBSFETs", IEEE Wide Bandgap Power Devices and Applications Conf., pp. 108-113, 2018.

[3] A. Kanale and B. J. Baliga, "Enhancing Short Circuit Capability of 1.2 kV SiC Power MOSFETs using a Gate-Source Shorted Si Depletion-Mode MOSFET in Series with the Source", IEEE Int. Conf. on Power Electronics and Drive Systems, Paper 827, pp. 1-6, 2019.

[4] X. Chen, et al, "Different JFET Designs on Conduction and Short-Circuit Capability for 3.3 kV Planar-Gate Silicon Carbide MOSFETs", IEEE Journal of Electron Devices Society, Vol. 8, pp. 841-845, 2020.

[5] H. Du and F. Iannuzzo, "A Mitigation Strategy for the Short-Circuit Degradation in SiC MOSFETs", IEEE Workshop on Wide Bandgap Power Devices and Applications in Asia (WiPDA Asia), pp. 1-4, 2020.

[6] Wolfspeed product page: https://www.wolfspeed.com/c2m0280120d.

[7] A. Kanale and B. J. Baliga, "Comparison of Current Suppression Methods to Enhance Short Circuit Capability of 1.2 kV SiC Power MOSFETs: A New Approach using a Series-connected, Gate-Source-Shorted Si Depletion-Mode MOSFET vs Reduced Gate Bias Operation", IEEE Industrial Electronics Conf., pp. 5114-5119, 2019.

[8] A. Agarwal, A. Kanale, K. Han, and B. J. Baliga, "Switching and Short-Circuit Performance of 27 nm Gate Oxide, 650 V SiC Planar-Gate MOSFETs with 10 to 15 V Gate Drive Voltage", IEEE Int. Symp. Power Semiconductor Devices and ICs, pp. 250-253, 2020.

[9] H. Hatta, T. Tominaga, S. Hino, N. Miura, S. Tomohisa and Y. Yamakawa, "Suppression of short-circuit current with embedded source resistance in SiC-MOSFET", Materials Science Forum, Vol. 924, pp. 727-730, 2018.

[10] D. Kim and W. Sung, "Improved Short-Circuit Ruggedness for 1.2 kV 4H-SiC MOSFET using a Deep P-Well Implemented by Channeling Implantation", IEEE Electron Device Letters, Vol. 42, pp. 1822-1825, 2021.

[11] B. J. Baliga, U.S. Patent Application Filed and Pending Office Action, 2019.

[12] A. Kanale and B. J. Baliga, "Enhancing Short Circuit Capability of 1.2-kV Si IGBT Using a Gate-Source Shorted Si Depletion Mode MOSFET in Series with the Emitter", IEEE Tran. Power Electronics, Vol. 35, pp. 6350-6361, 2020.

[13] A. Kanale and B. J. Baliga, "Enhancing Short Circuit Capability of 1.2 kV SiC Power MOSFETs using a Gate-Source Shorted Si Depletion-Mode MOSFET in Series with the Source", IEEE Int. Conf. on Power Electronics and Drive Systems (PEDS), Paper 827, pp. 1-6, 2019.

[14] A. Kanale and B. J. Baliga, "Achieving Short Circuit Capability for 600 V GaN FETs Using a Gate-Source-Shorted Si Depletion-Mode MOSFET in Series with the Source", IEEE Workshop on Wide Bandgap Power Devices and Applications in Asia (WiPDA Asia), pp. 1-6, 2020.

[15] IXYS Power Semiconductor product page, https://www.littelfuse.com/products/power-semiconductors/ixys-power-semiconductors-and-ics.aspx.

[16] A. Kanale and B. J. Baliga, "Theoretical Optimization of the Si GSS-DMM Device in the BaSIC Topology for SiC Power MOSFET Short-Circuit Capability Improvement", IEEE Access, Vol. 9, pp. 70039-70047, 2021.

[17] A. Kanale and B. J. Baliga, "A New User-Configurable Method to Improve Short-Circuit Ruggedness of 1.2-kV SiC Power MOSFETs", IEEE Tran. Power Electronics, Vol. 36, pp. 2059-2067, 2021.

[18] A. Kanale and B. J. Baliga, "Selection Methodology for Si Power MOSFETs used to enhance SiC Power MOSFET Short-Circuit Capability with the BaSIC(EMM) Topology", IEEE Tran. Power Electronics, Vol. 36, pp. 8243-8252, 2021.

[19] A. Kanale and B. J. Baliga, "Comparison of Current Suppression Methods to Enhance Short Circuit Capability of 1.2 kV SiC Power MOSFETs: A New Approach using a Series-connected, Gate-Source-Shorted Si Depletion-Mode MOSFET vs Reduced Gate Bias Operation", IEEE Industrial Electronics Conf., pp. 5114-5119, 2019.

[20] A. Kanale and B. J. Baliga, "Excellent Static and Dynamic Scaling of Power Handling Capability of the BaSIC(DMM) Topology with 1.2 kV SiC Power MOSFETs", IEEE Workshop on Wide Bandgap Power Devices and Applications (WiPDA), pp. 14-17, 2021.

Chapter 16

Bi-Directional Switch

The SiC devices discussed in the previous sections all have unidirectional voltage blocking capability which is suitable for voltage-source-converters (VSCs). The VSC power circuit topology became popular in the 1980s after the commercialization of the Si IGBT[1]. Prior to this time, the current source inverter (CSI) was popular due to availability of Si thyristors with bi-directional blocking capability[2]. Another attractive power electronics topology is the matrix converter which eliminates the need for storage elements, such as the electrolytic DC link capacitor for VSIs and the DC bus inductor for the CSIs[3]. This topology is consequently more efficient and smaller in weight and size. However, it requires a bi-directional switch.

A bi-directional switch has the following attributes: (a) both forward and reverse high voltage blocking capability; (b) conduction of current with low on-state voltage drop in the first and third quadrants under gate control; (c) fast turn-on and turn-off capability in both quadrants to minimize switching losses; (d) large forward biased safe-operating-area (FBSOA) in both quadrants with saturation current controlled by the gate voltage. The first bi-directional switch, named the TRIAC, was based on Si thyristor technology[4]. It was popular for phase control of AC power delivery in the 1960s. Its lack of FBSOA resulted in production of electro-magnetic interference with the cathode ray tube based television sets. It is not suitable for modern matrix converters.

16.1 Multi-Device Implementations

Until recently, the construction of matrix converters had to be performed by using multiple devices to achieve the characteristics of a bi-directional switch. Various multi-device bi-directional switch options that have been explored are shown in Fig. 16.1 The first case (a) is a bidirectional switch formed with 5 devices consisting of a Si IGBT (device Q1) inside a diode bridge (4 diodes D1, D2, D3 and D4) to provide bi-directional voltage blocking and current flow capability[3]. It can be implemented using commonly available asymmetric blocking IGBTs that have excellent on-state voltage drop and FBSOA. For this implementation, the on-state voltage drop of the bi-directional switch in each quadrant consists of the voltage drop across 2 diodes and the IGBT, which is a relatively large value of 8.6 V as shown in Fig. 16.1. The switching losses of asymmetric blocking IGBTs are much lower than symmetric blocking IGBTs but are high compared with SiC power MOSFETs.

Comparison of Bi-Directional Switch Implementations				
Switch Configuration	Description	Number of components	On-State Voltage Drop (V)	Switching Loss
	Diode Bridge + Asymmetric IGBT	5	8.6 [2 diodes + 1 IGBT]	High
	Case (a)			
	Asymmetric IGBTs + Freewheeling diodes	4	5.8 [1 diode + 1 IGBT]	High
	Case (b)			
	Back-to-back symmetric IGBTs	2	2.2 [1 symmetric IGBT]	Very High
	Case (c)			
	SiC Power MOSFETs + JBS diodes	4	3.1 [1 diode + 1 MOSFET]	Low
	Case (d)			
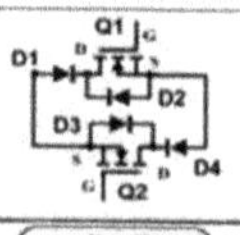	Back-to-back SiC Power MOSFETs + antiparallel and series JBS diodes	6	3.1 [1 diode + 1 MOSFET]	Low
	Case (e)			
	Four-terminal SiC Monolithic BiDFET	1	1.0 [1 BiDFET]	Low
	Case (f)			

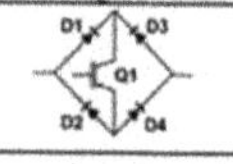

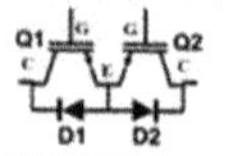

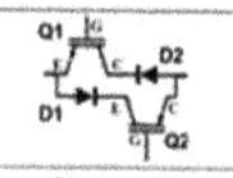

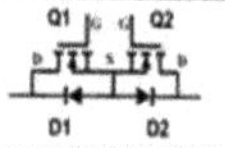

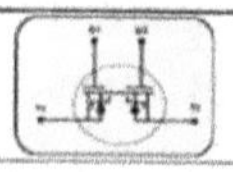

Fig. 16.1 Bi-directional switch implementations for matrix converters.

The second case (b) shown in Fig. 16.1 utilizes 4 devices consisting of the commonly available Si asymmetric blocking IGBTs (Devices Q1 and Q2) with anti-parallel diodes (D1 and D2)[5]. The on-state voltage drop of the bi-directional switch in each quadrant consists of the voltage drop across one diode and one IGBT, which is a relatively large value of 5.8 V as shown in Fig. 16.1. As previously mentioned, the switching losses of asymmetric blocking IGBTs are much lower than symmetric blocking IGBTs but are high compared with SiC power MOSFETs.

The third case (c) shown in Fig. 16.1 makes use two symmetric IGBT connected in a back-to-back configuration[6]. Although a separate series diode is shown in the circuit, it is actually located within the symmetric blocking IGBT structure. This reduces the parts count to only 2 components. The on-state voltage drop of this bi-directional switch in each quadrant is that of a symmetric blocking IGBT, which is a relatively low value of 2.2 V, as shown in Fig. 16.1. However, the switching losses of symmetric blocking IGBTs are much larger than asymmetric blocking IGBTs[4] and very high compared with SiC power MOSFETs.

The fourth case (d) is based on using SiC power MOSFETs with an anti-parallel SiC JBS diode[7]. Two of these units are then connected in series as shown in Fig. 16.1. This approach is therefore implemented using 4 discrete devices. The on-state voltage drop of this bi-directional switch in each quadrant consists of the voltage drop across one SiC JBS diode and one SiC power MOSFET, which is 3.1 V as shown in Fig. 16.1. The switching losses of the SiC power MOSFETs and diodes are low due to operation in the unipolar manner.

The fifth case (e) is based on using two SiC power MOSFETs in anti-parallel configuration. A SiC JBS diode is placed in series with each SiC power MOSFET because they lack reverse blocking capability[8]. This approach is implemented using 6 discrete devices because each SiC power MOSFET also needs a SiC JBS diode in anti-parallel with it. The on-state voltage drop of this bi-directional switch in each quadrant consists of the voltage drop across one SiC JBS diode and one SiC power MOSFET, which is 3.1 V as shown in Fig. 16.1. The switching losses of the SiC power MOSFETs and diodes are low due to operation in the unipolar manner.

In conclusion, it has been necessary to utilize multiple discrete devices to create bi-directional switches. The approaches using the Si IGBT have relatively high on-state drop and switching losses. The approaches using the multiple discrete SiC devices have high on-state voltage drop and low switching losses.

16.2 The Monolithic Gen-1 BiDFET

A bi-directional SiC based switch, called the Bi-Directional Field Effect Transistor (BiDFET), was proposed in 2019 with patent issued in 2020[9]. The architecture of this concept is illustrated in the upper part of Fig. 16.2. Two adjacent SiC power JBSFETs (JBSFET-1 and JBSFET-2) that are simultaneously fabricated on a wafer are utilized. They have a common

N^+ substrate and drain metallization at the bottom of the wafer. Unlike discrete JBSFETs, no external connection is made to the drain contact. A four-terminal AC switch is formed by using the source and gate electrodes of the two JBSFETs. Details of the construction of each JBSFET is shown at the bottom of Fig. 16.2. The cells within each JBSFET contain a MOSFET and JBS diode. Each JBSFET has its own edge termination to support high voltages.

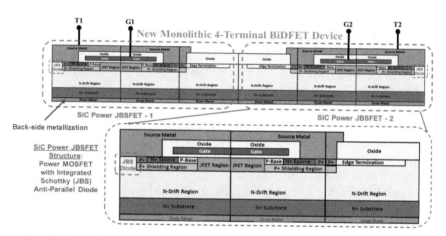

Fig. 16.2 Monolithic bi-directional SiC switch created by connecting two SiC power JBSFETs in tandem.

Terminal T1 of JBSFET-1 is used as the reference terminal during operation of the BiDFET. With gate G1 shorted to terminal T1 and gate G2 shorted to terminal T2, the BiDFET can support high voltage in the first quadrant with positive bias applied to terminal T2 due to blocking by JBSFET-1. The JBS diode in JBSFET-2 is forward biased during this time. The BiDFET can support high voltage in the third quadrant with negative bias applied to terminal T2 due to blocking by JBSFET-2. The JBS diode in JBSFET-1 is forward biased during this time.

The BiDFET can conduct current in the first and third quadrants if a positive gate drive voltage is applied to gate G1 with respect to terminal T1 and to gate G2 with respect to terminal T2. This turns on the channels of both JBSFET-1 and JBSFET-2 providing a unipolar conduction path. The current flow between the devices does not flow laterally even though they have a common N-drift region. This path has a high resistance. The current flows vertically from the source to the drain for each JBSFET and their common drain electrode and package on which the device is mounted. The on-state resistance is determined by the resistances of the two JBSFETs, which can be reduced by increasing their active area.

The BiDFET has the excellent high voltage output characteristics exhibited by each of the internal JBSFETs. Consequently, switching gate G1 of JBSFET-1, while keeping the positive voltage of gate G2, allows unipolar low loss turn-on and turn-off of the device current in the first quadrant. Similarly, switching gate G2 of JBSFET-2, while keeping the positive voltage of gate G1, allows unipolar low loss turn-on and turn-off of the device current in the third quadrant.

The JBS diodes within the two JBSFETs prevent bipolar current flow through the MOSFET body diodes during the dead-time in circuit operation. Current flow via the body diodes can produce bipolar degradation induced reliability problems and high switching losses as discussed in chapter 13.

A major advantage of the proposed BiDFET concept is that the device can be fabricated in a commercial foundry using the existing manufacturing process and chip design for SiC JBSFETs. The use of two identical JBSFETs within the monolithic chips makes the performance perfectly symmetrical in both the first and third quadrants. This a unique feature not achieved by other approaches using SiC devices based on two-sided wafer processing. The proposed approach shown in Fig. 16.2 is scalable in blocking voltage by altering the drift region doping and thickness as done for SiC power MOSFETs.

16.2.1 Monolithic BiDFET Demonstration

The first experimental demonstration of a monolithic BiDFET was reported in 2018 using 1.2 kV SiC JBSFETs[10] with small active area of 0.045 cm². These devices exhibited the desired symmetrical 1.2 kV blocking capability in both quadrants with on-state resistance of 300 mΩ. The on-resistance could then to scaled down by fabrication of JBSFETs with larger active area.

16.2.2 Low On-Resistance BiDFET Demonstration

The active area of the 1.2 kV monolithic SiC BiDFET was increased by ten-fold to 0.45 cm² in 2020 to create a device with on-resistance of 50 mΩ in both quadrants[11]. This device is referred to as the Gen-1 SiC BiDFET here. The JBSFET cells in these devices had a pitch of 6.1 μm; channel length of 0.5 μm, JFET width of 1.5 μm, and Schottky contact width of 1 μm for the cross-section shown in Fig. 16.3(a). The devices had an overall chip size of 1.04 cm x 1.10 cm as shown in Fig. 16.3(b). Two gate pads were designed for each JBSFET to allow driving the chip more effectively. Gate runners were employed in the active area for each JBSFETs to reduce the internal gate resistance. The devices were packaged in a custom designed four-terminal module as shown in Fig. 16.3(c). Multiple wire bonds were distributed over the entire active area to reduce the package parasitic resistance to less than 1 mΩ. A view of the final molded module with four-terminals is shown in Fig. 16.3(d).

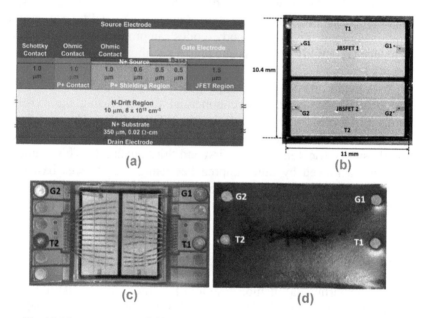

Fig. 16.3 Large area monolithic Gen-1 SiC BiDFET: (a) Internal JBSFET cross-section; (b) Overall chip view; (c) Chip in custom 4-terminal package; (d) Encapsulated 4-terminal BiDFET module.

The packaged monolithic Gen-1 SiC BiDFET devices had symmetric blocking characteristics with breakdown voltage greater than 1400 V as shown in Fig. 16.4. They could carry 20 A with an on-state voltage drop of 1 V in both quadrants as shown in Fig. 16.5, consistent with the expected value in Fig. 16.1. The measured on-resistance in both quadrants was 50 mΩ at a gate bias of 20 V applied to both gate G1 and G2. This corresponds to a JBSFET specific on-resistance of 11.25 mΩ-cm^2. The relatively large value for the specific on-resistance is due to the low annealing temperature of 900 °C used for the source contacts and the large cell pitch. This was required to make low leakage current Schottky contacts for the internal JBS diodes. The devices also exhibited good output characteristics in both quadrants as shown in Fig. 16.5. The reverse transfer (gate-drain) capacitance was found to be half that of the internal JBSFETs, which is beneficial for reducing switching losses. The measured on-state voltage drop of the JBS diode was about 2 V at 20 A ensuring suppressing of bipolar current flow via the MOSFET body diode.

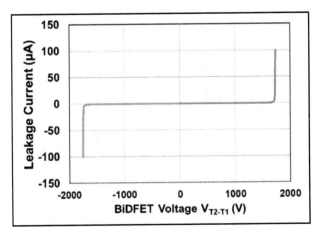

Fig. 16.4 Symmetric blocking characteristics of the large area Gen-1 SiC BiDFET.

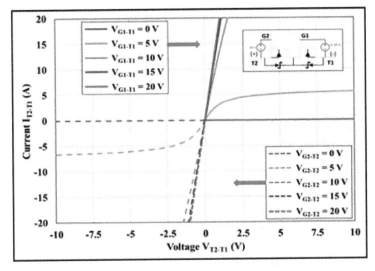

Fig. 16.5 Symmetric on-state and output characteristics of the large area Gen-1 SiC BiDFET.

16.2.3 Gen-1 Device Switching Performance

The switching characteristics of the Gen-1 SiC BiDFET for a typical inductive load were obtained using double-pulse testing with a DC supply voltage of 800 V[12]. The performance of the Gen-1 SiC BiDFET was compared with that of the internal JBSFET by using the two configurations illustrated in Fig. 16.6. A commercial SiC JBS diode was used across the load inductor for both cases. At a current of 10 A, the Gen-1 SiC BiDFET turn-on loss (E_{ON}) was 149 μJ and turn-off loss (E_{OFF}) was 109 μJ, resulting in a total switching loss ($E_{SW,T}$) of 258 μJ. In comparison, the internal JBSFET J11 had an E_{ON} of 214 μJ and an E_{OFF} of 146 μJ, resulting in an $E_{SW,T}$ of 360 μJ. The Gen-1 SiC BiDFET exhibits 40 % lower switching loss consistent with lower C_{GD} measured for the device.

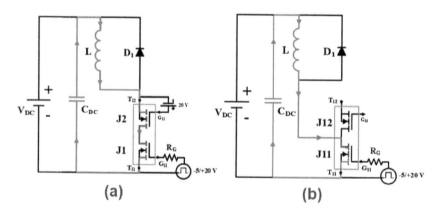

Fig. 16.6 Double-pulse test configurations for evaluating switching performance of:
(a) monolithic Gen-1 SiC BiDFET; (b) Internal JBSFET.

Switching loss measurements were also obtained using the test configurations shown in Fig. 16.7 with and without the positive DC gate bias applied to the gate for JBSFET-2 (J12). In case (a), the current flows via the internal JBS diode while in case (b) it flows via the MOSFET channel. It was found that the switching losses were identical with and without the DC gate bias applied to the gate of JBSFET-2.

The reverse recovery current in the body diodes of SiC power MOSFETs produces significant switching power losses as discussed in a chapter 13. This should not occur for the BiDFET due to the use of JBSFETs. The evaluation of the monolithic Gen-1 SiC BiDFET under these conditions was performed using the test configurations in Fig. 16.8. The current flowing in the load inductor increases when the lower switch is turned on as shown in case (a). The inductor current circulates via the JBS diode within the upper switch when the lower switch is turned off.

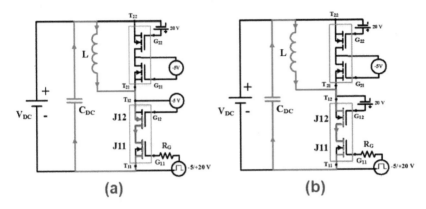

Fig. 16.7 Double-pulse test configurations for evaluating switching performance of monolithic Gen-1 SiC BiDFET: (a) current flow via JBS diode; (b) current flow via channel.

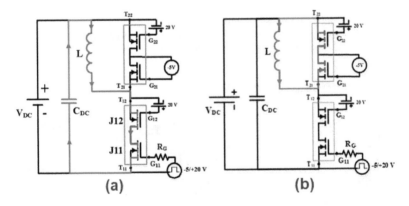

Fig. 16.8 Double-pulse test configurations for evaluating switching performance of monolithic Gen-1 SiC BiDFET: (a) current flow via channels in lower device; (b) current flow via JBS diode in upper device.

The waveforms for the device voltage and current are shown in Fig. 16.9 together with the gate voltage applied to the lower switch. A spike in the current is observed when the lower device is turned-on at 2.4 μs. This current is usually ascribed to the body diode reverse recovery. However, the same spike in current occurs at the initial time when the current is zero. From this observation, it can be concluded that the current spike is associated with the output capacitance of the upper device and the high dV/dt at these instances. This was confirmed by performing the measurements at elevated temperatures up to 140 °C. No change in the magnitude of the current spike was observed unlike in the case of reverse recovery currents that increase with temperature.

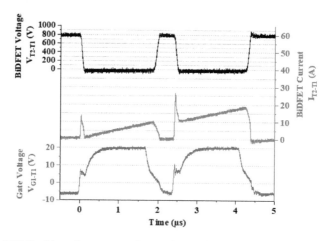

Fig. 16.9 Double-pulse test waveforms observed for the monolithic Gen-1 SiC BiDFET. Black upper trace is voltage across the device; Red middle trace is the current flowing through the device; Blue lower trace is the gate voltage.

16.3 The Monolithic Gen-2 BiDFET

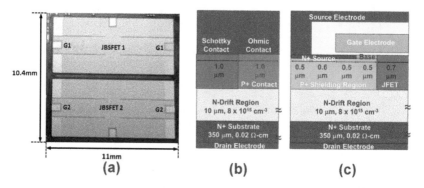

Fig. 16.10 Large area monolithic Gen-2 SiC BiDFET: (a) Overall chip design with JBS diodes in corners of each JBSFET; (b) Cross-section of internal JBS Diode; (c) Cross-section of MOSFET cells.

A monolithic Gen-2 SiC BiDFET was created by separating the JBS diodes from the MOSFET cells and locating them at the four corners of each JBSFET[13]. Separating the JBS diodes from the MOSFET cells allows annealing the source contact metal of the MOSFET cells at a high temperature (1000 °C) to achieve a low contact resistance. In addition, the MOSFET cell size can be significant reduced to achieve a lower specific on-resistance. The JBS diodes can be fabricated using either Titanium or Nickel as the Schottky barrier with a lower contact annealing temperature (< 900 °C) to achieve a small leakage current.

The JBS diodes can be observed in the top view of the chip shown in Fig. 16.10(a) due to different shading of the metal. The JBS diodes were designed with the cross-section shown in Fig. 16.10(b) where the width of the Schottky contact is 2 μm between the P^+ protection regions. The doping under the Schottky contact is enhanced using the doping profile used for the JFET regions within the MOSFET cells. The active area of the JBS diodes was chosen to be one-tenth of the active area of the JBSFET.

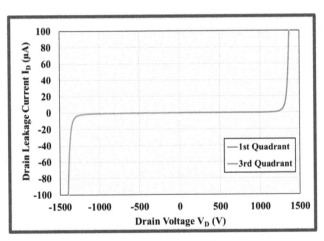

Fig. 16.11 Symmetric blocking characteristics of the large area Gen-2 SiC BiDFET.

A cross-section of the MOSFET cells is shown in Fig. 16(c). The contact to the P^+ shielding region is made orthogonal to the cross-section. The cell pitch is reduced to 2.8 μm compared with 6.1 μm for the JBSFET in the Gen-1 design (see Fig. 16.3). The smaller cell pitch increases the channel density. The specific on-resistance of the MOSFET in the Gen-2 design is reduced to 4.5 mΩ-cm² due to a combination of the smaller cell pitch and reduced source contact resistance compared to 11.25 mΩ-cm² for the JBSFETs in the Gen-1 design. Consequently, the on-resistance of each JBSFET in the Gen-2 design is reduced to under 12 mΩ in spite of the MOSFET cells occupying 90 % of the active area. The monolithic Gen-2 SiC BiDFET then has a designed on-resistance of less than 25 mΩ.

The monolithic Gen-2 SiC BiDFET has symmetrical blocking characteristics as shown in Fig. 16.11 with blocking voltage exceeding 1400 V. The on-state characteristics of the monolithic Gen-2 SiC BiDFET are shown in Fig. 16.12. The device has the same on-state resistance of 25 mΩ in both the first and third quadrants. Consequently, a remarkable reduction of on-resistance by a factor of 2-times was achieved for the Gen-2 SiC BiDFET with the same die size as the Gen-1 SiC BiDFET.

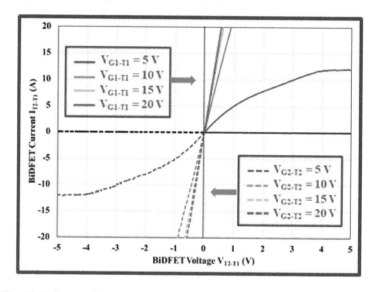

Fig. 16.12 Symmetric on-state and output characteristics of the large area Gen-2 SiC BiDFET.

Two Gen-1 SiC BiDFETs can be packaged in parallel to achieve the same on-state resistance of 25 mΩ as the single Gen-2 SiC BiDFET. A comparison of these options is shown in Table 16.1. The many favorable features of the Gen-2 SiC BiDFET design strategy are listed in the last column. The die area is reduced by a factor of 2-times reducing the die cost and improving manufacturability. The input capacitance of the Gen-2 SiC BiDFET is reduced by 30 % due to difference in MOSFET cell structure and area. The output capacitance of the Gen-2 SiC BiDFET is reduced by 75 % due to the smaller active area. This results in a reduction in the turn-off switching loss by 80 % leading to a reduction in total switching loss by 30 %.

Table 16.1: Comparison of Gen-1 and Gen-2 BiDFETs

Parameter, Units	Gen 1 (2 Chips)	Gen 2 (1 Chip)	Improvement
Chip Area, cm^2	2.28	1.14	2x
R$_{DS,ON}$, mΩ	25	27	-
g$_M$, S	15	15	-
C$_{ISS}$, pF	15100	11730	1.3x
C$_{OSS}$, pF	1050	600	1.75x
C$_{RSS}$, pF	70	70	-
E$_{ON}$, μJ	1350	1120	1.2x
E$_{OFF}$, μJ	460	250	1.8x
E$_{TOTAL}$, μJ	1810	1370	1.3x

16.4 Gen-1 BiDFET in Matrix Converter Application

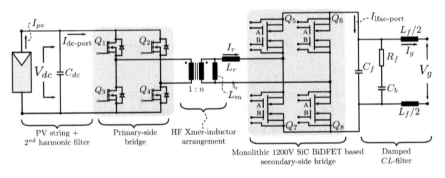

Fig. 16.13 Single-phase matrix converter for photovoltaic power generation based on monolithic SiC BiDFETs.

A single-phase, single-stage, isolated AC/DC converter has been demonstrated for solar power conversion utilizing BiDFET enabled single-phase matrix converter on the grid-side[14]. This BiDFET enabled matrix converter provides significant improvements over conventional AC/DC isolated converters implemented with a DC link using bulky unreliable electrolytic capacitors. The BiDFET-based matrix converter needs a smaller number of switches and no electrolytic capacitors, which provides a lower volume and higher reliability solution for PV domestic applications.

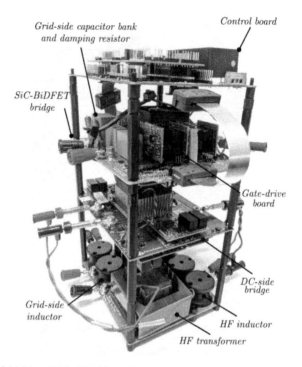

Fig. 16.14 Monolithic SiC BiDFET based matrix converter for photovoltaic power generation.

The hardware prototype was built with a stack of four PCBs as shown in Fig. 16.14. The upper PCB has the control board which supplies the auxiliary power, accepts sensor signals, generates PWM gate signals and protects the converter against faults through hardware and software trip settings. The second PCB has the grid-side full-bridge matrix converter enabled by the 1.2 kV Gen-1 BiDFET. The third PCB has the PV-side full-bridge converter implemented using 650 V enhancement-mode GaN transistors. The fourth PCB has the filter and high-frequency AC-link board, which includes the grid-side inductors, PV-side second-harmonic filter capacitors, high-frequency inductor, and high-frequency transformer.

16.5 Summary

The SiC BiDFET switch has fully gate controlled symmetrical characteristics in both the first and third quadrant of operation. The demonstrated large area, monolithically implemented devices can support 1400 V in both quadrants and exhibit an on-state resistance of 25 mΩ for the Gen-2 chips. The devices exhibit saturated gate controlled output characteristics with a wide forward-biased-safe-operating-area. Their unipolar operation allows fast turn-on and turn-off switching transients with low losses at high operating frequencies. A single-phase matrix converter has been demonstrated using these devices for residential solar power generation.

References

[1] B. J. Baliga, "The IGBT Device", Second Edition, Elsevier, 2022.

[2] T. Jahns and B. Sarlioglu, "The Incredible Shrinking Motor Drive", IEEE Power Electronics Magazine, pp. 18-27, September 2020.

[3] P. W. Wheeler, J. Rodriguez, J. C. Clare, L. Epringham, and A. Weinstein, "Matrix Converters: A Technology Review", IEEE Trans. Industrial Electronics, vol. 49, no. 2, pp. 276-288, April 2002.

[4] B. J. Baliga, "Fundamentals of Power Semiconductor Devices", Second Edition, Springer, 2019.

[5] R. Moghe, R. P. Kandula, A Iyer, and D. Divan, "Loss Comparison between SiC, Hybrid Si/SiC, and Si Devices in Direct AC/AC Converters", IEEE Energy Conversion Congress and Exposition, pp. 3848-3855, 2012.

[6] M. Takei, Y. Harada and K. Ueno, "600V-IGBT with Reverse Blocking Capability", IEEE Int. Symp. On Power Semiconductor Devices and ICs, pp. 413-416, 2001.

[7] S. Safari, A. Castellazzi and P. Wheeler, "Experimental and Analytical Performance Evaluation of SiC Power Devices in the Matrix Converter", IEEE Trans. Power Electronics, Vol. 29, pp. 2584-2596, 2014.

[8] H. F. Ahmed, et al, "A Single-Phase Buck–Boost Matrix Converter with only Six Switches and without Commutation Problem", IEEE Trans. Power Electronics, Vol. 32, pp. 1232-1244, 2017.

[9] B. J. Baliga, "Monolithically Integrated AC Switch having JBSFETs therein with Commonly-connected drain and Cathode Electrodes", U. S. Patent 10,804,393, Filed June 7, 2019, Issued October 13, 2020.

[10] B. J. Baliga and K. Han, "Monolithic SiC Bi-Directional Field Effect Transistor (BiDFET): Concept, Implementation, and Electrical Characteristics", in Govt. Microcircuit Appl. And Critical Tech. Conf., 2018.

[11] K. Han, A. Agarwal, A. Kanale, B. J. Baliga, S. Bhattacharya, T-H. Cheng, D. Hopkins, V. Amarasinghe, and J. Ransom, "Monolithic 4-Terminal 1.2 kV/20 A 4H-SiC Bi-Directional Field Effect Transistor (BiDFET) with Integrated JBS Diodes", IEEE Int. Symp. On Power Semiconductor Devices and ICs, pp. 242-245, 2020.

[12] A. Kanale, T-H. Cheng, S. S. Shah, K. Han, A. Agarwal, B. J. Baliga, D. Hopkins and S. Bhattacharya, "Switching Characteristics of a 1.2 kV, 50 mΩ SiC Monolithic Bidirectional Field Effect Transistor (BiDFET) with Integrated JBS Diodes", IEEE Applied Power Electronics Conf., pp. 1267-1274, 2021.

[13] B. J. Baliga, D. Hopkins, S. Bhattacharya, A. Agarwal, T-H. Cheng, R. Narwal, A. Kanale, S. S. Shah, and K. Han, "The BiDFET Device and Its Impact on Converters", IEEE Power Electronics Magazine, pp. 20-27, March 2023.

[14] S. Bhattacharya, R. Narwal, S. S. Shah, B. J. Baliga, A. Agarwal, A. Kanale, K. Han, D. Hopkins, and T-H. Cheng, "Power Conversion Systems enabled by SiC BiDFET Device", IEEE Power Electronics Magazine, pp. 39-43, March 2023.

Chapter 17

Insulated Gate Bipolar Transistors

The replacement of bipolar-mode silicon devices with unipolar-mode SiC devices was proposed to reduce the on-state and switching losses in power electronic circuits[1]. This has been successfully achieved by the demonstration of high performance 4H-SiC power MOSFETs as described in chapters 11 and 12. Due to increasing SiC wafer size with reduced manufacturing cost, it has now become feasible to replace Si IGBTs with blocking voltages up to 6-kV with SiC power MOSFETs. This enables increasing the operating frequency which allows reduction of the cost, size and weight of inductors and filters in the power electronics.

However, for blocking voltages above 10 kV, the specific on-resistance for even 4H-SiC unipolar transistors becomes large, as described in chapter 4, creating high on-state power losses. The reduced on-state current density for these devices increases their die size and cost for applications such as high power motors and solid-state-transformers for smart grids. This has motivated the investigation of IGBTs made from 4H-SiC material.

It is possible to make both n-channel and p-channel IGBTs using 4H-SiC as in the case of silicon IGBTs[2]. The development of p-channel SiC IGBTs took precedence over n-channel IGBTs because the quality of N^+ substrates required for the p-channel devices was much superior to that of P^+ substrates required for the n-channel devices.

It is necessary to shield the gate oxide from the high electric fields developed in the semiconductor in the case of all SiC IGBTs. This can be accomplished using a P^+ shielding region as shown for the planar-gate MOSFETs in chapter 11, and the incorporation of a junction at the bottom of the trenches as shown for the trench-gate MOSFET in chapter 12[3].

The first p-channel SiC IGBT structures with 10-kV blocking voltage capability were reported in 2005 with the trench-gate process[4].

Subsequently, planar-gate p-channel silicon carbide IGBT structures with 9-kV blocking voltage capability were reported in 2007[5] and 12-kV devices were reported in 2008[6]. Although this work demonstrated that conductivity modulation of the drift region can be achieved in the SiC IGBT structure similar to that observed in silicon devices, the on-state voltage drop obtained for the SiC IGBT was significantly worse that than shown in chapter 11 for the 10-kV silicon carbide power MOSFET structure.

More recent interest has therefore shifted to even higher blocking voltage ratings from 15-kV to 20-kV. The on-state characteristics of asymmetric 4H-SiC p-channel IGBTs having a 175 μm thick P-base region with doping concentration of 2×10^{14} cm^{-3} were reported for the planar device architecture in 2007[7]. The devices had on-state voltage drop of 8.5 volts at an on-state current density of 25 A/cm^2. The high-level lifetime in the P-base region was measured at 0.46 μs. The measured blocking voltage capability of the devices was only 5-kV although the authors assumed that the parameters for the drift region are suitable for a 20-kV device. The optimization of p-channel asymmetric IGBT structures in 4H-SiC for blocking voltages between 15 and 20 kV has also been reported[8].

A comparison of the high frequency performance of 15-kV asymmetric and symmetric blocking p-channel IGBTs has been reported[9]. This study concludes that the lifetime in the buffer layer has to be optimized to obtain the best performance in the asymmetric p-channel 4H-SiC IGBT structure. However, current technology for silicon carbide does not allow selective adjustment of the lifetime in the buffer layer.

Progress with the development of n-channel 4H-SiC IGBT has accelerated since 2007 when the successful fabrication of a device with 13-kV blocking voltage capability was reported[10]. The modulation of the conductivity of the drift region was verified in these devices from the on-state characteristics. Despite a low inversion layer mobility of 18 cm^2/V-s observed in the high-voltage structures, an on-state voltage drop of 3.8 volts was obtained an on-state current density of 25 A/cm^2 with a gate bias of 20 volts. The devices exhibited a voltage rise-time of 0.25 μs and a current fall-time of 0.1 μs when operated from a 7-kV power supply at a current density of 175 A/cm^2. Since that time, the blocking voltage of the n-channel IGBT has been steadily scaled until 10 kV devices were reported[11] in 2010, 12.5 kV devices were reported[12] in 2012, 21 kV devices were reported[13] in 2013, and 22-kV device were reported[14] in 2014.

The progress in development of high voltage silicon carbide power devices was reviewed in 2008[15]. The report concludes that the most appropriate applications for SiC MOSFET structures are in the range of 4 to 10 kV blocking voltages while that for SiC IGBTs are in the range of 15 to 30 kV blocking voltages. Based up on this, the discussion of silicon carbide IGBTs will be focused on 20-kV rated devices in this chapter. The characteristics of the p-channel and n-channel planar inversion-mode silicon carbide IGBT structures are compared here.

The basic operating principles and characteristics for the Si IGBT have been described in detail in the textbook[16]. The operating principles of the asymmetric 4H-SiC IGBT structure can be expected to be similar to those for the asymmetric Si IGBT structure. However, the doping concentration in the drift region for the 4H-SiC structure is much larger than that for the Si device structure. Consequently, although the minority carrier concentration in the space-charge region during the switching of the silicon carbide and silicon devices is nearly the same, it is much smaller than the doping concentration in the silicon carbide devices and greater than the doping concentration in the silicon devices. In the case of the asymmetric Si IGBT structure, the space-charge region does not reach-through the drift region during the voltage transient leaving stored charge in the drift region at the end of the voltage transient. In contrast, the space-charge region reaches-though the drift region when the collector voltage is much less than the collector supply voltage in the case of the typical asymmetric 4H-SiC IGBT structure. This alters the shape of the voltage and current transients as discussed in this chapter with a high dV/dt that could be a problem. A SiC asymmetric IGBT drift layer design that avoids this problem is described in this chapter.

17.1 n-Channel Asymmetric Structure

The asymmetric n-channel 4H-SiC IGBT structure with the planar gate architecture is illustrated in Fig. 17.1 with its doping profile. Since the asymmetric IGBT structure is intended for use in DC circuits, its reverse blocking capability does not have to match the forward blocking capability allowing the use of an N-buffer layer adjacent to the P^+ collector region. The N-buffer layer has a much larger doping concentration than the lightly doped portion of the N-base region. The electric field in the asymmetric IGBT takes a trapezoidal shape allowing supporting the forward blocking voltage with a thinner N-base region. This allows achieving a lower on-state voltage drop and superior turn-off characteristics.

As in the case of silicon devices, the doping concentration of the buffer layer and the lifetime in the N-base region must be optimized to perform a trade-off between on-state voltage drop and turn-off switching losses[16]. Unlike the silicon device, the silicon carbide structure has uniform doping concentration for the various layers produced by using either epitaxial growth or by using multiple ion-implantation energies to form a box profile.

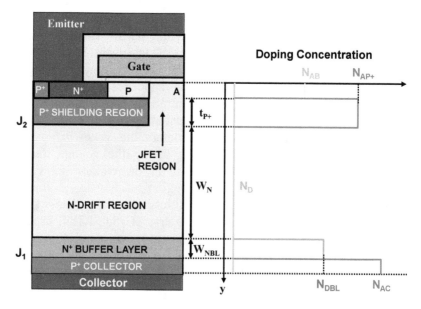

Fig. 17.1 Asymmetric n-channel SiC IGBT structure and its doping profile.

17.1.1 Blocking Characteristics

The design of the 20-kV asymmetric 4H-SiC n-channel IGBT structure is discussed in this section. The physics for blocking voltages in the first and third quadrants by the IGBT structure is discussed in detail in the textbook[16]. When a positive bias is applied to the collector terminal of the asymmetric 4H-SiC IGBT structure, the junction (J_2) between the P$^+$ shielding region and the N-base (drift) region becomes reverse biased while the junction (J_1) between the P$^+$ collector region and the N-buffer layer becomes forward biased. The forward blocking voltage is supported across the junction (J_2) between the P^+ shielding region and the N-base (drift) region with a depletion layer extending mostly within the N-base region. The doping concentration and width of the JFET region must be designed to allow suppression of the electric field at point A as discussed in chapter 11 for the 4H-SiC power MOSFET structure.

The forward blocking capability of the asymmetric n-channel 4H-SiC IGBT structure is determined by the open-base transistor breakdown phenomenon. The maximum blocking voltage occurs when the common base current gain of the NPN transistor of the n-channel structure becomes equal to unity. For the asymmetric IGBT structure, the emitter injection efficiency is smaller than unity due to the high doping concentration of the N-buffer layer. The emitter injection efficiency for the P^+ collector/N-buffer junction (J_1) can be obtained by using an analysis similar to that described in the textbook for the bipolar power transistor[16]:

$$\gamma_E = \frac{D_{pNBL} L_{nC} N_{AC}}{D_{pNBL} L_{nC} N_{AC} + D_{nC} W_{NBL} N_{DBL}} \qquad [17.1]$$

where D_{pNBL} and D_{nC} are the diffusion coefficients for minority carriers in the N-buffer and P^+ collector regions; N_{AC} and L_{nC} are the acceptor concentration and diffusion length for minority carriers in the P^+ collector region; N_{DBL} and W_{NBL} are the donor concentration and width of the N-buffer layer. In determining the diffusion coefficients and the diffusion length, it is necessary to account for impact of the high doping concentrations in the P^+ collector region and N-buffer layer on the mobility. In addition, the lifetime within the highly doped P^+ collector region is reduced due to heavy doping effects, which shortens the diffusion length.

The open-base transistor breakdown condition for the asymmetric n-channel silicon carbide IGBT structure is given by:

$$\alpha_{PNP} = (\gamma_E . \alpha_T)_{PNP} M = 1 \qquad [17.2]$$

Based up on this expression, it can be concluded that the breakdown voltage for the asymmetric 4H-SiC IGBT structure will occur when the multiplication co-efficient is only slightly above unity. Using the avalanche breakdown criteria when the multiplication co-efficient becomes equal to infinity will lead to significant error in the design of the drift region for the IGBT structure.

When the collector bias exceeds the reach-through voltage (V_{RT}), the electric field is truncated by the high doping concentration of the N-buffer layer making the un-depleted width of the NPN transistor base region equal to the width of the N-buffer layer. The base transport factor is then given by:

$$\alpha_T = \frac{1}{\cosh\left(W_{NBL} / L_{pNB}\right)} \qquad [17.3]$$

which is independent of the collector bias. Here, $L_{p,NB}$ is the diffusion length for holes in the N-buffer layer. This analysis neglects the depletion region extension within the N-buffer layer due to its high doping level. The diffusion length for holes ($L_{p,NB}$) in the N-buffer layer depends upon the diffusion coefficient and the minority carrier lifetime in the N-buffer layer. The diffusion coefficient varies with the doping concentration in the N-buffer layer based upon the concentration dependence of the mobility. In addition, the minority carrier lifetime has been found to be dependent upon the doping concentration[17] in the case of silicon devices. Although this phenomenon has not been verified for silicon carbide, it is commonly used when performing numerical analysis of silicon carbide devices. The effect can be modeled by using the relationship:

$$\frac{\tau_{LL}}{\tau_{p0}} = \frac{1}{1+\left(N_D / N_{REF}\right)} \qquad [17.4]$$

where N_{REF} is a reference doping concentration whose value will be assumed to be 5×10^{16} cm^{-3} for 4H-SiC.

The multiplication factor for a P-N junction is given by:

$$M = \frac{1}{1-\left(V_A / BV_{PP}\right)^n} \qquad [17.5]$$

with the avalanche breakdown voltage of the P-base/N-base junction (BV_{PP}) *without the punch-through phenomenon*. The value for n of 6 for Si is also assumed for 4H-SiC. In order to apply this formulation to the punch-through case relevant to the asymmetric 4H-SiC IGBT structure, it is necessary to relate the maximum electric field at the junction for the punch-through case to the non-punch-through case[16]. The electric field at the interface between the lightly doped portion of the N-base region and the N-buffer layer is given by:

$$E_1 = E_m - \frac{qN_DW_N}{\varepsilon_S} \qquad [17.6]$$

The voltage supported by the device is given by:

$$V_C = \left(\frac{E_m + E_1}{2}\right)W_N = E_mW_N - \frac{qN_D}{2\varepsilon_S}W_N^2 \qquad [17.7]$$

From this expression, the maximum electric field is given by:

$$E_m = \frac{V_C}{W_N} + \frac{qN_DW_N}{2\varepsilon_S} \qquad [17.8]$$

The corresponding equation for the non-punch-through case is:

$$E_m = \sqrt{\frac{2qN_DV_{NPT}}{\varepsilon_S}} \qquad [17.9]$$

Equating these maximum electric fields, the non-punch-through voltage (V_{NPT}) that determines the multiplication coefficient 'M' corresponding to the applied collector bias (V_C) for the punch-through case is given by:

$$V_{NPT} = \frac{\varepsilon_S E_m^2}{2qN_D} = \frac{\varepsilon_S}{2qN_D}\left(\frac{V_C}{W_N} + \frac{qN_DW_N}{2\varepsilon_S}\right)^2 \qquad [17.10]$$

by using Eq. [17.8]. The multiplication coefficient for the asymmetric 4H-SiC IGBT structure can be computed by using this non-punch-through voltage:

$$M = \frac{1}{1 - \left(V_{NPT}/BV_{PP}\right)^n} \qquad [17.11]$$

The multiplication coefficient increases with increasing collector bias. The open-base transistor breakdown voltage (and the forward blocking capability of the asymmetric IGBT structure) is determined by the collector voltage at which the multiplication factor becomes equal to the reciprocal of the product of the base transport factor and the emitter injection efficiency.

The n-channel asymmetric 4H-SiC IGBT structure must have a forward blocking voltage of 22,000 V for a 20-kV rated device. In the case of avalanche breakdown, there is a unique value for the doping concentration of 3.2 x 10^{14} cm^{-3} for the drift region with a width of 272 μm to obtain this blocking voltage. In the case of the asymmetric 4H-SiC IGBT structure, it is advantageous to use a lower doping concentration for the lightly doped portion of the N-base region in order to reduce its width. The strong conductivity modulation of the N-base region during on-state operation favors a smaller thickness for the N-base region independent of its original doping concentration. A doping concentration of 2.0 x 10^{14} cm^{-3} for the N-base region will be assumed for the n-channel asymmetric 4H-SiC IGBT structure analyzed in this section. This typical for very high voltage 4H-SiC IGBTs reported in the literature[14].

The doping concentration of the N-buffer layer must be sufficiently large to prevent reach-through of the electric field to the P$^+$ collector region. Although the electric field at the interface between the N-base region and the N-buffer layer is slightly smaller than at the blocking junction (J$_2$), a worse case analysis can be done by assuming that the electric field at this interface is close to the critical electric field for breakdown in the drift region. The minimum charge in the N-buffer layer to prevent reach-through can be then obtained using:

$$N_{DBL}W_{NBL} = \frac{\varepsilon_S E_C}{q} \qquad \text{[17.12]}$$

Using a critical electric for breakdown in silicon carbide of 1.47 x 10^6 V/cm for a doping concentration of 2.0 x 10^{14} cm^{-3} in the N-base region, the minimum charge in the N-buffer layer to prevent reach-through for a silicon carbide asymmetric IGBT structure is found to be 8 x 10^{12} cm^{-2}. An N-buffer layer with doping concentration of 5 x 10^{16} cm^{-3} and thickness of 5 μm has a charge of 2.5 x 10^{13} cm^{-2} that satisfies this requirement.

The asymmetric n-channel 4H-SiC IGBT structure will be assumed to have a P$^+$ collector region with doping concentration of 1 x 10^{19} cm^{-3}. It will be assumed that all the acceptors are ionized even at room temperature although the relatively deep acceptor level in silicon carbide may lead to incomplete dopant ionization. In this case, the emitter injection efficiency computed using Eq. [17.1] is 0.971. When the device is close to breakdown, the entire N-base region is depleted and the base transport factor computed by using Eq. [17.3] in this case is 0.903. In computing these values, a lifetime of 1 μs was assumed for the N-base region resulting in a lifetime of 0.5 μs in the N-buffer layer due to the scaling according to Eq. [17.4]. Based up on Eq. [17.2], open-base transistor breakdown will then occur when the multiplication coefficient becomes equal to 1.14 for the above values for the injection efficiency and base transport factor.

The forward blocking capability for the silicon carbide n-channel asymmetric IGBT structure can be computed by using Eq. [7.2] for various widths for the N-base region. The analysis requires determination of the voltage V_{NPT} by using Eq. [17.10] for each width of the N-base region. The resulting values for the forward blocking voltage are plotted in Fig. 17.2. From this graph, the N-base region width required to obtain a forward blocking voltage of 23,000-V is 165 µm.

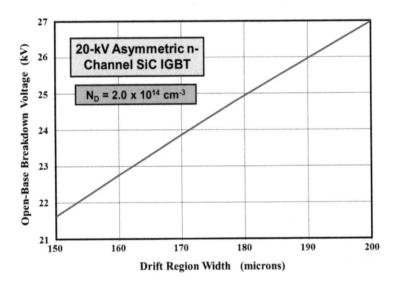

Fig. 17.2 Optimization of drift region width for the 20-kV asymmetric n-channel 4H-SiC IGBT structure.

A forward blocking voltage of 16 kV was reported[18] for an n-channel 4H-SiC IGBT fabricated using a drift region with doping concentration of 4×10^{14} cm^{-3} and thickness of 150 µm. The forward blocking voltage of 22.6 kV has been reported[16] for an n-channel asymmetric 4H-SiC IGBT by using a drift region thickness of 180 mm in the case of an N-base doping concentration of 2×10^{14} cm^{-3}. This larger drift region thickness is due to the smaller N-buffer layer thickness of 2 µm used by the authors. A blocking voltage of 27.5 kV was achieved[19] by using a drift region with doping concentration of 1×10^{14} cm^{-3} and thickness of 210 µm. These experimental results are consistent with the solutions obtained using the above analytical model.

17.1.2 On-State Voltage Drop

A generally applicable analytical model has been developed for the silicon asymmetric IGBT structure which is valid for any injection level in the buffer layer[20]. This analytical model can also be applied to silicon carbide devices. The carrier distribution profiles in the on-state for the asymmetric IGBT structure are shown in the textbook[16]. The hole and electron concentrations in the N-base region are equal due to charge neutrality and the low doping concentration required for the drift region. The hole concentration in the N-buffer layer can be lower or higher than the doping concentration (N_{DBL}) in the buffer layer for silicon carbide devices. In the case of 4H-SiC devices, the buffer layer doping is uniform with a range of 1 to 5 x 10^{17} cm^{-3} achieved by epitaxial growth[12].

An expression for the hole concentration in the buffer layer at junction (J_1) has been derived[16]:

$$p_{NB}^2(0) + \left(\frac{D_{pNB} N_{AP+} L_{nP+} + D_{nP+} N_{DB} L_{pNB}}{D_{nP+} L_{pNB}} \right) p_{NB}(0)$$
$$- \frac{N_{AP+} L_{nP+} J_C}{q D_{nP+}} = 0 \qquad [17.13]$$

The solution of this quadratic equation for the hole concentration in the buffer layer at junction (J_1) is:

$$p_{NB}(0) = \frac{1}{2}\left(\sqrt{b^2 - 4c} - b \right) \qquad [17.14]$$

where

$$b = \frac{D_{pNB} N_{AP+} L_{nP+} + D_{nP+} N_{DB} L_{pNB}}{D_{nP+} L_{pNB}} \qquad [17.15]$$

and

$$c = -\frac{N_{AP+} L_{nP+} J_C}{q D_{nP+}} \qquad [17.16]$$

Since the unified analytical model presented is valid for all injection levels in the N-buffer layer, it can be used to predict the variation of the injected hole concentration with lifetime in the N-base region and the doping concentration in the N-buffer layer for the asymmetric 4H-SiC IGBT structure.

The holes diffuse through the buffer layer producing a concentration [p(W$_{NB-}$)] inside the buffer layer at the boundary between the N-buffer layer and the N-base region:

$$p\left(W_{NB-}\right)=p_{NB}\left(0\right)e^{-\left(W_{NBL}/L_{pNB}\right)} \qquad [17.17]$$

where W$_{NBL}$ is the thickness of the buffer layer. The hole concentration [p(W$_{NB-}$)] in the N-base region at the boundary between the N-buffer layer and the N-base region can be obtained by equating the hole current density on the two sides of this boundary[16]:

$$p\left(W_{NB+}\right)=\frac{L_a \tanh\left[\left(W_N + W_{NBL}\right)/L_a\right]}{2qD_p}J_p\left(W_{NB-}\right) \qquad [17.18]$$

with

$$J_p\left(W_{NB-}\right)=J_p\left(0\right)e^{-\left(W_{NBL}/L_{pNB}\right)} \qquad [17.19]$$

The hole concentration profile in the N-base region as dictated by high-level injection conditions is given by[16]:

$$p(y)=p\left(W_{NB+}\right)\frac{\sinh\left[\left(W_N + W_{NBL} - y\right)/L_a\right]}{\sinh\left[\left(W_N + W_{NBL}\right)/L_a\right]} \qquad [17.20]$$

which is valid for y > W$_{NBL}$.

The free carrier distribution obtained by using the above equations is provided in Fig. 17.3 for the case of the 20-kV asymmetric n-channel IGBT structure with an N-base region thickness of 165 μm and a buffer layer thickness of 5 μm. The hole lifetime (τ_{p0}) in the N-base region was varied for these plots from 0.1 to 10 μs. Note that the high-level lifetime (τ_{HL}) in these cases is two-times the hole lifetime (τ_{p0}). It can be observed that the hole concentration [p$_{NB}$(0)] decreases at the collector side of the N-buffer layer (at y = 0) from 1.8 x 10^{17} cm^{-3} to 2.25 x 10^{16} cm^{-3}. In addition, the hole concentration is significantly reduced at the emitter side when the lifetime in the N-base region decreases. The carrier density falls below 1 x 10^{15} cm^{-3} over a significant portion of the N-base region when the lifetime becomes smaller than 1 μs. These results indicate that the on-state voltage drop will increase rapidly when the hole lifetime (τ_{p0}) in the N-base region is reduced below 1 μs. However, the smaller stored charge in the N-base region and buffer layer will reduce the turn-off time and energy loss per cycle.

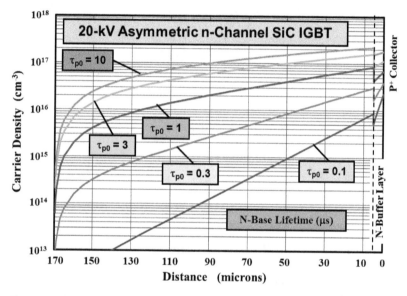

Fig. 17.3 Injected carrier profiles in the 20-kV n-channel asymmetric 4H-SiC IGBT structure: lifetime dependence.

The on-state voltage drop for the 20-kV asymmetric n-channel IGBT structure can be obtained by using the equations derived in the textbook[16] in section 9.5.5. The on-state voltage drop for the asymmetric IGBT structure can be obtained by using:

$$V_{ON} = V_{P+NBL} + V_B + V_{MOSFET} \qquad [17.21]$$

where V_{P+NBL} is the voltage drop across the P$^+$ collector/N-buffer layer junction (J$_1$), V_B is the voltage drop across the N-base region after accounting for conductivity modulation due to high-level injection conditions, and V_{MOSFET} is the voltage drop across the MOSFET portion. In the asymmetric IGBT structure, the junction (J$_1$) between the P$^+$ collector region and the N-buffer layer operates at neither high-level nor low-level injection conditions. Consequently, the voltage drop across the junction (J_1) must be obtained using:

$$V_{P+NB} = \frac{kT}{q} \ln \left(\frac{p_{NB}(0) N_{BL}}{n_i^2} \right)$$

[17.22]

The voltage drop across the N-base region can be obtained by integrating the electric field inside the N-base region. The voltage drop is obtained by taking the sum of two parts[17]. The first part is given by:

$$V_{B1} = \frac{2 L_a J_C \sinh(W_N / L_a)}{qp(W_{NB+})(\mu_n + \mu_p)} \left\{ \tanh^{-1}\left[e^{-(W_{ON}/L_a)} \right] - \tanh^{-1}\left[e^{-(W_N/L_a)} \right] \right\}$$

[17.23]

The depletion width (W_{ON}) across the P-base/N-base junction (J_2) in the on-state depends on the on-state voltage drop. It can be obtained by an iterative process. The voltage drop associated with the second part is given by:

$$V_{B2} = \frac{kT}{q} \left(\frac{\mu_n - \mu_p}{\mu_n + \mu_p} \right) \ln \left[\frac{\tanh(W_{ON}/L_a)\cosh(W_{ON}/L_a)}{\tanh(W_N/L_a)\cosh(W_N/L_a)} \right]$$

[17.24]

For the planar gate IGBT structure considered here, the voltage drop across the MOSFET portion includes the channel, accumulation, and JFET regions[16]. The contribution from channel is given by:

$$V_{CH} = \frac{J_C L_{CH} W_{CELL}}{2\mu_{ni} C_{OX} (V_G - V_{TH})}$$

[17.25]

The contribution from JFET region is given by:

$$V_{JFET} = \frac{J_C \rho_{JFET} (t_{P+} + W_0) W_{CELL}}{W_{JFET} - 2W_0}$$

[17.26]

The contribution from accumulation layer is given by:

$$V_{ACC} = \frac{J_C K_A W_{JFET} W_{CELL}}{4\mu_{nA} C_{OX} (V_G - V_{TH})}$$

[17.27]

The on-state voltage drop (at an on-state current density of 25 A/cm^2) computed for the 20-kV asymmetric n-channel 4H-SiC IGBT structure by using the above equations is provided in Fig. 17.4 as a function of the high-level lifetime in the N-base region. This asymmetric 4H-SiC IGBT structure had the optimized N-base region width of 165 μm and N-buffer layer width of 5 μm. The N-buffer layer doping concentration was kept at 5×10^{16} cm^{-3} for all the cases. From the figure, it can be observed that the on-state voltage drop is close that of the collector/N-buffer layer junction (~ 3.2 V) when the high-level lifetime is greater than 2 μs. The on-state voltage drop increases rapidly when the high-level lifetime is reduced below 0.6 μs due an increase in the voltage drop across the N-base region. This is consistent with the lack of conductivity modulation of the drift region when the lifetime (τ_{p0}) becomes less than 0.3 μs as shown in Fig. 17.3. The on-state voltage drop is predicted as 3.65 V for a high-level lifetime of 1 μs in the N-base region using the analytical model. It increases rapidly to 7.5 V for the case of a high-level lifetime of 0.4 μs.

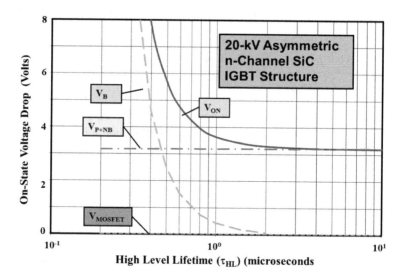

Fig. 17.4 On-state voltage drop for the 20-kV asymmetric 4H-SiC n-channel IGBT structure: N-base lifetime dependence.

The on-state voltage drop for a 16-kV n-channel 4H-SiC IGBT has been reported[19] to be 5 V at an on-state current density of 100 A/cm^2. The on-state voltage drop for a 22 kV, 1 cm^2 4H-SiC n-channel IGBT has been reported[15] as 7.5 V at 20-A. The lifetime in the drift region was not provided in these papers. The on-state voltage drop for an n-channel

4H-SiC IGBT has been reported[21] to increase when the buffer layer thickness is increased from 2 to 5 μm. This is consistent with the above analytical model because the injected excess carrier density in the N-base region is reduced when the buffer layer thickness is increased. The on-state voltage drop for an n-channel 4H-SiC IGBT capable of supporting 27.5-kV was reported[20] as 11.7 V due to its large (210 μm) thick drift layer.

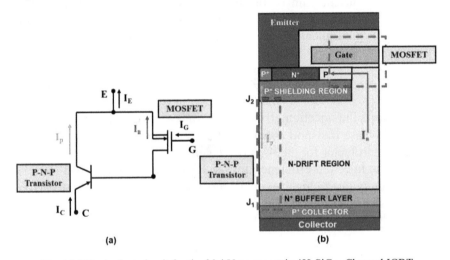

Fig. 17.5 Equivalent circuit for the 20-kV asymmetric 4H-SiC n-Channel IGBT structure in the on-state.

The equivalent circuit for an n-channel IGBT structure[16] based upon the P-N-P Transistor/MOSFET model consists of an n-channel MOSFET providing the base drive current to a P-N-P transistor as shown in Fig. 17.15(a). The P-N-P transistor and MOSFET portions are identified by the red dashed boxes in cross-section shown in Fig. 17.5(b). The emitter current for the IGBT structure consists of the hole current (I_p) flow (green arrow) via the P-N-P transistor and the electron current (I_n) flow (red arrow) via the MOSFET portion:

$$I_E = I_p + I_n \qquad [17.28]$$

The electron current serves as the base drive current for the P-N-P transistor. Consequently, these currents are inter-related by the common base current gain of the P-N-P transistor:

$$I_p = \alpha_{PNP} I_E = \alpha_{PNP} I_C \qquad [17.29]$$

and:

$$I_n = \left(1 - \alpha_{PNP}\right)I_E = \left(1 - \alpha_{PNP}\right)I_C \qquad [17.30]$$

because, under steady-state operating conditions, the gate current (I_G) for the IGBT structure is zero due to the high impedance of the MOS gate structure.

The current gain of the P-N-P transistor is determined by the product of the emitter injection efficiency and the base transport factor because the multiplication coefficient is unity at the low on-state bias voltages:

$$\alpha_{PNP} = \gamma_{E,ON} . \alpha_{T,NB} . \alpha_{T,NBL} \qquad [17.31]$$

where $\gamma_{E,ON}$ is the injection efficiency of transistor emitter in the on-state, $\alpha_{T,NB}$ is the base transport factor for the N-base region, and $\alpha_{T,NBL}$ is the base transport factor for the N-buffer layer.

The injection efficiency for the IGBT structure in the on-state is less than unity due to high-level injection conditions in the N-base region and N-buffer layer region. The injection efficiency in the on-state can be obtained by using:

$$\gamma_{E,ON} = \frac{J_p\left(J_1\right)}{J_{C,ON}} \qquad [17.32]$$

where $J_p(J_1)$ is the hole current density at junction J_1, which can computed using:

$$J_P\left(J_1\right) = \frac{qD_{pNB}P_{NB}\left(0\right)}{L_{pNB}} \qquad [17.33]$$

The base transport factor for the N-base region in the on-state can be obtained by using[16]:

$$\alpha_{T,N-Base,0} = \frac{J_p\left(W_N\right)}{J_p\left(W_{NB}+\right)} \qquad [17.34]$$

where $J_p(W_N)$ is the hole current density at junction J_2 and $J_p(W_{NB}+)$ is the hole current density at interface between the N-base region and the N-buffer layer. These current densities can be obtained by using[16]:

$$J_p\left(W_{NB}+\right)=\left[\left(\frac{\mu_p}{\mu_p+\mu_n}\right)+\left(\frac{\mu_n}{\mu_p+\mu_n}\right)K_{AS}\right]J_C \qquad [17.35]$$

and

$$J_p\left(W_N\right)=\left\{\frac{\left(\dfrac{\mu_p}{\mu_p+\mu_n}\right)-\left(\dfrac{\mu_n K_{AS}}{\mu_p+\mu_n}\right)}{\left[\sinh\left(\dfrac{W_N}{L_a}\right)\tanh\left(\dfrac{W_N}{L_a}\right)-\cosh\left(\dfrac{W_N}{L_a}\right)\right]}\right\}J_C \qquad [17.36]$$

The base transport factor in the conductivity modulated lightly doped portion of the N-base region is enhanced by the combination of drift and diffusion due to the high-level injection conditions.

The base-transport factor associated with the N-buffer layer can be obtained from the decay of the hole current within the N-buffer layer as given by low-level injection theory[16]:

$$\alpha_{T,N-Buffer}=\frac{J_p\left(W_{NB}-\right)}{J_p\left(y_N\right)}=e^{-W_{NBL}/L_{pNB}} \qquad [17.37]$$

The case of the 20-kV asymmetric 4H-SiC n-channel IGBT structure with a N-base region width of 165 μm and a low-level lifetime of 1 μs in the N-base region can be analyzed using the above analytical solutions. The device will be assumed to have an N-buffer layer doping concentration of 5 x 10^{16} cm^{-3} and thickness of 5 μm; and P$^+$ collector region (emitter region of the internal PNP transistor) doping concentration of 1 x 10^{19} cm^{-3}. With these device parameters, the injected concentration of holes [$p_{NB}(0)$] in the N-buffer layer at the junction (J_1) is found to be 6.9 x 10^{16} cm^{-3} by using Eq. [17.14]. Using this value in Eq. [17.32], the injection efficiency in the on-state is found to be 0.959. With these parameters, the base transport factor for the N-base region is found to be 0.285 by using Eq. [17.34] and the base transport factor for the N-buffer layer is found to be 0.631 by using Eq. [17.37]. Combining these values, the common base current gain of the PNP transistor (α_{PNP}) in the on-state is found to be 0.172. Based up on this analysis, it can be concluded that only 17 percent of the emitter current of the 20-kV asymmetric 4H-SiC n-channel IGBT structure is due to the hole current component (I_p) and most of the current flow consists of the electron current (I_n) at the emitter side. This has been confirmed by numerical simulations[21].

17.1.3 Turn-Off Characteristics

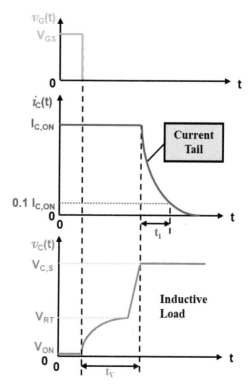

Fig. 17.6 Turn-off waveforms for the asymmetric n-channel 4H-SiC IGBT structure for an inductive load.

The turn-off behavior for the asymmetric 4H-SiC IGBT structure can be expected to be similar to that for the silicon asymmetric IGBT structure. However, the doping concentration of the drift region in the silicon carbide devices is two orders to magnitude larger than that for the silicon devices. This has a significant impact on the turn-off waveforms.

In the case of the silicon device, the hole concentration in the space charge region during the voltage rise-time becomes larger than the doping concentration in the drift region. This additional charge in the space charge region reduces its width to less than the width of the N-base region during the entire voltage transient. This holds true because the DC supply voltage is typically two-thirds of the voltage rating of the Si IGBT. Consequently, the space-charge-region does not reach-though to the N-buffer layer at the end of the voltage rise-time when the collector voltage becomes equal to the DC supply voltage. During the current fall-time, the stored charge remaining in the N-base region must be first removed until the space-charge-region punches through to the N-buffer layer. This is followed by the recombination of the stored charge in the buffer layer. For the asymmetric silicon IGBT structure, a single phase is observed for the voltage transient while the current decays in two phases[21].

In contrast, the hole concentration in the space charge region during the voltage rise-time for the asymmetric 4H-SiC IGBT structure is much smaller than the doping concentration of the drift region. Consequently, the space-charge-region reaches-through to the buffer layer during the voltage rise-time at a collector bias that is well below the DC supply voltage. The electric field in the N-base region takes a trapezoidal shape after the space-charge-region reaches-through to the buffer layer, allowing the collector voltage to rise at a much more rapid rate until it reaches the supply voltage. All the stored charge in the N-base region is therefore removed during the voltage rise-time. During the current fall-time, the stored charge in the buffer layer is removed by recombination. This occurs with a single current decay transient.

In order to turn-off the IGBT structure, the gate voltage must simply be reduced from the on-state value (nominally 15 volts) to zero as illustrated in Fig. 17.6. The magnitude of the gate current can be limited by using a resistance in series with the gate voltage source. The waveform for the gate voltage shown in the figure is for the case of zero gate resistance. Once the gate voltage falls below the threshold voltage, the electron current from the channel ceases. In the case of an inductive load, the collector current for the IGBT structure is then sustained by the hole current flow due to the presence of stored charge in the N-base region. The collector voltage begins to increase in the IGBT structure immediately after the gate voltage reduces below the threshold voltage.

17.1.3.1 Voltage Rise-Time:

The analysis of the turn-off waveform for the collector voltage transient for the asymmetric 4H-SiC IGBT structure can be performed by using the charge control principle. The concentration p_{WNB+} in the on-state at the interface between the lightly doped portion of the N-base region and the N-buffer layer was previously derived for the silicon carbide asymmetric IGBT structure in section 17.1.2. To develop the analysis of the collector voltage transient, it will be assumed that the hole concentration profile in the N-base region does not change due to recombination. In this case, the electric field profile in the asymmetric 4H-SiC IGBT structure during the collector voltage transient is illustrated in Fig. 17.7. As the space charge region expands towards the collector side, holes are removed from the stored charge region at its boundary. The holes then flow through the space charge region at their saturated drift velocity due to the high electric field in the space charge region.

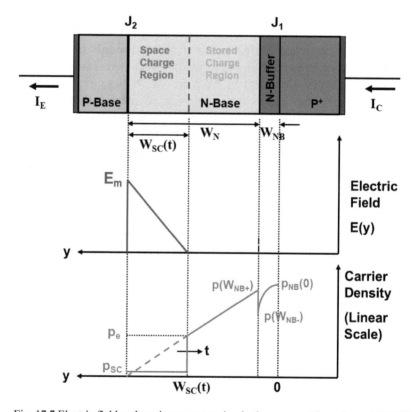

Fig. 17.7 Electric field and carrier concentration in the asymmetric n-channel 4H-SiC IGBT structure during the voltage transient with inductive load.

The concentration of holes at the edge of the space-charge region (p_e) increases during the turn-off process as the space-charge width (W_{SC}) increases:

$$p_e(t) = p(W_{NB+}) \frac{\sinh\left[W_{SC}(t)/L_a\right]}{\sinh\left[(W_N + W_{NB})/L_a\right]}$$
[17.38]

This equation is based on the hole carrier distribution given by Eq. [17.20] which is similar in shape to the linear distribution illustrated in Fig. 17.7. According to the charge-control principle, the charge removed by the expansion of the space-charge layer must equal the charge removed due to collector current flow:

$$J_{C,ON} = qp_e(t)\frac{dW_{SC}(t)}{dt} = qp(W_{NB+})\frac{\sinh\left[W_{SC}(t)/L_a\right]}{\sinh\left[(W_N + W_{NB})/L_a\right]}\frac{dW_{SC}(t)}{dt}$$
[17.39]

by using Eq. [17.38]. Integrating this equation on both sides and applying the boundary condition of width $W_{SC}(0)$ for the space-charge layer at time zero provides the solution for the evolution of the space-charge region width with time:

$$W_{SC}(t) = L_a \, a\cosh\left\{ \frac{J_{C,ON}\sinh\left[(W_N + W_{NBL})/L_a\right]}{qL_a p(W_{NB+})}t + \cosh\left[W_{SC}(0)/L_a\right] \right\}$$
[17.40]

The space-charge layer expands towards the right-hand-side as indicated by the horizontal time arrow in Fig. 17.7 with the hole concentration profile in the stored charge region remaining unchanged.

The collector voltage supported by the asymmetric silicon carbide IGBT structure is related to the space charge layer width by:

$$V_C(t) = \frac{q(N_D + p_{SC})W_{SC}^2(t)}{2\varepsilon_S}$$
[17.41]

The hole concentration (p_{SC}) in the space-charge layer can be related to the collector current density under the assumption that the carriers are moving at the saturated drift velocity in the space-charge layer:

$$p_{SC} = \frac{J_{C,ON}}{q v_{sat,p}}$$ [17.42]

The hole concentration in the space-charge region (psc) remains constant during the voltage rise-time because the collector current density is constant. Consequently, the slope of the electric field profile in the space-charge region also becomes independent of time. This analytical model for turn-off of the asymmetric 4H-SiC IGBT structure under inductive load conditions predicts a non-linear increase in the collector voltage with time.

The collector voltage increases in accordance with the above model until the space charge region reaches-through to the N-base region. The reach-through voltage during the turn-off of the asymmetric 4H-SiC IGBT must be computed with inclusion of the positive charge due to the presence of holes in the space-charge-region associated with the collector current flow:

$$V_{RT}\left(J_{C,ON}\right) = \frac{q\left(N_D + p_{SC}\right)W_N^2}{2\varepsilon_S}$$ [17.43]

For the asymmetric 4H-SiC n-channel IGBT structure, the hole concentration in the space-charge-region (psc) computed using Eq. [17.42] is 1.8×10^{13} cm^{-3} at an on-state current density of 25 A/cm^2 based up on a saturated velocity of 8.6×10^6 cm/s for holes. This is much smaller than the doping concentration of the N-base region (typically 1.5×10^{14} cm^{-3}). For the case of the 20-kV asymmetric silicon carbide IGBT structure with an N-base width of 165 microns and doping concentration of 1.5×10^{14} cm^{-3}, the reach-through voltage is found to be 4262 V. In contrast, the reach-through voltage under forward blocking operation is only 3150 V.

The time at which reach-through occurs can be derived from Eq. [17.40] by setting the space-charge-region width equal to the width of the N-base region:

$$t_{RT} = \frac{q L_a p\left(W_{NB} +\right)}{J_{C,ON}}\left\{\frac{\cosh\left[W_N / L_a\right] - \cosh\left[W_{SC}\left(0\right)/ L_a\right]}{\sinh\left[\left(W_N + W_{NB}\right)/ L_a\right]}\right\}$$ [17.44]

Once the space-charge-region reaches-through the N-base region, all the stored charge in the N-base region has been removed by the voltage transient. However, there is still substantial stored charge in the N-buffer layer. The expansion of the space-charge-region is now curtailed by the high doping concentration of the N-buffer layer.

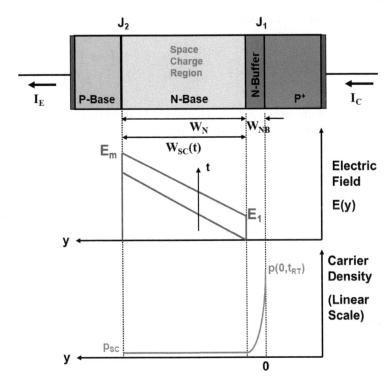

Fig. 17.8 Electric field and carrier distribution in the asymmetric 4H-SiC IGBT structure during the second phase of the voltage rise-time with inductive load.

The end of the first phase of the turn-off process occurs when the collector voltage rises to the reach-through voltage (V_{RT}). At this time, the space-charge-region has reached the edge of the N-buffer layer. This forces the hole concentration at the edge of the space-charge-region (at $y = W_{NB}$ in Fig. 17.8) to the hole concentration (p_{SC}) inside the space-charge-region, which is close to zero when compared with the injected hole concentration at the junction (J_1). The hole concentration in the N-buffer layer at junction (J_1) changes abruptly when reach-through occurs in order to maintain the same current density because the collector current density is held fixed during the voltage rise-time.

The hole concentration [$p(0,t_{RT})$] in the N-buffer layer at junction (J_1) during the second phase of the voltage rise-time can be obtained by analysis of current transport in the N-buffer layer. The hole concentration distribution in the N-buffer layer has the same boundary conditions as the base region of a bipolar transistor operating in its active region with finite recombination in the base region[16]:

$$p(y) = p(0, t_{RT}) \left\{ \frac{\sinh\left[(W_{NBL} - y)/L_{pNB} \right]}{\sinh\left(W_{NBL} / L_{pNB} \right)} \right\}$$ [17.45]

The hole current density ($J_p(0)$) in the buffer layer at the junction (J_1) is equal to the collector current density ($J_{C,ON}$):

$$J_p(0) = qD_{pNB} \left. \frac{dp}{dy} \right|_{y=0} = J_{C,ON}$$ [17.46]

The hole concentration ($p(0,t_{RT})$) at junction J_1 can be obtained by substituting Eq. [17.45] for the hole carrier distribution:

$$p(0, t_{RT}) = \frac{J_{C,ON} L_{pNB} \tanh\left(W_{NBL} / L_{pNB} \right)}{qD_{pNB}}$$ [17.47]

Substituting this into Eq. [17.45] gives the hole distribution in the buffer layer:

$$p(y) = \frac{J_{C,ON} L_{pNB}}{qD_{pNB}} \left\{ \frac{\sinh\left[(W_{NBL} - y)/L_{pNB} \right]}{\cosh\left(W_{NBL} / L_{pNB} \right)} \right\}$$ [17.48]

This hole distribution in the buffer layer is illustrated in Fig. 17.8.

During the second phase of the voltage rise-time, the electric field in the N-base region must increase with a punch-through distribution because of the high doping concentration of the N-buffer layer. As the electric field at the interface between the N-base region and the N-buffer layer grows with increasing collector voltage, a small depletion layer is formed in the N-buffer layer. The formation of the depletion region in the N-buffer layer requires removal of electrons from the donors within the N-buffer layer with an electron current (displacement current) flow towards the collector contact. The electron current available at the interface between the N-base region and the N-buffer layer is determined by the hole current in the N-buffer layer. The hole current at the interface between the N-base region and the N-buffer layer can be obtained from the hole concentration profile given by Eq. [17.48]:

$$J_p\left(W_{NB}\right) = qD_{pNB}\left.\frac{dp}{dy}\right|_{y=W_{NBL}} = \frac{J_{C,ON}}{\cosh\left(W_{NBL}/L_{pNB}\right)} \qquad [17.49]$$

Consequently, the displacement current is given by:

$$J_D = J_n\left(W_{NBL}\right) = J_{C,ON} - J_p\left(W_{NBL}\right) = J_{C,ON}\left[1 - \frac{1}{\cosh\left(W_{NBL}/L_{pNB}\right)}\right]$$

$$[17.50]$$

The capacitance of the space-charge-region during the second phase of the voltage rise-time is independent of the collector voltage because the space-charge-region width is essentially equal to the width of the N-base region because the depletion width in the N-buffer layer is very small due to its high doping concentration. The (specific) capacitance of the space-charge-region can be obtained using:

$$C_{SCR} = \frac{\varepsilon_S}{W_N} \qquad [17.51]$$

The rate of rise of the collector voltage based up on charging the space-charge-region capacitance is given by:

$$\frac{dV_C}{dt} = \frac{J_D}{C_{SCR}} \qquad [17.52]$$

Using Eq. [17.50]:

$$\frac{dV_C}{dt} = \frac{J_{C,ON}}{C_{SCR}}\left[1 - \frac{1}{\cosh\left(W_{NBL}/L_{pNB}\right)}\right] \qquad [17.53]$$

The collector voltage waveform after reach-through is then given by:

$$V_C\left(t\right) = V_{RT}\left(J_{C,ON}\right) + \frac{J_{C,ON}}{C_{SCR}}\left[1 - \frac{1}{\cosh\left(W_{NBL}/L_{pNB}\right)}\right]t \qquad [17.54]$$

According to this analytical model, the collector voltage should increase linearly with time after the space-charge-region reaches-through the N-base region. The end of the voltage rise-time occurs when the collector voltage becomes equal to the collector supply voltage ($V_{C,S}$). Using this criterion in Eq. [17.54], the collector voltage rise-time interval is obtained:

$$t_V = t_{RT} + \frac{\varepsilon_S}{J_{C,ON} W_N} \left[\frac{\cosh\left(W_{NBL} / L_{pNB}\right)}{\cosh\left(W_{NBL} / L_{pNB}\right) - 1} \right] \left[V_{C,S} - V_{RT}\left(J_{C,ON}\right) \right]$$

[17.55]

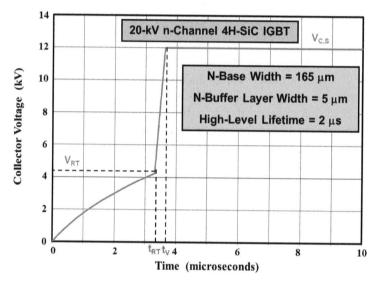

Fig. 17.9 Collector voltage waveform for the asymmetric n-channel 4H-SiC IGBT structure during inductive load turn-off.

Consider the case of the 20-kV asymmetric 4H-SiC n-channel IGBT structure with a N-base region width of 165 µm and a low-level lifetime of 1 µs in the N-base region; N-buffer layer doping concentration of 5 x 10^{16} cm^{-3} and thickness of 5 µm; and P$^+$ collector region (emitter region of the internal PNP transistor) doping concentration of 1 x 10^{19} cm^{-3}. The collector voltage waveform predicted by the above analytical model is provided in Fig. 17.9 for the case of a high-level lifetime of 2 µs and collector supply voltage of 12,000 V. A collector current density of 25 A/cm^2 was used in this example. It can be observed that the collector voltage increases in a non-linear manner until a reach-through time (t_{RT}) of 3.3 µs. The reach-through collector voltage (V_{RT}) is

4260 V. After the reach-through of the space-charge-region, the collector voltage increases in a linear manner with a high [dV/dt] of 2.43×10^{10} V/s. The collector voltage becomes equal to the collector supply voltage of 12,000 V at time (t_V) of 3.63 μs. This behavior of the voltage transient has been observed with numerical simulations[21] and experimental tests[22].

17.1.3.2 Current Fall-Time:

At the end of the collector voltage transient in the asymmetric 4H-SiC IGBT, the space-charge-region has extended through the entire N-base region leaving stored charge only in the N-buffer layer. The collector current decays due to the recombination of this stored charge under low-level injection conditions. Unlike in the case of the silicon IGBT, the collector current transient occurs in a single phase as described by:

$$J_C(t) = J_{C,ON} e^{-t/\tau_{BL}} \qquad [17.56]$$

where t_{BL} is the low-level lifetime in the N-buffer layer.

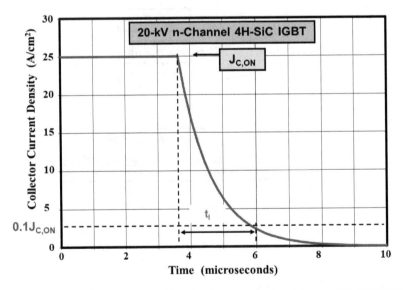

Fig. 17.10 Collector current waveform for the asymmetric n-Channel 4H-SiC IGBT structure during inductive load turn-off.

The collector current waveform for the 20-kV n-channel 4H-SiC asymmetric IGBT structure obtained by using the above model is provided in Fig. 17.10. The current fall-time is defined as the time taken for the current to reduce to 10 percent of the on-state value. In this case, the current fall time obtained by using Eq. [17.56] is:

$$t_I = 2.303 \, \tau_{BL} \qquad\qquad [17.57]$$

For the above example, the current-fall time is found to be 2.3 µs if no scaling of the lifetime with buffer layer doping is taken into account. The results of numerical simulations support the analytical models derived here[21]. In addition, the turn-off waveforms for the 22 kV asymmetric 4H-SiC n-channel IGBT are very similar to those described by the analytical model[22].

17.1.4 Lifetime Dependence

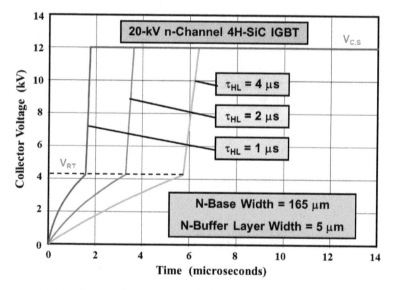

Fig. 17.11 Collector voltage transients during turn-off for the 20-kV asymmetric n-channel 4H-SiC IGBT structure with inductive load: drift lifetime dependence.

Optimization of the power losses for the IGBT structure requires performing a trade-off between the on-state voltage drop and the switching losses[16]. One approach to achieve this is by adjusting the lifetime in the drift (N-base) region. A reduction of the lifetime in the drift region also alters the lifetime in the N-buffer layer in the case of silicon devices. A relationship between the lifetime in the drift region and the buffer layer has not yet been established for silicon carbide devices. Consequently, it will be assumed that the lifetime in the N-buffer layer is the same as that in the N-base region for silicon carbide structures for this section. The impact of independently optimizing the lifetime in the buffer layer has been analyzed for 15-kV asymmetric 4H-SiC IGBT structures[10].

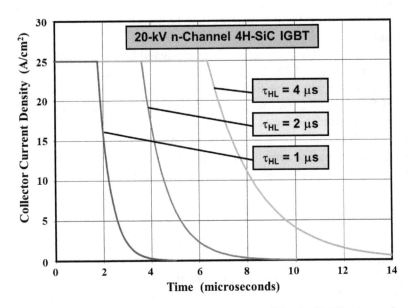

Fig. 17.12 Collector current transients during turn-off for the 20-kV asymmetric n-channel 4H-SiC IGBT structure with inductive load: drift lifetime dependence.

The impact of reducing the lifetime in the drift region on the on-state voltage drop for the 20-kV asymmetric n-channel 4H-SiC IGBT structure was previously discussed in section 17.1.2. As in the case of silicon devices, the on-state voltage drop increases when the lifetime is reduced. The analytical model developed for turn-off of the asymmetric 4H-SiC IGBT structure can be used to analyze the impact of changes to the lifetime in the drift region on the turn-off characteristics. The collector voltage transients predicted by the analytical model are shown in Fig. 17.11 for the case of the 20-kV asymmetric 4H-SiC IGBT structure operating with an on-state current density of 25 A/cm^2. The voltage rise-time increases when the lifetime is increased because of the larger concentration for the holes in the N-base region that are being removed during the collector voltage transient. The voltage rise-times obtained by using the analytical model are 1.77, 3.63, and 6.38 μs for high-level lifetime values of 1, 2, and 4 μs, respectively. In all cases, the reach-through voltage of has the same value (4262 V) as predicted by Eq. [17.42]. However, the rate of increase in the collector voltage [dV/dt] during the second phase of the voltage transient becomes larger when the lifetime is reduced. The collector voltage [dV/dt] increases from 1.24 x 10^{10} V/s to 4.66 x 10^{10} V/s when the high-level lifetime is reduced from 4 to 1 μs. These high dV/dt transients may be an issue in power electronic applications.

The collector current transients predicted by the analytical model are shown in Fig. 17.12. It can be observed that the current transient becomes longer when the lifetime in the N-base region increases. The current fall-time increases when the lifetime is increased because of the reduced recombination rate in the N-buffer layer during the current transient. According to the analytical model, the current fall-times obtained by using the analytical model are 1.15, 2.30, and 4.61 μs for high-level lifetime values of 1, 2, and 4 μs, respectively.

17.1.5 Switching Energy Loss

The power loss incurred during the turn-off switching transient limits the maximum operating frequency for the IGBT structure. Power losses during the turn-on of the IGBT structure are also significant but strongly dependent on the reverse recovery behavior of the fly-back rectifiers in circuits. Consequently, it is common practice to use only the turn-off energy loss per cycle during characterization of IGBT devices. The turn-off losses are associated with the voltage rise-time interval and the current fall-time interval. The energy loss for each event can be computed by integration of the power loss, as given by the product of the instantaneous current and voltage. During the voltage rise-time interval, the anode current is constant while the voltage increases in a non-linear manner as a function of time until reach-through occurs. In order to simplify the analysis, the energy loss during this interval can be computed using:

$$E_{OFF,V1} = \frac{1}{2} J_{C,ON} V_{RT} t_{RT}$$ [17.58]

with t_{RT} given by Eq. [17.44]. During the second phase of the voltage rise-time, the collector voltage increases linearly with time while the collector current is constant. The energy loss during this interval can be computed using:

$$E_{OFF,V2} = \frac{1}{2} J_{C,ON} \left(V_{C,S} - V_{RT} \right) \left(t_V - t_{RT} \right)$$ [17.59]

For the typical switching waveforms for the 20-kV asymmetric n-channel 4H-SiC IGBT structure shown in Fig. 17.9 with a collector supply voltage of 12,000 V, the energy loss per unit area during the collector voltage rise-time is found to be 0.24 J/cm² if the on-state current density is 25 A/cm².

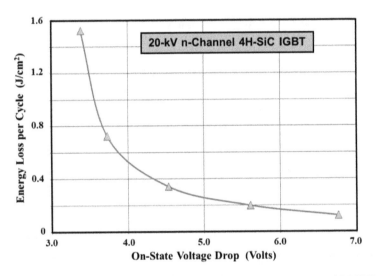

Fig. 17.13 Trade-off curve for the 20-kV asymmetric n-channel 4H-SiC IGBT structure: by lifetime variation in N-base (drift) region.

During the collector current fall-time interval, the collector voltage is constant while the current decreases exponentially with time. The energy loss during the collector current fall-time interval can be computed using:

$$E_{OFF,I} = J_{C,ON} V_{C,S} \tau_{BL}$$ [17.60]

For the typical switching waveform for the 20-kV asymmetric n-channel 4H-SiC IGBT structure shown in Fig. 17.10 with a collector supply voltage of 12,000 V, the energy loss per unit area during the collector current fall-time is found to be 0.30 J/cm² if the on-state current density is 25 A/cm². The total energy loss per unit area ($E_{OFF,V} + E_{OFF,I}$) during the turn-off process for the 20-kV asymmetric n-channel 4H-SiC IGBT structure is then found to be 0.54 J/cm^2.

Using the results obtained from the numerical simulations[20], the on-state voltage drop and the total energy loss per cycle can be computed. These values are plotted in Fig. 17.13 to create a trade-off curve to optimize the performance of the 20-kV asymmetric n-channel 4H-SiC IGBT structure by varying the lifetime in the N-base region. Devices used in lower frequency circuits would be chosen from the left-hand-side of the trade-off curve while devices used in higher frequency circuits would be chosen from the right-hand-side of the trade-off curve.

17.1.6 Maximum Operating Frequency

The maximum frequency for operation of the 20-kV asymmetric n-channel 4H-SiC IGBT structure is limited by the junction temperature reaching a reliability based limit. The junction temperature is determined by the total power loss and thermal impedance. The total power loss is obtained by combining the on-state and switching power losses:

$$P_{D,TOTAL} = \delta\, P_{D,ON} + E_{OFF}\, f \qquad [17.61]$$

where δ is the duty cycle (device on-time divided by period of switching cycle) and f is the switching frequency.

High-Level Lifetime (μs)	On-State Voltage Drop (Volts)	On-State Power Dissipation (W/cm²)	Energy Loss per Cycle (J/cm²)	Maximum Operating Frequency (Hz)
4	3.39	42.3	1.523	104
2	3.73	46.6	0.725	212
1	4.54	56.7	0.341	420
0.6	5.61	70.1	0.198	656
0.4	6.76	84.5	0.122	947

Table 17.1 Power loss analysis for the 20-kV asymmetric n-channel 4H-SiC IGBT structure.

In the case of the baseline 20-kV asymmetric n-channel 4H-SiC IGBT device structure with a high-level lifetime of 2 μs in the N-base region, the on-state voltage drop is 3.73 V at an on-state current density of 25 A/cm^2. For the case of a 50 % duty cycle, the on-state power dissipation contributes 47 W/cm² to the total power loss. For this lifetime value, the energy loss per cycle during the voltage rise-time obtained from the numerical simulations is 0.425 J/cm² and the energy loss per cycle during the current fall-time obtained from the numerical simulations is 0.300 J/cm². Using a total turn-off energy loss per cycle of 0.725 J/cm² in Eq. [17.61] yields a maximum operating frequency of about 212 Hz.

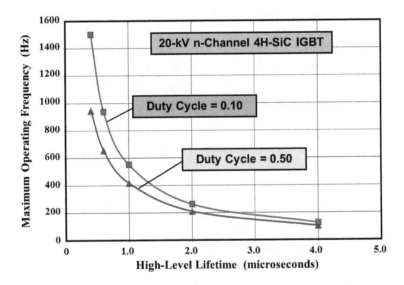

Fig. 17.14 Maximum operating frequency for the 20-kV asymmetric n-channel 4H-SiC IGBT structure.

The maximum operating frequency for the 20-kV asymmetric n-channel 4H-SiC IGBT structure can be increased by reducing the lifetime in the N-base region. The on-state voltage drop and the energy loss per cycle can be computed by using the results obtained from the numerical simulations[20]. These values are provided in Table 17.1 together with the maximum operating frequency as a function of the high level lifetime in the N-base region under the assumption of a 50 % duty cycle and a total power dissipation limit of 200 W/cm². The maximum operating frequency is plotted in Fig. 17.14 as a function of the high-level lifetime in the N-base region. It can be observed that the maximum operating frequency can be increased up to 950 Hz by reducing the high-level lifetime to 0.4 μs. The IGBT is often operated with pulse-width-modulation to synthesize variable frequency output power for motor control. In these applications, the duty cycle can be much shorter than 50 percent. In this case, the maximum operating frequency for the 20-kV asymmetric n-channel 4H-SiC IGBT structure can be increased. As an example, the maximum operating frequency for the 20-kV asymmetric n-channel 4H-SiC IGBT structure operated at a 10 percent duty cycle is included in Fig. 17.14. It can be seen that the maximum operating frequency can now exceed 1500 Hz.

The hard switching frequency limit of operation has been studied[23] for 15-kV n-channel 4H-SiC IGBTs. The authors concluded that operation at 6 kHz was feasible with liquid cooling and a junction temperature of 150 °C. The higher values for the switching frequency for these devices when compared with the analytical values plotted in Fig. 17.14 is due to the lower blocking voltage rating and liquid cooling to tolerate larger power dissipation.

17.2 Optimized n-Channel Asymmetric Structure

In the previous section, it was shown that the 20-kV asymmetric n-channel 4H-SiC IGBT structure exhibits a collector voltage turn-off waveform consisting of two phases. In the first phase, the collector voltage increases gradually up to a reach-through voltage and then during the second phase the collector voltage increases very rapidly with time until it reaches the collector supply voltage. This produces a high [dV/dt] which is not desirable during circuit operation. The second phase can be prevented from occurring by optimization of the doping concentration and width of the N-base region so that the reach-through of the space-charge-region occurs when the collector voltage becomes equal to the collector supply voltage[20]. The design and performance of this optimized 20-kV asymmetric 4H-SiC IGBT structure is discussed in this section.

17.2.1 Structural Optimization

An expression (see Eq. [17.43]) for the reach-through voltage was derived in the previous section. It can be concluded from this equation that the reach-through voltage is a function of the width and the doping concentration of the drift region, as well as the on-state current density. During optimization, it is necessary to choose these values after obtaining the hole concentration in the space-charge-region using the on-state current density. Although Eq. [17.43] indicates that the reach-through voltage can be increased by solely increasing the doping concentration of the N-base region, this approach results in a reduction of the blocking voltage. Consequently, the width and the doping concentration of the N-base region must be optimized together to simultaneously obtain the desired open-base breakdown voltage of 21-kV and a reach-through voltage equal to a collector supply voltage of 12-kV (as an example).

The width of the N-base region required to achieve a blocking voltage of 21-kV is shown in Fig. 17.15 based up on using open base transistor breakdown physics. A low-level lifetime of 1 µs was assumed in the drift region for the analysis. An N-buffer layer doping concentration of 5 x 10^{16} cm^{-3} was assumed with a thickness of 5 µm for this baseline device structure. For each value of the N-base doping concentration, its width was varied until the common-base current gain became equal to unity.

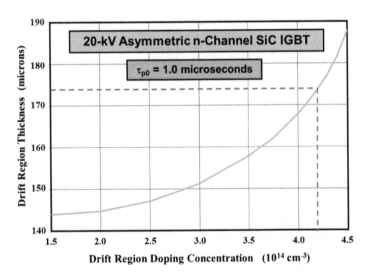

Fig. 17.15 Optimization of drift region width for the 20-kV asymmetric 4H-SiC n-channel IGBT structure.

The reach-through voltage can be computed by using Eq. [17.43] using the optimum width for the N-base region corresponding to each doping concentration. The resulting values for the reach-through voltage are plotted in Fig. 17.16 as a function of the drift region doping concentration. From this plot, it can be observed that a reach-through voltage of 12-kV is obtained when the drift region doping concentration is 4.2 x 10^{14} cm^{-3}. For this drift region doping concentration, an open-base breakdown voltage of 21-kV is obtained if a drift region width of 175 μm is used according to Fig. 17.15. These values must be chosen for the optimized 20-kV n-channel asymmetric 4H-SiC IGBT structure to avoid the high dV/dt transient during turn-off.

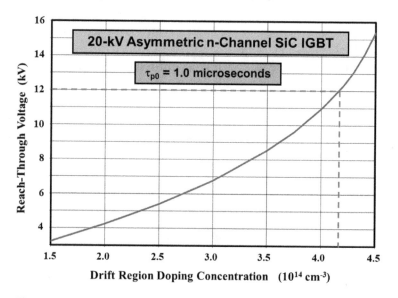

Fig. 17.16 Reach-through voltage for the 20-kV asymmetric 4H-SiC n-channel IGBT structure.

17.2.2 Blocking Characteristics

The physics of operation of the optimized 20-kV n-channel asymmetric 4H-SiC IGBT structure is similar to that of the structure discussed in the previous section. However, the electric field profile and the reach-through voltage for the optimized structure are altered due to the larger doping concentration and thickness of the drift region. Due to the larger doping concentration of 4.2 x 10^{14} cm^{-3} for the optimized 20-kV n-channel asymmetric 4H-SiC IGBT structure, the slope of the electric field profile in the N-base region can be expected to be nearly 3-times larger than for the previous structure. In addition, the reach-through voltage for the depletion region increases from 4000 V to 12,000 V due to the larger doping concentration and thickness of the N-base region as predicted by using Eq. [17.43]. These conclusion have been verified by numerical simulations[20].

17.2.3 On-State Voltage Drop

The physics of operation in the on-state for the optimized 20-kV n-channel asymmetric 4H-SiC IGBT structure is identical to that for the structure discussed in the previous section. Based up on the high-level injection model for the IGBT structure, the on-state voltage drop for the optimized structure can be expected to be slightly greater than that for the previous structure for the same lifetime in the N-base region due to its larger width. This has been verified by numerical simulations[20]. The elimination of the high [dV/dt] during the turn-off transient in the 4H-SiC IGBT must be traded-off against the higher on-state power loss.

17.2.4 Turn-Off Characteristics

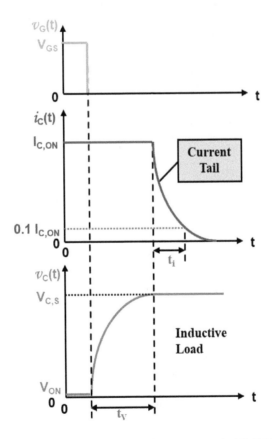

Fig. 17.17 Turn-off waveforms for the optimized asymmetric 4H-SiC IGBT structure with inductive load.

The turn-off behavior for the optimized 20-kV n-channel asymmetric 4H-SiC IGBT structure can be expected to be quite different from that for the 20-kV n-channel asymmetric 4H-SiC IGBT structure discussed in the previous section. In the optimized structure, the collector voltage should increase during a single phase to the DC supply voltage and the collector current should then decay by the recombination of holes in the N-buffer layer. The rise of the collector voltage is described by the physics developed for the previous structure during the first phase (see Eq. [17.40]). The current fall occurs with the same physics that governs the recombination of holes in the buffer layer for both structures (see Eq. [17.56]).

In order to turn-off the IGBT structure, the gate voltage must simply be reduced from the on-state value (nominally 15 volts) to zero as illustrated in Fig. 17.17. The magnitude of the gate current can be limited by using a resistance in series with the gate voltage source. The waveform for the gate voltage shown in the figure is for the case of zero gate resistance. Once the gate voltage falls below the threshold voltage, the electron current from the channel ceases. In the case of an inductive load, the collector current for the IGBT structure is then sustained by the hole current flow due to the presence of stored charge in the N-base region. The collector voltage begins to increase in the IGBT structure immediately after the gate voltage reduces below the threshold voltage.

17.2.4.1 Voltage Rise-Time:

The analysis of the turn-off waveform for the collector voltage transient for the optimized asymmetric IGBT structure can be performed by using the same approach as described in the previous section. In the case of the optimized structure, the voltage should increase to the collector supply voltage in a single phase as described by Eq. [17.41]. The collector voltage supported by the optimized asymmetric 4H-SiC IGBT structure is related to the space charge layer width given by Eq. [17.40]. The collector voltage increases in accordance with the above model until the space charge region reaches-through the N-base region when the collector voltage becomes equal to the DC supply voltage.

The time at which the collector voltage transient is completed is given by Eq. [17.44]. Once the space-charge-region reaches-through the N-base region, all the stored charge in the N-base region has been removed by the voltage transient. However, there is still substantial stored charge in the N-buffer layer. The expansion of the space-charge-region is now curtailed by the high doping concentration of the N-buffer layer.

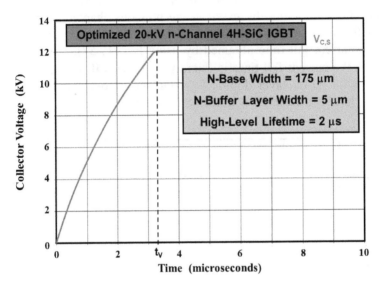

Fig. 17.18 Collector voltage waveform for the optimized asymmetric n-channel 4H-SiC IGBT structure during inductive load turn-off.

Consider the case of the optimized 20-kV asymmetric silicon carbide n-channel IGBT structure with a N-base region width of 175 μm and a high-level lifetime of 2 μs in the N-base region; N-buffer layer doping concentration of 5×10^{16} cm^{-3} and thickness of 5 μm; and P$^+$ collector region (emitter region of the internal PNP transistor) doping concentration of 1×10^{19} cm^{-3}. The collector voltage waveform predicted by the above analytical model is provided in Fig. 17.18 for this structure. A collector current density of 25 A/cm^2 was used in this example. It can be observed that the collector voltage increases monotonically until a reach-through time (t_{RT}) of 3.3 μs when it becomes equal to the collector supply voltage of 12,000 V. This time is identical to the first phase for the IGBT device in the previous section (see Fig. 17.9).

17.2.4.2 Current Fall-Time:

At the end of the collector voltage transient, the space-charge-region has extended through the entire N-base region leaving stored charge only in the N-buffer layer in the case of the optimized 20-kV asymmetric silicon carbide n-channel IGBT structure. The collector current therefore decays due to the recombination of this stored charge under low-level injection conditions. As in the case of the 20-kV asymmetric silicon carbide n-channel IGBT structure discussed in the previous chapter, the collector current transient occurs in a single phase as described by Eq. [17.56] with the current fall time obtained by using Eq. [17.57]. For the above example, the current-fall time is found to be 2.3 μs if no scaling of the lifetime with buffer layer doping is taken into account. This switching behavior has been verified by numerical simulations[20].

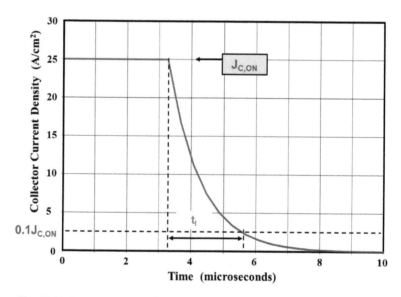

Fig. 17.19 Collector current waveform for the optimized asymmetric n-Channel 4H-SiC IGBT structure during inductive load turn-off.

The collector current waveform for the optimized 20-kV n-channel 4H-SiC asymmetric IGBT structure obtained by using the model is provided in Fig. 17.19. The current fall-time is defined as the time taken for the current to reduce to 10 percent of the on-state value. The current-fall time is found to be 2.3 μs if no scaling of the lifetime with buffer layer doping is taken into account.

17.2.5 Lifetime Dependence

As in the case of the structure discussed in the previous section, it will be assumed that the lifetime in the N-buffer layer is the same as that in the

N-base region for the optimized silicon carbide structure. The on-state voltage drop increases when the lifetime is reduced as discussed in section 17.2.3. The analytical model developed for turn-off of the optimized asymmetric IGBT structure presented in section 17.2.4 can be used to analyze the impact of changes to the lifetime in the drift region on the turn-off characteristics.

The collector voltage transients predicted by the analytical model for three values of high-level lifetime in the drift region are shown in Fig. 17.20 for the case of the optimized 20-kV asymmetric 4H-SiC IGBT structure operating with an on-state current density of 25 A/cm². The voltage rise-time increases when the lifetime is increased because of the larger concentration for the holes in the N-base region that are being removed during the collector voltage transient. The voltage rise-times obtained by using the analytical model are 1.5, 3.3, and 5.8 μs for high-level lifetime values of 1, 2, and 4 μs, respectively. In all cases, the collector voltage increases monotonically to the collector supply voltage of 12,000 V as expected.

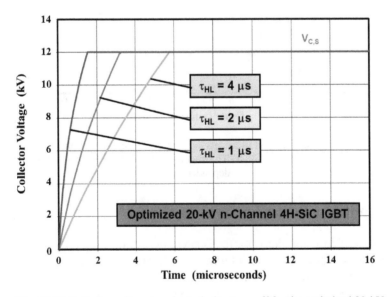

Fig. 17.20 Collector voltage transients during turn-off for the optimized 20-kV asymmetric n-channel 4H-SiC IGBT structure with inductive load: drift lifetime dependence.

The collector current transients predicted by the analytical model for various lifetime values in the drift region for the optimized 20 kV asymmetric SiC IGBT are shown in Fig. 17.21. It can be observed that the current transient becomes longer when the lifetime in the N-base region increases. The current fall-time increases when the lifetime is increased because of the reduced recombination rate in the N-buffer layer during the current transient. According to the analytical model, the current fall-times obtained by using the analytical model are 1.15, 2.30, and 4.61 μs for high-level lifetime values of 1, 2, and 4 μs, respectively.

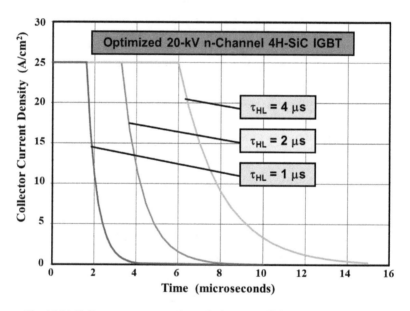

Fig. 17.21 Collector current transients during turn-off for the optimized 20-kV asymmetric n-channel 4H-SiC IGBT structure with inductive load: drift lifetime dependence.

17.2.6 Switching Energy Loss

The turn-off loss for the optimized asymmetric 4H-SiC IGBT structure during the voltage rise-time interval is different from that for the device structure discussed in the previous section. Since the collector voltage transient for the optimized structure occurs in a single phase until it reaches the collector supply voltage, the energy loss during this interval can be computed using:

$$E_{OFF,V} = \frac{1}{2} J_{C,ON} V_{C,S} t_V$$ [17.62]

For the typical switching waveforms for the optimized 20-kV asymmetric n-channel 4H-SiC IGBT structure shown in Fig. 17.18 with a collector supply voltage of 12,000 V, the energy loss per unit area during the collector voltage rise-time is found to be 0.50 J/cm² if the on-state current density is 25 A/cm² which is more than that for the previous structure.

During the collector current fall-time interval, the collector voltage is constant while the current decreases exponentially with time. The energy loss during the collector current fall-time interval can be computed using:

$$E_{OFF,I} = J_{C,ON} V_S \tau_{BL}$$
[17.63]

For the typical switching waveform for the optimized 20-kV asymmetric n-channel 4H-SiC IGBT structure with a collector supply voltage of 12,000 V, the energy loss per unit area during the collector current fall-time is found to be 0.30 J/cm² if the on-state current density is 25 A/cm². This is the same as that for the structure discussed in the previous section. The total energy loss per unit area ($E_{OFF,V} + E_{OFF,I}$) during the turn-off process for the optimized 20-kV asymmetric n-channel 4H-SiC IGBT structure is found to be 0.80 J/cm². It can be concluded that, in order to eliminate an abrupt change in the collector voltage for the asymmetric silicon carbide IGBT structure, it is necessary to tolerate an increase in the switching power loss.

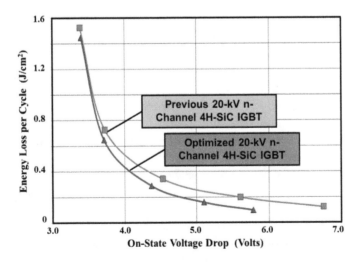

Fig. 17.22 Trade-off curve for the optimized 20-kV asymmetric n-channel 4H-SiC IGBT structure: drift lifetime dependence.

The on-state voltage drop and the total energy loss per cycle can be computed for the optimized 20 kV asymmetric SiC IGBT structure using the results obtained from the numerical simulations[20]. These values are plotted in Fig. 17.22 to create a trade-off curve for the performance of the optimized 20-kV asymmetric n-channel 4H-SiC IGBT structure by varying the lifetime in the N-base region. A duty cycle of 50 % was assumed for this example. Devices used in lower frequency circuits would be chosen from the left-hand-side of the trade-off curve while devices used in higher frequency circuits would be chosen from the right-hand-side of the trade-off curve. It can be seen that the optimized structure has a superior trade-off curve when compared to the previous structure due to its reduced on-state voltage drop in spite of larger switching losses.

17.2.7 Maximum Operating Frequency

High-Level Lifetime (μs)	On-State Voltage Drop (Volts)	On-State Power Dissipation (W/cm²)	Energy Loss per Cycle (J/cm²)	Maximum Operating Frequency (Hz)
4	3.397	42.5	1.45	109
2	3.714	46.4	0.648	237
1	4.376	54.7	0.290	502
0.6	5.106	63.8	0.160	854
0.4	5.781	72.3	0.099	1291

Table 17.2 Power loss analysis for the optimized 20-kV asymmetric n-channel 4H-SiC IGBT structure.

The maximum operating frequency for operation of the optimized 20-kV asymmetric n-channel 4H-SiC IGBT structure can be obtained by combining the on-state and switching power losses (see Eq. [17.61]. In the case of the baseline optimized 20-kV asymmetric n-channel 4H-SiC IGBT device structure with a high-level lifetime of 2 μs in the N-base region, the on-state voltage drop is 3.714 V at an on-state current density of 25 A/cm². For the case of a 50 % duty cycle, the on-state power dissipation contributes 46 W/cm² to the total power loss. For this lifetime value, the energy loss per cycle during the voltage rise-time obtained from the numerical simulations[20] is 0.348 J/cm² and the energy loss per cycle during the current fall-time obtained from the numerical simulations[20] is 0.300 J/cm². Using a total turn-off energy loss per cycle of 0.648 J/cm^2 in Eq. [17.61] yields a maximum operating frequency of 237 Hz.

The maximum operating frequency for the optimized 20-kV asymmetric n-channel 4H-SiC IGBT structure can be increased by reducing the lifetime in the N-base region. Using the results obtained from the numerical simulations[20], the on-state voltage drop and the energy loss per cycle can be computed. These values are provided in Table 17.2 together with the maximum operating frequency as a function of the high level lifetime in the N-base region under the assumption of a 50 % duty cycle and a total power dissipation limit of 200 W/cm^2. The maximum operating frequency is plotted in Fig. 17.21 as a function of the high-level lifetime in the N-base region. It can be observed that the maximum operating frequency can be increased up to 1300 Hz by reducing the high-level lifetime to 0.4 µs.

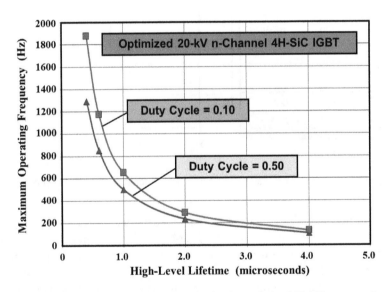

Fig. 17.23 Maximum operating frequency for the optimized 20-kV asymmetric n-channel 4H-SiC IGBT structure.

The IGBT is often operated with pulse-width-modulation to synthesize variable frequency output power for motor control. In these applications, the duty cycle can be much shorter than 50 percent. In this case, the maximum operating frequency for the optimized 20-kV asymmetric n-channel 4H-SiC IGBT structure can be increased. As an example, the maximum operating frequency for the optimized 20-kV asymmetric n-channel 4H-SiC IGBT structure operated at a 10 percent duty cycle is included in Fig. 17.23. It can be seen that the maximum operating frequency can now approach 2000 Hz.

17.3 p-Channel Asymmetric Structure

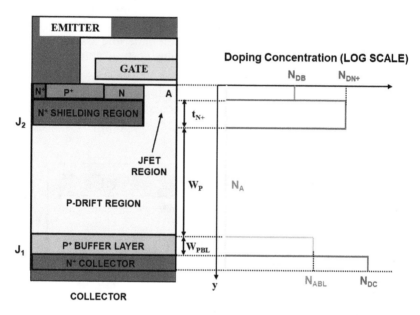

Fig. 17.24 Asymmetric p-channel 4H-SiC IGBT structure and its doping profile.

The asymmetric p-channel 4H-SiC IGBT structure with the planar gate architecture is illustrated in Fig. 17.24 with its doping profile. As mentioned at the beginning of this chapter, the asymmetric p-channel silicon carbide IGBT structure received more attention initially than the n-channel structure because of concerns with the high resistance of available P$^+$ silicon carbide substrates. Since the asymmetric IGBT structure is intended for use in DC circuits, its reverse blocking capability does not have to match the forward blocking capability allowing the use of a P-buffer layer adjacent to the N$^+$ collector region. The P-buffer layer has a much larger doping concentration than the lightly doped portion of the P-base region. The electric field in the asymmetric IGBT takes a trapezoidal shape allowing supporting the forward blocking voltage with a thinner P-base region. This allows achieving a lower on-state voltage drop and superior turn-off characteristics. As in the case of silicon devices[16], the doping concentration of the buffer layer and the lifetime in the P-base (drift-region) region must be optimized to perform a trade-off between on-state voltage drop and turn-off switching losses. Like the asymmetric n-channel 4H-SiC IGBT structure, the asymmetric p-channel 4H-SiC IGBT structure has uniform doping concentration for the various layers produced by using either epitaxial growth or by using multiple ion-implantation energies to form a box profile.

17.3.1 Blocking Characteristics

The design of the 20-kV asymmetric 4H-SiC p-channel IGBT structure is discussed in this section. The physics for blocking voltages is similar to the n-channel structure discussed in section 17.1. The forward blocking capability of the asymmetric 4H-SiC p-channel IGBT structure is determined by the open-base transistor breakdown phenomenon. In the case of the asymmetric 4H-SiC p-channel IGBT structure, the maximum blocking voltage occurs when the common base current gain of the NPN transistor becomes equal to unity. For the asymmetric p-channel IGBT structure, the emitter injection efficiency is smaller than unity due to the high doping concentration of the P-buffer layer. The emitter injection efficiency for the N^+ collector/P-buffer junction (J_1) can be obtained by using an analysis similar to that described in the textbook for the bipolar power transistor[16]:

$$\gamma_E = \frac{D_{nPBL} L_{pC} N_{DC}}{D_{nPBL} L_{pC} N_{DC} + D_{pC} W_{PBL} N_{ABL}} \qquad [17.64]$$

where D_{nPBL} and D_{pC} are the diffusion coefficients for minority carriers in the P-buffer and N^+ collector regions; N_{DC} and L_{pC} are the doping concentration and diffusion length for minority carriers in the N^+ collector region; N_{ABL} and W_{PBL} are the doping concentration and width of the P-buffer layer. In determining the diffusion coefficients and the diffusion length, it is necessary to account for impact of the high doping concentrations in the N^+ collector region and P-buffer layer on the mobility. In addition, the lifetime within the highly doped N^+ collector region is reduced due to heavy doping effects, which shortens the diffusion length.

The open-base transistor breakdown condition for the asymmetric p-channel 4H-SiC IGBT structure is given by:

$$\alpha_{NPN} = \left(\gamma_E . \alpha_T \right)_{NPN} M = 1 \qquad \text{[17.65]}$$

Based up on this expression, it can be concluded that the breakdown voltage for the 4H-SiC p-channel asymmetric IGBT structure will occur when the multiplication co-efficient is slightly above unity.

When the collector bias exceeds the reach-through voltage (V_{RT}), the electric field is truncated by the high doping concentration of the N-buffer layer making the un-depleted width of the NPN transistor base region equal to the width of the N-buffer layer. The base transport factor is then given by:

$$\alpha_T = \frac{1}{\cosh\left(W_{PBL} / L_{nPB} \right)} \qquad \text{[17.66]}$$

which is independent of the collector bias. Here, $L_{n,PB}$ is the diffusion length for electrons in the P-buffer layer. This analysis neglects the depletion region extension within the P-buffer layer. The diffusion length for electrons (L_{pPB}) in the P-buffer layer depends upon the diffusion coefficient and the minority carrier lifetime in the P-buffer layer. The diffusion coefficient varies with the doping concentration in the P-buffer layer based upon the concentration dependence of the mobility. In addition, the minority carrier lifetime has been found to be dependent upon the doping concentration[17] in the case of silicon devices. Although this phenomenon has not been verified for silicon carbide, it is commonly used when performing numerical analysis of silicon carbide devices. The effect can be modeled by using the relationship:

$$\frac{\tau_{LL}}{\tau_{n0}} = \frac{1}{1 + \left(N_A / N_{REF} \right)} \qquad \text{[17.67]}$$

where N_{REF} is a reference doping concentration whose value will be assumed to be 5×10^{16} cm^{-3}.

The multiplication factor for a P-N junction is given by:

$$M = \frac{1}{1 - \left(V_C / BV_{PP} \right)^n} \qquad \text{[17.68]}$$

with a value of n = 6 and the avalanche breakdown voltage of the N-base/P-base junction (BV_{PP}) *without the punch-through phenomenon*. In order to apply this formulation to the punch-through case relevant to the asymmetric p-channel silicon carbide IGBT structure, it is necessary to relate the maximum electric field at the junction for the two cases. The electric field at the interface between the lightly doped portion of the P-base region and the P-buffer layer is given by:

$$E_1 = E_m - \frac{qN_A W_P}{\varepsilon_S} \qquad [17.69]$$

The applied collector voltage supported by the device is given by:

$$V_C = \left(\frac{E_m + E_1}{2}\right) W_P = E_m W_P - \frac{qN_A}{2\varepsilon_S} W_P^2 \qquad [17.70]$$

From this expression, the maximum electric field is given by:

$$E_m = \frac{V_C}{W_P} + \frac{qN_A W_P}{2\varepsilon_S} \qquad [17.71]$$

The corresponding equation for the non-punch-through case is:

$$E_m = \sqrt{\frac{2qN_A V_{NPT}}{\varepsilon_S}} \qquad [17.72]$$

Equating these maximum electric fields, the non-punch-through voltage that determines the multiplication coefficient 'M' corresponding to the applied collector bias 'V$_A$' for the punch-through case is given by:

$$V_{NPT} = \frac{\varepsilon_S E_m^2}{2qN_A} = \frac{\varepsilon_S}{2qN_A}\left(\frac{V_C}{W_P} + \frac{qN_A W_P}{2\varepsilon_S}\right)^2 \qquad [17.73]$$

The multiplication coefficient for the asymmetric silicon carbide IGBT structure can be computed by using this non-punch-through voltage:

$$M = \frac{1}{1 - \left(V_{NPT} / BV_{PP}\right)^n} \qquad [17.74]$$

The multiplication coefficient increases with increasing collector bias. The open-base transistor breakdown voltage (and the forward blocking capability of the asymmetric IGBT structure) is determined by the collector voltage at which the multiplication factor becomes equal to the reciprocal of the product of the base transport factor and the emitter injection efficiency.

The silicon carbide p-channel asymmetric IGBT structure must have a forward blocking voltage of 22,000 V for a 20-kV rated device. In the case of avalanche breakdown, there is a unique value for the doping concentration of 3.2×10^{14} cm^{-3} for the drift region with a width of 272 μm to obtain this blocking voltage. In the case of the asymmetric silicon carbide IGBT structure, it is advantageous to use a much lower doping concentration for the lightly doped portion of the P-base region in order to reduce its width. The strong conductivity modulation of the P-base region during on-state operation favors a smaller thickness for the P-base region independent of its original doping concentration. A doping concentration of 1.5×10^{14} cm^{-3} will be assumed for the P-base region.

The doping concentration of the P-buffer layer must be sufficiently large to prevent reach-through of the electric field to the N$^+$ collector region. Although the electric field at the interface between the P-base region and the P-buffer layer is slightly smaller than at the blocking junction (J$_2$), a worse case analysis can be done by assuming that the electric field at this interface is close to the critical electric field for breakdown in the drift region. The minimum charge in the P-buffer layer to prevent reach-through can be then obtained using:

$$N_{ABL}W_{PBL} = \frac{\varepsilon_S E_C}{q} \qquad [17.75]$$

Using a critical electric for breakdown in silicon carbide of 2×10^6 V/cm for a doping concentration of 1.5×10^{14} cm^{-3} in the buffer layer, the minimum charge in the P-buffer layer to prevent reach-through for a silicon carbide p-channel asymmetric IGBT structure is found to be 1.07×10^{13} cm^{-2}. A P-buffer layer with doping concentration of 5×10^{16} cm^{-3} and thickness of 5 μm has a charge of 2.5×10^{13} cm^{-2} in which satisfies this requirement.

The asymmetric p-channel 4H-SiC IGBT structure will be assumed to have an N$^+$ collector region with doping concentration of 1×10^{19} cm^{-3}. It will be assumed that all the donors are ionized even at room temperature although the relatively deep donor level in silicon carbide may lead to incomplete dopant ionization. In this case, the emitter injection efficiency computed using Eq. [17.64] is 0.997. When the device is close to breakdown, the entire P-base region is depleted and the base transport factor computed by using Eq. [17.66] in this case is 0.988. In computing these values, a lifetime of 1 μs was assumed for the P-base region resulting in a lifetime of 0.5 μs in the P-buffer layer due to the scaling according to Eq. [17.67]. The base transport factor is much larger for the p-channel IGBT than the n-channel device due to larger diffusion length for electrons compared with hole. Based up on Eq. [17.65], open-base transistor breakdown will then occur when the multiplication coefficient becomes equal to 1.02 for the above values for the injection efficiency and base transport factor. In comparison with the n-channel asymmetric 4H-SiC IGBT structure, the multiplication factor corresponding to open-base transistor breakdown has a much smaller value for the p-channel device. Consequently, it becomes necessary to utilize a thicker drift region for the p-channel device when compared with the n-channel device.

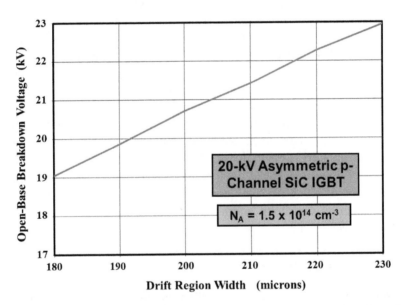

Fig. 17.25 Optimization of drift region width for the 20-kV asymmetric p-channel 4H-SiC IGBT structure.

The forward blocking capability for the 4H-SiC p-channel asymmetric IGBT structure can be computed by using Eq. [17.65] for various widths for the P-base region. The analysis requires determination of the voltage V_{NPT} by using Eq. [17.73] for each width of the P-base region. The resulting values for the forward blocking voltage are plotted in Fig. 17.25. From this graph, a forward blocking voltage of 22,300 V can be obtained by using a P-base region width of 220 μm. This value is substantially larger than the N-base width of 160 μm for the n-channel device. The larger drift region width required for the p-channel device, due to the larger gain of the NPN transistor, increases its on-state voltage drop and the stored charge making its trade-off curve worse than for the n-channel device structure.

   In terms of experimental results, p-channel 4H-SiC IGBT were reported[24] in 2006 with a blocking voltage of 5.8 kV. This was achieved using a drift region with doping concentration of 2-6 x 10^{14} cm^{-3} and thickness of 50 μm. The blocking voltage was increased[25] to 7.5 kV by using a drift region with doping concentration of 2-6 x 10^{14} cm^{-3} and thickness of 100 μm. These devices had a thin (1 μm) buffer layer with high doping of 1-2 x 10^{17} cm^{-3}. In 2008, p-channel 4H-SiC IGBTs with the P-drift region doping concentration of 2-3 x 10^{14} cm^{-3} and thickness of 100 μm were reported[26] with blocking voltage of 11.5 kV.

   In terms of 4H-SiC IGBTs with ultra-high (~ 15 kV) blocking voltage capability, the blocking voltage capability of n-channel and p-channel 4H-SiC IGBTs with same drift region doping concentration of 2 x 10^{14} cm^{-3} and thickness of 140 μm has been compared[27]. It was found that the n-channel 4H-SiC IGBT had superior blocking voltage capability consistent with the above analytical model. In 2014, p-channel 4H-SiC IGBTs were reported[28] with blocking voltage capability of 14.7 kV achieved using a drift region doping concentration of 5.2 x 10^{14} cm^{-3} and thickness of 152 μm. These devices has a P-buffer layer with doping concentration of 1.0 x 10^{17} cm^{-3} and thickness of 1 μm. A two zone JTE edge termination with total width of 400 μm was employed to achieve this breakdown voltage.

17.3.2 On-State Voltage Drop

The minority carrier (electron) distribution profiles for the p-channel asymmetric 4H-SiC IGBT structure can be expected to be governed by the same high-level injection physics previously described for the n-channel structure in section 17.1. In this section, the characteristics of the 20-kV p-channel asymmetric 4H-SiC IGBT structure will be described using the results of numerical simulations[20].

   The on-state characteristics of the 20-kV asymmetrical p-channel 4H-SiC IGBT structure were obtained by using a gate bias voltage of 10 V for the case of various values for the lifetime in the drift region. This device structure has a buffer layer doping concentration of 5 x 10^{16} cm^{-3} and thickness of 5 μm. The on-state voltage drop increases as expected with reduction of the lifetime (τ_{p0}, τ_{n0}). The on-state voltage drop at a hole lifetime (τ_{p0}) value of 2 μs is found to be 4.65 V at an on-state current density of 25 A/cm^2.

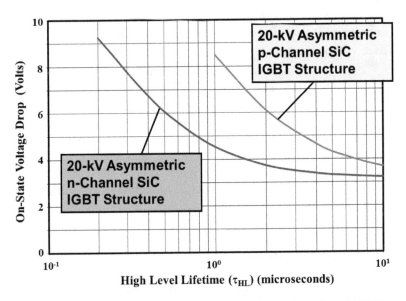

Fig. 17.26 On-state voltage drop for the 20-kV asymmetric p-channel IGBT structure: drift region lifetime dependence.

The variation of the on-state voltage drop as a function of the lifetime in the drift region obtained by using the numerical simulations is compared with that for the n-channel device structure in Fig. 17.26. It can be clearly seen that the n-channel 4H-SiC IGBT structure has a lower on-state voltage drop than that of the p-channel 4H-SiC device structure for all lifetime values. This is consistent with other analyses reported in the literature[29] and measured results on fabricated devices[28].

In early planar p-channel IGBTs reported in 2006, the on-state voltage drop was found[25] to be very high at room temperature. This was significantly improved[26] by 2007 by the addition of a 'current suppressing layer (CSL)' which has a doping concentration of 5-8 x 10^{15} cm^{-3} just under the N-base regions compared with the doping concentration of 2-6 x 10^{14} cm^{-3} in the P-drift region. The CSL layer reduces the JFET region resistance as well. In 2008, p-channel 4H-SiC IGBTs with the P-drift region doping concentration of 2-3 x 10^{14} cm^{-3} and thickness of 100 μm were reported[27] with a good on-state voltage drop of 4.5 V at an on-state current density of 40 A/cm^2.

In 2014, p-channel 4H-SiC IGBTs were reported[29] with blocking voltage capability of 15 kV. They exhibited a very high on-state voltage drop at room temperature. The on-state voltage drop reduced to -8.5 V at an on-state current density of 100 A/cm^2 at 250 °C. The authors related this improvement to an increase in the minority carrier lifetime from 0.75 to 2 μsec with increase in temperature to 250 °C.

17.3.3 Turn-Off Characteristics

The turn-off behavior for the asymmetric p-channel 4H-SiC IGBT structure can be expected to be similar to that for the n-channel structure as discussed in section 17.1.3. The same theoretical analysis should therefore be applicable for both devices. In this section, the turn-off characteristics of the 20-kV p-channel asymmetric silicon carbide IGBT structure will be described using only the results of numerical simulations[20].

17.3.4 Lifetime Dependence

From an applications perspective, the optimization of the power losses for the IGBT structure requires performing a trade-off between the on-state voltage drop and the switching losses. One approach to achieve this is by adjusting the lifetime in the drift (P-base) region. A reduction of the lifetime in the drift region also alters the lifetime in the P-buffer layer in the case of silicon devices. However, the relationship between the lifetime in the drift region and the buffer layer has not yet been established for silicon carbide devices. Consequently, it will be assumed that the lifetime in the P-buffer layer is the same as that in the P-base region for silicon carbide structures.

The numerical simulations[20] showed a decrease in the time taken for the collector voltage to increase to the reach-through voltage when the lifetime in the P-base region is reduced. In the simulation results, the reach-through voltage remains independent of the lifetime in the N-base region as predicted by the analytical model. After reach-through of the space-charge-region occurs, the collector voltage increases linearly with time. The [dV/dt] values for the collector voltage transients increase with reduced lifetime in the drift region as predicted by the analytical model. The [dV/dt] values are 0.83, 1.2, 2.5, 3.3, and 5.0 x 10^9 V/s for high-level lifetime values of 10, 6, 4, 2, and 1 μs, respectively.

The numerical simulations of the 20-kV asymmetric p-channel 4H-SiC IGBT structure also show[20] a substantial increase in the collector current fall-time when the lifetime increases. For all the lifetime values, the collector current decays exponentially with time as predicted by the analytical model. The collector current fall-time values are 15, 10, 7, 3.5 and 1.8 μs, for high-level lifetime values of 10, 6, 4, 2, and 1 μs, respectively. The turn-off time for the p-channel 4H-SiC IGBT has been found[30] to be much (2-times) longer than that for the n-channel structure. This is due to the larger current gain of the internal NPN transistor that is supporting the bipolar current flow.

Good switching performance with an inductive load was demonstrated[31] for 4H-SiC p-channel IGBTs in 2008. The devices with 100 μm thick P-drift regions has a turn-off time of ~ 1 μs. The voltage rise-time consisted of two phases as discussed above in the analytical models. The switching performance of p-channel 4H-SiC IGBTs with breakdown voltage of 14.8 kV was reported[28] in 2014 for the case of inductive load turn-off. However, the data was taken using a 16 kV 4H-SiC P-i-N rectifier with a large junction capacitance across the inductor. This results in soft-switching behavior with the turn-off [dV/dt] controlled by the capacitance[32]. The collector voltage then increases linearly with time in the first phase unlike in the case of hard switching. The turn-off time was 5 μs for a collector DC supply voltage of 6 kV.

17.3.5 Switching Energy Loss

The power loss incurred during the turn-off switching transient limits the maximum operating frequency for the IGBT structure. Power losses during the turn-on of the IGBT structure are also significant but strongly dependent on the reverse recovery behavior of the fly-back rectifiers in circuits. Consequently, it is common practice to use only the turn-off energy loss per cycle during characterization of IGBT devices. The turn-off losses are associated with the voltage rise-time interval and the current fall-time interval. The energy loss for each event can be computed by integration of the power loss, as given by the product of the instantaneous current and voltage.

During the voltage rise-time interval, the anode current is constant while the voltage increases in a non-linear manner as a function of time until reach-through occurs. In order to simplify the analysis, the energy loss during this interval will be computed using Eq. [17.58]. During the second phase of the voltage rise-time, the collector voltage increases linearly with time while the collector current is constant. The energy loss during this interval can be computed using Eq. [17.59]. For the typical switching waveforms for the 20-kV asymmetric p-channel 4H-SiC IGBT structure with a negative collector supply voltage of 12,000 V, the energy loss per unit area during the collector voltage rise-time is found to be 0.24 J/cm^2 if the on-state current density is 25 A/cm^2.

During the collector current fall-time interval, the collector voltage is constant while the current decreases exponentially with time. The energy loss during the collector current fall-time interval can be computed using Eq. [17.60]. For the typical switching waveforms for the 20-kV asymmetric p-channel 4H-SiC IGBT structure with a negative collector supply voltage of 12,000 V, the energy loss per unit area during the collector current fall-time is found to be 0.30 J/cm^2 if the on-state current density is 25 A/cm^2. The total energy loss per unit area ($E_{OFF,V} + E_{OFF,I}$) during the turn-off process for the 20-kV asymmetric p-channel 4H-SiC IGBT structure is found to be 0.54 J/cm^2.

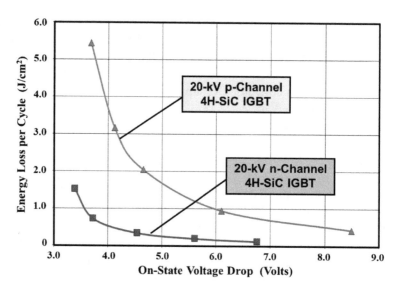

Fig. 17.27 Trade-off curve for the 20-kV asymmetric p-channel 4H-SiC IGBT structure: lifetime in P-base (drift) region.

The on-state voltage drop and the total energy loss per cycle were obtained for the 20-kV p-channel asymmetric 4H-SiC IGBT structure using the results obtained from the numerical simulations[20]. These values are plotted in Fig. 17.27 to create a trade-off curve to optimize the performance of the 20-kV asymmetric p-channel 4H-SiC IGBT structure by varying the lifetime in the N-base region. Devices used in lower frequency circuits would be chosen from the left-hand-side of the trade-off curve while devices used in higher frequency circuits would be chosen from the right-hand-side of the trade-off curve. For comparison purposes, the trade-off curve for the 20-kV n-channel asymmetric 4H-SiC IGBT structure is also shown in Fig. 17.27. It can be concluded that the performance of the 20-kV n-channel asymmetric 4H-SiC IGBT structure is far superior to that of the p-channel 4H-SiC device. Consequently, more attention has been given to develop the n-channel 4H-SiC IGBT structure than the p-channel device.

17.3.6 Maximum Operating Frequency

The maximum operating frequency for operation of the 20-kV asymmetric p-channel 4H-SiC IGBT structure can be obtained by combining the on-state and switching power losses (see Eq. [17.61]). In the case of the baseline 20-kV asymmetric p-channel 4H-SiC IGBT device structure with a high-level lifetime of 4 μs in the P-base (drift) region, the on-state voltage drop is 4.65 V at an on-state current density of 25 A/cm^2. For the case of a 50 % duty cycle, the on-state power dissipation contributes 58.1 W/cm^2 to the total power loss. For this lifetime value, the energy loss per cycle during the voltage rise-time obtained from the numerical simulations[20] is 1.44 J/cm^2 and the energy loss per cycle during the current fall-time obtained from the numerical simulations[21] is 0.60 J/cm^2. Using a total turn-off energy loss per cycle of 2.04 J/cm^2 in Eq. [17.85] yields a maximum operating frequency of only 69 Hz.

High-Level Lifetime (μs)	On-State Voltage Drop (Volts)	On-State Power Dissipation (W/cm^2)	Energy Loss per Cycle (J/cm^2)	Maximum Operating Frequency (Hz)
10	3.69	46.1	5.44	28
6	4.12	51.5	3.17	47
4	4.65	58.1	2.04	69
2	6.11	76.3	0.95	131
1	8.49	106	0.43	219

Table 17.3 Power loss analysis for the 20-kV asymmetric p-channel 4H-SiC IGBT structure: Lifetime in drift layer dependence.

The maximum operating frequency for the 20-kV asymmetric p-channel 4H-SiC IGBT structure can be increased by reducing the lifetime in the P-base region. Using the results obtained from the numerical simulations, the on-state voltage drop and the energy loss per cycle can be computed. These values are provided in Table 17.3 together with the maximum operating frequency as a function of the high level lifetime in the N-base region under the assumption of a 50 % duty cycle and a total power dissipation limit of 200 W/cm^2.

The maximum operating frequency is plotted in Fig. 17.28 as a function of the high-level lifetime in the P-base region. It can be observed that the maximum operating frequency can be increased up to 200 Hz by reducing the high-level lifetime to 1 μs. For comparison purposes, the maximum operating frequency for the 20-kV n-channel asymmetric 4H-SiC IGBT structure is also shown in Fig. 17.28. It can be concluded that the maximum operating frequency of the 20-kV n-channel asymmetric 4H-SiC IGBT structure is much greater to that of the p-channel 4H-SiC device.

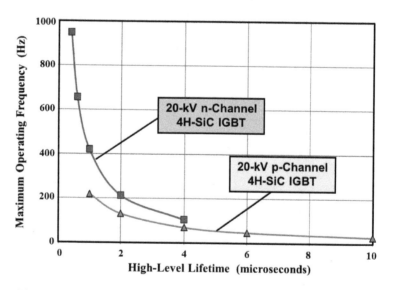

Fig. 17.28 Maximum operating frequency for the 20-kV asymmetric p-channel 4H-SiC IGBT structure: drift region lifetime dependence.

17.4 Latch-Up and S-O-A

The issue to destructive failure from latch-up of the parasitic thyristor within the silicon IGBT structure needed to be addressed during the initial stages of its development in the early 1980s[2]. With increasing maturity of its design and manufacturing process, the immunity from latch-up is now taken for granted. However, this cannot be assumed for the 4H-SiC IGBTs now under development.

For an n-channel IGBT with linear cell geometry, the latch-up current density is given by[16]:

$$J_{L,n-Ch} = \frac{V_{bi}}{\alpha_{PNP,ON} \, \rho_{SP} \, L_{N+} \, p} \qquad [17.76]$$

where V_{bi} is the built-in potential of junction between the N^+ emitter and P-base regions, $\alpha_{PNP,ON}$ is the current gain of the P-N-P transistor, ρ_{SP} is the sheet resistance of the P-base region, L_{N+} is the length of the N^+ emitter in the cell cross-section, and p is the cell pitch. Fortunately, the built-in potential for the junction in 4H-SiC is three times bigger than for silicon which increases the latch-up current level. Unfortunately, the sheet resistance of the P-base region is very high for 4H-SiC IGBTs due to incomplete ionization of P-type dopants despite the use of a P^+ shielding region. In the case of a P^+ shielding region with doping concentration of 1×10^{18} cm^{-3}, the ionized acceptor concentration is only 2.2×10^{16} cm^{-3}. Using a hole mobility of 54.8 cm^2/V-s for this doping level, the sheet resistance is found to be 50,000 Ω/sq for a typical P^+ region thickness of 1 μm.

For a p-channel IGBT with linear cell geometry, the latch-up current density is given by[16]:

$$J_{L,p-Ch} = \frac{V_{bi}}{\alpha_{NPN,ON} \, \rho_{SN} \, L_{P+} \, p} \qquad [17.77]$$

where V_{bi} is the built-in potential of junction between the P^+ emitter and N-base regions, $\alpha_{NPN,ON}$ is the current gain of the N-P-N transistor, ρ_{SN} is the sheet resistance of the N-base region, L_{P+} is the length of the P^+ emitter in the cell cross-section, and p is the cell pitch. Again, the built-in potential for the junction in 4H-SiC is three times bigger than for silicon which increases the latch-up current level. Fortunately, the sheet resistance of the N-base region is low for 4H-SiC IGBTs due to the use of an N^+ shielding region despite incomplete ionization of N-type dopants. In the case of an N^+ shielding region with doping concentration of 1 x 10^{18} cm^{-3}, the ionized donor concentration is 5.25 x 10^{17} cm^{-3}. Using an electron mobility of 324 cm^2/V-s for this doping level, the sheet resistance is found to be 370 Ω/sq for a typical N^+ region thickness of 1 μm. Consequently, the latch-up current density for the p-channel SiC IGBT is far (135x) larger than for the n-channel device.

The latch-up performance of 4H-SiC IGBTs has not been reported in the literature. However, it has been shown that the p-channel 4H-SiC IGBT has excellent reverse-biased-safe-operating-area[32]. Devices designed with a breakdown voltage of 7.5 kV were switched off from an on-state current density of 200 A/cm^2 with a DC supply voltage of 4 kV without failure.

17.5 Trench-Gate Structure

As in the case of silicon IGBTs[16,33], it can be expected that trench gate 4H-SiC IGBT would also have improved on-state characteristics. However, as in the case of 4H-SiC trench-gate power MOSFETs discussed in chapter 12, a high electric field develops across the gate oxide during blocking high voltages leading to device failure. This problem can be solved by using a P^+ shielding region at the bottom on the trenches[3] for n-channel devices.

Trench-gate 4H-SiC p-channel IGBTs were reported[34] in 2003 without the use of shielding regions under the trench gate oxide. These devices exhibited very low breakdown voltage of -85 volts in spite of using a drift region with doping level of 5 x 10^{15} cm^{-3} and thickness of 12 μm. The threshold voltage for the devices was very high ($\sim$ -30 V). The devices had a large knee voltage of -7.1 V and an on-state voltage drop of -11.25 V at low on-state current density of 1 A/cm^2.

17.6 Summary

The physics of operation and design principles for the asymmetric 4H-SiC IGBT structure have been described in this chapter. The analysis, which includes both n-channel and p-channel structures, demonstrates that the 20-kV n-channel asymmetric 4H-SiC IGBT structure offers excellent characteristics for utility applications. However, the usual method used to design the drift region of the asymmetric IGBT leads to a high [dV/dt] during switching. A design methodology for the drift region doping and thickness is provided to avoid a high [dV/dt] during the turn-off event for the silicon carbide IGBT structure.

The characteristics of both n-channel and p-channel 4H-SiC IGBTs reported in the literature have been provided to describe the progress with this technology. The analytical models derived in this chapter are consistent with the experimental results. The highest blocking voltage achieved for 4H-SiC IGBTs is 27.5 kV making them a candidate for utility applications.

References

[1] B. J. Baliga, "Semiconductors for High Voltage Vertical Channel Field Effect Transistors", Journal of Applied Physics, Vol. 53, pp. 1759-1764, 1982.

[2] B. J. Baliga, "The IGBT Device", Second Edition, Springer Science, 2023.

[3] B. J. Baliga, "Silicon Carbide Switching Device with Rectifying Gate", U.S. Patent 5,396,085, Filed December 28, 1993, Issued March 7, 1995.

[4] Q. Zhang, et al, "10kV Trench Gate IGBTs on 4H-SiC", IEEE International Symposium on Power Semiconductor Devices and ICs, pp. 159-162, 2005.

[5] Q. Zhang, et al, "9 kV 4H-SiC IGBTs with 88 mΩ-cm^2 of $R_{diff,on}$", Material Science Forum Vols. 556-557, pp. 771-774, 2007.

[6] Q. Zhang, et al, "12-kV p-Channel IGBTs with Low On-Resistance in 4H-SiC", IEEE Electron Device Letters, Vol. 29, pp. 1027-1029, 2008.

[7] Y. Sui, X. Wang, and J. A. Cooper, "High-Voltage Self-Aligned, p-Channel DMOS-IGBTs in 4H-SiC", IEEE Electron Device Letters, Vol. 28, pp. 728-730, 2007.

[8] T. Tamaki, et al, "Optimization of On-State and Switching Performances for 15-20 kV 4H-SiC IGBTs", IEEE Transactions on Electron Devices, Vol. 55, pp. 1920-1927, 2008.

[9] W. Sung, et al, "Design and Investigation of Frequency Capability of 15-kV 4H-SiC IGBT", IEEE International Symposium on Power Semiconductor Devices and ICs, pp. 271-274, 2009.

[10] M. K. Das, et al, "A 13-kV 4H-SiC n-channel IGBT with Low $R_{diff,on}$ and Fast Switching", International Conference on Silicon Carbide and Related Materials, October 2007.

[11] Q. Zhang, et al, "SiC Power Devices for Microgrids", IEEE Transactions on Power Electronics, Vol. 25, pp. 2889-2896, 2010.

[12] S. Ryu, et al, "Ultra High Voltage (>12 kV), High Performance 4H-SiC IGBTs", IEEE International Symposium on Power Semiconductor Devices and ICs, pp. 257-260, 2012.

[13] S. Ryu, et al, "Ultra High Voltage IGBTs in 4H-SiC", IEEE Workshop on Wide Bandgap Power Devices and Applications", pp. 36-39, 2013.

[14] E. V. Brunt, et al, "22 kV, 1 cm², 4H-SiC n-IGBTs with improved Conductivity Modulation", IEEE International Symposium on Power Semiconductor Devices and ICs, pp. 358-361, 2014.

[15] R. J. Callanan, et al, "Recent Progress in SiC DMOSFETs and JBS Diodes at CREE", IEEE Industrial Electronics Conference, pp. 2885-2890, 2008.

[16] B. J. Baliga, "Fundamentals of Power Semiconductor Devices", Chapter 9, Springer-Science, New York, 2008.

[17] B. J. Baliga and M. S. Adler, "Measurement of Carrier Lifetime Profiles in Diffused Layers of Semiconductors", IEEE Transactions on Electron Devices, Vol. ED-25, pp. 472-477, 1978.

[18] Y. Yonezawa, et al, "Low V_f and Highly Reliable 16 kV Ultra-high Voltage SiC Flip-Type n-channel Implantation and Epitaxial IGBT", IEEE International Electron Devices Meeting, pp. 6.6.1-6.6.4, 2013.

[19] J. W. Palmour, "Silicon Carbide Power Device Development for Industrial Markets", IEEE International Electron Devices Meeting, pp. 1.1.1-1.1.8, 2014.

[20] B. J. Baliga, "Advanced High Voltage Power Device Concepts", Chapters 5 and 7, Springer-Science, New York, 2011.

[21] G. Wang, et al, "Static and Dynamic Performance Characterization and Comparison of 15 kV SiC MOSFET and 15 kV SiC n-IGBTs", IEEE International Symposium on Power Semiconductor Devices and ICs, pp. 229-232, 2015.

[22] A. Kadavelugu, et al, "Understanding dV/dt of 15 kV SiC n-IGBT and its Control using Active Gate Driver", IEEE Energy Conversion Congress and Exposition, pp. 2213-2220, 2014.

[23] A. Kadavelugu, et al, "Experimental Switching Frequency Limits of 15 kV SiC N-IGBT Module", IEEE Energy Conversion Congress and Exposition Asia, 2013.

[24] Q. Zhang, et al, "Design and Fabrication of High Voltage IGBTs on 4H-SiC", IEEE International Symposium on Power Semiconductor Devices and ICs, pp. 1-4, 2006.

[25] Q. Zhang, et al, "New Improvement Results on 7.5 kV 4H-SiC p-IGBTs with $R_{diff,on}$ of 26 $m\Omega$-cm^2 at 25 °C", IEEE International Symposium on Power Semiconductor Devices and ICs, pp. 281-284, 2007.

[26] A. Agarwal, et al, "Prospects of Bipolar Power Devices in Silicon Carbide", IEEE Industrial Electronics Conference, pp. 2879-2884, 2008.

[27] S-H. Ryu, et al, "High Performance, Ultra High Voltage 4H-SiC IGBTs", IEEE Energy Conversion Congress and Exposition, pp. 3603-3608, 2012.

[28] T. Deguchi, et al, "Static and Dynamic Performance Evaluation of > 13 kV SiC P-Channel IGBTs at High Temperatures", IEEE International Symposium on Power Semiconductor Devices and ICs, pp. 261-264, 2014.

[29] J. A. Cooper, et al, "Power MOSFETs, IGBTs, and Thyristors in SiC", IEEE International Electron Devices Meeting, pp. 7.2.1-7.2.4, 2014.

[30] J. W. Palmour, et al, "SiC Power Devices for Smart Grid Systems", IEEE International Power Electronics Conference, pp. 1006-1013, 2010.

[31] Q. Zhang, et al, "Design and Characterization of High-Voltage 4H-SiC p-IGBTs", IEEE Transactions on Electron Devices, Vol. 55, pp. 1912-1919, 2008.

[32] A. Kadavelugu, et al, "Zero Voltage Switching Characterization of 12 kV SiC N-IGBTs", IEEE International Symposium on Power Semiconductor Devices and ICs, pp. 350-353, 2014.

[33] H. R. Chang and B. J. Baliga, "500-V n-Channel Insulated Gate Bipolar Transistor with a Trench Gate Structure", IEEE Transactions on Electron Devices, Vol. ED-36, pp. 1824-1829, 1989.

[34] R. Singh, et al, "High Temperature SiC Trench Gate p-IGBT", IEEE Transactions on Electron Devices, Vol. 50, pp. 774-784, 2003.

Chapter 18

SiC Power Device Manufacturing

Silicon Carbide power devices have been recently commercialized to take advantage of the high breakdown electric field strength, good electron mobility, and favorable thermal conductivity of this material. These devices are expected to replace Si IGBTs in applications that need higher operating frequency to reduce the size, weight, and cost of passive circuit elements. The biggest impediment to market adoption of these devices is their high manufacturing cost. The manufacturing cost can be reduced by employing a high volume Si foundry that has been upgraded to handle some unique process steps peculiar to manufacturing SiC devices.

A three year effort to create a process technology that can be utilized to manufacture SiC JBS rectifiers, power MOSFETs, and JBSFETs at a foundry was undertaken at NCSU under the support of the PowerAmerica Institute. The JBSFET is a power MOSFET structure in which the JBS rectifier has been integrated to improve circuit performance and reduce cost. The NCSU technology was named **PRESiCE**™ for 'PRocess Engineered for manufacturing SiC Electronic-devices'. This process produces diodes and MOSFETs with characteristics on par with commercially available devices from companies. It is described in this chapter as an example of a manufacturing technology for SiC power devices.

A commercially viable process technology needs to be rigorously qualified. This was achieved by running three consecutive process lots, with six 6-inch SiC wafers per lot, at a commercial foundry X-Fab, TX, with identical process steps. Extensive characterization of the JBS diodes and MOSFETs was performed on all the devices on the wafers using a Signatone semi-automated probe station with a B1505 Keysight Curve Tracer. This allowed evaluation of statistical data for the mean value and stand deviation for various device electrical parameters. Wafer maps were generated to visually assess the process uniformity and consistency.

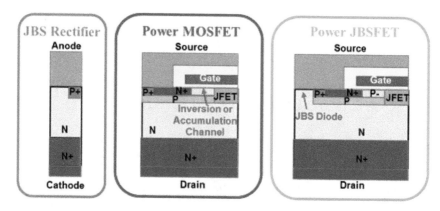

Fig. 18.1 SiC power devices manufactured using the PRESiCE™ technology:
JBS diodes, power MOSFETs, and power JBSFETs.

The PRESiCE™ technology allows manufacturing the devices
shown in Fig. 18.1. The JBS rectifier is a Schottky diode with a P$^+$
shielding region that was described in chapter 6. The power MOSFET
is the shielded planar-gate structure that was described in chapter 11.
The JBSFET is a power MOSFET with integrated JBS diode that was
described in chapter 13.

18.1 PRESiCE™ Technology

The PRESiCE™ technology developed by North Carolina State
University for manufacturing SiC power MOSFETs requires performing
11 photolithographic masking steps. The device designs used 1.0 μm
minimum feature size and 0.2 μm alignment tolerance per foundry design
rules. The basic process sequence for manufacturing SiC power
MOSFETs with the PRESiCE™ technology is illustrated in Fig. 18.2,
18.4, 18.5, and 18.6. All devices were fabricated using 4H-SiC wafers
with a drift region thickness of 10 μm and N-type doping concentration of
8 x 10^{15} cm^{-3} to achieve a device rating of 1.2 kV with actual breakdown
voltages above 1600 V. Ion-implantation at 600 °C was used with an oxide
hard mask to form the P-base and N$^+$ source regions. Excellent yield and
parametric distributions were obtained for 0.5 μm channel length devices
even though the process is non-self-aligned with 0.2 μm alignment
tolerance.

It is essential to include a rugged, high performance edge termination at the periphery of all the power devices to ensure good performance. The hybrid-JTE edge termination[1], described in chapter 3, is an excellent choice because it achieves over 95 % of the ideal breakdown voltage with wide tolerance of the JTE implant dose. This termination requires a JTE zone and P^+ floating field rings.

The first mask (shown in Fig. 18.2 as M1) is used to etch trenches on the wafers for creating alignment marks for all subsequent masks. This is a unique requirement for SiC manufacturing, not needed in the case of Si chips, because the very high ion implant anneal temperature (1600 °C) requires removal of all layers on the SiC wafer surface and coverage with a carbon cap.

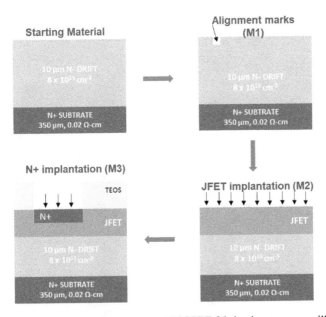

Fig. 18.2 Typical SiC planar-gate power MOSFET fabrication sequence: illustrates photolithography steps with masks M1, M2, and M3.

The ion implanted regions can in principle be formed in any sequence and then annealed together to activate the dopants. One sequence of ion implants is described here as an example. It is important to point out that the energy and dose of the ion implants must be chosen after taking into account loss of a SiC surface layer due to oxidation to form the gate oxide. The ion implants can be masked by defining an oxide layer with thickness of about 1.5 μm.

The second mask (shown in Fig. 18.2 as mask M2) is used to form the JFET region inside the MOSFET cells. This is a low dose nitrogen ion implant with multiple energies to create a uniform n-type doping profile with a concentration of about 3 x 10^{16} cm^{-3} to a depth of about 1 µm. The JFET doping enhancement must extend to the depth of the P$^+$ shielding region. It can be extended slightly further to form a current spreading layer (CSL layer) to reduce the specific on-resistance as discussed in chapter 11.

The third mask (shown in Fig. 18.2 as mask M3) is used to form the N$^+$ source region. The N$^+$ source region is shallow in depth (typically 0.2 µm) with a high surface concentration to obtain a low specific ohmic contact resistance. A surface concentration above 5 x 10^{19} cm^{-3} is sufficient to reduce the specific contact resistance to below 1 x 10^5 Ω-cm^2 for nickel contact metal annealed at 1000 °C. The typical doping profile for the N$^+$ ion implant is shown in red in Fig. 18.3. Its peak lies slightly below the surface to allow for the SiC layer removed during the gate oxide growth.

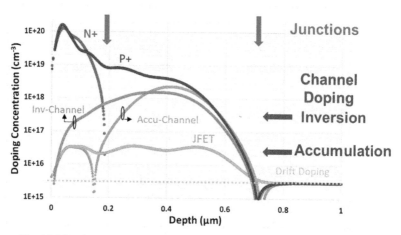

Fig. 18.3 Doping profiles for various regions within the SiC planar-gate power MOSFET after ion implantation.

The fourth mask (shown in Fig. 18.4 as mask M4) is used to form the P$^+$ shielding region. The energy and dose for the ion implantation of Aluminum for forming this region is chosen to achieve a depth of about 0.7 µm as shown in Fig. 18.3. The energy for the ion implant is chosen to leave a n-type surface layer with doping concentration of 3 x 10^{16} cm^{-3} (same as JFET region) and a thickness of about 0.15 µm for the case of accumulation channel devices. This corresponds to the blue line in the figure. These parameters produce enhancement-mode devices with a threshold voltage of about 2 V in the case of a gate oxide thickness of 550 Å. Additional p-type Aluminum ion implants are performed with lower energy to create the P-base region of the inversion-channel devices. This corresponds to the orange line in the figure. P-type doping at the surface of the P-base region must be about 2×10^{17} cm^{-3} to achieve a threshold voltage of 3 V in the case of a gate oxide thickness of 550 Å.

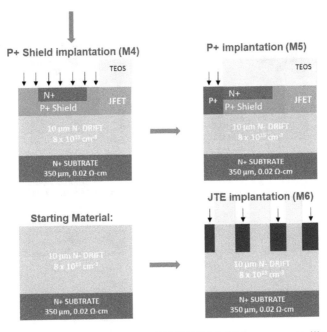

Fig. 18.4 Typical SiC planar-gate power MOSFET fabrication sequence: illustrates photolithography steps with masks M4, M5, and M6.

The fifth mask (shown in Fig. 18.4 as mask M5) is used to form a P$^+$ region. This region connects to the P-base region via the P$^+$ shielding region. A high surface concentration for this region is desirable to obtain a low specific contact resistance. A surface concentration above 5×10^{19} cm^{-3} is sufficient to reduce the specific contact resistance to below 1×10^5 Ω-cm^2 for nickel contact metal annealed at 1000 °C. The typical doping profile for the P$^+$ ion implant is shown in black in Fig. 18.3. Its peak lies slightly below the surface to allow for the SiC layer removed during the gate oxide growth.

The sixth mask (shown in Fig. 18.4 as mask M6) is used to form a multiple floating zone JTE regions in the edge termination. This portion of the device structures lies outside the MOSFET cells.

All the ion implanted regions are simultaneously annealed to activate the dopants. A high activation level can be obtained by using a temperature of 1675 °C for a duration of 30 min. However, this temperature can lead to dissociation of SiC at the surface that is highly detrimental. Dissociation is prevented by using a carbon cap as shown in Fig. 18.5.

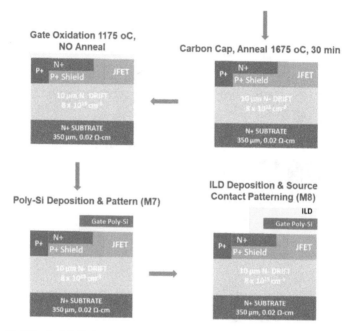

Fig. 18.5 Typical SiC planar-gate power MOSFET fabrication sequence: illustrates photolithography steps with masks M7 and M8.

The gate oxide is thermally grown after removal of the carbon cap. A sacrificial oxide of 200 Å can be first grown and removed to remove surface damage. The thermal oxidation is performed at 1175 °C followed by a NO anneal to reduce the interface state density. This is important to improving the channel mobility.

The gate electrode is then deposited on the gate oxide as shown in Fig. 18.5. This is typically formed using highly phosphorus doped polysilicon layer with a coating of silicide to reduce its sheet resistance to below 5 Ω/sq. The gate electrode is patterned using the seventh mask (shown in Fig. 18.5 as mask M7). This is a critical alignment step because the gate electrode must overlap the N^+ source region beyond the channel portion.

The inter-layer-dielectric (ILD) is now deposited to cover the gate electrode. It is a TEOS (tetraeythlorthosilicate) film formed using low pressure chemical vapor deposition. The layer must be free of pinholes to avoid gate-to-source short-circuits. It must be conformal to cover the edges of the gate electrode. The ILD is patterned using the eight mask (shown in Fig. 18.5 as mask M8). This is a critical alignment step because its opening must allow ohmic contacts to be made to the N^+ and P^+ regions. At the same time, the opening in the ILD must not encroach on the gate electrode. The SiC power MOSFET have channel widths (orthogonal to the cross-sections shown in the above figures) of more than 10 meters. Poor alignment of the ILD contact mask M8 along the cell fingers can lead to short-circuits between the gate and source making the devices inoperable.

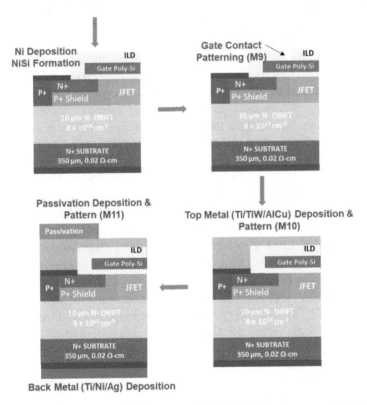

Fig. 18.6 Typical SiC planar-gate power MOSFET fabrication sequence: illustrates photolithography steps with masks M9, M10, and M11.

The ohmic contact to the N^+ source and P^+ contact regions is achieved by using a 1000 Å nickel layer annealed at 750 °C to form a nickel silicide at the SiC surface as shown in Fig. 18.6. The rest of the deposited nickel layer can be etched away from the ILD layer. A nickel layer is also evaporated on the back-side of the wafer and annealed to form an ohmic contact to the N^+ substrate (device drain electrode). Contact for the gate electrode is then opened using the ninth mask (shown in Fig. 18.6 as mask M9). This contact opening is shown at the MOSFET cell in Fig. 18.6 for convenience. The opening is actually located at the gate pads on the chip and not in the MOSFET cells.

The top metal layer is deposited as shown in Fig. 18.6. It consists of a stack of Ti 1500 Å, TiN 1000 Å, and AlCu 4 μm. The Ti film provides good ohmic contact to the nickel silicide layer. The thick AlCu layer allows attaching thick (typically 10 mils) wires on the source electrode with low resistance between the wire-bonds. The TiN layer serves as a barrier layer. The top metal stack must be patterned using the tenth mask (shown in Fig. 18.6 as mask M10) to define the source and gate electrodes. This includes any gate runners on the chip to distribute the drive signals.

A protective passivation layer is then applied over the top of the chip. This consists of 5000 Å of silicon nitride formed using low pressure chemical vapor deposition, and a polyimide coating. These layers are patterned using the eleventh mask (shown in Fig. 18.6 as mask M11) to expose the surfaces where the aluminum wire-bonds are attached.

The final step in the process is to deposit the back side metal. This is a stack of Ti 1000 Å, Ni 4000 Å, and Ag 10,000 Å. The silver layer allows attaching the chip to the package. It is common practice to thin the SiC N^+ substrate from 350 μm to 100 μm to reduce its parasitic resistance from 0.70 to 0.2 mΩ-cm^2. This is important because the specific on-resistance of 1200 V rated SiC planar-gate power MOSFETs is only 2.5 mΩ-cm^2. Special wafer handling equipment is required to thin the substrate without breakage.

The above process is for the manufacturing of SiC planar-gate power MOSFETs. The JBS rectifiers can be manufactured using many of the same process steps to fabricate the alignment mark, JTE edge termination, and P^+ region needed for this device structure. The Schottky contact can be made using either Ti or Ni as the barrier metal. Titanium produces a lower barrier height with a rectifier knee voltage of about 0.8 V while Nickel produces a larger barrier height with a rectifier knee voltage of about 1.1 V. The Ni Schottky contact is annealed at 750 °C to form a silicide. High leakage current is observed when the anneal temperature is made above 900 °C for the Ni contact.

The process described is similar to that used to manufacture SiC power devices by companies. This process has been implemented over a time span of 5 years in a commercial SiC foundry by NCSU to successfully make high performance SiC power devices.

18.2 Process Qualification Methodology

It is necessary to perform process qualification in order to manufacture power semiconductor devices using any developed technology[2]. It is typical to run three consecutive process lots (Lot 1, 2 and 3) at the commercial foundry with identical process steps. This effort was undertaken at NCSU in 2019. Each of the SiC wafers contained about 50 devices of each type shown in Fig. 18.1. A Signatone semi-automated probe station was used with a B1505 Keysight Curve Tracer to obtain extensive wafer-level data on all of the 150 devices of each type on each wafer. This allowed creating wafer maps to visually assess the uniformity and to generate statistical distribution of the device parameters.

The on-state voltage drop and leakage current were documented in the case of the JBS diode. The on-resistance, threshold voltage, and gate-drain capacitance were acquired for the power MOSFETs and JBSFETs. In addition, the third quadrant voltage drop was obtained for the JBSFETs to evaluate bypassing of the body diode by the integrated JBS diode. Its value should be less than 2.5 V to ensure inactivation of the P-N body-diode within the MOSFET structure. Wafer maps were created for each parameter to examine the yield. Statistical distribution of the measured parameters were plotted to document the average value and the standard deviation. The leakage current data provided in this paper is taken at 1000 V for the 1.2 kV rated devices. Very little change in leakage current is observed between 1000 V and 1200 V for the linear cell MOSFET devices. It starts increasing rapidly only beyond 1400 V with a breakdown voltage of about 1600 V at a leakage current of 100 μA.

The process qualification was achieved by examining the distribution of the above device parameters: (a) within a wafer; (b) wafer-to-wafer within a lot; and (c) wafer-to-wafer from lot-to-lot. The parametric spread (typical and maximum or minimum values) given in commercial product datasheets served as the benchmark to determine the yield and quality of the process. A breakdown voltage above 1600 V was found for all the fabricated devices, well above the 1.2 kV rating, as demonstrated in the blocking characteristics shown in previous technical publications on these devices (see chapter 11). The yield was not limited by the blocking voltage due to excellent performance of the hybrid-Junction Termination Extension (JTE) edge termination applied to all the devices.

18.2.1 Statistical Distributions: JBS Rectifiers

The JBS rectifier is a Schottky rectifier with a P-N junction in parallel as discussed in chapter 6. The P-N junction is used to suppress large leakage currents during the reverse blocking mode. The case of a nickel Schottky contact is described here.

<u>Within-Wafer and Wafer-to-Wafer-within-a-Lot Data</u>:

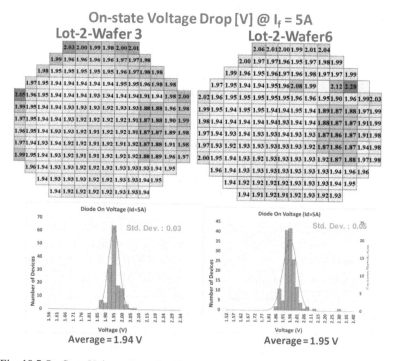

Fig. 18.7 On-State Voltage Drop for SiC JBS rectifiers: Within-Wafer and Wafer-to-Wafer-within-a-Lot distribution data.

Wafer maps and statistical distribution data for the on-state voltage drop for JBS rectifiers are shown in Fig. 18.7 for two wafers from Lot 2. The distribution is uniform for each wafer. It has an average value of 1.94 V with a standard deviation of 0.03 V for the 150 devices measured on wafer 3. A similar very uniform distribution is observed across wafer 6 with an average value of 1.95 V and a standard deviation of 0.05 V for 150 devices on this wafer. Comparing the data from the two wafers, it can be concluded that the variation of the on-state voltage drop from Wafer-to-Wafer-within-a-Lot is also very small.

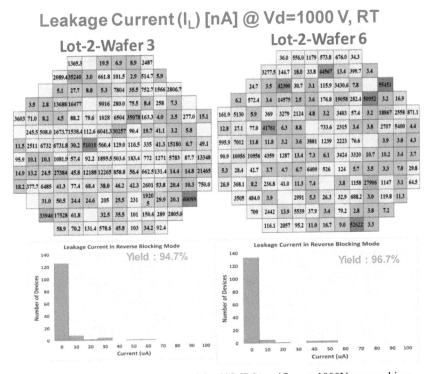

Fig. 18.8 Leakage currents measured for SiC JBS rectifiers at 1000V reverse bias: Within-Wafer and Wafer-to-Wafer-within-a-lot variation.

Fig. 18.8 shows wafer maps of the leakage currents measured at 1000 V for the JBS rectifiers on wafers 3 and 6 from Lot 2. Note that the values are given in nA. The statistical distribution of the leakage current is given below the wafer maps. The leakage current is low (well below 100 μA used in datasheets for SiC JBS rectifiers).

Lot-to-Lot Distribution Data:

Data on the on-state voltage drop for the JBS rectifiers from one wafer from each of the three qualification lots is shown in Fig. 18.9. A uniform distribution is observed for each wafer. The average values for the three wafers are 2.00 V, 1.94 V, and 2.06 V. A standard deviation of 0.03-0.07 V is observed for 150 devices on each wafer. It can be concluded from this data that Lot-to-Lot variations of on-state voltage drop are very small.

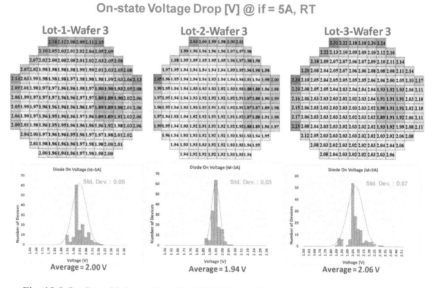

Fig. 18.9 On-State Voltage Drop for SiC JBS rectifiers at 5 A: Lot-to-Lot variation.

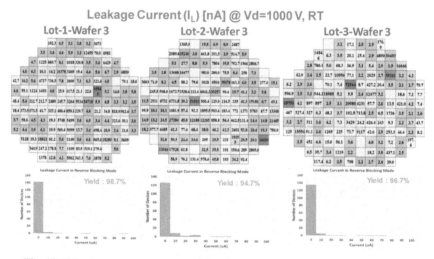

Fig. 18.10 Leakage currents measured for SiC JBS rectifiers at 1000V reverse bias: Lot-to-Lot variation.

The leakage currents measured at 1000 V for JBS rectifiers on wafers from the three lots are shown in Fig. 18.10. The statistical distribution of the leakage current is given at the bottom of the wafer maps. The leakage current is in the nA range, well below the 100 μA used in datasheets.

Summary: Based up on the measured data, the yield is found to be above 90 % for the JBS rectifiers manufactured using the PRESiCE™ technology. The leakage current for Schottky rectifiers is often a yield limiting factor. This problem is overcome with the JBS rectifier structure. The average leakage currents for JBS diodes made with the PRESiCE™ technology are well below the industry standard leakage current of 100 μA. The on-state voltage drop for these JBS diodes is about 2 V which is suitable for their use as antiparallel diode with Si Insulated Gate Bipolar Transistors (IGBTs) and SiC power MOSFETs. The Gen-3 PRESiCE™ technology can therefore be used to fabricate commercial JBS diode products in the foundry.

18.2.2 Statistical Distributions: Power MOSFETs

The 1.2 kV rated power MOSFETs were found to have excellent breakdown voltages (> 1600 V) and low (nA range) leakage currents due to the robust edge termination and cell design. These device parameters did not limit the yield. The distributions for three other parameters (on-resistance, threshold voltage, and gate-drain capacitance) must be evaluated while doing the process qualification. Power MOSFET datasheets provide the typical value for on-resistance together with a maximum value that is 30 % greater. The fabrication process should keep the standard deviation sufficiently small to avoid exceed this limit. In datasheet for power MOSFETs, maximum and minimum values for the threshold voltage that are 30 % above and below the typical value are commonly used. The standard deviation produced by the process should avoid exceeding these boundaries. Just the typical value is given in datasheets for the gate-drain capacitance. However, this is an important device parameter that limits the switching losses for the SiC power MOSFET. It was therefore included during the process qualification.

Within-Wafer and Wafer-to-Wafer-within-a-Lot Data:

Wafer maps for the on-resistance of SiC power MOSFETs are shown in Fig. 18.11 for two wafers from Lot 3. The statistical distribution is shown below the wafer maps. The distribution observed for wafer 4 has an average value of 170 mΩ with standard deviation of only 6 mΩ for 150 devices. This is a variation of only 3.5 %. A similar tight distribution is seen for wafer 5 an average value of 175 mΩ for 150 devices. Based up on the data from both wafers, it can be concluded that variations from Wafer-to-Wafer-within-a-Lot for the PRESiCE™ technology are well within acceptable limits of 30 % in manufacturers datasheets.

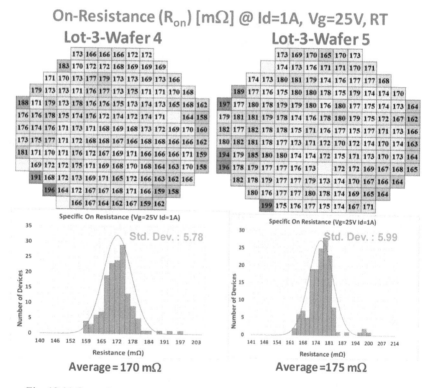

Fig. 18.11 On-resistance measured for SiC power MOSFETs: Within-Wafer and Wafer-to-Wafer-within-a-Lot variation of On-Resistance.

The threshold voltage of a power MOSFET must be sufficiently large, typically at least 2 V, to prevent devices from inadvertently turning on due to voltage spikes in power circuits. It must also be sufficiently low to allow using reasonable gate drive voltages, typically 15-20 V, for SiC power MOSFETs. Wafer maps for threshold voltage variation are shown in Fig. 18.12 for two wafers from Lot 3. The statistical distribution is shown below the wafer maps. The distribution is uniform across wafer 4: a standard deviation < 0.15 V with an average value of 3.94 V for the 150 MOSFETs. This is less than 4 %, well below the margins given in data-sheets. For wafer 5, the standard deviation is also < 0.15 V with an average value of 3.95 V for 150 MOSFETs indicating excellent uniformity within industry standards. Using the data from both wafers, it can be concluded that variations from Wafer-to-Wafer-within-a-Lot are sufficiently low for manufacturing the MOSFETs.

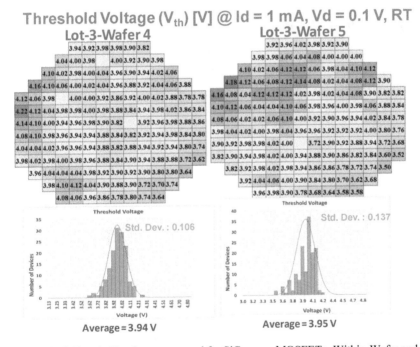

Fig. 18.12 Threshold voltage measured for SiC power MOSFETs: Within-Wafer and Wafer-to-Wafer-within-a-Lot.

The switching losses are determined by the gate-drain capacitance (C_{GD}) of a power MOSFET in inverters used for electric vehicle motor drive applications. A smaller C_{GD} reduces the transition time for the drain voltage resulting in lower switching energy loss. Wafer maps for the C_{GD}, measured at a drain bias of 1000 V, are shown in Fig. 18.13 for two wafers from Lot 3. The statistical distribution is shown below the wafer maps.

The C_{GD} for wafer 4 has a standard deviation < 0.6 pF with an average value of 10.38 pF for 150 MOSFETs. In the case of wafer 5, the standard deviation is < 0.3 pF with an average value of 9.90 pF for 150 MOSFETs. This confirms very small variations in the capacitance across a wafer. Using the data from the two wafers, it can be concluded that C_{GD} variations from Wafer-to-Wafer-within-a-Lot are very small.

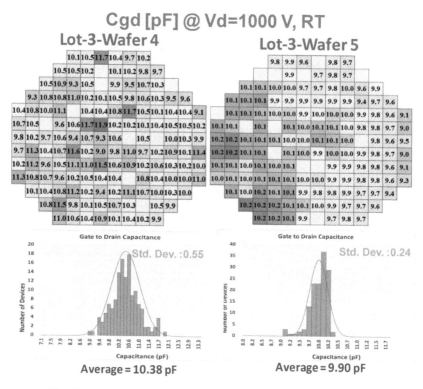

Fig. 18.13 Gate-Drain Capacitance measured for SiC power MOSFETs:
Within-Wafer and Wafer-to-Wafer-within-a-Lot.

Lot-to-Lot Distribution Data:

Wafer maps of the on-resistance of the SiC power MOSFETs measured for one wafer from each of the three lots are shown in Fig. 18.14. The corresponding statistical distribution is provided below the wafer maps. The distribution is very uniform within each wafer. The average values are 181 mΩ, 164 mΩ, and 175 mΩ for the three wafers, with a standard deviation < 6 mΩ for 150 MOSFETs on each wafer. The variation in on-resistance is below 4 %, well within the 30 % margin used for commercial datasheets. The data confirms that on-resistance variations on wafers from three Lots fall within the specifications in datasheets and are therefore not a yield limiting factor for the PRESiCE™ technology.

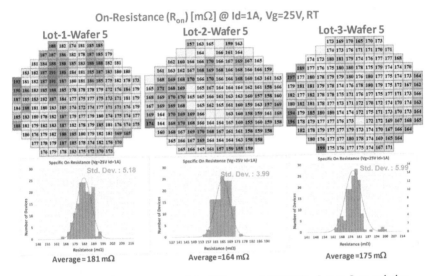

Fig. 18.14 On-Resistance measured for SiC power MOSFETs: Lot-to-Lot variation.

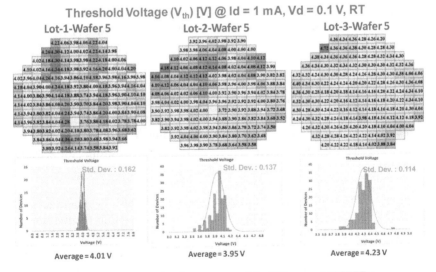

Fig. 18.15 Threshold Voltage measured for SiC power MOSFETs: Lot-to-Lot variation.

Wafer maps of the threshold voltage variation of SiC power MOSFETs for one wafer from each of the three lots are shown in Fig. 18.15 with the statistical distribution below each wafer map. There is very little variation from lot to lot: a standard deviation < 0.2 V with an average value of 4.0 V for 150 MOSFETs on each wafer. From this data, it can be concluded that Lot-to-Lot threshold voltage variations are not a yield limiting factor for the PRESiCE™ technology.

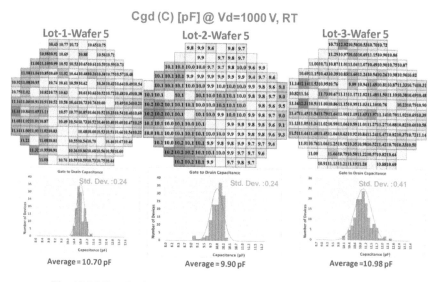

Fig. 18.16 Gate-Drain Capacitance measured for SiC power MOSFETs: Lot-to-Lot variation.

Wafer maps and statistical distributions of the gate-drain capacitance (C_{GD}) are shown in Fig. 18.16 for one wafer from each of the three lots. A very uniform distribution is observed from Lot-to-Lot: a standard deviation < 0.5 pF with an average value of about 10 pF for 150 MOSFETs within each wafer. This parameter is therefore not a yield limiting factor.

<u>Summary</u>: From the measured data on power MOSFETs manufactured using the PRESiCE™ technology, it can be concluded that the maximum on-resistance for 90 % of the devices are less than 1.3x of the typical value, demonstrating a yield of above 90 %. The threshold voltage for the SiC power MOSFETs is within +/− 30 % of the typical value as required by datasheets.

18.2.3 Statistical Distributions: Power JBSFETs

The JBS diode and MOSFET structures discussed in the previous sections have been integrated into a single monolithic device called the JBSFET (see chapter 13). The JBSFET cross-section, shown in Fig. 18.1, contains a JBS diode formed by making a gap in the P^+ shielding region. A Schottky contact is made to the drift region using nickel metallization silicided at 900 °C. The process simultaneously makes good ohmic contacts to the P^+ and N^+ regions. The Schottky contact size is optimized to achieve an on-state voltage drop of below 2.5 V in the third quadrant to by-pass the P-N body diode in the MOSFET while avoiding large leakage current in the blocking mode.

<u>Within-Wafer and Wafer-to-Wafer-within-a-Lot Data</u>:

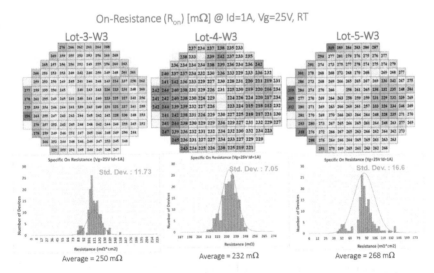

Fig. 18.17 On-Resistance measured for SiC power JBSFETs: Lot-to-Lot variation.

The on-resistance of the JBSFET is larger than that of the MOSFET for the same die size due to a reduced channel density (see chapter 13). To compensate for this, an accumulation-channel was used instead of the inversion-channel in the MOSFETs. The accumulation layer mobility has been found to be 30 % larger than the inversion layer mobility in 4H-SiC MOSFETs. Process qualification was performed like discussed for the power MOSFET in the previous section. The distributions for the on-resistance, threshold voltage, leakage current, and third quadrant on-state voltage drop for accumulation-channel JBSFETs are shown in this chapter. The capacitance distributions for JBSFETs are not shown because they resemble those discussed in the previous section for the power MOSFETs. Only the variations from lot-to-lot are included here.

Wafer maps and statistical distributions of the on-resistance for the SiC power JBSFETs are shown in Fig. 18.17 for wafers from three lots. The average values are 250 mΩ, 232 mΩ, and 268 mΩ for the three wafers. The on-resistance is uniform within each wafer. The standard deviation is < 20 mΩ for 150 JBSFETs on each wafer. The variation in on-resistance is below 8 %, well within the 30 % margin used for commercial datasheets. From the data, it can be surmised that variations in on-resistance from Lot-to-Lot are very small and that this is not a yield limiting factor.

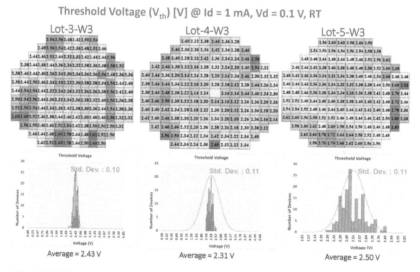

Fig. 18.18 Threshold voltage measured for SiC power MOSFETs: Within-Wafer and Wafer-to-Wafer-within-a-Lot.

Wafer maps of the threshold voltage for the SiC power JBSFETs are shown in Fig. 18.18 for one wafer from each of the three lots. The average value for the threshold voltage for accumulation-channel devices is smaller than for inversion-channel devices. The distribution is very tight from Lot-to-Lot with a standard deviation of about 0.1 V from an average value of 2.4 V for 150 JBSFETs in each wafer. From the data, it can be surmised that threshold voltage variations from Lot-to-Lot are very small and that this parameter is not a yield limiting factor.

Schottky diodes are well known to produce high leakage currents when blocking large voltage. This problem is particularly severe for SiC devices due to large Schottky barrier lowering and tunneling effects. The shielding of the Schottky contact by the P$^+$ regions is critical to suppressing the leakage current in products. Consequently, the leakage current could become the yield limiting factor in JBSFETs due to the integrated Schottky contact.

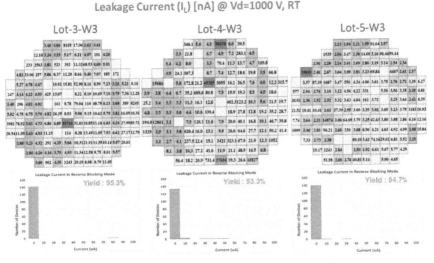

Fig. 18.19 SiC power JBSFETs manufactured using PRESiCE^{TM} technology: Lot-to-Lot variation of Leakage Current.

Wafer maps and statistical distributions of leakage current measured at 1000 V for JBSFETs are shown in Fig. 18.19 for one wafer from each of the three qualification lots. It can be observed from the data that the magnitude of the leakage current is in the nA range, well below typical datasheet specifications of 100 μA, in spite of integration of the JBS diode. This outcome is achieved with the proper choice of the width of the Schottky contact within the JBSFET cells.

The reason for integration of the JBS diode into the power MOSFET structure is to provide a path for current to by-pass the body-diode in the third quadrant. This requires designing the JBS diode such that its on-state voltage drop is about 2.5 V, which is significantly below the 3.5 V required to obtain current flow via the body diode. Wafer maps and statistical distributions for the on-state voltage drop in the third quadrant for the power JBSFETs are shown in Fig. 18.20 for one wafer from each of the three lots. The average on-state voltage ranges from 2.2 to 2.4 V ensuring that the body-diode activation is suppressed.

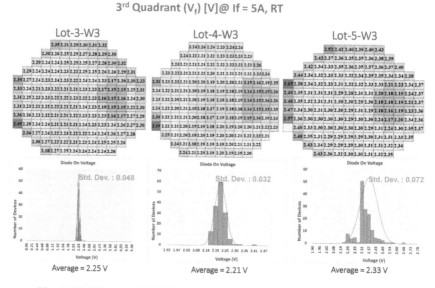

Fig. 18.20 SiC power JBSFETs manufactured using PRESiCE™ technology: Lot-to-Lot variation of 3rd Quadrant Voltage Drop.

Summary: The above data demonstrates that the PRESiCE™ technology is capable of producing SiC JBSFETs with maximum on-resistance well within the 30 % limit, with yields above 90 %. The threshold voltage variation for these SiC power JBSFETs falls within the +/− 30 % of the typical value. The third quadrant current flow via the integrated JBS diode keeps the on-state voltage drop below 2.5 V as desired while simultaneously not incurring a high leakage current through the Schottky contact. These features meet the criteria for manufacturing SiC JBSFET products.

18.3 Summary

The PRESiCE™ technology was developed by NCSU at a 6 inch commercial foundry, X-Fab, to manufacture 1.2 kV SiC JBS rectifiers, power MOSFETs, and JBSFETs. This technology was developed over a three year time frame with funding from the PowerAmerica Institute created by the Department of Energy in 2015. The technology was qualified by running three consecutive process lots. The wafer maps and parametric distributions obtained for the fabricated devices show excellent control of uniformity across each wafer, from wafer-to-wafer within a lot, and wafer-to-wafer from lot-to-lot. The overall yield for all the different types of devices manufactured using the PRESiCE™ technology exceeds 90 % at a die size of 3 mm x 3 mm. These excellent results were achieved by using strict process control protocols at the foundry and by using all in-house processes compared with performing the hot ion-implants at an external service.

References

[1] W. Sung and B. J. Baliga, "A Near Ideal Edge Termination Technique for 4500V 4H-SiC Devices: The Hybrid Junction Termination Extension", IEEE Electron Device Letters, Vol. 37, pp. 1609-1612, 2016.

[2] B. J. Baliga, "Third Generation PRESiCE™ Technology for Manufacturing SiC Power Devices in a 6-inch Commercial Foundry", IEEE Journal of the Electron Device Society, Vol. 9, pp. 1111-1117, 2020.

Chapter 19

Synopsis

The motivation for the development of wide bandgap semiconductor based power devices arises from the improvements in efficiency for many applications. The impact of improving the efficiency of power electronics on energy savings has been recognized for a long time[1]. This paper points out that adoption of adjustable speed motor drives and compact fluorescent lamps can lead to huge energy savings, referred to a 'negawatts'. The commercialization of the silicon Insulated Gate Bipolar Transistor (IGBT) has already led to enormous savings in electricity and gasoline[2,3]. The myriad applications for the IGBT in various sectors of the economy has also been documented[4]. During the past 30 years, this technology has produced an electrical energy savings of over 103,400 terra-watt-hours and a gasoline savings of 1.86 trillion pounds. A reduction in carbon dioxide emissions by over 150 trillion pounds has resulted from the improved efficiencies[4].

The introduction of wide bandgap semiconductor based power devices that can replace the silicon IGBT offers the promise to make even further improvements in the efficiency if their cost becomes competitive. These benefits have been promoted in many papers over the years[5,6,7,8]. The revenue for SiC power MOSFETs was $ 1.3 billion in 2022 and is expected to reach $ 6.3 billion in 2031. The main applications for the SiC power devices were initially for power factor correction and photovoltaics. The big escalation in revenue is expected to come from deployment of electric vehicles and their charging stations. The use of wide bandgap power devices in electric and hybrid electric vehicles is promising in the future because of range extension and simplification of the cooling system.

The potential applications for SiC power devices based power devices will be reviewed in this concluding chapter. The applications for silicon carbide power devices are growing due to earlier commercialization of Schottky (JBS) power rectifiers followed by power MOSFETs.

The prospective applications for SiC power devices are: (a) motor control for the industrial sector; (b) uninterruptible power supplies for data centers; (c) renewable energy (solar and wind) power systems; (d) electric and hybrid electric vehicles; and (e) power factor correction.

19.1 SiC Power Device Evolution

The first SiC power devices to be commercialized were JBS rectifiers described in chapter 6. The very first high voltage SiC Schottky rectifiers were reported in 1992 with low on-state voltage drop and absence of large reverse recovery currents[9]. The Junction Barrier controlled Schottky (JBS) rectifier concept, first proposed[10] for silicon devices in the 1980s, was applied to SiC devices in the 1990s to reduce the leakage current[11,12]. Commercial 4H-SiC JBS rectifiers became available in the early 2000s making their applications feasible. The SiC JBS rectifier has very favorable characteristics for applications due to its smaller on-state voltage drop and significantly smaller reverse recovery losses when compared with silicon P-i-N rectifiers. They have found various applications as antiparallel diodes for silicon IGBTs leading to a market of $ 2.1 billion in 2022.

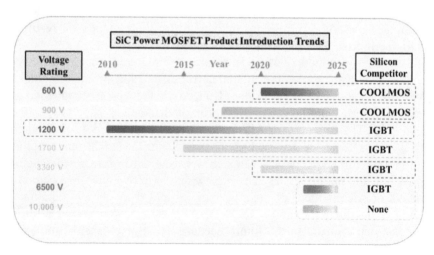

Fig. 19.1 SiC power MOSFET product evolution.

The development of SiC power MOSFETs took a much longer time frame due to problems with the MOS interface. Although the first high performance planar SiC power MOSFET was reported[13] in 1997, the commercialization of these devices did not occur until 2010. The SiC power MOSFET has smaller on-state voltage drop and switching losses than silicon IGBTs for blocking voltage up to at least 5-kV. SiC power MOSFETs are commercially available with voltage ratings of 600-V, 900-V, 1200-V, and 1700-V with products under development for higher voltages. This has encouraged their use in various applications to improve the efficiency even though their cost is still much greater (2-3 times) than that of silicon IGBTs.

The evolution of SiC power MOSFET product introduction is shown in Fig. 19.1. The pace of introduction and voltage rating for the SiC power MOSFETs was decided by the competing Si power switch technology. The relatively high switching losses in Si IGBTs provided a window of opportunity for penetration of the market with unipolar SiC power MOSFETs that exhibit low switching losses despite their higher cost. SiC power MOSFETs with 1200 V rating were first introduced to the market in 2010. Subsequently, devices with 1700 V rating were introduced in 2015 to compete with Si IGBTs. The cost of these SiC power MOSFETs was larger than that of the Si IGBTs. The justification for replacing the Si IGBT had to include operating the power circuits at higher frequencies to reduce the size and cost of passive elements (inductors and capacitors) and filters.

The availability of unipolar Si super-junction MOSFETs (COOLMOS^{TM}) made the completion more difficult for SiC power MOSFETs at voltage ratings of 600 V and 900 V. However, the poor reverse recovery performance of the body diode in the COOLMOS devices made their replacement with SiC power MOSFETs attractive. SiC power MOSFETs with 900 V rating were introduced in the market in 2017 followed by 600 V rated devices in 2020. These devices have a very large potential market due to rapid deployment of electric vehicles and their charging infrastructure.

SiC power MOSFETs with 3300 V rating became commercially available in 2020. Device with even higher blocking voltages can be expected to be introduced in the market post 2025. The market for these devices in traction drives is relatively smaller but an important one. Devices with ratings above 10 kV for power distribution applications may be delayed due to the even smaller market and slow adoption by utilities.

19.2 SiC Device Applications

It has been recognized by the power device industry that the biggest potential market for SiC power devices would be in the electric vehicle and charging infrastructure. However, this market was challenging due to the very strict protocols for reliability and field trials. The qualification cycles for the automotive industry for Si devices was a prolonged period of 3-5 years.

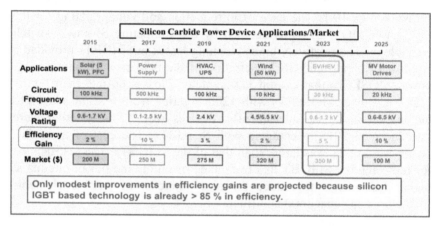

Fig. 19.2 SiC power device applications.

The initial commercial applications for SiC power devices were identified to be residential solar power generation and power supplies. These applications were realized in 2015-2017 as shown in Fig. 19.2. This figure provides the circuit operating frequency, device voltage rating, and market size for each application. The 1.2 kV voltage ratings for the first SiC power MOSFETs were adequate for this application.

The HVAC and wind power generation applications need devices with larger voltage ratings delaying their deployment. High power motor drives that require devices with voltage ratings above 3.3 kV are options in the future. The electric vehicle application needs devices with voltage ratings of 0.6 to 1.2 kV with future growth to well above the $350 Million shown in the figure. This application is highlighted by the red box in Fig. 19.2 due to enormous future market potential.

It is worth noting that power electronics using the Si IGBT already offers very high efficiencies exceeding 85-90 %. Consequently, the gain in efficiency by replacing them with SiC power MOSFET is modest – ranging from 2-10 %. The motivation for replacing Si IGBTs with SiC power MOSFETs comes from other system benefits, such as smaller size and weight for the inverter in electric vehicles. A gain in range of the electric vehicle by about 10 % has been projected with these devices.

19.3 SiC Device Application Examples

Some examples of applications for SiC power devices are provided in this chapter. More applications will emerge as the cost of SiC power devices declines and more components become available from suppliers. Most SiC power device manufacturers around the world are making major investments in the production of large diameter 4H-SiC substrates and in production facilities for manufacturing the power devices.

19.3.1 Boost PFC Converters using SiC JBS Rectifiers

One major application space for SiC JBS rectifiers is in power factor correction (PFC) circuits[14]. The performance of the boost PFC circuit is limited by reverse-recovery related power losses in the silicon P-i-N power rectifier. This power loss can be mitigated by performing soft-switching but this introduces snubber inductors and capacitors. Utilizing the SiC JBS rectifier eliminates the reverse-recovery problem allowing operation at significantly higher frequencies. This allows reduction of the size of the boost inductor while maintaining a high efficiency.

A bridgeless boost PFC converter with SiC power rectifiers is becoming the next generation of high performance front-end converter in applications. These PFC converters can be used in computers and uninterruptible power supplies. The size of the EMI filters, boost inductor, and heat sink has been shown[15,16] to be reduced by using SiC diodes operating at 1 MHz. The SiC JBS rectifier has also been used with a silicon COOLMOS transistor to achieve high performance in PFC circuits[17,18]. Enhanced performance of continuous conduction mode active PFC circuits has been demonstrated by using SiC diodes[19].

19.3.2 Photovoltaic Inverters: SiC JBS Rectifiers

A typical grid connected photovoltaic system contains the solar cells for generation of electrical energy, a buck-boost DC-DC converter followed by a DC-to-AC inverter, and a LCL filter[20]. SiC JBS rectifiers have been used as boost diodes in the converter stage with silicon IGBTs since 2005 in PV applications and as flyback diodes in the inverter stage[21]. The replacement of silicon P-i-N rectifiers with SiC Schottky rectifiers has been found to increase the efficiency by 2 %. An increase in efficiency by 0.8 % at the same power level has also been reported[22] by replacing silicon P-i-N rectifiers with SiC Schottky rectifiers. However, the output power can be increased by 85 % by using the SiC diodes and the switching frequency can be increased from 16 kHz to 48 kHz. This reduces the size and weight of passive components.

19.3.3 Automotive Traction Inverters: SiC JBS Rectifiers

Another potential high volume application space for SiC diodes is electric and hybrid electric vehicles. Here, the SiC JBS rectifiers are used as flyback diodes across silicon IGBTs as first proposed in 1994[23]. The power losses were demonstrated to be reduced by 33.6 % by replacing silicon P-i-N rectifiers with SiC Schottky rectifiers in a 55-kW three-phase automotive traction inverter[24].

Many hybrid electric vehicles, such as the Prius from Toyota, make use of a DC-to-DC boost converter between the battery and the electric motors. It has been demonstrated that the power losses can be reduced by using the Si COOLMOS transistor and the SiC JBS diode to achieve an efficiency of 99 percent[25].

19.3.4 Photovoltaic Inverters: SiC MOSFETs

An all SiC device based PV inverter solution can be achieved due to the availability of 1.2-kV SiC power MOSFETs. The most prevalent silicon IGBT based PV inverter topology is the three-level, Dual-Neutral-Point-Clamped (3L-DNPC) topology[20]. The approach requires three IGBT modules each with 4 IGBTs and 2 diodes. The operating frequency is limited to 16 kHz due to the high switching losses in the IGBTs. The low operating frequency increases the size of the DC link capacitor and the LCL output filter increasing their cost.

With a PV inverter made using SiC power MOSFETs, the topology can be simplified to a two-level, full bridge with split capacitor (2L-FB)[20]. The switching frequency can be increased to 50-kHz by using the SiC devices due to their smaller switching losses. This reduces the size, weight and cost of the inverter because the number of device is reduced to 6. Cost of the SiC-MOSFET based 2L-FB PV inverter has been calculated to be 8.8 % less than that for a Si-IGBT based 3L-DNPC inverter due to the reduced cost for the PCB, heat-sink, DC-link capacitors, and the LCL-filter despite the higher total semiconductor device cost.

The advantages of replacing silicon IGBTs with SiC power MOSFETs have been identified encouraging implementation into PV systems. A 2 % improvement in efficiency has been demonstrated by replacing silicon IGBTs with SiC power MOSFETs in Japan[26].

The reduction of cost of PV inverters by replacing silicon IGBTs with SiC power MOSFETs has also been analyzed[27]. The authors conclude that SiC-based PV inverters can be operated only at switching frequencies up to 50-kHz due to electromagnetic interference. The inverter efficiency increases by 0.8 % for the single phase case and 2 % for the three-phase case when SiC power MOSFETs and SiC diodes instead of Si devices. These improvements provide a modest annual cost savings of 20-30 Euros per year. The power density for the PV inverter can be improved from 0.38 kW/kg with silicon IGBTs to 1 kW/kg by using an all-SiC implementation[28]. This is attractive to commercial roof-top solar panel installers.

The inverter cost for PV installations in Europe has been analyzed for the case of silicon and SiC components[29]. The authors concluded that the cost of SiC-based PV inverters is higher than that of Si-based inverters by 226-293 % due to higher prices for SiC devices. They project equal cost for both inverters can be achieved if the cost of SiC devices is reduced in half. The SiC-based inverters will achieve lower levelized cost of generated electricity by 4-7 % and higher energy production by 1.6-4 %.

19.3.5 Automotive Traction Inverters: SiC MOSFETs

Hybrid-Electric and Electric vehicles require power management from the battery. Many stages of DC-to-DC and DC-to-AC are inherent in the automobile. The silicon IGBT has been extensively used for the development of all the hybrid-electric and electric cars on the road today[4]. The cost of power semiconductor devices is a significant fraction of the power electronics in the vehicles[30]. In addition, a significant (33 to 50 %) size reduction of the power conversion unit is projected[31] by replacing silicon devices with SiC power MOSFETs. Furthermore, a similar reduction in the size of capacitors and inductors is achieved by the higher frequency of operation enabled by SiC power MOSFETs. An air-cooled inverter with power density of 60-kW/L can be designed by using the SiC power MOSFETs.

Although the low switching power losses of SiC power MOSFETs when compared with Si IGBTs is attractive for improving the efficiency, large voltage oscillations of the DC bus voltage have been observed[32]. Actual power losses in the SiC power MOSFETs have been measured to be ten-times smaller than for Si IGBT as projected in 1994[23]. The impact of these reduced power losses has been estimated to extend the range of the electric vehicle by 5 percent[33]. The high voltages generated at the DC bus due to oscillations can also damage the winding insulation in motors[34]. A gain in efficiency by about 2 percent has been reported by replacing Si IGBTs and PiN diodes with SiC power MOSFETs and JBS diodes in an electric vehicle drive-train[35].

The Toyota Motor Company has studied the benefits of replacing Si IGBTs and PiN rectifiers with SiC power MOSFETs and JBS diodes[36]. The Si devices are replaced with the SiC devices in the power control unit (PCU) consisting of the boost converter and inverter stages. The SiC devices could be operated at a higher frequency due to reduced switching losses. Driving tests using the Japanese JC08 test cycle showed an increase in fuel efficiency by 5 percent. The larger switching frequency is expected to produce a reduction in PCU size by 80 percent.

19.3.6 Locomotive Traction Inverters: SiC MOSFETs

The benefits of using SiC power MOSFETs and JBS diodes in place of the Si IGBT and PiN rectifier have been shown to apply to railway traction applications as well[37]. In this application, small mass and volume are a premium. Reducing converter losses is also important to minimize the size of the cooling system. Increasing operating frequency allows reduction of the size of the passive filtering components.

It was demonstrated that the SiC module could be operated at 15 kHz with the same power losses as in the Si module at 1 kHz. At a fixed frequency of 10-kHz, the power loss with the SiC module was reduced by 40 percent compared with the Si module.

19.3.7 Industrial Motor Drive: SiC MOSFETs

Silicon IGBTs have become the workhorse for industrial motor drives[4]. Silicon carbide devices offer significant reduction in power losses for this application. A motor drive has been implemented using SiC devices for an Allen Bradley 50 hp 3-phase induction motor[38]. An improvement in efficiency by 2.5 % was observed when the inverter was operated at 8-kHz and 5 % at 16-kHz. The main problem with using SiC devices was found to be the high dV/dt which can damage the motor winding insulation. This can be mitigated by increasing the gate drive resistance at the expense of larger power losses.

The economics of replacing Si devices with SiC devices has also been examined for various countries with differing electricity cost[37]. Based upon an efficiency gain of 0.8 %, the annual energy cost savings for China, USA, Japan, Germany and Denmark are $ 80, $ 120, $ 270, $ 360, and $ 420, respectively. Based upon a cost differential of $ 200 for the SiC drive, a payback period of 29, 19, 9, 7, and 6 years was computed for these countries.

The viability and advantages of SiC power MOSFETs for industrial drives has been analyzed taking into account not only reduction in the switching power losses but other considerations such as short circuit withstand capability and vulnerability to cosmic ray induced failures[39]. It was found that short-circuit withstand time was inversely proportional to the drain bias voltage as expected from analytical models [40]. Derating of the SiC power MOSFETs was found to be necessary to avoid cosmic ray induced failures as observed for Si IGBTs.

19.3.8 Data Centers using SiC MOSFETs

Large data centers consume 120 terra-watt-hours of electricity annually and operate at a low efficiency of 67 % due to many power conversion stages[41]. The power distribution efficiency can be improved to 73 % by using a DC bus architecture that makes use of SiC power devices. The 400-V DC architecture consists of a front end rectifier (FER) stage to create the 400-V DC bus, an intermediate bus converter (IBC) on the server motherboard to reduce the voltage to 10 V DC, and a point-of-load (POL) converter to reduce the voltage to 1 V for the microprocessor and memory chips.

SiC power devices are used for the FER stage to obtain a power loss reduction by 50 %, a volume reduction by 20 % and a weight reduction by 10 %. An efficiency of 98 % was observed using the SiC devices.

19.3.9 Electric Vehicle Chargers: SiC MOSFETs

Many automobile manufacturers are migrating to all-electric vehicles. This approach requires deployment of vehicle charging network with an efficient charger that derives its energy from a power grid based on renewable energy. It is estimated that there will be 50-80 million electric vehicles on the road in 2025 with 140-245 million by 2030[42]. The range of an electric vehicle is limited to less than 300 miles. A well distributed charging network is essential to overcome range anxiety for consumers. 10 million chargers have already been deployed around the world but a far greater number is required to satisfy the emerging demand.

Both on-board and off-board chargers are under consideration[43]. The on-board charger is located within the electric vehicle. It can be plugged into the commonly available AC power source in homes and buildings. Its power level ranges up to 40 kW[44]. They add weight and take up space inside the vehicle. This a slow charging approach suitable for use overnight in homes or while at work. It has been employed in the Tesla Model 3 and Toyota RAV4 vehicles as examples.

One example of an on-board charger design that makes use of SiC power devices is a 6.6 kW two-stage architecture[45]. It makes use a variable DC link voltage ranging from 500-840 V in the first stage and 250-450 V in the second stage. A relatively high switching frequency of over 300 kHz is used for the first stage and 500 kHz for the second stage. The design produced a power density of 37 W/in^3 with efficiency above 96 %.

An off-board charger located at charging stations distributed within cities and along highways is essential to encourage adoption of electric vehicles by consumers. Their power level ranges up to 100 kW. It is essential to reduce the charging time to under 10 minutes to appease consumers that have become accustomed to filling gas tanks. Typically, the 20 kW, 3-phase chargers can achieve 80 % battery capacity in 2.5-3.5 hours[43].

Three-phase off-board chargers operating off the 380 V AC grid can charge the battery within 1 hour. They have been deployed by Tesla, BMW, Nissan, and Hyundai. Superchargers with 250 kW capability are now available that can charge the battery to 80 % within 15 min. Tesla has operated 16,000 superchargers at 1826 stations worldwide.

Wireless or inductive charging of electric vehicles is another option that has been studied[4]. This approach relies on transferring power from a power source with winding imbedded in the road to a coil located within the vehicle. This is attractive for electric busses which make stops at well-defined locations where the charging coils can be imbedded on the road. This is another potential market for SiC power devices in the future.

19.4 Summary

A great deal of interest has been generated in the power electronic community by the availability of SiC power devices. For blocking voltages above 600 V, SiC power devices offers significant reduction in power losses and the ability to increase the circuit operating frequency when compared with existing bipolar silicon devices, including the IGBT. This produces many system advantages, namely smaller size for the passive components and output filters as well as higher efficiency. The adoption of this wide bandgap semiconductor technology in applications is constrained by concerns regarding reliability and the higher cost of the devices. Recent studies indicate that the devices have been engineered to provide good reliability. Major programs are underway around the world to reduce the manufacturing cost[46]. This bodes a promising future for a technology that was envisioned more than 40 years ago[47].

References

[1] A. B. Lovins, "The Negawatt Revolution", Across the Board – The Conference Board Magazine, Vol. XXVII, Issue 9, pp. 18-23, 1990.

[2] B. J. Baliga, "The Role of Power Semiconductor Devices on Creating a Sustainable Society", IEEE Applied Power Electronics Conference, Invited Plenary Paper, March 18, 2013.

[3] B. J. Baliga, "Social Impact of Power Semiconductor Devices", IEEE International Electron Devices Meeting, Abstract 2.1.1, pp. 20-23, December 2014.

[4] B. J. Baliga, "The IGBT Device: Physics, Design, and Applications of the Insulated Gate Bipolar Transistor", Second Edition, Elsevier Press, Amsterdam, 2023.

[5] I. Omura, "Future Role of Power Electronics", International Conference on Integrated Power Electronics Systems, Paper 14.2, March 2010.

[6] N. Kaminski, "SiC and GaN Devices – Competition or Coexistence?", IEEE Integrated Power Electronic Systems Conference, pp. 1-11, 2012.

[7] A. Bindra, "Wide-Bandgap-Based Power Devices", IEEE Power Electronics Magazine, pp. 42-47, March 2015.

[8] B. J. Baliga, "40 Years of Progress in SiC Power Devices", SiC 2020, November 2020, Busan, Korea.

[9] M. Bhatnagar, P. M. McLarty, and B. J. Baliga, "Silicon Carbide High Voltage (400 V) Schottky Barrier Diode", IEEE Electron Device Letters, Vol. EDL-13, pp. 501-503, 1992.

[10] B. J. Baliga, "The Pinch Rectifier: A Low Forward Drop High Speed Power Diode", IEEE Electron Device Letters, Vol. EDL-5, pp. 194-196, 1984.

[11] R. Held, N. Kaminsi, and E. Niemann, "SiC Merged p-n/Schottky Rectifiers for High Voltage Applications", Silicon Carbide and Related Materials – 1997, Material Science Forum, Vol. 264-268, pp. 1057-1060, 1998.

[12] F. Dahlquist, et al, "Junction barrier Schottky Diodes in 4H-SiC and H-SiC", Silicon Carbide and Related Materials – 1997, Material Science Forum, Vol. 264-268, pp. 1061-1064, 1998.

[13] P. M. Shenoy and B. J. Baliga, "The Planar 6H-SiC ACCUFET", IEEE Electron Device Letters, Vol. EDL-18, pp. 589-591, 1997.

[14] M. M. Javanovic and Y. Jang, "State-of-the-Art, Single-Phase, Active Power-Factor-Correction Techniques for High-Power Applications – An Overview", IEEE Transactions on Industrial Electronics, Vol. 52, pp. 701-708, 2005.

[15] M. Hernando, et al, "Comparing Si and SiC Diodes Performance in a Commercial AC-to-DC Rectifier with Power Factor Correction", IEEE Power Electronics Specialists Conference, Vol. 4, pp. 1979-1982, 2003.

[16] P-O. Jeannin, et al, "1 MHz Power Factor Correction Boost Converter with SiC Schottky Diode", IEEE Industrial Applications Society Meeting, pp. 1267-1272, 2004.

[17] B. Lu, et al, "Performance Evaluation of CoolMOS and SiC Diode for Single-Phase Power factor Correction Applications", IEEE Applied Power Electronics Conference, Vol. 2, pp. 651-657, 2003.

[18] L. Lorenz, G. Deboy, and I. Zverev, "Matched Pair of CoolMOS Transistor with SiC-Schottky Diode – Advantages in Applications", IEEE Transactions on Industrial Applications, Vol. 40, pp. 1265-1272, 2004.

[19] W-S. Choi and S-M. Young, "Effectiveness of a SiC Schottky Diode for Super-Junction MOSFETs on Continuous Conduction Mode PFC", IEEE International Symposium on Power Electronics, Electrical Drives, Automation and Motion, pp. 562-567, 2010.

[20] C. Sintamarean, et al, "Wide-band Gap Devices in PV Systems – Opportunities and Challenges", IEEE International Power Electronics Conference, pp. 1912-1919, 2014.

[21] A. Mumtaz, "Photovoltaic Systems: Technology Trends and Challenges through to 2020", IEEE International Symposium on Power Semiconductor Devices and ICs Short Course, 2014.

[22] E. Theodossu, "Efficiency Improvement in Booster Power Modules with SiC Components", Bodo Power Systems, pp. 32-35, March 2014.

[23] B. J. Baliga, "Power Semiconductor Devices for Variable Frequency Drives", Proceedings of the IEEE, Vol. 82, pp. 1112-1122, 1994.

[24] B. Ozpineci, et al, "A 55-kW Three-Phase Inverter with Si IGBT and SiC Schottky Diodes", IEEE Transactions on Industrial Applications, Vol. 45, pp. 278-285, 2009.

[25] W. Martinez, et al, "Efficiency Optimization of a Single-Phase Boost DC-DC Converter for Electric Vehicle Applications", IEEE Industrial Electronics Society Annual Conference, pp. 4279-4285, 2014.

[26] R. Ammo and H. Fujita, "Analysis and Reduction of Power Losses in PV Converters for Grid Connection to Low-Voltage Three-Phase Three-Wire Systems", IEEE International Power Electronics Conference, pp. 2027-2034, 2014.

[27] B. Burger, D. Kranzer, and O. Statler, "Cost Reduction of PV-Inverter with SiC-DMOSFETs", IEEE International Conference on Integrated Power Systems, pp. 1-5, 2008.

[28] J. Mookken, B. Agrawal, and J. Liu, "Efficient and Compact 50kW Gen2 SiC Device based PV String Inverter", IEEE Power Electronics, Intelligent Motion, Renewable Energy and Energy Management Conference, pp. 780-786, 2014.

[29] S. Saridakis, E. Koutroulis, and F. Blaabjerg, "Optimization of SiC-Based H5 and Conergy-NPC Transformerless PV Inverters", IEEE Journal of Emerging and Selected Topics on Power Electronics, Vol. 3, pp. 555-567, 2015.

[30] M. Marz, et al, "Power Electronics Systems Integration for Electric and Hybrid Vehicles", IEEE Conference on Integrated Power Electronic Systems, Paper 6.1, 2010.

[31] K. Hamada, "Power Semiconductor Device and Module Technologies for Hybrid Vehicles", IEEE International Symposium on Power Semiconductor Devices and ICs Short Course, 2014.

[32] P. Shamsi, et al, "Performance Evaluation of Various Semiconductor Technologies for Automotive Applications", IEEE Applied Power Electronics Conference, pp. 3061-2066, 2013.

[33] K. Kumar, et al, "Impact of Sic MOSFET Traction Inverters on Compact-Class Electric Car Range", IEEE International Conference on Power Electronics, pp. 1-6, 2014.

[34] M. J. Scott, et al, "Design Considerations for Wide Bandgap based Motor Drive Systems", IEEE Electric Vehicles Conference, pp. 1-6, 2014.

[35] S. Jahdi, et al, "An Evaluation of Silicon Carbide Unipolar Technologies for Electric Vehicle Drive-Trains", IEEE Journal of Emerging and Selected Topics in Power Electronics, Vol. 2, pp. 517-528, 2014.

[36] K. Hamada, et al, "SiC – Emerging Power Device Technology for Next-Generation Electrically Powered Environmentally Friendly Vehicles", IEEE Transactions on Electron Devices, Vol. 62, pp. 278-285, 2015.

[37] J. Fabre, P. Ladoux, and M. Piton, "Characterization and Implementation of Dual-SiC MOSFET Modules for Future Use in Traction Converters", IEEE Transactions on Power Electronics, Vol. 30, pp. 4079-4090, 2015.

[38] J. Rice and J. Mookken, "Economics of High Efficiency SiC MOSFET based 3-ph Motor Drive", Power Conversion and Intelligent Motion, pp. 1003-1010, 2014.

[39] A. Bolotnikov, et al, "Overview of 1.2kV – 2.2kV SiC MOSFETs targeted for Industrial Power Conversion Applications", IEEE Applied Power Electronics Conference, pp. 2445-2452, 2015.

[40] B. J. Baliga, "Fundamentals of Power Semiconductor Devices", Springer-Science, pp. 960-964, New York, 2008.

[41] Y. Cui, et al, "High Efficiency Data Center Power Supply using Wide Bandgap Power Devices", IEEE Applied Power Electronics Conference, pp. 3437-3443, 2014.

[42] A. Waheed, et al, "Efficient Electric Vehicle Charger Based on Wide Band-gap Materials for V2G and G2V", International Conference on Engineering and Emerging Technologies, pp. 1-5, 2022.

[43] S. A. Q Mohammed and J-W. Jung, "A Comprehensive State-of-the-Art Review of Wired/Wireless Charging Technologies for Battery Electric Vehicles: Classification/Common Topologies/Future Research Issues", IEEE Access, Vol. 9, pp. 19572-19585, 2021.

[44] W. Martinez, W. Lin, and C. Suarez, "EMC implications of implementing WBG devices in battery charger modules for electric vehicles", International Power Electronics Conference, pp. 2516-2521, 2022.

[45] B. Li, "A High-Efficiency High-Density Wide-Bandgap Device-Based Bidirectional On-Board Charger", IEEE Journal of Emerging and Special Topics in Power Electronics, Vol. 6, pp. 1627-1636, 2018.

[46] A. Agarwal, et al, "Wide Band gap Semiconductor Technology for Energy Efficiency", Material Science Forum, Vol. 858, pp. 797-802, 2016.

[47] B. J. Baliga, "Semiconductors for High Voltage Vertical Channel Field Effect Transistors", J. Appl. Phys., Vol. 53, pp. 1759-1764, 1982.

Homework Problems

The contents of this book were used to teach a graduate course at North Carolina State University for many semesters. The homework assignments given to the students are provided here for the assistance of other instructors who wish to use this book in their class.

Home Work 1: Material Properties and Breakdown

Problem 1: Determine the intrinsic carrier concentration for silicon and 4H-SiC at 300, 400 and 500 °K. Provide your answers in a Tabular form for comparing the values at each temperature.

Problem 2: Calculate the built-in potential for silicon and 4H-SiC at 300, 400 and 500 °K using a doping concentration of 1×10^{19} cm^{-3} on the P-side and 1×10^{16} cm^{-3} on the N-side of the junction. Provide your answers in a Tabular form for comparing the values at each temperature.

Problem 3: Determine the electric field at which the impact ionization coefficient for silicon and 4H-SiC becomes 10^4 cm^{-1} using Baliga's Power Laws. Provide your answers in a Tabular form for comparing the values.

Problem 4: Determine the mobility for electrons in Silicon and 4H-SiC at doping concentrations of: 1×10^{14} cm^{-3}, 1×10^{15} cm^{-3}, 1×10^{16} cm^{-3}, 1×10^{17} cm^{-3}, 1×10^{18} cm^{-3}, 1×10^{19} cm^{-3}. Provide your answers in a Tabular form with values for each mobility.

Problem 5: Name the deep levels that determines lifetime in 4H-SiC. What are the positions of these deep levels? What is the threshold energy required to create these deep levels by electron irradiation? Determine the 160 keV Electron Fluence required to obtain a lifetime of 0.2 microseconds.

Problem 6: Calculate the breakdown voltage for a junction termination using the single optimally located floating field ring with a depth of 1 μm for a 4H-SiC drift region with doping concentration of 1 x 10^{16} cm^{-3}. Determine the spacing for the single optimally located floating field ring. What is the mask dimension required for this design?

Problem 7: What is the optimum dose for a single zone JTE region for 4H-SiC? What is its minimum width for a breakdown voltage of 3000 volts?

Problem 8: What is the Positive Bevel Angle required to reduce the Surface Electric Field to 40 percent of the Bulk value? You should use the analytical Model B for your calculations.

Problem 9: Calculate the width of the drift region for a 4H-SiC punch-through diode to achieve a breakdown voltage of 15000 volts if the drift region doping concentration is 1 x 10^{14} cm^{-3}.

Home Work 2: Schottky and JBS Rectifiers

Problem 1: Calculate the on-state voltage drop for a 4H-SiC Schottky barrier rectifier designed to block 1000V. You can assume the following: (1) parallel-plane breakdown voltage; (2) On-state current density of 200 A/cm^2; (c) Barrier height of 1.6 eV; (d) Operation at room temperature (300 °K); (e) Substrate thickness of 350 microns and resistivity of 0.020 Ω-cm (f). Provide the voltage drop across the Schottky barrier and the series resistance as well as the total voltage drop.

Problem 3: A 4H-SiC Schottky barrier rectifier is designed to block 1000-V. (a) Calculate the leakage current density without Schottky barrier lowering and tunneling. (b) Calculate the leakage current density with Schottky barrier lowering but without tunneling. (c) Calculate the leakage current density with Schottky barrier lowering and tunneling. (d) What is the barrier reduction in eV due to the image force? Use the following assumptions: (1) parallel-plane breakdown voltage; (2) Reverse bias voltage of 800V; (3) Barrier height of 1.6 eV; (4) No impact ionization; (5) No generation or diffusion current.

Problem 5: A 4H-SiC JBS rectifier is designed to block 1000V. The P-N junction depth is 1 micron. The cell pitch (p) is 2 micron. The P-region width (s) is 1 micron. (a) Calculate the On-State Voltage Drop. What is the contribution from the Schottky contact and from the series resistance? (b) Calculate the difference in on-state voltage drop of the JBS rectifier and the on-state voltage drop of the Schottky rectifier in Problem 1. You can assume the following: (1) parallel-plane breakdown voltage; (2) On-state current density of 200 A/cm^2; (3) Barrier height of 1.6 eV; (4) Operation at room temperature (300 °K); (5) Substrate thickness of 350 microns and resistivity of 0.020 Ω-cm; (6) Depletion width at on-state calculated using an on-state voltage drop of 1.5 volts; (7) Doping of the P$^+$ region is 1 x 10^{19} cm^{-3}.

Problem 6: A 4H-SiC JBS rectifier is designed to block 1000V. The P-N junction depth is 1 micron. The cell pitch (p) is 2 micron. The P-region width (s) is 1 micron. (a) Calculate the leakage current at 300 °K for a reverse bias of 800V. (b) Calculate the ratio of the leakage current for the Schottky rectifier in Problem 2 to that for the JBS rectifier.

You can assume the following: (1) parallel-plane breakdown voltage; (2) On-state current density of 200 A/cm^2; (3) Barrier height of 1.6 eV; (4) Operation at room temperature (300 °K); (5) Substrate thickness of 350 microns and resistivity of 0.020 Ω-cm; (6) Depletion width at on-state calculated using an on-state voltage drop of 1.5 volts; (7) Doping of the P$^+$ region is 1 x 10^{19} cm^{-3}.

Home Work 3: P-i-N and MPS Rectifiers

Problem 1: Design a 4H-SiC P-i-N rectifier with reverse blocking voltage of 15-kV. The drift region has a doping concentration of 1 x 10^{14} cm^{-3}. The lifetime in the drift region is 1 microsecond. (a) What is the thickness of the drift region? (b) What is the on-state voltage drop at a current density of 100 A/cm^2? (c) What is the stored charge in the drift region? (d) The diode is switched off with a ramp rate of 5 x 10^7 A/cm^2-s. The reverse recovery occurs with the space charge layer extending through the entire drift region before the voltage reaches the supply voltage of 10 kV. What is the reverse recovery time (t$_{RR}$)? (e) What is the peak reverse recovery current density under the conditions in part (d)? (f) What is the voltage at which the space charge layer penetrates the entire drift region?

You can assume the following: (1) parallel-plane breakdown voltage; (d) Operation at room temperature (300 °K).

Problem 2: Design a 4H-SiC MPS rectifier with reverse blocking voltage of 15-kV. The drift region has a doping concentration of 1 x 10^{14} cm^{-3}. The lifetime in the drift region is 10 microseconds. (a) What is the thickness of the drift region? (b) What is the on-state voltage drop at a current density of 100 A/cm^2? Provide the components: Voltage drop across the Schottky contact; Voltage drop across the middle region; Voltage drop across the drift/N$^+$ substrate. (c) What is the stored charge in the drift region? (d) The diode is switched off with a ramp rate of 5 x 10^7 A/cm^2-s. The reverse recovery occurs with the space charge layer extending through the entire drift region before the voltage reaches the supply voltage of 10 kV. What is the reverse recovery time (t_{RR})? (e) What is the peak reverse recovery current density under the conditions in part (d)? (f) What is the voltage at which the space charge layer penetrates the entire drift region?

You can assume the following: (1) parallel-plane breakdown voltage; (2) Operation at room temperature (300 °K); (3) Schottky barrier height of 2.0 eV; (4) Cell pitch (p) of 3 microns; (5) Schottky contact width of 1 micron; (6) P-N junction depth of 1 micron.

Home Work 4: Silicon GD-MOSFET and SJ-MOSFET

Problem 1: Design a silicon GD-MOSFET structure with blocking voltage of 150-V. (a) What is the length of the Source Electrode in the trench? (b) What is the optimum thickness of the trench oxide around the source electrode? (c) What is the optimum doping gradient? (d) Calculate the specific on-resistance for the device. Provide all the components: channel resistance, accumulation resistance, drift resistance in the trench portion. You can neglect the second component of the drift region resistance and the substrate resistance. (e) Compare the GD-MOSFET specific on-resistance to that for the ideal specific on-resistance for the one-dimensional case.

You can assume the following: (1) breakdown voltage is not limited by edge termination; (2) Operation at room temperature (300 °K); (3) Inversion layer mobility of 200 cm^2/V-s; (4) Accumulation layer mobility of 1000 cm^2/V-s; (5) Gate Oxide thickness of 500 angstroms; (6) mesa width of 1 micron; (7) trench width of 2 microns; (8) P-base junction depth of 1 micron; (9) N$^+$ source depth of 0.2 microns; (10) gate electrode depth of 1.2 microns; (11) threshold voltage of 2 volts; (12) gate bias of 10 volts; (13) initial doping in the mesa region of 1 x 10^{16} cm^{-3}.

Problem 2: Design a silicon SJ-MOSFET structure with blocking voltage of 500-V. (a) What is the length of the drift region (P & N columns)? (b) What is the optimum dose for the P and N drift regions? (c) What is the optimum doping concentration for the P and N drift regions if their width is 10 microns? (d) Calculate the specific on-resistance for the device. Provide all the components: channel resistance, accumulation resistance, drift resistance in the portion with P-regions. You can neglect the second component of the drift region resistance and the substrate resistance. (e) Compare the SJ-MOSFET specific on-resistance to that for the ideal specific on-resistance for the one-dimensional case.

You can assume the following: (1) breakdown voltage is not limited by edge termination; (2) Operation at room temperature (300 °K); (3) Inversion layer mobility of 200 cm^2/V-s; (4) Accumulation layer mobility of 1000 cm^2/V-s; (5) Gate Oxide thickness of 500 angstroms; (6) P-base junction depth of 1 micron; (7) N^+ source depth of 0.2 microns; (8) threshold voltage of 2 volts; (9) gate bias of 10 volts.

Home Work 5: SiC Power MOSFETs

Problem 1: Design an optimized 4H-SiC Shielded Planar-Gate Power MOSFET linear cell structure to obtain a blocking voltage of 1000 volts. The edge termination limits the breakdown voltage to 80 % of the parallel-plane value. (a) Determine the drift region doping concentration assuming all the blocking voltage is supported by the drift region. (b) Determine the drift region thickness assuming all the blocking voltage is supported by the drift region. (c) Calculate the P-base doping concentration (assuming it is uniformly doped) to obtain a threshold voltage of 5 volts. The gate oxide thickness is 500 angstroms. The fixed charge in the gate oxide is 2 x 10^{11} cm^{-2}. Ignore work function difference for gate electrode. (d) Calculate the depletion width within the P-base region when the structure is supporting 1000 volts if the P-base region is not shielded. Calculate the depletion width within the P+ shielding region (doping concentration of 1 x 10^{18} cm^{-3}) when the structure is supporting 1000 volts. (e) Determine the optimum gate length to obtain the minimum specific on-resistance for your linear cell design using the parameters provided at the end of the problem. (f) What is the minimum specific on-resistance for your optimum linear cell design using the parameters provided at the end of the problem? Provide the components (R_{ch}, R_A, R_J, R_D, R_{SUB}) in absolute values of $m\Omega$-cm^2 and as a percentage of the total. (g) Provide a graph of the specific on-resistance versus the gate length (ranging from 4 to 10 microns) showing all the components, including the total. (h) Calculate the specific on-resistance for the ideal drift region for blocking 1000 volts in $m\Omega\text{-}cm^2$. Compare your design to this value by taking the ratio of your design value to the ideal value.

Parameters and Assumptions: (1) Inversion Mobility = 20 cm^2/Vs. (2) Accumulation Mobility = 100 cm^2/Vs. (3) Cell Polysilicon window width = 5 microns (4) N^+ Substrate resistivity of 0.02 Ohm-cm and thickness of 200 microns. (5) Gate Bias = 15 volts. (6) K factor for accumulation spreading = 0.6. (7) P-Base Extension beyond Polysilicon Gate Edge = 1.2 microns. (8) N^+ Source Extension beyond Polysilicon Gate Edge = 0.2 microns. (8) P^+ Junction Depth = 1 micron

Problem 2: Design a 4H-SiC Shielded Trench-Gate Power MOSFET linear cell structure to obtain a blocking voltage of 1000 volts. The edge termination limits the breakdown voltage to 80 % of the parallel-plane value. Use the drift region doping concentration from Problem 1. Use the drift region thickness from Problem 1. (a) What is the specific on-resistance for your device using the parameters provided at the end of the problem? Provide the components (R_{ch}, R_{J1}, R_{J2}, R_D, R_{SB}) in absolute values of $m\Omega\text{-}cm^2$ and as a percentage of the total. (b) Calculate the specific on-resistance for the ideal drift region for blocking 1000 volts in $m\Omega\text{-}cm^2$. Compare your design to this value by taking the ratio of your design value to the ideal value.

Parameters and Assumptions: (1) P-base junction depth = 0.7 microns. (2) N+ source junction depth = 0.2 microns. (3) Trench depth = 1.5 microns. (4) P^+ region thickness/junction depth = 0.2 microns. (5) Gate oxide thickness = 500 angstroms. (6) Inversion Mobility = 20 cm^2/Vs. (7) Accumulation Mobility = 100 cm^2/Vs. (8) N^+ Substrate resistivity of 0.02 Ohm-cm and thickness of 200 microns. (9) Gate Bias = 15 volts; Threshold voltage = 5 volts. (10) Mesa width = 2.5 microns. (11) Trench width = 1 micron. (12) JFET region doping = 5 x 10^{16} cm^{-3}.

Home Work 6: SiC IGBTs

Problem 1: (a) Determine the width of the N-drift region for an n-channel 4H-SiC IGBT to obtain a blocking voltage of 15 kV if it's doping concentration is 1.5 x 10^{14} cm^{-3}. The N-Buffer layer has a doping concentration of 5 x 10^{16} cm^{-3} and its thickness is 5 microns. The lifetime (Low-Level, High-Level, Space-Charge-Generation) in the N-drift layer is 2 microsecond. Scale the lifetime in the N-Buffer layer using a reference doping of 5 x 10^{16} cm^{-3}. The P$^+$ Collector region has a doping concentration of 1 x 10^{19} cm^{-3} and its thickness is 10 microns. (b) Calculate the injected hole concentration at the P$^+$ collector/N-Buffer Layer junction for the planar-gate asymmetric n-Channel 4H-SiC IGBT structure under the operating conditions defined in part (e). Assume a diffusion length for electrons of 1 micron in the P$^+$ collector region. (c) What is the hole concentration in the N-buffer layer at the interface between the N-drift and N-buffer regions? (d) What is the hole concentration in the N-drift region at the interface between the N-drift and N-buffer regions? (e) Determine the on-state voltage drop at an on-state current density of 50 A/cm^2 for the planar-gate asymmetric n-channel 4H-SiC IGBT structure using the two-dimensional model. Provide the values for the voltage drop across the P$^+$/N junction, the N-base region, and the MOSFET (using only the channel resistance). (f) The planar-gate asymmetric n-channel 4H-SiC IGBT structure is switched off under inductive load conditions from the on-state operating conditions defined in part (e). (g) Calculate the voltage rise-time to reach a collector DC supply voltage of 10 kV. (h) Calculate the reach-through voltage. (i) Calculate the reach-through time. (j) Calculate the [dV/dt] during the second phase of the voltage waveform. (k) What is the current fall-time? (l) Obtain the total energy loss per cycle. Provide the energy loss during the voltage rise-time and the current fall-time.

Use the following parameters: (1) Cell pitch of 10 microns. (2) Channel length of 1.0 microns. (3) Inversion mobility of 15 cm^2/V-s. (4) Gate oxide thickness of 500 angstroms. (5) Gate bias of 15 volts. (6) Threshold voltage of 5 volts. (7) Lifetime (Low-Level, High-Level, Space-Charge-Generation) in the N-drift layer of 2 microsecond. (8) All the dopants are fully ionized.

Problem 2: (a) Determine the width of the P-drift region for a p-channel 4H-SiC IGBT to obtain a blocking voltage of 15 kV if it's doping concentration is 1.5 x 10^{14} cm^{-3}. The P-Buffer layer has a doping concentration of 5 x 10^{16} cm^{-3} and its thickness is 5 microns. The lifetime (Low-Level, High-Level, Space-Charge-Generation) in the P-drift layer is 2 microsecond. Scale the lifetime in the P-Buffer layer using a reference doping of 5 x 10^{16} cm^{-3}. The N$^+$ Collector region has a doping concentration of 1 x 10^{19} cm^{-3} and its thickness is 10 microns. (b) Calculate the injected electron concentration at the N$^+$ collector/P-Buffer Layer junction for the planar-gate asymmetric p-Channel 4H-SiC IGBT structure under the operating conditions defined in part (e). Assume a diffusion length for holes of 1 micron in the N^+ collector region. (c) What is the electron concentration in the P-buffer layer at the interface between the P-drift and P-buffer regions? (d) What is the electron concentration in the P-drift region at the interface between the P-drift and P-buffer regions? (e) Determine the on-state voltage drop at an on-state current density of 50 A/cm^2 for the planar-gate asymmetric p-channel 4H-SiC IGBT structure using the two-dimensional model. Provide the values for the voltage drop across the P^+/N junction, the N-base region, and the MOSFET (using only the channel resistance). (f) The planar-gate asymmetric p-channel 4H-SiC IGBT structure is switched off under inductive load conditions from the on-state operating conditions defined in part (e). (g) Calculate the voltage rise-time to reach a collector DC supply voltage of 10 kV. (h) Calculate the reach-through voltage. (i) Calculate the reach-through time. (j) Calculate the [dV/dt] during the second phase of the voltage waveform. (k) What is the current fall-time? (l) Obtain the total energy loss per cycle. Provide the energy loss during the voltage rise-time and the current fall-time.

Use the following parameters: (1) Cell pitch of 10 microns. (2) Channel length of 1.0 microns. (3) Inversion mobility of 15 cm^2/V-s. (4) Gate oxide thickness of 500 angstroms. (5) Gate bias of 15 volts. (6) Threshold voltage of 5 volts. (7) Lifetime (Low-Level, High-Level, Space-Charge-Generation) in the N-drift layer of 2 microsecond.

Index